Fundamental Problems in Statistical Mechanics III

Proceedings of the 1974 Wageningen Summer School

E.G.D. Cohen Editor

North-Holland/American Elsevier

FUNDAMENTAL PROBLEMS IN STATISTICAL MECHANICS III

FUNDAMENTAL PROBLEMS IN STATISTICAL MECHANICS III

Proceedings of the International Summer School on Fundamental Problems in Statistical Mechanics III, Wageningen, The Netherlands, July 29-August 15, 1974

Editor

E. G. D. Cohen

Rockefeller University
NEW YORK, N.Y.
U.S.A.

1975

NORTH-HOLLAND PUBLISHING COMPANY – AMSTERDAM • OXFORD
AMERICAN ELSEVIER PUBLISHING COMPANY, INC. – NEW YORK

ISBN North-Holland 0 7204 0324 3
ISBN American Elsevier 0 444 10829 7

Publishers:
NORTH-HOLLAND PUBLISHING COMPANY - AMSTERDAM
NORTH-HOLLAND PUBLISHING COMPANY, LTD. - OXFORD

Sole distributors for the U.S.A. and Canada:
AMERICAN ELSEVIER PUBLISHING COMPANY, INC.
52 VANDERBILT AVENUE
NEW YORK, N.Y. 10017

PRINTED IN THE NETHERLANDS

PREFACE

This book contains all the lectures of the 1974 Summer School on Fundamental Problems in Statistical Mechanics held from July 29 - August 15 in Wageningen, The Netherlands. Like the lectures of the previous summer school, these are critical reviews of some of the developments in statistical mechanics which have come to the foreground since the preceding summer school was held. Again, emphasis was placed more on clarity of presentation and an understanding of problems as a whole, rather than on specialized methods. Comparison with the two previous volumes will show to what extent the interest in the years between two summer schools has changed or remained the same. Although the lectures are mainly intended as introductory expositions, they often include recent developments. In fact, these developments have sometimes been so recent, that no clear general opinion as to their significance yet exists!

Again, there is only incidental treatment of problems in quantum statistical mechanics and its application to the problems of superfluids and superconductors. This is related to the occurrence of several other summer schools devoted entirely to this subject, held at the same time as this.

The summer school was organized by NUFFIC (Netherlands Foundation for International Cooperation) in cooperation with the Rockefeller University; financial support was also given by Stichting Physica, het Lorentz fonds, and het Ministerie van onderwijs en wetenschappen.

The school was attended by about 70 students from 25 countries. The scientific organizing committee was composed of:

E.G.D. Cohen, The Rockefeller University, New York

M.H. Ernst, University of Utrecht

J.M.J. van Leeuwen, Technical University of Delft

Ch.G. van Weert, University of Amsterdam

The program consisted of 40 regular lectures given during the mornings by 11 lecturers and a number of seminars given during the afternoons and evenings. No seminars could be published this time, in view of the large number of regular lectures.

Thanks are due to the registrar and administrator of the school, Drs. R. Doop of NUFFIC, and to the hostess, Ms. E. van Walsum. We are also grateful to the secretary, Mrs. C.A.H. Baurdoux-Hermans who, together with Mrs. A. Kitselar, typed all the manuscripts. Special thanks must go to Dr. Ch.G. van Weert, who, in order to reduce the price of this book, took it upon himself to supervise the preparation of all the manuscripts and deliver them print-ready to the publisher.

It is hoped that this book will prove useful and stimulating to all those interested in statistical mechanics.

E.G.D. Cohen

CONTENTS

CRITICAL PHENOMENA

B. WIDOM

Department of Chemistry, Cornell University, Ithaca, New York 14850

In these lectures we shall cover two of the topics that are of great current interest in the theory of equilibrium critical phenomena. The first of these, Wilson's renormalization-group theory, is certainly the most significant development in the subject in the years since the preceding Nuffic Summerschool on Fundamental Problems in Statistical Mechanics, where the subject of phase transitions was reviewed by Kasteleyn[1]. The second of the topics to be covered here is that of higher-order critical points, particularly tricritical points. The renormalization-group theory also affords a view of higher-order critical points, as will be mentioned briefly, but our treatment of this second topic will be mostly phenomenological.

We shall begin with a brief review of the Kadanoff theory of scaling and homogeneity[2]. An alternative formulation[3,4] leads to the same results, but it is Kadanoff's that provides the appropriate framework for the subsequent discussion of the renormalization-group theory.

1. KADANOFF'S SCALING THEORY[2]

It is convenient here to use the language appropriate to the Ising model of a ferromagnet, rather than the language of a fluid. At the critical point, the correlation length ξ of the spin-spin correlation function $G(r) = \langle s(0)s(r)\rangle$ is infinite. Near the critical point it is finite, but much greater than the lattice spacing, so it is possible to find a number L which is much greater than 1 yet such that L lattice spacings is still much less than ξ. Imagine the Ising lattice divided into cells L lattice spacings on a side, each containing L^d spins (figure 1). It was supposed by Kadanoff that the net magnetization in

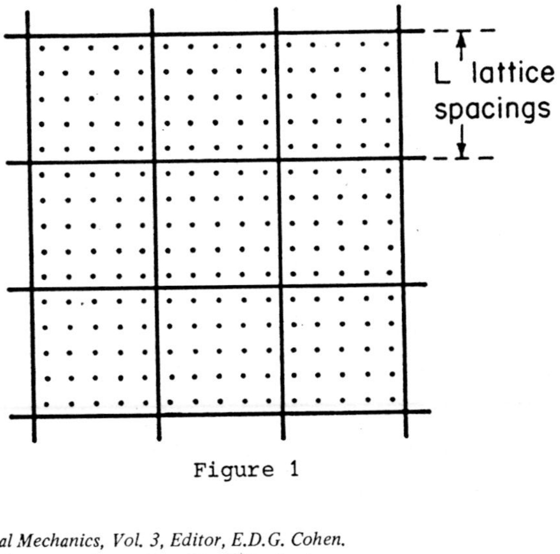

Figure 1

Fundamental Problems in Statistical Mechanics, Vol. 3, Editor, E.D.G. Cohen.

each cell plays the rôle of an elementary spin in a new Ising model, in which what were the cells are now the new spin sites. The correlation length ξ is the same in the new picture as in the original, but measured as a number of lattice spacings it is smaller in the new picture by a factor of L, so the new, re-scaled Ising model appears to be further from its critical point than the original model was from its. Then with $t = (T-T_c)/T_c$ a dimensionless measure of the deviation of the temperature from the critical temperature, and with h the magnetic field, the new re-scaled model will appear to be at values of t and h that are larger than the original (because further from the critical point); and the factors by which the new, effective t and h exceed the original will themselves increase with L. Thus, the new, effective t and h may be $L^y t$ and $L^x h$, respectively, where x and y are two positive exponents.

Let $f(t,h)$ be the singular part of the free energy per spin. The full free energy per spin may in addition contain an analytic background term that is irrelevant to the critical phenomenon and so need not scale in the way f will be found to. In the re-scaled model the cells are of sub-macroscopic size $(L\ll\xi)$, so the contribution to the free energy that comes from within the cells is analytic and is not included in f. If the system is of dimensionality d, then $L^d f(t,h)$ is the singular contribution to the free energy per group of L^d spins in the original Ising model, while $f(L^y t, L^x h)$ is the same quantity expressed from the point of view of the re-scaled model, where it appears as the contribution per spin. Thus,

$$L^d f(t,h) = f(L^y t, L^x h) \quad . \tag{1.1}$$

But this must hold identically for all the allowable values of L, and the only way (1.1) can be an identity in L is for f to be of the form

$$f(t,h) = t^{d/y}\phi(t\,h^{-y/x}) \tag{1.2}$$

where ϕ is a function of a single variable; that is, $f(t,h)$ must be homogeneous in the variables t and $h^{y/x}$, with degree of homogeneity d/y.

In the now conventional notation, the heat capacity is said to diverge at the critical point proportionally to $|t|^{-\alpha}$, so the singular part of the free energy density at $h = 0$ behaves as $|t|^{2-\alpha}$. Then $\phi(+\infty)$ and $\phi(-\infty)$ must be finite, non-zero constants, and the exponent y must be related to α by

$$d/y = 2 - \alpha \ . \tag{1.3}$$

On the critical isotherm $(t = 0)$, if h is to vary with the δ power of the magnetization M (this is again conventional notation), then f must vary as

$h^{1+1/\delta}$, because $M = (\partial f/\partial h)_t$. But for small values u of its argument the function $\phi(u)$ must behave as $u^{-d/y}$, in order that there be a $t = 0$ limit; so then

$$d/x = 1 + 1/\delta \quad . \tag{1.4}$$

As a consequence of the homogeneity of f expressed in (1.2), the critical-point exponents $2-\alpha$ and δ may be re-expressed at will in terms of two others, the exponent β that determines the rate of vanishing of the spontaneous magnetization, $M \sim |t|^{\beta}$, and the exponent γ that determines the rate of divergence of the susceptibility, $\chi = (\partial M/\partial h)_t \sim |t|^{-\gamma}$ [2,4]. These relations are[4,5]

$$2 - \alpha = \gamma + 2\beta \quad , \quad \delta = 1 + \gamma/\beta \quad . \tag{1.5}$$

Thus, from (1.3)-(1.5), the thermodynamic critical-point exponents α, β, γ, δ, are all expressible in terms of the exponents x and y in (1.1).

If the correlation length ξ diverges at the critical point proportionally to $|t|^{-\nu}$, then relations involving the exponent ν are obtained when similar arguments are applied to the correlation function $G(r)$ rather than to the free energy density f. Take $h = 0$ for simplicity, but indicate the correlation function's explicit t-dependence by now calling it $G(t,r)$. In the re-scaled Ising model the new, effective t is $L^y t$, as above, while the new, effective distance is r/L. At the same time the amplitude of the correlation function may scale with a power p, say, of L. Then as in the analogous eq. (1.1), we have

$$G(t,r) = L^p G(L^y t, L^{-1} r) \tag{1.6}$$

as an identity in L, so G must be of the form

$$G(t,r) = r^p g(t^{1/y} r) \quad . \tag{1.7}$$

This shows the correlation length ξ to be identifiable as $t^{-1/y}$, and the critical-point exponent p to be what is conventionally[6] called $-(d-2+\eta)$; that is, we have the identifications

$$p = -(d - 2 + \eta) \tag{1.8}$$

$$1/y = \nu \quad . \tag{1.9}$$

Further, entirely as a consequence of the homogeneity of $G(t,r)$ as expressed in (1.7), we have the correlation-function exponents ν and η related to the thermodynamic susceptibility exponent γ by[6]

$$(2 - \eta)\nu = \gamma \quad . \tag{1.10}$$

This scaling picture was the direct inspiration for the more recent renormalization-group theory of the critical point[7,8)]. The assumption that the net magnetization of groups of L^d spins interact as the single spins of a re-scaled Ising model was the fundamental unproved postulate in the theory that was just outlined. In the renormalization-group theory it is seen that this postulate is figuratively, but not literally, correct. In reality the appropriate block spin variables prove to be the sums of the long-wavelength Fourier components of the spin density, down to components of wavelength L, say; and such sums are roughly, but not exactly, the sums of the spins in blocks of volume L^d. The homogeneity of the correlation function and the thermodynamic homogeneity are unaffected by this modification, so all the results derived in this section continue to hold. But the renormalization-group theory, in addition to justifying the ideas of scaling and homogeneity and leading to the usual relations among critical-point exponents, provides the means of calculating the separate values of those exponents, and as such is a most important advance. We discuss that next.

2. WILSON'S RENORMALIZATION-GROUP THEORY[7,8]; INTRODUCTION

We shall here ask how the earlier scaling picture — groups of spins playing the rôles of single spins in a re-scaled Ising model — might come about, without at this point asking whether it does come about. In this first instance, then, we conjecture a mathematical mechanism of scaling.

It is convenient to treat a continuous-spin rather than discrete-spin Ising model. Let

$$s_1, s_2, \ldots, s_N \qquad (-\infty < s_i < \infty)$$

be the spins at the N sites of the lattice. Associated with each configuration, that is, with each set of values of the s_i, there is an energy E and a Boltzmann factor $B_N(s_1, \ldots, s_N; a_0, b_0, \ldots) = \exp(-E/kT)$. Here $a_0, b_0, \ldots$ are all the parameters that are present in the Boltzmann factor — the temperature T, the magnetic field h, and as many spin-spin interaction-energy parameters as there might be. The probability of occurrence of the spin configuration in which each s_i lies in an infinitesimal range ds_i about some prescribed value s_i, is

$$\frac{B_N ds_1 \ldots ds_N}{\int_{-\infty}^{\infty} \cdots \int_{-\infty}^{\infty} B_N ds_1 \ldots ds_N} \quad . \tag{2.1}$$

Now change to new variables σ_i $(i = 1, \ldots, N)$, each a function of all of the original s_i, and each again taking all values from $-\infty$ to ∞ :

$$\sigma_i = \sigma_i(s_1, \ldots, s_N) \qquad (-\infty < \sigma_i < \infty) \quad . \tag{2.2}$$

The probability of occurrence of a spin configuration in which each of the $\sigma_1, \sigma_2, \ldots, \sigma_{N/\ell}$, say, lies in an infinitesimal range $d\sigma_i$ about some prescribed value σ_i, irrespective of the values of the remaining $N - N/\ell$ of the σ_i, is

$$\frac{\left(\int_{-\infty}^{\infty} \cdots \int_{-\infty}^{\infty} B_N J \, d\sigma_{\frac{N}{\ell}+1} \cdots d\sigma_N\right) d\sigma_1 \cdots d\sigma_{N/\ell}}{\int_{-\infty}^{\infty} \cdots \int_{-\infty}^{\infty} \left(\int_{-\infty}^{\infty} \cdots \int_{-\infty}^{\infty} B_N J \, d\sigma_{\frac{N}{\ell}+1} \cdots d\sigma_N\right) d\sigma_1 \cdots d\sigma_{N/\ell}} \tag{2.3}$$

where J is the Jacobian of the transformation (2.2).

Now suppose that it is possible to choose the new variables σ_i in such a way that the multiple integral in the parentheses in the numerator and denominator of (2.3), proves, when evaluated, to be of the form $c^N B_{N/\ell}(\sigma_1, \ldots, \sigma_{N/\ell}; a_1, b_1, \ldots)$, with c^N some constant, independent of the spin variables (so that it cancels in (2.3)); that is, proves to be proportional to the Boltzmann factor for a continuous-spin model identical in form to the original model, but with N/ℓ spins instead of N spins, and with parameters $a_1, b_1, \ldots$ that may have values different from, but otherwise play the same rôles as, those of the original $a_0, b_0, \ldots$. It must ultimately be demonstrated that there are such σ_i, but for the present we assume it. If $\sigma_1, \ldots, \sigma_{N/\ell}$ were simply the sums of the spin variables s_i in blocks, each block containing ℓ of the original spins, it would be precisely the earlier scaling picture. What emerges later is that there is indeed a transformation to new spin variables σ_i of the kind we are supposing, at least approximately; and that the $\sigma_1, \ldots, \sigma_{N/\ell}$ are indeed roughly, though not exactly, the sums of the s_i in blocks of size ℓ.

Because the new model is identical in form to the old model, it must be possible to transform it yet again, this time to a model with N/ℓ^2 spins and parameters $a_2, b_2, \ldots$; and so on, indefinitely. At each stage the parameters $a_n, b_n, \ldots$ depend only on their values $a_{n-1}, b_{n-1}, \ldots$ at the preceding stage, not on how many iterations of the transformation have already occurred; because at each stage the model is identical in form to the original one, and its parameters might originally have had any values. Thus, there are functions $\alpha, \beta, \ldots$, independent of n, such that

$$a_n = \alpha(a_{n-1}, b_{n-1}, \ldots)$$

$$b_n = \beta(a_{n-1}, b_{n-1}, \ldots) \qquad (2.4)$$

$$\vdots$$

The functions $\alpha, \beta, \ldots$ are presumed to be non-singular; the singularities characteristic of the critical point arise not from any singular feature of the transformation (2.4), but from the iteration of the transformation a large number of times. The group of transformations defined by the recurrence relations (2.4) is called the "renormalization group", and (2.4) the "renormalization-group equations", by analogy with renormalization in quantum field theory.

At a fixed-point of the transformation (2.4), the values of the parameters are left unchanged by the transformation; that is, $a_n = a_{n-1}$, $b_n = b_{n-1}$, etc. The values $a^*, b^*, \ldots$ of the parameters at such a fixed-point are then determined as the solution (or solutions, if there is more than one fixed-point) of the simultaneous algebraic equations

$$a^* = \alpha(a^*, b^*, \ldots)$$

$$b^* = \beta(a^*, b^*, \ldots) \qquad (2.5)$$

$$\vdots$$

In the neighbourhood of such a fixed point the parameters satisfy the linearized recurrence relations

$$a_n - a^* = A_a(a_{n-1} - a^*) + A_b(b_{n-1} - b^*) + \ldots$$

$$b_n - b^* = B_a(a_{n-1} - a^*) + B_b(b_{n-1} - b^*) + \ldots \qquad (2.6)$$

$$\vdots$$

where

$$A_a = \partial\alpha(a^*, b^*, \ldots)/\partial a^*, \qquad A_b = \partial\alpha(a^*, b^*, \ldots)/\partial b^*, \ \ldots$$

$$B_a = \partial\beta(a^*, b^*, \ldots)/\partial a^*, \qquad B_b = \partial\beta(a^*, b^*, \ldots)/\partial b^*, \ \ldots \qquad (2.7)$$

$$\vdots \qquad\qquad \vdots$$

If (2.6) had been a single equation, $a_n - a^* = \lambda(a_{n-1} - a^*)$, say, its solution $a_n - a^*$ would have been simply $a_n - a^* = (a_0 - a^*)\lambda^n$. More generally, the solution of the simultaneous eqs. (2.6) is

$$a_n - a^* = d_{11}\lambda_1^n + d_{12}\lambda_2^n + \dots$$

$$b_n - b^* = d_{21}\lambda_1^n + d_{22}\lambda_2^n + \dots \qquad (2.8)$$

$$\vdots$$

where $\lambda_1, \lambda_2, \dots$ are the eigenvalues of the matrix of coefficients in (2.6),

$$\begin{bmatrix} A_a & A_b & \dots \\ B_a & B_b & \dots \\ \vdots & \vdots & \end{bmatrix} \qquad (2.9)$$

The coefficients d_{ij} depend on the initial values $a_0 - a^*$, $b_0 - b^*$, etc., but the ratio of d_{ij}'s for fixed j is independent of those initial values; for d_{ij} is the $i^{\underline{th}}$ component of the $j^{\underline{th}}$ right-eigenvector of the matrix (2.9), and the initial values $a_0 - a^*$, etc., only determine the weight with which that eigenvector, and the associated λ_j^n, is represented in (2.8).

Each time the transformation is iterated the number of spin variables is less by the factor ℓ than it had been, so after n iterations of the transformation, groups of ℓ^n of the original spin variables are playing the rôles of single spins. Then ℓ^n is analogous to what in section 1 we called L^d; and when the appropriate $\sigma_1, \dots, \sigma_{N/\ell}$ prove to be something like sums of the original s_i in blocks of ℓ spins, as they will, the analogy is very close. Thus, we identify

$$\ell^n = L^d \quad . \qquad (2.10)$$

The dimensionality d is of course fixed, as is ℓ; it is n and L that vary as the transformation is iterated, and they provide alternative measures of how far the re-scaling has gone.

Some of the eigenvalues λ_j that appear in the solution (2.8) are greater than 1 and some may be less than 1. Those "normal modes" of the system (i.e., linear combinations of the $a_n - a^*$, $b_n - b^*$,... that are exactly proportional to single ones of the λ_j^n) that are associated with λ_j's that exceed 1, correspond to re-scaled parameters like t and h that increase with each iteration of the transformation. These two do so proportionally to L^y and L^x (in the notation of section 1), or to $(\ell^{y/d})^n$ and $(\ell^{x/d})^n$ (in the present notation), respectively. Such parameters, or combinations of parameters containing them, are said to be "relevant". For an ordinary critical point there are only two independent, relevant variables, e.g., t and h. Any other parameters, such as the ratio of second- to first-neighbour interaction energies, are "irrelevant", and for them the only non-zero d_{ij} in (2.8) are those associated with eigenvalues λ_j of magnitude <1. Thus, as the re-scaling proceeds, the irrelevant parameters approach their fixed-point values; while the relevant parameters, which like t and h may be chosen to vanish at the critical point, grow, because (as explained in section 1) the system is in effect further from its critical point with each iteration.

The character of the solution (2.8) of the linearized renormalization-group equations is most readily seen in a simple example in which we suppose there are only two parameters, a_0 and b_0, with a_0 relevant and b_0 irrelevant, and with $\lambda_1>1$ and $0<\lambda_2<1$. Because b_0 is irrelevant, λ_1^n, which grows with n, must not appear in b_n, so $d_{21} = 0$ in (2.8). Then

$$a_n - a^* = [(a_0 - a^*) - s(b_0 - b^*)]\,\lambda_1^n + s(b_0 - b^*)\lambda_2^n$$

$$b_n - b^* = (b_0 - b^*)\lambda_2^n \quad , \tag{2.11}$$

where $s = d_{12}/d_{22}$, a constant, independent of the initial values $a_0 - a^*$ and $b_0 - b^*$. These are parametric equations (parameter n) relating $a_n - a^*$ to $b_n - b^*$. This is shown graphically in figure 2, where $a_n - a^*$ is plotted against $b_n - b^*$ for a variety of different initial values $a_0 - a^*$ and $b_0 - b^*$. Each curve,

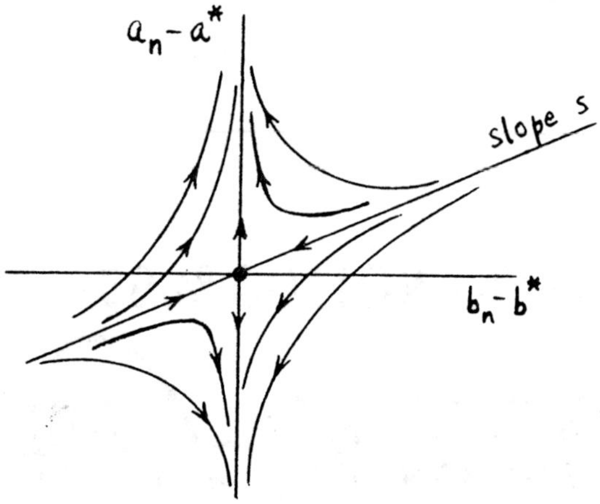

Figure 2

traced out by varying n, is the unique trajectory through the point $a_0 - a^*$, $b_0 - b^*$. The arrows show the direction of increasing n. The fixed-point of the transformation is at the origin, for that is where $a_n = a^*$, $b_n = b^*$ for all n.

For the system to be at its critical point, the relevant parameter a_0 must have the right value, which in general depends on the value of the irrelevant parameter b_0. (The critical temperature, for example, is a function of the ratio of second- to first-neighbour interaction energies.) There is then a one-parameter locus of critical points, on which a_0 is some definite function of b_0. But if the system is at such a critical point, it is again at such a point after each iteration; for the transformation that is being iterated only alters the language with which the system is described, not its physical condition. For example, the re-scaled t exceeds the original t by the factor L^y, but it still vanishes, for all L, if the original t vanishes. Thus, among the trajectories in figure 2, the one that passes through the point $a_0 - a^*$, $b_0 - b^*$ where a_0 has its critical value for the given b_0, is in fact a locus of such critical points; i.e., at each point on that trajectory a_n, b_n are related as at a critical point. Further, that special critical-point trajectory is the straight line of slope s, that passes through the origin. We can make that identification because in this example there is only one relevant parameter, which may be thought of as the temperature, and the quantity that then plays the part of the re-scaled t is the "normal mode"

$$t_n = (a_n - a^*) - s(b_n - b^*) = t_0 \lambda_1^n \quad . \tag{2.12}$$

But the critical point locus is that on which t, or in this case t_n, vanishes for all n; so it is indeed the line $(a_n - a^*) = s(b_n - b^*)$, as stated.

The closer to its critical point the system is — in this illustration, the smaller t_0, i.e., the closer to the critical-point line the starting point $a_0 - a^*$, $b_0 - b^*$ — the greater the number n of iterations that take place before the trajectory begins to depart significantly from the critical-point line, and the closer to the fixed-point — in this illustration, the origin — does the trajectory come before that departure occurs. The fixed-point is always a critical point, i.e., the critical-point line (more generally, the critical-point hyper-surface) in the parameter-space always passes through the fixed-point; and it is a general property of the trajectories determined by (2.8) that if the system is close to its critical point, the trajectory that describes the evolution of the parameters passes close to the fixed-point. Where it does, the linearization of (2.4) that led to (2.6) and (2.8) provides an accurate approximation. Thus, when the system is close enough to its critical point, (2.8) is a good approximation to the solution of (2.4) once n is large enough for the trajectory to have entered the neighbourhood of the fixed-point, and it remains a good approximation until the trajectory departs from that neighbourhood; and that departure occurs at ever larger values of n the closer the system is to its critical point.

We shall call the λ_1 of this illustration the "thermal" eigenvalue, and re-name it λ_T. Then from (2.10) and (2.12), we have that the effective, re-scaled t is the multiple $L^{(\ln\lambda_T/\ln\ell)d}$ of the original t, from which we identify the exponent y of section 1 as

$$y = (\ln\lambda_T/\ln\ell)d \quad , \tag{2.13}$$

and then the correlation-length exponent ν as

$$\nu = \ln \ell / d \ln \lambda_T \quad , \tag{2.14}$$

from (1.9).

This identification has the following interpretation: When the system is close to its critical point, the trajectory in parameter space should not begin to deviate significantly from the critical-point line (or, more generally, from the critical-point hypersurface), until, with increasing n, the linear dimension of the blocks of spins that constitute the effective spins of the re-scaled model, viz., L lattice spacings, comes to be of the order of magnitude of the correlation length, ξ; for not until then should there be any manifestation of the finiteness of ξ, that is, of the fact that the system is merely close to, but not at, its critical point. But it is $t_0\lambda_1^n$ in (2.12) that measures the deviation of the trajectory from the critical-point line, and this deviation is only significant when λ_1^n is large enough to counterbalance the small value of t_0; that is, when λ_1^n comes to be of the order of $1/t_0$. But if that is to happen when L lattice spacings is ξ, it follows from (2.10) that ξ must be of the order of $t_0^{-\ln\ell/d\ \ln\lambda_T}$ lattice spacings (now using the notation λ_T in place of λ_1); and that is precisely (2.14).

The result (2.14) is general, and is an example of the prescription this theory yields for calculating the critical-point exponents: Find the fixed-point of the renormalization-group equations (2.4) by solving the algebraic equations (2.5); linearize (2.4) about the fixed-point, as in (2.6); and find the eigenvalues of the matrix of coefficients of the linearized equations. For an ordinary critical point two of these eigenvalues will be greater than 1, the remainder less than 1. Those that are greater than 1 are the "thermal" eigenvalue λ_T and what we may call the "magnetic" eigenvalue λ_H. These are readily distinguished because the normal mode associated with λ_T does not appear in the magnetic-field-like parameter in (2.8), and that associated with λ_H does not appear in the temperature-like parameter. Of the two, λ_H is the larger, as will be seen in a moment. The re-scaled magnetic-field-like variable in (2.8) then grows as λ_H^n, or, from (2.10), as $L^{(\ln\lambda_H/\ln\ell)d}$. Then from section 1 we identify

$$x = (\ln\lambda_H/\ln\ell)d \quad , \tag{2.15}$$

which is analogous to (2.13); and from (1.4) we have

$$1 + 1/\delta = \ln\ell/\ln\lambda_H \quad , \tag{2.16}$$

which is analogous to (2.14). Thus, λ_H and λ_T yield directly ν (or, equivalently, y) and δ (or, equivalently, x). The other critical-point exponents are obtainable from these via (1.3), (1.5), and (1.10).

From (1.3), (1.5), (1.9), (2.14) and (2.16),

$$\ln\lambda_H/\ln\lambda_T = \beta\delta = \beta + \gamma \quad ,$$

which always exceeds 1; so of the two eigenvalues λ_H and λ_T, the former is the larger, as stated above.

We now have the framework of the renormalization-group theory, and we turn next to concrete realizations and applications of this scheme.

3. A MODEL HAMILTONIAN

The Hamiltonian that lends itself most readily to the renormalization-group analysis is of the Landau-Ginzburg form, with an associated Boltzmann factor

$$B = e^{-\int\{\frac{1}{2}|\nabla s(\vec{r})|^2 + Q[s(\vec{r})]\}d\tau_{\vec{r}}} \quad . \tag{3.1}$$

Here $s(\vec{r})$ is a continuous spin density (which is more convenient to treat than discrete spins s_i, though the difference is superficial); $Q(s)$ is some yet-to-be-specified function of the spin density; and $d\tau_{\vec{r}}$ is an element of volume at $\vec{r}$. By convention, an interaction-energy parameter, and $1/kT$, are absorbed in $s(\vec{r})$, leaving just ½ as the coefficient of the square gradient.

We shall suppose that $s(\vec{r})$ has no Fourier components of wavelength less than some fixed constant, <u>a</u> say, which sets a scale of length analogous to the lattice spacing in a lattice model. The integral over $\vec{r}$ in (3.1) is the analog of a sum over lattice sites i, and the square gradient $|\nabla s(\vec{r})|^2$ is the analog of the discrete $s_i^2 + s_{i'}^2 - 2s_i s_{i'}$ for a pair of <u>neighbouring</u> sites i and i'.

If $Q(s)$ were simply a multiple of s^2, then $Q[s(\vec{r})]$ would just provide another term analogous to s_i^2, and (3.1) would be the continuum form of the Gaussian model[9-11], with no external field. An additional term in $Q(s)$ linear in s would include the effect of such a field. A further term proportional to s^4, analogous to the discrete s_i^4, would, if its coefficient were positive, alter the weight that the Boltzmann factor B assigned to each spin configuration, in such a way as to make the model more Ising-model-like and less Gaussian-model-like[11]: The purely Gaussian weighting is uniform on every sphere $\sum_i s_i^2$ = constant, in the space of the s_i's; while on that same sphere, $\sum_i s_i^4$ is least, and $\exp(-\sum_i s_i^4)$ greatest, when all the s_i^2 are equal, as they are in the Ising model (where $s_i^2 = 1$, say, for all i).

Aside from a term linear in s arising from the interaction of the spins with an external magnetic field, $Q(s)$ must be even in s, and may be taken to be a power series in s^2. The infinitely many coefficients in this series mean infinitely many parameters a_0, b_0,..., in the language of section 2; but of these, only a small number prove to be relevant, the rest irrelevant.

It is shown by Wilson[8] that, starting with the Boltzmann factor (3.1), the transformation from the original spin density $s(\vec{r})$ to the "block-spin" density

$$\sigma(\vec{r}) = 2^{(d-2)/2} \int_{|\vec{q}|<\pi/a} \left(\int e^{i\vec{q}\cdot\vec{\rho}} s(\vec{\rho}) d\tau_{\vec{\rho}} \right) e^{-2i\vec{q}\cdot\vec{r}} d\tau_{\vec{q}} \quad , \tag{3.2}$$

where $\underline{a}$ is the basic length defined above, has, to some approximation, all the properties of the transformation discussed hypothetically in section 2. The quantity $\sigma(\vec{r}/2)$ calculated from (3.2) consists of the long-wavelength $(|\vec{q}|<\pi/a)$ Fourier components of $s(\vec{r})$, and has no component of wavelength less than $2a$, twice the minimum wavelength in $s(\vec{r})$. This is the basic feature of the block-spin variable; but then as a consequence of the length re-scaling — $2\vec{r}$ in place of $\vec{r}$ in the integrand in (3.2) — $\sigma(\vec{r})$ itself, like the original $s(\vec{r})$, again has $\underline{a}$ for its minimum wavelength.

Had the $\vec{q}$-integration in (3.2) been unrestricted (though the integrand vanishes for $|\vec{q}|>2\pi/a$ in any case, by definition of $\underline{a}$), instead of being restricted to $|\vec{q}|<\pi/a$, the resulting $\sigma(\vec{r})$ would have been proportional to $\int s(\vec{\rho})\,\delta(\vec{\rho}-2\vec{r})\,d\tau_{\vec{\rho}} = s(2\vec{r})$; but because of the restriction $|\vec{q}|<\pi/a$, the delta-function peak, while still centered at $2\vec{r}$, is now broadened to a width measured by 2a. Thus, $\sigma(\vec{r})$ is roughly, though not exactly, the total spin in a region of space of linear size 2a centered at $2\vec{r}$. This is the property of the block-spin variable σ that we anticipated earlier, now with the identification

$$\ell = 2^d \quad . \tag{3.3}$$

The factor $2^{(d-2)/2}$ in (3.2) is a spin re-scaling factor that restores the magnitude of the spin density to that of the original $s(\vec{r})$, so that in this transformation, and in each subsequent iteration of it, the spin variables retain their original magnitudes. (See section 9.) The length re-scaling mentioned earlier serves a similar purpose with respect to the distance variable. After n iterations of the transformation, the block-spin density consists only of those Fourier components of the original $s(\vec{r})$ that are of wavelength greater than $2^n a$; though because of the length re-scaling, the minimum wavelength is still formally $\underline{a}$ at every stage.

The once-transformed spin density $\sigma(\vec{r})$ here plays the part of the transformed spins $\sigma_1,\ldots,\sigma_{N/\ell}$ of section 2. The analog of the once-transformed Boltzmann factor, that is, of the quantity in parentheses in the numerator and denominator of (2.3), is obtained from (3.1) by integrating the functional $B\{s(\vec{r})\}$ over all possible short-wavelength components $(|\vec{q}|>\pi/a)$ of the $s(\vec{r})$ — analogous to the integration over $\sigma_{(N/\ell)+1},\ldots,\sigma_N$ in (2.3). The result is then a new Boltzmann factor, B', which is still a functional of the $\sigma(\vec{r})$, i.e., of the long-wavelength components of the original $s(\vec{r})$. If the new functional $B'\{\sigma(\vec{r})\}$ were again (to within a constant factor) of the form (3.1), though perhaps with a new function $Q_1(\sigma)$ in place of the original $Q(s)$, then B' would be just the quantity described schematically as $B_{N/\ell}(\sigma_1,\ldots, \sigma_{N/\ell}; a_1, b_1,\ldots)$ in section 2. The parameters $a_1, b_1,\ldots$ correspond to the function $Q_1(\sigma)$, just as the original $a_0, b_0,\ldots$ corresponded to the original function $Q(s)$. Wilson[8] shows that, to some approximation, it is indeed so that $B'\{\sigma(\vec{r})\}$, constructed as described above, is of the same form as the original $B\{s(\vec{r})\}$ in (3.1); and that if $Q_n(x)$ is the function Q after n iterations of this transformation (so that in this notation the Q above is Q_0), then, in the absence of an external field, $Q_n(x)$ is the solution of the approximate recurrence relation

$$Q_{n+1}(x) = -2^d \ln[I_n(2^{1-d/2}x)/I_n(0)] \tag{3.4}$$

where

$$I_n(x) = \int_{-\infty}^{\infty} e^{-y^2-\frac{1}{2}[Q_n(x+y)+Q_n(x-y)]} dy \quad . \tag{3.5}$$

These are approximate renormalization-group equations for the present model with no external field. The approximations entail $\eta = 0$[8]. A simple generalization of (3.4)-(3.5) that allows a non-vanishing value of the critical-point exponent η will be found in section 6, where recurrence relations remarkably like (3.4)-(3.5) will be seen to be <u>exact</u> for a special class of models.

An obvious solution of (3.4)-(3.5) is $Q_n(x)$ = a constant multiple of $4^n x^2$. This solution arises from a $Q_0(x)$ that is then also just a constant multiple of x^2, and so corresponds to the Gaussian model. The significant question is whether a $Q_0(x)$ that also contains terms proportional to higher powers of x will lead to an essentially different solution, and thus to an Ising-model-like critical point, of a character different from that of the Gaussian model. We shall see in the next section that such a solution may be explicitly derived from (3.4)-(3.5) when the dimensionality d is near 4, and that it illustrates some important general features of the theory.

4. THE WILSON-FISHER ε-EXPANSION[12]

If the dimensionality d in (3.4) is treated as a continuous variable, and if we imagine d to be near 4, so that

$$\varepsilon = 4 - d \tag{4.1}$$

is a small parameter, then we may verify by direct substitution that there are solutions of (3.4)-(3.5) of the form

$$Q_n(x) = v_n x^2 + u_n x^4 + \mathcal{O}(\varepsilon^3) \qquad [v_n,\ u_n \text{ both } \mathcal{O}(\varepsilon)] \quad . \tag{4.2}$$

To see this, we first substitute (4.2) into (3.5), and then the resulting I_n into (3.4), thus obtaining

$$Q_{n+1}(x) = 4(v_n + 3u_n - 9u_n^2 - 3v_n u_n)x^2 + (1 + \varepsilon \ln 2 - 9u_n)u_n x^4 + \mathcal{O}(\varepsilon^3) \quad . \tag{4.3}$$

Then (4.2) is indeed a solution, provided v_n, u_n satisfy the two coupled recurrence relations

$$v_{n+1} = 4(v_n + 3u_n - 9u_n^2 - 3v_n u_n) + \mathcal{O}(\varepsilon^3) \tag{4.4}$$

$$u_{n+1} = (1 + \varepsilon \ln 2 - 9u_n)u_n + \mathcal{O}(\varepsilon^3) \quad . \tag{4.5}$$

These are the renormalization-group equations for the two parameters u_n, v_n. These two parameters are all that are required to fix Q_n, to $\mathcal{O}(\varepsilon^2)$. The term $v_n x^2$ in $Q_n(x)$, alone, would characterize the Gaussian model, but the additional term $u_n x^4$, if it proves to be important, makes the model Ising-model-like. We are treating the case of no external field, so there is no term in $Q_n(x)$ linear in x.

The algebraic equations (2.5) that determine the fixed points of (4.4)-(4.5) are

$$0 = v^* + 4u^* - 12u^{*2} - 4v^*u^* + \mathcal{O}(\varepsilon^3) \tag{4.6}$$

$$0 = (\varepsilon \ln 2 - 9u^*)u^* + \mathcal{O}(\varepsilon^3) \quad . \tag{4.7}$$

These have two solutions. One is the "Gaussian-model fixed point",

$$v^* = -4u^* = 0 \qquad \text{(Gaussian fixed point)} \quad , \tag{4.8}$$

exact for all ε; this is the fixed point with which is associated, for example, the solution $Q_n = v_n x^2$, $v_n = 4^n v_0$ of the original equations (3.4)-(3.5), that we had noted before. The second is the "Ising-model fixed point",

$$v^* = -4u^* + \mathcal{O}(\varepsilon^2) = -\frac{4 \ln 2}{9}\varepsilon + \mathcal{O}(\varepsilon^2) \qquad \text{(Ising fixed point)} \quad . \tag{4.9}$$

The matrix of coefficients, (2.9), that is obtained when the recurrence relations (4.4)-(4.5) are linearized about either of the fixed points (4.8) or (4.9), is

$$\begin{bmatrix} 4(1-3u^*) + \mathcal{O}(\varepsilon^2) & 12(1-6u^*-v^*) + \mathcal{O}(\varepsilon^2) \\ \mathcal{O}(\varepsilon^2) & 1+\varepsilon\ln 2 - 18u^* + \mathcal{O}(\varepsilon^2) \end{bmatrix}, \tag{4.10}$$

with eigenvalues

$$\lambda_1 = 4(1-3u^*) + \mathcal{O}(\varepsilon^2) \quad , \quad \lambda_2 = 1 + \varepsilon\ln 2 - 18u^* + \mathcal{O}(\varepsilon^2) \quad . \tag{4.11}$$

Evaluated separately at the two fixed points, these are

$$\lambda_1 = 4 \quad , \quad \lambda_2 = 1 + \varepsilon\ln 2 + \mathcal{O}(\varepsilon^2) \qquad \text{(Gaussian fixed point)} \tag{4.12}$$

and

$$\lambda_1 = 4 - \frac{4\ln 2}{3}\varepsilon + \mathcal{O}(\varepsilon^2) \ , \ \lambda_2 = 1 - \varepsilon\ln 2 + \mathcal{O}(\varepsilon^2) \quad \text{(Ising fixed point)}. \tag{4.13}$$

The value of λ_1 given by (4.12) is exact, for all ε, and with it there is associated, in particular, the solution $\varrho_n = v_n x^2$, $v_n = 4^n v_0$ of (3.4)-(3.5).

Which of the two fixed points is the relevant one depends on the initial conditions and on the sign of ε. If $u_0 = 0$, we see from (4.4)-(4.5) that $u_n = 0$ and $v_n = 4^n v_0$. If, instead, u_0 is positive, but still small on a scale of ε, and if $\varepsilon<0$ $(d>4)$, then it is seen from (4.5) that u_n, while now not identically 0, nevertheless vanishes for large n, and does so as $(1+\varepsilon\ln 2)^n u_0$; while v_n is again $4^n v_0$, for large n, from (4.4). But this is just the solution of the renormalization-group equations (4.4)-(4.5) in the neighbourhood of the Gaussian fixed point $v^* = u^* = 0$, where the eigenvalues λ_1 and λ_2 given by (4.12) are $\lambda_1 = 4$ and $\lambda_2 = 1 + \varepsilon\ln 2$. Near this fixed point in the v_n, u_n plane the trajectories are like those in figure 2, with a_n and b_n identified as v_n and u_n, respectively, but with the slope s now negative: $s = d_{12}/d_{22} = -4 + \mathcal{O}(\varepsilon)$.

Thus, when $u_0 = 0$, or when $u_0 \gtrsim 0$ and $\varepsilon<0$, it is the Gaussian fixed point that is dominant in determining the character of the solution of the renormalization-group equations for large n; of the two fixed points (4.8) and (4.9), it is in this case the former that is relevant. When the conditions $u_0 \gtrsim 0$, $\varepsilon<0$ $(d>4)$ are satisfied, and when, in addition, the system is close to its critical point, which is at $v_0 = -4u_0 + \mathcal{O}(\varepsilon^2)$, the v_n, u_n trajectories then pass close to the Gaussian fixed point. Because it entails $u_n \to 0$ with increasing n, hence the vanishing of the x^4 term in (4.2), this fixed point corresponds always to the Gaussian model, as its name suggests, and the critical-point exponents it implies are those of that model, as we shall see.

If $u_0 \gtrsim 0$ still, but now $\varepsilon>0$ $(d<4)$, we see from (4.5) that u_n increases with increasing n; i.e., the x^4 term in (4.2) becomes increasingly important with each iteration of the transformation, and the properties of the system are then Ising-model-like. The dominant influence in determining the character of the solution of the renormalization-group equations is in this case that of the Ising fixed point (4.9). Near this fixed point the trajectories are again like those in figure 2, with a_n and b_n again identified as v_n and u_n, and again with $s = d_{12}/d_{22} = -4 + \mathcal{O}(\varepsilon)$. When the conditions $u_0 \gtrsim 0$, $\varepsilon>0$ $(d<4)$ are satisfied, and when, in addition, the system is close to its critical point, which is again at $v_0 = -4u_0 + \mathcal{O}(\varepsilon^2)$, the v_n, u_n trajectories pass close to the Ising fixed point. With increasing n the parameter u_n approaches its fixed-point value u^* given by (4.9), which is now non-zero. Thus, in this case the x^4 term in (4.2) remains important, the system is Ising-model-like, and its critical-point exponents are those of that model, as we shall see.

The initial condition $u_0 < 0$ is non-physical, for it would yield a divergent partition function, and so need not be considered further.

It is important to notice that when $\varepsilon<0$, in which case the eigenvalues (4.13) associated with the Ising fixed point are both greater than 1, it is the Gaussian fixed point that is relevant, and that there, from (4.12), $\lambda_1>1$, $\lambda_2<1$; and that when $\varepsilon>0$, in which case the eigenvalues associated with the Gaussian fixed point are both greater than 1, it is the Ising fixed point that is relevant, and that there, also, $\lambda_1>1$, $\lambda_2<1$. (When $u_0 = 0$ the Gaussian fixed point is the relevant one even when $\varepsilon>0$, as we saw; but then $u_n = 0$, $v_n = 4^n v_0$, so the fact that formally $\lambda_2>1$ in that case is of no consequence, and this exception to the rule that at the relevant fixed point $\lambda_1>1$, $\lambda_2<1$, may be ignored.) In the language of section 2, there is then only one "relevant" parameter. This is as expected, because there is no external field in this model, so there is only a temperature-like variable that can be relevant. The eigenvalue here called λ_1 is the one that exceeds 1, and so may be identified with the thermal eigenvalue λ_T, as in section 2.

With $\lambda_T = \lambda_1$ then given by (4.12) for $\varepsilon<0$ $(d>4)$ and by (4.13) for $\varepsilon>0$ $(d<4)$, and with ℓ given by (3.3), the critical-point exponent ν may be calculated from (2.14),

$$\nu = \frac{1}{2} \qquad (d>4) \tag{4.14}$$

$$\nu = \frac{1}{2} + \frac{1}{12}\varepsilon + \mathcal{O}(\varepsilon^2) \qquad (d<4) \tag{4.15}$$

The value $\nu = \frac{1}{2}$ is the classical, mean-field-theory result, and is indeed characteristic of the Gaussian model for $d>4$. The right-hand side of (4.15), truncated after its second term, cannot be expected to be quantitatively accurate for ε as large as 1 — in fact, it yields $\nu \approx 0.58$, while one expects $\nu = 0.64$

for $d = 3$ — but it nevertheless shows clearly why ν exceeds its classical value when $d<4$, and as such is a major achievement. We did not calculate the correlation function here, but had we done so we would have seen that $\eta = 0$ [8], as mentioned earlier. Therefore, from (1.10), the values of ν given by (4.14) and (4.15) are at the same time approximations to $\frac{1}{2}\gamma$. The value $\gamma = 1$ is the classical, mean-field-theory result, and is indeed characteristic of the Gaussian model for all $d>4$; and (4.15) shows why $\gamma > 1$ when $d<4$.

At $d = 4$ itself, we have $\varepsilon = 0$, and the two fixed points (4.8) and (4.9) coincide. In that borderline case the thermodynamic functions are modified by logarithmic factors, which we shall not consider further; but such factors leave unaltered the formal values of the critical point exponents, which are then the same as for a Gaussian model of $d>4$, where the exponents have their classical, mean-field-theory values. The dimensionality $d = 4$ is then the borderline dimensionality below which the critical point is non-classical, with d-dependent critical-point exponents, and at which it changes over to a classical critical point with critical-point exponents that are independent of d. The concept of a borderline dimensionality is an important one, to which we shall return in section 9, after we have discussed critical points of higher order.

Wilson[13] has shown that one may obtain the ε-expansion from a Feynman-graph expansion, starting with a generalized form of (3.1), but without further approximation, and, in particular, without use of the approximate recurrence relations (3.4)-(3.5), etc. The results are that the critical-point exponents calculated by the theory outlined above are verified to be correct to and including their terms of order ε, but not to $\mathcal{O}(\varepsilon^2)$; that the critical-point exponent η proves to be $\mathcal{O}(\varepsilon^2)$, with a very small coefficient: $\eta = \frac{1}{54}\varepsilon^2 + \mathcal{O}(\varepsilon^3)$; and that the critical-point exponents, when calculated correctly to $\mathcal{O}(\varepsilon^2)$ and then evaluated at $\varepsilon = 1$, are in very good (though not perfect) agreement with those determined numerically for the three-dimensional Ising model. With the inclusion of terms $\mathcal{O}(\varepsilon^3)$, however, the agreement becomes poorer[14], so the ε-expansion is asymptotic rather than convergent.

Starting with very general Hamiltonians in (3.1), there may be many fixed points, which compete with each other in determining the character of the n-times transformed Hamiltonian for large n, in the same way that the two fixed points in the theory just outlined competed with each other. Just as here it was the nature of the starting Hamiltonian that determined which of the fixed points would ultimately be the relevant one, so also, more generally, it is the initial Hamiltonian that determines, according to the values of its parameters, which fixed point will be relevant. That, in turn, determines the values of the critical-point exponents. Hamiltonians may then be grouped into "universality classes", such that all those in the same class — those with the values of their parameters in certain prescribed ranges — lead to the same fixed-point Hamiltonian, and are thus the

Hamiltonians of systems that share a common set of critical-point exponents. Two systems with different sets of exponents belong to different universality classes. This idea explains why, on the one hand, there may be many features of a Hamiltonian — the precise values of its interaction energies, the details of its lattice structure, etc. — that affect only the location of a critical point, but not its analytical character as expressed by the critical-point exponents; and why, on the other hand, not all Hamiltonians yield the same kind of critical point.

5. OTHER METHODS

Many of the practical, numerical results of the renormalization-group theory have come from the ε-expansion, but other methods have also been used.

One that is similar in spirit to the ε-expansion is the $\frac{1}{n}$-expansion,[15] where n is now the dimensionality of the spin, i.e., the number of spatial components of the (classical) spin vector. In this notation, $n = 1$ defines the Ising model, $n = 2$ the classical XY model, $n = 3$ the classical Heisenberg model, and $n = \infty$ the spherical model[16]. The latter is essentially the Gaussian model[10], and expansions about $n = \infty$ $(1/n = 0)$, like those about $d = 4$ $(\varepsilon = 0)$, exploit the fact that the renormalization-group equations are exactly soluble in the Gaussian-model limit.

A quite different and particularly important numerical method for the treatment of Ising models with discrete spins $s_i = \pm 1$, that arose from the renormalization-group ideas and is very close to Kadanoff's original block-spin picture, was developed by Niemeijer and van Leeuwen[17,18]. It is based on block-spin variables σ_i defined by $\sigma_i = +1$ or -1 according to the sign of the net spin Σs_i in a small cluster of sites. In evaluating the partition function, the Boltzmann factor is first summed over all spin configurations of the clusters for which the net spins are of one sign; i.e., for fixed values of the block-spin variables. The result is proportional to the Boltzmann factor of a new, effective Hamiltonian, that is a function of the block-spin variables, and contains nearest-neighbour, further-than-nearest-neighbour, and more-than-pair interactions. This transformation is then iterated, and leads to renormalization-group equations for the interaction-energy parameters. The larger the basic cluster, the more parameters that enter and undergo transformation, and the more accurate the approximation. The method has not yet been widely applied, but judging from its early applications[17,18] it is of considerable promise.

In the scheme outlined in section 2 there appeared a proportionality constant c^N that was such that the once-transformed Boltzmann factor was $c^N B_{N/\ell}$, with ℓ the number of spins in a block. That constant canceled from numerator and denominator of (2.3), and was not mentioned again, but it has a thermodynamic significance that we shall now consider. The quantity c itself is some intensive, analytic function of the parameters that are present in the original Boltzmann factor, $c = c(a_0, b_0, \ldots)$. After the second iteration of the transformation there then appears, as a second proportionality factor, the same function c, now of arguments $a_1, b_1, \ldots$, and now raised to the power N/ℓ; etc. Then the partition function $Z_N(a_0, b_0, \ldots)$ of the N-spin system is

$$Z_N(a_0,b_0,\ldots) = Z_1(a_{\log_\ell N}, b_{\log_\ell N}, \ldots) \prod_{n=1}^{\log_\ell N} c(a_{n-1}, b_{n-1}, \ldots)^{N/\ell^{n-1}} , \quad (5.1)$$

where the logarithms, as noted, are with base ℓ. The free energy per spin (including, but now not merely, its singular part) is then

$$f = -\ell kT \sum_{n=1}^{\infty} \ell^{-n} \ln c(a_{n-1}, b_{n-1}, \ldots) - kT \lim_{N\to\infty} \frac{1}{N} \ln Z_1(a_{\log_\ell N}, b_{\log_\ell N}, \ldots). \quad (5.2)$$

Each term in the infinite series is analytic in the parameters $a_0, b_0, \ldots$ that are present in the original Boltzmann factor, but the whole sum, which contributes part or all of the critical-point singularity in f, is not. The critical-point exponents alone are derivable from the recurrence relations for the $a_n, b_n, \ldots$, without reference to the function c, as in section 2; but this function c, that is in the otherwise neglected proportionality factor, is now seen to be of importance if one wishes to calculate the full equation of state. This point was emphasized by Nauenberg and Nienhuis[19], who thereby extended the method of Niemeijer and van Leeuwen.

6. BAKER MODELS[20]

The mechanism of the renormalization-group transformation, and the origin of the approximate recurrence relation (3.4)-(3.5), are illuminated by models that were introduced for this purpose by Baker[20]. (See also Dyson[21].) In these there is a hierarchy of spin groupings, and the interaction between groups, at each level of the hierarchy, depends only on the sums of the spins in the groups; so that the Kadanoff hypothesis is made to be correct, just by the structure of the Hamiltonian.

The models are best described first in their one-dimensional version, in which the interactions are as pictured in figure 3. There are interactions (the precise nature of which will be specified presently) between alternate pairs of spins ("level 0"), a weaker interaction between alternate pairs of such pairs ("level 1"), a still weaker interaction between alternate pairs of those pairs ("level 2"), etc. (We may construct similar models with any number $\ell = 2,3,4,\ldots$ of spins in the basic group[20]; here we take $\ell = 2$.) To begin with, we have N ($= 2^M$, say) sites, pictured as the dots in fig. 3, with a spin $s_{m,0}$ ($m = 1,2,3,\ldots,2^M$) at each site. The second subscript 0 on $s_{m,0}$ identifies these

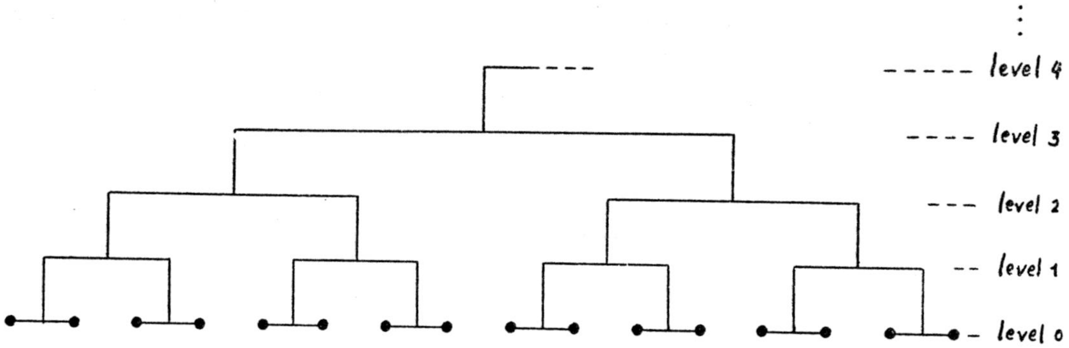

Figure 3

as the original, untransformed spin variables. They are continuous spins, but limited to

$$-1 \le s_{m,0} \le 1 \tag{6.1}$$

unlike the s_i of section 2, which range from $-\infty$ to ∞.

In terms of the $s_{m,0}$, we now define $N = 2^M$ new spin variables — half of them called $s_{m,1}$ and half $\hat{s}_{m,1}$ — by the orthogonal transformation

$$s_{m,1} = (s_{2m-1,0} + s_{2m,0})/\sqrt{2}$$

$$\hat{s}_{m,1} = (s_{2m-1,0} - s_{2m,0})/\sqrt{2} \quad , \tag{6.2}$$

$$m = 1,2,3,\ldots,2^{M-1} \; .$$

In this first transformation, as well as in each of the subsequent ones to which we shall proceed in a moment, the uncapped s's are sums of the previous uncapped s's, while the capped s's are differences of the previous uncapped s's. (This notation is the reverse of Baker's[20].)

We now leave the 2^{M-1} capped s's alone, and transform the 2^{M-1} uncapped s's a second time:

$$s_{m,2} = (s_{2m-1,1} + s_{2m,1})/\sqrt{2}$$

$$\hat{s}_{m,2} = (s_{2m-1,1} - s_{2m,1})/\sqrt{2} \quad , \tag{6.3}$$

$$m = 1,2,3,\ldots,2^{M-2} \; .$$

Continuing in this way to the general level n of this transformation, we leave the $2^{M-(n-1)}$ capped s's alone and transform the $2^{M-(n-1)}$ uncapped s's,

$$s_{m,n} = (s_{2m-1,n-1} + s_{2m,n-1})/\sqrt{2}$$

$$\hat{s}_{m,n} = (s_{2m-1,n-1} - s_{2m,n-1})/\sqrt{2} \quad , \qquad (6.4)$$

$$m = 1,2,3,\ldots,2^{M-n} \quad .$$

The model is now defined by its Hamiltonian, which depends explicitly on all the $\hat{s}_{m,n}$ of every level of transformation n, and, in addition, depends explicitly on all the original $s_{m,0}$:

$$\mathcal{H} = J \sum_{n=1}^{M} 2^{-(2-\eta)(n-1)} \sum_{m=1}^{2^{M-n}} (\hat{s}_{m,n})^2$$

$$- \frac{1}{2} J \frac{1-2^{-(3-\eta)M}}{1-2^{-(3-\eta)}} \sum_{m=1}^{2^M} (s_{m,0})^2 \quad , \qquad (6.5)$$

where J and η are two parameters. Because each $s_{m,n}$ is the sum of a neighbouring pair of spins from the previous level of transformation, and each $\hat{s}_{m,n}$ is the difference of such a neighbouring pair of spins, $s_{m,n}$ is like the total spin in a large block of the original spins $s_{m,0}$, while $\hat{s}_{m,n}$ is like the gradient of the spin density, or the difference between the sums of the original spins in neighbouring pairs of blocks. Thus, the various pieces $\Sigma_m(\hat{s}_{m,n})^2$ of the Hamiltonian (6.5) are analogous to $\int |\nabla s(\vec{r})|^2 d\tau_{\vec{r}}$ in Wilson's Hamiltonian (section 3); though it is an important characteristic of the present model that its Hamiltonian contains not just one such sum (over m), but a sum (over n) of such sums, one corresponding to each level of interaction, with weights $2^{-(2-\eta)(n-1)}$ that decrease with the level. The remaining part of (6.5), proportional to $\Sigma_m(s_{m,0})^2$, is analogous to the integral of the s^2 term in the earlier $Q(s)$ [$= Q_0(s)$] of section 3. It will appear later — with the introduction of $Q_0(s)$ in (6.7) below — that the restriction (6.1) also contributes to the effective $Q(s)$, which is then not merely proportional to s^2, but, it transpires, is qualitatively like that of section 3.

By tracing the recurrent transformation (6.4) backward, each $\hat{s}_{m,n}$ may ultimately be expressed in terms of the original spin variables $s_{m,0}$. If these expressions are then substituted for the $\hat{s}_{m,n}$ in (6.5), the terms $(s_{m,0})^2$ in the Hamiltonian are found[20] to cancel exactly, leaving $\mathcal{H}$ entirely a sum of products of pairs of distinct spins. Each such pair of distinct spins $s_{m,0}$ and $s_{m',0}$ contributes to the interaction energy the amount[20]

$$-J \frac{2^{3-\eta}-2}{2^{3-\eta}-1} \frac{s_{m,0}\, s_{m',0}}{2^{(3-\eta)(n-1)}} \qquad (6.6)$$

where now n is the level of first appearance of the product $s_{m,0}\, s_{m',0}$. (See fig. 3, where for the pair $s_{1,0}$, $s_{13,0}$, for example, the level of first appearance is seen to be $n = 3$.) When $\eta < 2$, the interaction (6.6) is ferromagnetic for positive J and antiferromagnetic for negative J. The reason for the appearance in (6.6) of the smaller weighting factor $2^{-(3-\eta)(n-1)}$ in place of the larger $2^{-(2-\eta)(n-1)}$ from (6.5), is that the product $s_{m,0}\, s_{m',0}$ contributes ferromagnetically (for $J > 0$ and $\eta < 2$) only at the level of its first appearance, but thereafter antiferromagnetically, so that its total contribution, while still ferromagnetic, is weaker than in its first appearance. Because n in (6.6) is the level of first appearance of the product $s_{m,0}\, s_{m',0}$, the quantity 2^n is a measure of the typical distance r between sites m and m', so according to (6.6) the effective spin-spin interaction energy in the present one-dimensional model falls off inversely with the $3-\eta$ power of the distance. As long as $\eta \leq 1$, this counts as a short-range interaction in one dimension, and we would then expect no phase transition in this one-dimensional model.[21)]

The partition function of the model defined by (6.5) is obtained by integrating $\exp(-\mathcal{H}/kT)$ over all the $s_{m,0}$, each ranging from -1 to 1. In this integration the $\hat{s}_{m,n}$ in (6.5) are to be understood as functions of the $s_{m,0}$, obtained recursively from (6.4). Now define a function $\mathcal{Q}_0(s)$,

$$\mathcal{Q}_0(s) = \begin{cases} -\frac{1}{2} K \dfrac{1-2^{-(3-\eta)M}}{1-2^{-(3-\eta)}} s^2 & \text{when} \quad -\sqrt{2} \leq s \leq \sqrt{2} \\ \infty & \text{otherwise,} \end{cases} \qquad (6.7)$$

where

$$K = J/kT \quad . \qquad (6.8)$$

This function is shown graphically as "Baker's $\mathcal{Q}_0(s)$" in fig. 4(a). Then from (6.5), (6.7) and (6.8), the partition function Z may be written

$$Z = \int_{-\infty}^{\infty} \cdots \int_{-\infty}^{\infty} \exp\Big[-K \sum_{n=1}^{M} 2^{-(2-\eta)(n-1)} \sum_{m=1}^{2^{M-n}} (\hat{s}_{m,n})^2 - \frac{1}{2} \sum_{m=1}^{2^M} \mathcal{Q}_0(\sqrt{2}\, s_{m,0}) \Big] \prod_{m=1}^{2^M} ds_{m,0} \quad . \qquad (6.9)$$

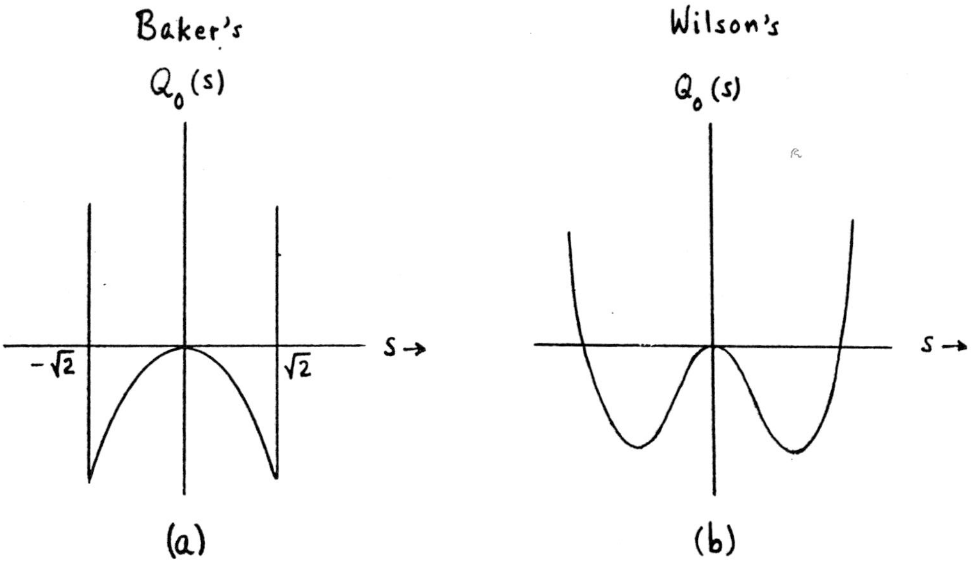

Figure 4

It was possible to extend the integrations from the intervals -1,1 to $-\infty, \infty$ because, by the definition of $Q_0(s)$ in (6.7), the integrand in (6.9) vanishes for any $s_{m,0}$ outside the range -1,1. It will emerge that $Q_0(s)$ plays a rôle in this model that is closely analogous to that of the $Q_0(s)$ [$= Q(s)$] in the Wilson theory, where the integrations in the partition function (the denominator of (2.1)) also range over $-\infty, \infty$. Wilson's $Q_0(s)$ is shown for comparison in fig. 4(b). From (4.2), it may be thought of roughly as $v_0 s^2 + u_0 s^4$ with $v_0 < 0$, $u_0 > 0$ — it was found in section 4, for example, that, to $\mathcal{O}(\varepsilon^2)$, the critical point was at $v_0 = -4u_0 < 0$ — and so has the shape shown. Its qualitative similarity to the $Q_0(s)$ in fig. 4(a) is clear. Indeed, when $v_0 \approx -4u_0$ its minima are at $s \approx \pm\sqrt{2}$.

If the integration variables in (6.9) are changed from the $s_{m,0}$ to the $s_{m,1}$ and $\hat{s}_{m,1}$ by means of the orthogonal transformation (6.2), the new element of volume is simply

$$\prod_{m=1}^{2^{M-1}} ds_{m,1}\, d\hat{s}_{m,1} \quad . \tag{6.10}$$

At the same time the factor in the integrand of (6.9) that contains the function Q_0, together with the factor that contains the $(\hat{s}_{m,1})^2$, from the term n = 1 in the first sum in the exponent, becomes

$$\prod_{m=1}^{2^{M-1}} \exp\left[-K\,(\hat{s}_{m,1})^2 - \tfrac{1}{2}Q_0(s_{m,1} + \hat{s}_{m,1}) - \tfrac{1}{2}Q_0(s_{m,1} - \hat{s}_{m,1})\right] \quad ; \tag{6.11}$$

where, to obtain (6.11), we re-expressed the sum of the $Q_0(\sqrt{2}\, s_{m,0})$ as

$$\sum_{m=1}^{2^M} Q_0(\sqrt{2}\, s_{m,0}) = \sum_{m=1}^{2^{M-1}} [Q_0(\sqrt{2}\, s_{2m-1,0}) + Q_0(\sqrt{2}\, s_{2m,0})] \quad , \tag{6.12}$$

and replaced $s_{2m-1,0}$ and $s_{2m,0}$ by $(s_{m,1} + \hat{s}_{m,1})/\sqrt{2}$ and $(s_{m,1} - \hat{s}_{m,1})/\sqrt{2}$, respectively, from (6.2).

The partition function (6.9) now has the new element of volume (6.10), and an integrand that is the product of (6.11) and the remaining factor

$$\exp[-K \sum_{n=2}^{M} 2^{-(2-\eta)(n-1)} \sum_{m=1}^{2^{M-n}} (\hat{s}_{m,n})^2] \tag{6.13}$$

By (6.4), each $\hat{s}_{m,n}$ for $m = 1,\ldots,2^{M-n}$ and $n \geq 2$, may be expressed in terms of all the $s_{m,1}$'s $(m = 1,\ldots,2^{M-1})$, but for given $s_{m,1}$'s is independent of the $\hat{s}_{m,1}$'s. Thus, the factor (6.13) in the integrand of the partition function is a function only of the integration variables $s_{m,1}$ and is independent of the integration variables $\hat{s}_{m,1}$. The only dependence of the integrand on the $\hat{s}_{m,1}$ is in the factor (6.11). But the latter is itself a product of 2^{M-1} factors, each of which depends on only a single one of the $\hat{s}_{m,1}$; so the multiple integral over the $\hat{s}_{m,1}$ is just a product of single integrals. The partition function then becomes

$$Z = \int_{-\infty}^{\infty} \cdots \int_{-\infty}^{\infty} \begin{pmatrix}\text{factor} \\ (6.13)\end{pmatrix} \times \prod_{m=1}^{2^{M-1}} [I_0(s_{m,1})ds_{m,1}] \tag{6.14}$$

where

$$I_0(x) = \int_{-\infty}^{\infty} e^{-Ky^2 - \frac{1}{2}[Q_0(x+y) + Q_0(x-y)]} dy \quad . \tag{6.15}$$

Now define a new function Q_1 by

$$Q_1(x) = -2 \ln[I_0(2^{\frac{1-\eta}{2}} x)/I_0(0)] \tag{6.16}$$

divide each of the integration variables $s_{m,1}$ in (6.15) by $2^{1-\eta/2}$, and, in the factor (6.13), change to a new summation index n equal to the earlier n-1. Then from (6.13)-(6.16),

$$Z = [2^{1-\eta/2} I_0(0)]^{2^{M-1}} \int_{-\infty}^{\infty} \cdots \int_{-\infty}^{\infty} \begin{pmatrix}\text{factor}\\ (6.18)\end{pmatrix}$$

$$\times \exp\left[-\frac{1}{2}\sum_{m=1}^{2^{M-1}} Q_1\left(\sqrt{2}\,\frac{s_{m,1}}{2^{1-\eta/2}}\right)\right] \prod_{m=1}^{2^{M-1}} d\,\frac{s_{m,1}}{2^{1-\eta/2}} \tag{6.17}$$

where the factor (6.18) is

$$\exp\left[-K\sum_{n=1}^{M-1} 2^{-(2-\eta)(n-1)} \sum_{m=1}^{2^{M-1-n}} (\hat{s}_{m,n+1}/2^{1-\eta/2})^2\right] \tag{6.18}$$

(With the new summation variable n, the weight factor $2^{-(2-\eta)(n-1)}$ in (6.13) should become $2^{-(2-\eta)n}$ in (6.18); but we continue to call it $2^{-(2-\eta)(n-1)}$, and then compensate for that by dividing the $\hat{s}_{m,n+1}$ in (6.18) by $2^{1-\eta/2}$.) But (6.17)-(6.18) is seen to have a structure identical to that of the partition function in its original form, (6.9), though now for a system with only half as many, $N/2 = 2^{M-1}$, spin variables, so that M is replaced by $M-1$. By the transformation equations (6.4), the $\hat{s}_{m,n+1}/2^{1-\eta/2}$ in (6.18) are related to the integration variables $s_{m,1}/2^{1-\eta/2}$ in (6.17) in the same way that the $\hat{s}_{m,n}$ of (6.9) are related to the original integration variables $s_{m,0}$. The original function Q_0 has been replaced by the quite different function Q_1, related to Q_0 by (6.15)-(6.16), but this is as anticipated in the Wilson theory. We see further, on comparing (6.17)-(6.18) with (6.9), that we may identify the quantity c that was referred to in sections 2 and 5, which is such that the once-transformed Boltzmann factor is $c^N B_{N/\ell}$. Here $\ell = 2$ and $N = 2^M$, and we find

$$c = [2^{1-\eta/2} I_0(0)]^{1/2} \quad . \tag{6.19}$$

The transformation that led from (6.9) to (6.17)-(6.18) may now be repeated arbitrarily many times. The Q_n that appears after the nth iteration of the transformation is determined by Q_{n-1} in the same way that Q_1 is determined by Q_0; i.e., by the generalization

$$Q_{n+1}(x) = -2\ln\left[I_n(2^{\frac{1-\eta}{2}}x)/I_n(0)\right] \tag{6.20}$$

$$I_n(x) = \int_{-\infty}^{\infty} e^{-Ky^2 - \frac{1}{2}[Q_n(x+y) + Q_n(x-y)]}\,dy \tag{6.21}$$

of (6.15)-(6.16). It emerges later, in the higher-dimensional versions of these models, that the parameter η in the Hamiltonian is the same as the critical-point exponent η, so to compare (6.20)-(6.21) with Wilson's approximate renormalization-group equations (3.4)-(3.5), which we know entail $\eta = 0$, we should set $\eta = 0$ here; and, at the same time, we should take $d = 1$ in (3.4), for (6.20)-(6.21) refers explicitly to a one-dimensional model. We then see that (6.20)-(6.21) is the same as (3.4)-(3.5), except that $K = 1$ in the latter. But that difference is superficial, for if $Q_n(x; K)$ is the solution of (6.20)-(6.21), then $Q_n(x; K) = Q_n(\sqrt{K}\, x; 1)$; i.e., the problem of solving (6.20)-(6.21) for general K is the same as that of solving it for $K = 1$.

This derivation of (6.20)-(6.21) as an exact recurrence relation for the present model is formally similar to, and illuminates, the derivation[8] of the approximate recurrence relation (3.4)-(3.5).

We now go on to general dimensionality d. One way of extending the interaction scheme of fig. 3. to general d is illustrated in figure 5(a) for the square net, $d = 2$, but the same basic idea can clearly be applied to a hypercubical lattice of any d. The lattice sites are shown as heavy dots, and the successive levels of interaction are distinguished by —— , --- , ... , etc. With spin variables and their transformations suitably generalized from (6.4), with a Hamiltonian that is a generalization of that in (6.5) suited to the interaction scheme of fig. 4(a), and with a Q_0 analogous to that in (6.7), Baker[20] finds the recurrence relation

$$Q_{n+1}(x) = -\, 2^{d} \ln \left[I_n(2^{1-d/2-\eta/2}\, x)/I_n(0) \right] \tag{6.22}$$

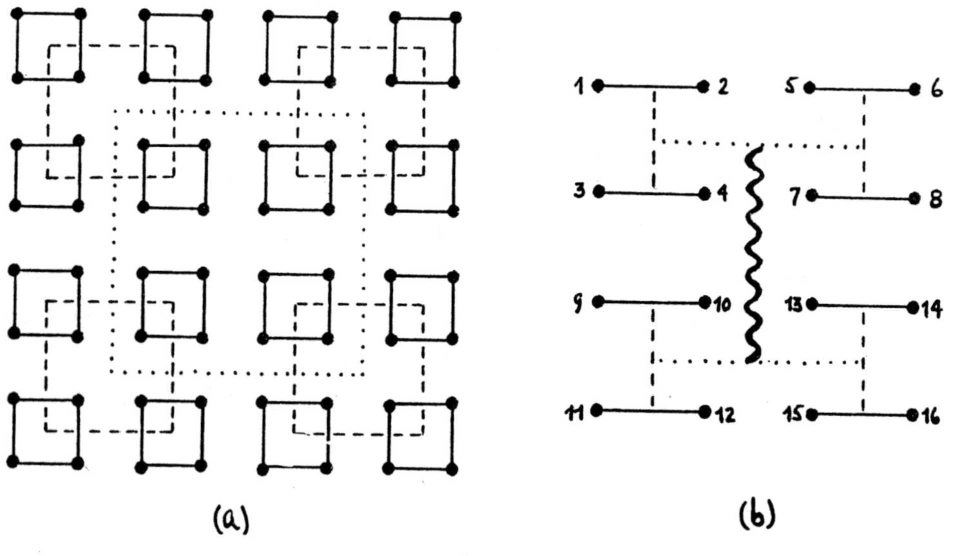

Figure 5

with

$$I_n(x) = (2^d-1) \text{ - fold multiple integral, generalization of (6.21)} \quad . \tag{6.23}$$

We see that (6.22) is the same as (3.4) with a general η; but (6.23), though the multiple integrals have a structure highly reminiscent of that of the single integral (3.5) (again, the presence of K makes no real difference), is nevertheless not the same as (3.5).

There is an alternative generalization of the one-dimensional model, corresponding to the interaction scheme that is illustrated for the square net, $d = 2$, in fig. 5(b). The lattice sites are again shown as heavy dots, now numbered, and the successive levels of interaction are distinguished by ——, ---, ..., ∿∿, etc. The same spins that, in the interaction scheme of fig. 5(a), were all first in mutual interaction at the nth level (i.e., at level number $n-1$, counting from $n=0$), are now, in the interaction scheme of fig. 5(b), all first in mutual interaction at the $(nd)^{th}$ level. The interaction scheme of fig. 5(b) is identical to the one-dimensional one shown in fig. 3 — to see this, we have merely to rearrange the lattice sites of fig. 5(b) linearly, in the order in which they are numbered — but this model is now distinguished from the earlier one-dimensional one by its Hamiltonian, which for d dimensions, with $N = 2^{Md}$ sites, is taken to be

$$\mathcal{H} = J \sum_{n=1}^{Md} 2^{-(2-\eta)(n-1)/d} \sum_{m=1}^{2^{Md-n}} (\hat{s}_{m,n})^2$$

$$- \frac{1}{2} J \frac{1-2^{-(d+2-\eta)M}}{1-2^{-(d+2-\eta)/d}} \sum_{m=1}^{2^{Md}} (s_{m,0})^2 \quad , \tag{6.24}$$

of which (6.5) is only the special case $d = 1$. The $\hat{s}_{m,n}$ are still determined in terms of the $s_{m,0}$ by (6.4), though now with Md in place of M.

Two spins that are r lattice spacings apart in the d-dimensional lattice of fig. 5(b), become separated by the much greater distance of about r^d lattice spacings, when the lattice is stretched out into its equivalent one-dimensional form. The effective spin-spin interactions in the Hamiltonian (6.5) of the one-dimensional system were seen to fall off inversely with the $3-\eta$ power of the distance. Similarly, in the Hamiltonian (6.24), the effective spin-spin interactions fall off inversely with the $d+2-\eta$ power of the distance in the d-dimensional system[20], but then with only the $(d+2-\eta)/d = 1+(2-\eta)/d$ power of the distance in the one-dimensional system that is equivalent to it. Viewed in the d-dimensional system, this is a short-range interaction (for $\eta \le 1$); but then, so long as $2-\eta < d$, this same interaction is of long range in the equivalent one-dimensional system. In $d > 1$ dimensions, a system with short-range interactions may undergo a phase transition, but a one-dimensional system does so only when its interactions are of long range.

We shall not calculate the correlation function here, but, had we done so, we would have seen that the parameter η in the Hamiltonian becomes the critical-point exponent η.[20] That a critical-point exponent should be related so directly to a parameter in the Hamiltonian is ordinarily unexpected, and is an artificiality of these models.

The necessary condition $2-\eta < d$ for the interactions in the equivalent one-dimensional system to be of long range, so that there may be a phase transition in the d-dimensional system, becomes, in two dimensions, $\eta > 0$. That a critical point with short-range forces in two dimensions requires $\eta > 0$ has long been known. It explains why the Ornstein-Zernike theory, which entails $\eta = 0$, is inconsistent with the existence of a critical point in two dimensions, why the spherical model and ideal Bose gas, for both of which $\eta = 0$, have no phase transition in two dimensions, and why Wilson[8] was not able to obtain sensible results for $d = 2$ from the approximate renormalization-group equations (3.4)-(3.5).

The recurrence relations arising from the Hamiltonian (6.24) are simple generalizations of (6.20)-(6.21),

$$Q_{n+1}(x) = -2 \ln [I_n(2^{(1-d/2-\eta/2)/d} x)/I_n(0)] \tag{6.25}$$

$$I_n(x) = \int_{-\infty}^{\infty} e^{-Ky^2 - \frac{1}{2}[Q_n(x+y)+Q_n(x-y)]} dy \quad , \tag{6.26}$$

with now only a single integral in (6.26) in place of the multiple integral in (6.23). When we compare these with the approximate (3.4)-(3.5) of the Wilson theory, we see that (except for the presence of the K, which we know to be inconsequential) (6.26) is the same as (3.5), whereas (6.25) differs from (3.4), not only in allowing for a general η but also by replacing 2^d by 2 both in the coefficient of the logarithm and in the argument of the I_n function. When, earlier, we compared (3.4)-(3.5) with (6.22)-(6.23), we saw that (3.4) was the same as (6.22) (with $\eta = 0$), but that (3.5) differed from (6.23). We have, then, the curious circumstance that Wilson's approximation amounts to combining the Q_{n+1}-to-I_n relation (with $\eta = 0$) from one Baker model, with the I_n-to-Q_n relation from another.[20]

With this description of the Baker models we conclude our outline of the renormalization-group theory (though we shall refer to some aspects of it again in section 9), and turn now to the second major subject of these lectures, critical points of higher order.

7. CRITICAL POINTS OF HIGHER ORDER

The temperature-composition ($T-x_{He^3}$) phase diagram for solutions of the two helium isotopes He^3, He^4 is shown schematically in fig. 6(a). Above the temperature

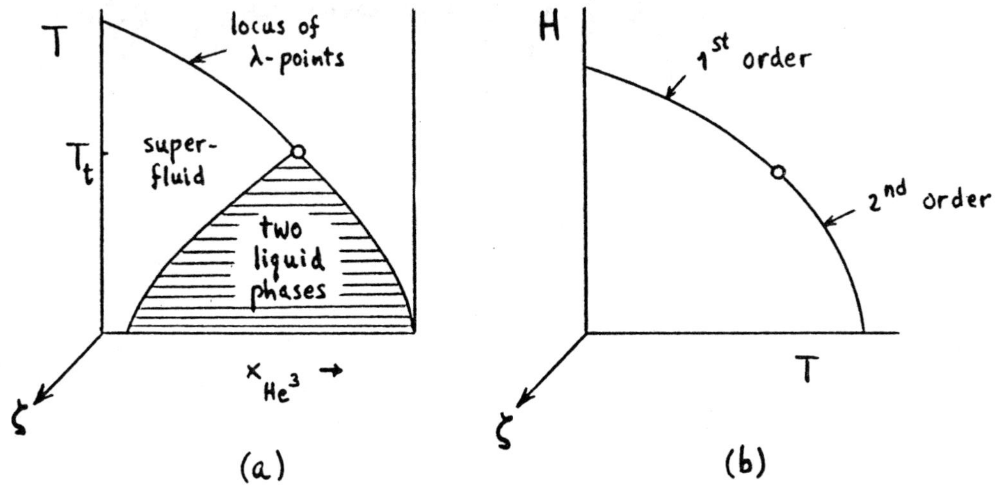

Figure 6

T_t the superfluid phase transition is of "second order"; it occurs at a λ-point, the locus of which is shown in the figure. The highest temperature point on this locus is the λ-point of pure He^4 ($x_{He^3} = 0$). Below T_t the superfluid phase transition is of first order, and the superfluid and non-superfluid phases are separated as two distinct layers. Some of the tielines in the two-liquid-phase region are shown in the figure. The two liquid phases that are in equilibrium come to be more and more alike as the temperature increases, and become identical at their consolute point (critical solution point), which is also the point at which the λ-line terminates, at T_t.

If we now extend the thermodynamic space with the addition of a hypothetical intensive field ζ (shown as a third dimension in fig. 6(a)), that is imagined to couple to the superfluid order parameter, then the superfluid phase may be distinguished as either of two phases of opposite symmetry, that is, two phases in which the order parameter has mean values that are equal in magnitude but opposite in sign. The superfluid order vanishes at the λ-line, and so in particular at the consolute point. As this point is then approached from lower temperatures, the two superfluid "phases" become identical to each other as well as to the non-superfluid phase. Such a point at which three previously distinct phases become identical (instead of two, as at an ordinary critical point) is a tricritical point. Because the field ζ is purely hypothetical, this tricritical point in the He^3-He^4 solutions is recognized in practice only as the point at which the 2nd-order transition turns into a 1st-order transition, or the reverse.

A formally identical phenomenon is seen in metamagnets (certain materials in which there are competing antiferromagnetic and ferromagnetic interactions), and is described schematically in the magnetic field-temperature (H-T) plane in fig. 6(b). The antiferromagnetic ordering occurs as a "second-order" transition along one portion of the phase-transition curve and as a first-order transition along the other. The 2nd-order portion of the curve is again a λ-line, at which the antiferromagnetic order (difference in sublattice magnetizations) vanishes. The 1st-order portion corresponds to the two-liquid-phase region of fig. 6(a), and is here seen as a line rather than a region only because we chose to plot the field H rather than the magnetization to which H is conjugate. Either system can equally well be described with either kind of diagram. Again, we extend the thermodynamic space with the addition of a ζ-axis (see the figure), with ζ now the field that couples to the antiferromagnetic order parameter; i.e., with ζ the staggered field, thermodynamically conjugate to the difference of sublattice magnetizations, as distinct from H, which is the ordinary, uniform field, conjugate to the total magnetization. With the field ζ we can distinguish two antiferromagnetic phases of opposite symmetry, so the line of 1st-order transitions in fig. 6(b) is, from this point of view, a line of three-phase equilibrium; i.e., a line of triple points. The tricritical point that separates the phase-transition curve in fig. 6(b) into a 2nd-order line and a 1st-order line is in this way again seen, as in the He^3-He^4 system, to be a point at which three phases become identical.

This view of such critical points is a fundamental advance due to Griffiths (ref. 22, 23)). The fields ζ that are introduced are not experimentally variable; only $\zeta = 0$ is physically realizable (though this statement should be qualified slightly for the metamagnet). In these lectures we shall not be concerned further with the systems described in figs. 6(a),(b) — they will be discussed much more thoroughly in the lectures of Professor Cohen — but we shall instead treat the higher order critical points that arise from the equilibrium and simultaneous merging of three or more real, visibly distinct, fluid phases, where all the relevant thermodynamic variables are physically realizable and no hypothetical fields are required.

In fig. 7(a) we show two fluid phases, α and β, in equilibrium. As their critical point is approached the interface between them thickens, spreads into both phases, and disappears; the two fluids have now become identical and we have only a single, homogeneous phase. In fig. 7(b) we show three fluid phases, α, β, and γ, in equilibrium. If two of them, say α and β, become identical, that is no

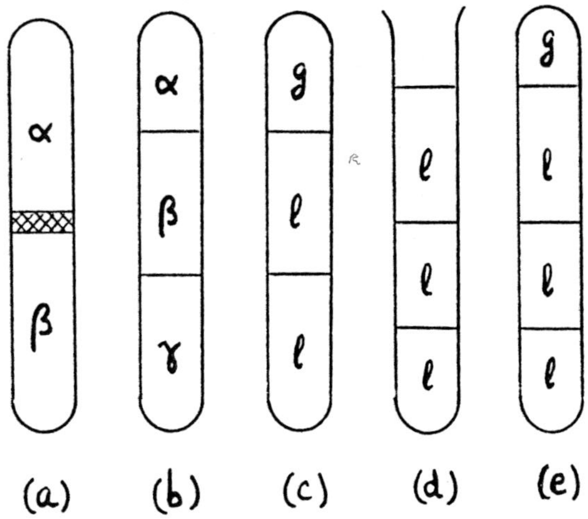

Figure 7

different from the ordinary critical point described in (a). (When such a critical point of two phases is achieved in the presence of a distinct third phase, as in this example, it is called a critical end point, because in certain geometrical representations it is seen as the point at which a line of critical points terminates on the boundary of a three-phase region; we shall see such a geometrical representation later.) But if the two interfaces separating the three phases in (b) vanish simultaneously, and the three phases become simultaneously identical, then that is a tricritical point.

The theoretical possibility of such higher order critical points, where three or more phases become simultaneously identical, was known to van der Waals and Kohnstamm.[24,25] We may derive a necessary condition for such points from the phase rule.[26,27] The phase rule in its usual form is $f = c - p + 2$, where f is the number of thermodynamic degrees of freedom, c the number of distinct chemical components, and p the number of phases. But each condition of criticality — each requirement that the interface between a pair of phases disappear and the two phases become identical — is an additional constraint and lowers f by 1. At what we may call a pth-order critical point, where all p phases become identical (so that with this nomenclature an ordinary critical point is of 2nd order), there are $p - 1$ such interfaces — imagine the phases stacked one above the other, according to their densities, as in figure 7 — so $p - 1$ such conditions of criticality. Therefore, at that point,

$$f = c - p + 2 - (p - 1) = c - 2p + 3 \quad . \tag{7.1}$$

But f cannot be negative; so as a necessary condition for a pth-order critical point,

$$c \geq 2p - 3 \quad . \tag{7.2}$$

For an ordinary critical point, where $p = 2$, this yields $c \geq 1$. For a tricritical point, $p = 3$, it yields $c \geq 3$: To achieve a tricritical point we must have a mixture of at least three distinct chemical species. For a fourth-order critical point, $p = 4$, we have $c \geq 5$; etc.

We may ask why, if three components are necessary for a tricritical point, such a point is seen in the two-component system of fig. 6(a) and in the one-component system of fig. 6(b). The answer is that the necessary condition derived from the phase rule is the condition for the thermodynamic space to be of high enough dimensionality for a higher-order critical point to be found in it even without a lucky accident, or without the intervention of any special symmetry. The thermodynamic space of a three-component system is of dimensionality $f = c - p + 2 = 3 - 1 + 2 = 4$. (This is the number of thermodynamic variables required to fix the state of the homogeneous system; i.e., the number of degrees of freedom f when there is only one phase.) A tricritical point in a three-component system is thus an isolated, invariant ($f = 0$) point in a four-dimensional space. For that single point to be found lying in an arbitrarily chosen section of that space, of dimensionality less than four, would ordinarily require a miracle; but because of the special symmetries of the systems in fig. 6, their tricritical points are already found in the $T - x_{He^3}$ and $H - T$ planes.

A typical classical fluid system with a tricritical point is the mixture carbon dioxide + ethyl alcohol + water.[28] Because the tricritical point in a three-component system is invariant, it occurs at a unique pressure, temperature, and chemical composition, which in the mixture cited are[28] 91.7 atm, 47.4°C, and mole fractions $x_{CO_2} = 0.83$, $x_{EtOH} = 0.15$, $x_{H_2O} = 0.02$. Most such mixtures of three simple substances should have tricritical points, but because they are isolated points in thermodynamic spaces of four dimensions they can be hard to find. Although, as we have seen, the theoretical possibility of the existence of such points has long been recognized, only ten or so examples of tricritical points in classical fluid mixtures are so far known, most of them found in the last twelve years by physical chemists in the Soviet Union.

The three fluid phases that are in equilibrium in the three-component systems at temperatures well below that of the tricritical point, are recognizable as two liquids and a gas, and are so labeled in fig. 7(c). In four-component systems it is possible to achieve a tricritical point at which all three of the phases that become identical are ordinary liquids,[27,29] and where the phenomenon may be studied while the system is open to the atmosphere, as in fig. 7(d), or while the liquids in question remain always in equilibrium with their vapor, in a closed vessel, as in fig. 7(e). In those cases the addition of the fourth component adds the additional thermodynamic degree of freedom that makes it possible to specify that three liquid phases become identical, and to specify at the same time that the pressure be 1 atmosphere, or that a fourth phase be also present. The temperature and the three independent composition variables (so, again, a total of four variables) are then all uniquely determined at the tricritical point. Such systems give to the experimenter the advantage of being able to work with ordinary liquids at or near atmospheric pressure. It is likewise possible in a five-component liquid system to find a tricritical point at 1 atmosphere and room temperature; it then occurs at a unique set of values of the four composition variables.

For the rest of our discussion of higher order critical points we shall refer explicitly only to those systems in which the number of chemical components is the smallest possible, but similar principles apply to the others as well.

If ρ_1, ρ_2, ρ_3 are the densities of the three chemical components in any phase of a three-component system, the composition of that phase is represented by a single point in the isothermal ρ_1, ρ_2, ρ_3 space of the mixture (figure 8(a)). The compositions of three phases in equilibrium, as in fig. 7(b), are represented simultaneously by three such points, one for each phase. The triangle determined by

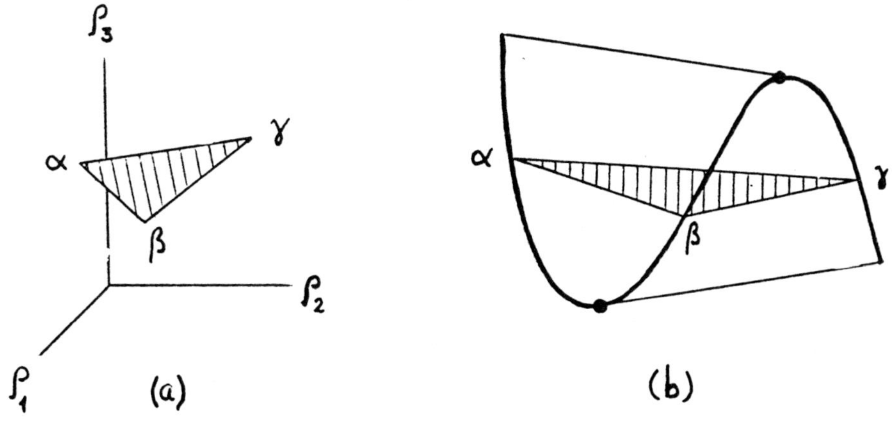

Figure 8

these three points as vertices is shown shaded in fig. 8(a). The overall composition ρ_1, ρ_2, ρ_3 of the mixture, all three phases taken together, is represented by a single point in the interior of this triangle. As the position of this point varies within the triangle, it represents mixtures with varying relative amounts of the three phases α, β, and γ, but with the three separate phases always of fixed composition, represented by the vertices of the triangle. Even at the fixed temperature of the isothermal ρ_1, ρ_2, ρ_3 space of fig. 8(a), however, there are infinitely many such triangles, which together constitute a region of three-phase coexistence in that space. This region, still in the space of fig. 8(a), is shown enlarged in fig. 8(b). It may be thought of as a stack of infinitely many, infinitely closely spaced triangles, of which a representative one is shown. The surface that bounds the three-phase region is a ruled surface, for through every point of it there is a line that lies entirely in the surface; viz., one of the sides, $\alpha\beta$, $\beta\gamma$, or $\gamma\alpha$, of one of the triangles of which the region is composed.

The point at which the side $\alpha\beta$ of the generating triangle is of vanishing length is shown as a dot in the lower part of fig. 8(b). That is a critical end point, referred to earlier, where the phases α and β become identical while still in equilibrium with the distinct phase γ. It corresponds in fig. 7(b) to the disappearance, within the tube, of the $\alpha\beta$ interface, while the $\beta\gamma$ interface remains. Though it is not shown, there is in the isothermal ρ_1, ρ_2, ρ_3 space of fig. 8 a one-parameter locus of $\alpha\beta$ critical points; this curve terminates at the critical end point. Also shown as a dot in fig. 8(b) is a second critical end point, where the side $\beta\gamma$ of the generating triangle vanishes, corresponding to the phases β and γ becoming identical, and the interface between them disappearing, while they are still in equilibrium with the distinct phase α. It is the terminus of a one-parameter locus of $\beta\gamma$ critical points in the composition space.

The whole of fig. 8 is for a single temperature. At a slightly higher temperature there would be a qualitatively similar figure, but with the three-phase region slightly smaller. Finally, at the temperature T_t of the tricritical point, the three-phase region has shrunk to a point, which is the tricritical point itself. Its coordinates ρ_1, ρ_2, ρ_3 determine the unique density and chemical composition in the tricritical state of the mixture.

It is important to know precisely how the three-phase region of fig. 8(b) shrinks with increasing temperature. This, and other quantitative details of the approach to the tricritical point, was determined by Griffiths[30)] from a generalization of the earlier phenomenological theory of Landau.[31)] We outline the basic ideas of this theory in the next section.

8. GRIFFITHS-LANDAU THEORY[30-32)]

We shall first review briefly the classical thermodynamic theory of the ordinary liquid-vapor critical point of a pure fluid. Near the critical point at p_c, V_c, T_c the pressure $p(V,T)$ as a function of the volume V and temperature T, may be expanded in powers of $T - T_c$ and $V - V_c$,

$$p - p_c = a(T - T_c) + b(T - T_c)(V - V_c) + c(V - V_c)^3 \qquad (8.1)$$

with constant coefficients a, b and c. To the approximation (8.1), the p,V isotherms are cubic in $V - V_c$ and the p,T isochores are linear in $T - T_c$. These are

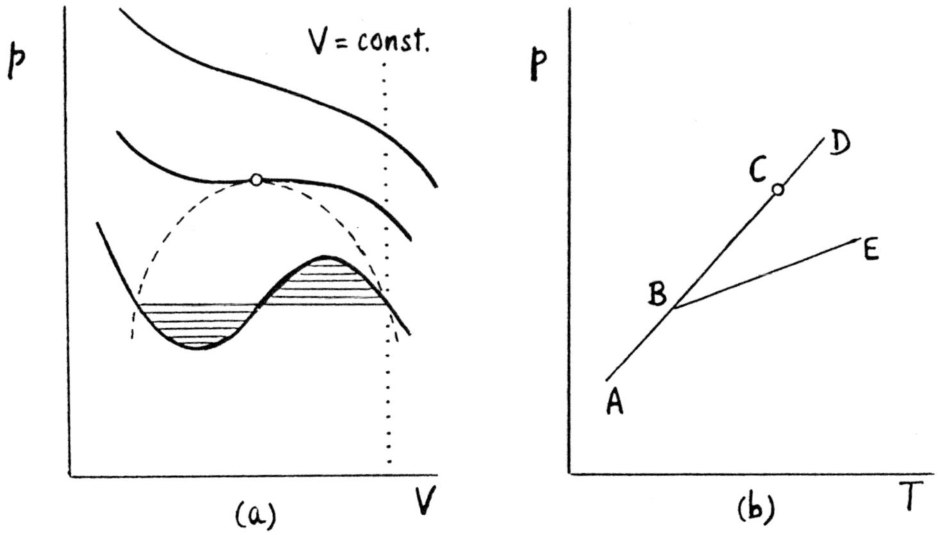

Figure 9

shown in figs. 9(a), (b). For $T < T_c$ the analytic p,V isotherm is reconstructed by the equal-areas rule, as shown in (a). The coexistence curve in the p,V plane is the locus of the end points of the horizontal line segments yielded by this construction, and is shown as the dashed curve in the figure. One isochore, V = const., is also shown in (a) as a vertical dotted line. The pressure as a function of the temperature along that isochore is given by ABE in fig. 9(b). The critical isochore $V = V_c$ is the line AD in (b), the portion AC, up to the critical point at C, being the equilibrium vapor pressure. The non-critical isochore ABE coincides with the vapor pressure line along AB, but departs from it at B, corresponding to the point in fig. 9(a) at which the vertical dotted line, followed upward through the two-phase region, meets the coexistence curve and enters the one-phase region.

The values of the critical-point exponents may now be read directly from (8.1) and fig. 9. According to (8.1), the compressibility $-V^{-1}(\partial V/\partial p)_T$ on the critical isochore diverges as $(T-T_c)^{-1}$, so $\gamma = 1$. On the critical isotherm $p - p_c \sim -(V-V_c)^3$, so $\delta = 3$. The point B in fig. 9(b), which, as we have seen, corresponds to a point on the coexistence curve, is at the intersection of the general non-critical isochore BE, given by (8.1), with the critical isochore, given by $p - p_c = a(T-T_c)$. Thus, the coexistence curve is determined by the roots, other than $V = V_c$, of the equation $0 = b(T-T_c)(V-V_c) + c(V-V_c)^3$, hence by $T_c - T \sim (V-V_c)^2$; so $\beta = 1/2$. The three exponents $\beta = 1/2$, $\gamma = 1$, $\delta = 3$ satisfy the second of eqs. (1.5).

The generalization of (8.1) appropriate to a critical point of order $q/2$, say, with q an even integer, is

$$b_1 = b_2\psi + b_3\psi^2 + b_4\psi^3 + \dots + b_{q-2}\psi^{q-3} + \psi^{q-1} \quad . \tag{8.2}$$

For an ordinary (second-order) critical point, we have $q = 4$, as in (8.1); for a tricritical point, $q = 6$. The thermodynamic variable ψ is, or is related to, the mean value of some order parameter, and is analogous to $V - V_c$. It is a density, or composition, or some function of such variables, and, like $V - V_c$, has different values in different phases. The remaining variables $b_1, b_2, \ldots, b_{q-2}$ are $q-2$ thermodynamic fields (such as temperature, pressure, and the chemical potentials, or functions of them), each having a common value in all phases that are in equilibrium. The field b_1 is the thermodynamic conjugate of ψ, and plays the role of $p - p_c - a(T - T_c)$ in (8.1). There are now $q-3$ independent coefficients $b_2, b_3, b_4, \ldots, b_{q-2}$, where in (8.1) there is only the single $T - T_c$. Note that there is no term in ψ^{q-2} in (8.2), just as there is none in $(V - V_c)^2$ in (8.1). One can always choose the thermodynamic functions so that this is so.[30] Had they been so chosen that a term in ψ^{q-2} was present, its coefficient "b_{q-1}" would not have been another independent thermodynamic variable: We may think of this system, in which there is a critical point of order $q/2$, as containing $q-3$ chemical components, which we know to be the minimum necessary. The full thermodynamic space is then of dimensionality $f = (q-3) - 1 + 2 = q-2$; i.e., to determine the state of the system one must specify the values of $q-2$ thermodynamic variables, and any thermodynamic function is a function of $q-2$ others. In (8.2), the field b_1 that is conjugate to ψ is being expressed as a function of the $q-2$ independent variables $b_2, b_3, b_4, \ldots, b_{q-2}, \psi$. The coefficient of the terminal ψ^{q-1} in (8.2) is likewise not another independent variable; it is some non-zero constant, like c in (8.1), and we may at will[30] choose it to be 1, as we have done.

The form of (8.2) appropriate to a tricritical point is that with $q = 6$,

$$b_1 = b_2\psi + b_3\psi^2 + b_4\psi^3 + \psi^5 \quad . \tag{8.3}$$

In all physically realizable states of the He^3-He^4 mixture and of the metamagnet, $b_3 = 0$, because of the special symmetry of those systems. (We could have augmented the thermodynamic spaces of fig. 6, and thus have shown their true four-dimensional character, by adding to each an axis for a hypothetical b_3 variable, just as we have already added the hypothetical ζ.) The present b_1 is the ζ of fig. 6, the field conjugate to the order parameter ψ; but whereas ζ was hypothetical, the present b_1 is a physically realizable function of temperature, pressure, and chemical potentials, that may be varied at will by the experimenter. The remaining variables b_2 and b_4 in (8.3) also have their analogs in the symmetrical systems of fig. 6. This is shown in fig. 10, based on fig. 6(b). This three-dimensional H,T,ζ space is the section $b_3 = 0$ of the full four-dimensional space. Deviations from the tricritical point may then be described in a b_1, b_2, b_4 coordinate system with origin at the tricritical point, as shown.[23,30] The b_4 axis is in the H,T plane, where it is tangent to the phase transition curve at the tricritical point;

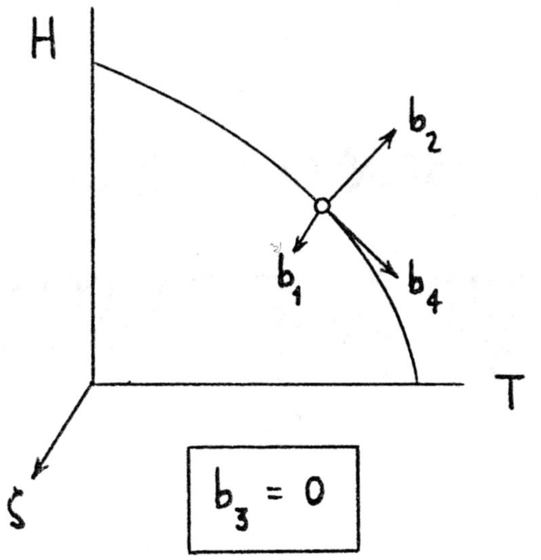

Figure 10

the b_2 axis is also in the H,T plane, but may otherwise be in any direction oblique to b_4; while the axis of b_1 (= ζ) may be in any direction oblique to the H,T plane.

Plots of b_1 vs ψ at fixed b_2, b_3,..., b_{q-2}, as derived from (8.2), would be the analogs of the p,V isotherms of fig. 9(a). This is illustrated for q = 6 by the four curves in fig. 11. (See also Bausch[33] and Bartis[34].) Each one shows b_1, as ordinate, plotted as a function of ψ, as abscissa. They all go through the origin of the b_1,ψ coordinate system. In each plot b_2, b_3, and b_4 are fixed, but their values vary from one plot to another. In (a)-(c), the equal-areas rule has been applied. In (a) we see a range of values of ψ in which two phases, called α and β, are in equilibrium at a constant b_1, and a different range of ψ, at a different constant b_1, in which two phases β and γ are in equilibrium. The fixed values of b_2, b_3, and b_4 in (a) are all independent; but if they were related to each other in a special way, the two constant values of b_1 at which the phase equilibria occur could be made equal. This is the condition for three phases to be in equilibrium, as in (b), which corresponds to the picture in fig. 7(b). In fig. 11(b), then, only two of the variables b_2, b_3, b_4 are independent; the third has a definite value, depending on the values of the other two. If now b_2, b_3, b_4 satisfy still another relation, in addition to the first, then two of the three phases that are in equilibrium, α and β or β and γ, may be made to be identical, while they are still in equilibrium with the distinct third phase, γ or α. This is a critical end point, and is shown in (c) for the case where α, β have merged to form a critical phase while γ remains distinct.[34] The horizontal tieline that connects the two phases in (c) corresponds to the tieline that forms the bottom edge of the three-phase region depicted in fig. 8(b). In 11(c), only one of the

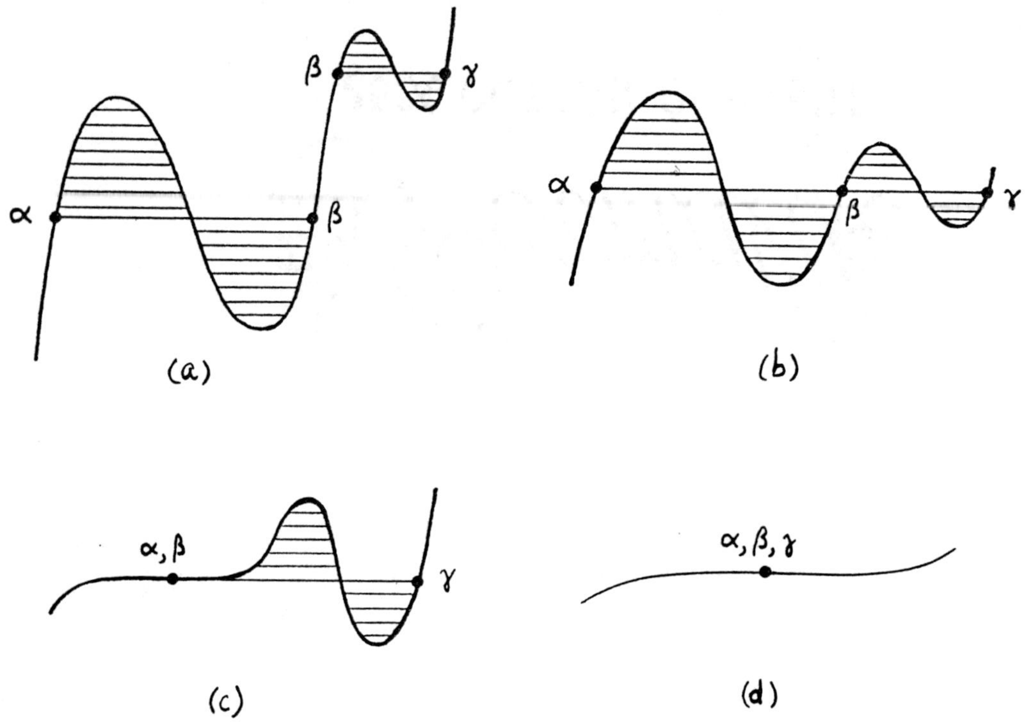

Figure 11

variables b_2, b_3, b_4 is independent, the values of the other two being determined by that one. If now even that remaining independent variable is given a particular value (viz., 0), the previously distinct phase γ is made to merge with the critical phase $\alpha\beta$, with the result shown in (d). Here $b_2 = b_3 = b_4 = 0$, and the curve is given by $b_1 = \psi^5$. The point marked α, β, γ is the tricritical point, at which also $b_1 = \psi = 0$.

Other shapes of plots of b_1 vs ψ are also possible, according to the values at which b_2, b_3, and b_4 are fixed. Figure 12(a) shows a case in which there is only one phase, whatever the value of b_1 or ψ. In fig. 12(b) there is seen a range of ψ over which two phases coexist, but not also a second range as in fig. 11(a). We may think of figures 11(a), 12(b), and 12(a), in that order, as a sequence in which we go through a $\beta\gamma$ critical point and then through an $\alpha\beta$ critical point. In fig. 12(c) the equal-areas construction is made in such a way as to show a metastable $\alpha\beta$ phase equilibrium at one b_1, and a metastable $\beta\gamma$ equilibrium at a lower b_1. The <u>same</u> b_1 vs ψ curve is shown again at (d), but now with the equal-areas construction made so as to show the stable $\alpha\gamma$ equilibrium, at a value of b_1 intermediate between those of the two metastable equilibria in (c).

We see from (8.2) that if $b_2, b_3, \ldots, b_{q-2}$ are fixed, then b_1 is a polynomial

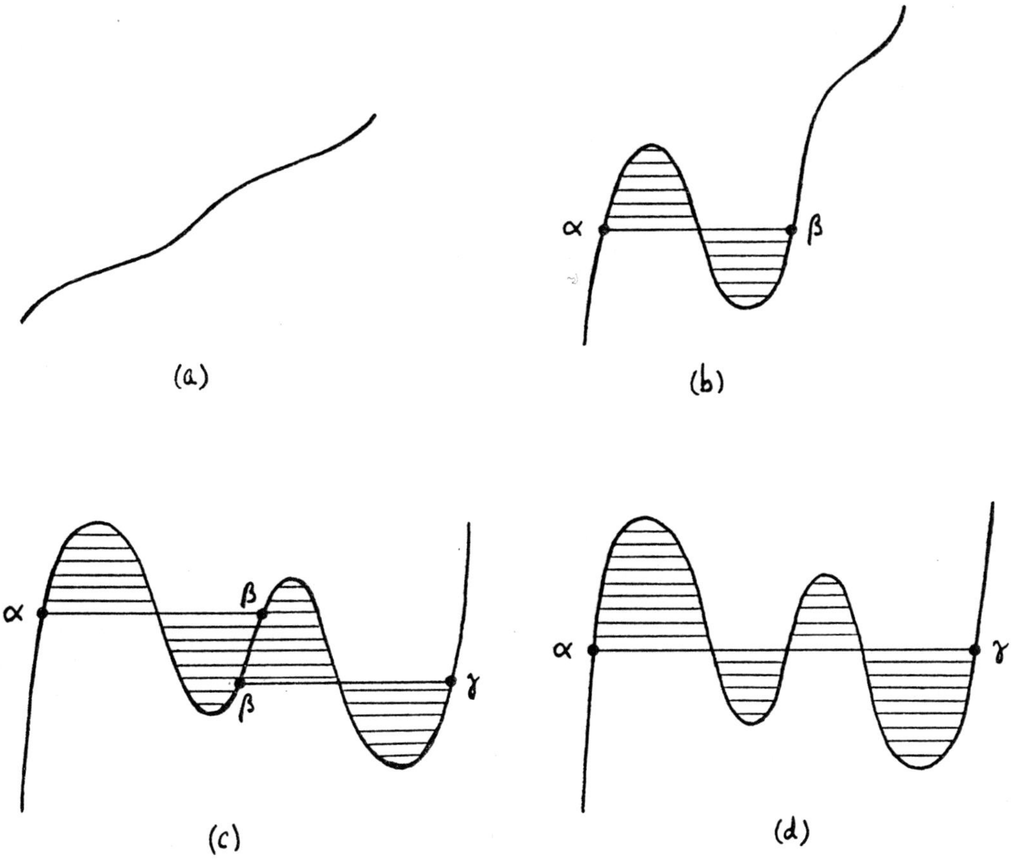

Figure 12

in ψ of degree $q-1$, an odd integer. In the general figure of the type 11(b) the horizontal line obtained from the equal-areas rule then makes $q-1$ intersections with the curve. Of these intersections, alternate ones, including the first and last — hence, $q/2$ of them — correspond to the stable phases $\alpha, \beta, \ldots,$ while the intervening $q/2-1$ of them correspond to "labile" phases, these being all unstable as homogeneous fluids. That at most $q/2$ stable fluids can coexist, according to this picture, confirms the identification of q in (8.2) as twice the order of the critical point.

We may read values of critical-point exponents from (8.2), just as we did from (8.1). The generalized susceptibility is $(\partial\psi/\partial b_1)_{b_2,\ldots,b_{q-2}}$, which is the rate at which the mean value of the order parameter changes with the ordering field at fixed values of the non-ordering fields. We see from (8.2) that it diverges proportionally to $1/b_2$ when $b_2 \to 0$ at $\psi = 0$; i.e., it diverges inversely as the first power of the variable that is here playing the role that is played by $T-T_c$ at an ordinary critical point (see fig. 10). Thus, $\gamma = 1$. Figure 11(d) is the analog of the critical isotherm at an ordinary critical point, and for general q is given by $b_1 = \psi^{q-1}$. Thus, $\delta = q-1$ (= 5 for a tricritical point). The "spontaneous" values of ψ are the non-zero roots of (8.2) with $b_1 = 0$, and so, when

$b_3 = b_4 = \ldots = b_{q-2} = 0$ and $b_2 < 0$ (see fig. 10), are $\pm\psi = (-b_2)^{1/(q-2)}$. (This is the direct generalization of our earlier calculation for an ordinary critical point, $q = 4$, where we found the coexistence curve from the intersection of the non-critical isochore, determined by (in the present notation) $b_1 = b_2\psi + \psi^3$, with the critical isochore, determined by $b_1 = 0$.) We then identify $\beta = 1/(q-2)$ (= 1/4 for a tricritical point). There are clearly many additional critical-point exponents that we could define[23] and identify, but these three provide a sufficient illustration.

To summarize, at a critical point of order $q/2$ the phenomenological equation (8.2) implies

$$\beta = 1/(q-2), \qquad \gamma = 1, \qquad \delta = q - 1 \quad . \tag{8.4}$$

These still satisfy the second of eqs. (1.5).

Griffiths' theory[30] of the tricritical point starts not with (8.3), but with an associated free energy; but the two formulations are equivalent, with our b_i related to his a_i by $b_1 = -a_1/6$, $b_2 = a_2/3$, $b_3 = a_3/2$, $b_4 = 2a_4/3$. By explicit calculation, Griffiths finds the form of the three-phase region in the isothermal ρ_1, ρ_2, ρ_3 space, which we showed schematically in fig. 8(b), and determines the manner in which it shrinks to a point as the temperature T approaches the tricritical-point temperature T_t. Figure 13 gives a somewhat stylized representation of the results. Here $t = T_t - T$; and the figure shows the three-phase region first

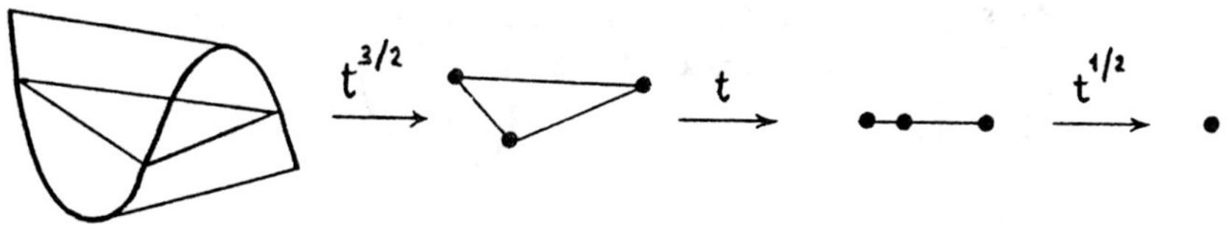

Figure 13

becoming very flat, as the thickness of the stack of triangles vanishes proportionally to $t^{3/2}$, then also becoming very slender as the largest altitude of the triangles vanishes proportionally to t, and finally approaching a point (the tricritical point) as the length of the longest side of the triangles vanishes proportionally to $t^{1/2}$.

The three critical-point exponents associated with the shrinking of the three-phase region, which are thus predicted by the phenomenological theory based on (8.3) to be 3/2, 1, and 1/2, are important elements in the characterization of the tricritical point. Work to determine these three exponents by experiment is in progress in our laboratory at Cornell, and in other laboratories as well.

Another critical-point exponent important in the characterization of the tricritical point is that associated with the vanishing of the interfacial tensions. Let σ be the interfacial tension and μ the exponent, so that $\sigma \sim t^{\mu}$. For the interfacial tension between the superfluid and non-superfluid phases in the two-liquid-phase region of the He^3-He^4 mixtures (fig. 6(a)), Papoular[35] predicts $\mu = 2$. The calculation is based on scaling relations that connect μ to other critical-point exponents[3,36,37], together with the classical, mean-field-theory values for those exponents (like those that follow from the phenomenological equation (8.3)). An analogous calculation[38] for tricritical points in the classical, multicomponent fluid mixtures that we are now considering, yields the same result, $\mu = 2$. In our experiments at Cornell we hope to test this prediction, too.

It may be asked why the exponents, such as those shown in fig. 13, or $\mu = 2$, which follow from a phenomenological theory of the classical form, are treated seriously as theoretical predictions, when it is known that the critical-point exponents yielded by the corresponding phenomenological theory of ordinary critical points ($q = 4$) are certainly wrong. The answer to this question is bound up with the important idea of <u>borderline dimensionality</u>, to which we now turn in our final section.

9. BORDERLINE DIMENSIONALITY

We saw in section 4 that for an ordinary critical point $d = 4$ is the borderline dimensionality below which the critical point is non-classical, with d-dependent exponents, and at which it changes over to a classical critical point, with exponents that are then independent of d for all $d > 4$. That $d = 4$ would be such a borderline dimensionality had already been inferred by Stell[39] on other grounds.

Any of the d-dependent relations among critical-point exponents, such as

$$(2 - \eta)/d = (\delta - 1)/(\delta + 1) \quad , \tag{9.1}$$

which follows from (1.3), (1.5), (1.9), and (1.10), continues to hold at the borderline dimensionality, though that is the highest dimensionality at which it does.[40] At the same time, at the borderline dimensionality the exponents have their classical, mean-field values, though that is the lowest dimensionality in which they do. Hence, the borderline dimensionality can be found as the solution d^* of the equation that is obtained by substituting the classical values of the exponents into any of the d-dependent scaling relations such as (9.1). The classical value of η, at which it sticks[39] for $d \geq d^*$, is 0; while we have just seen in (8.4) that for a critical point of order $q/2$ the classical value of δ is $q - 1$.

Hence, from (9.1), the borderline dimensionality d^* is related to the order of the critical point, $q/2$, by

$$(d^* - 2)(q - 2) = 4 \quad . \tag{9.2}$$

For an ordinary critical point (second order, $q = 4$) this yields $d^* = 4$, which we already knew. For a tricritical point ($q = 6$) it yields $d^* = 3$, so three dimensions is the borderline dimensionality for tricritical points, as first found by Riedel and Wegner.[41)] This is the reason why, when $d = 3$, we expect classical exponents such as those shown in fig. 13 or the surface-tension exponent $\mu = 2$, to be correct for a tricritical point (though the thermodynamic functions themselves would be modified by logarithmic factors[41)], as is characteristic of $d = d^*$), while at the same time they are wrong for ordinary critical points. For critical points of still higher order we have $d^* < 3$.

We gave here the simplest possible derivation of (9.2), but the same result may be derived also from the renormalization-group theory[42-43)], or alternatively from the "Ginzburg criterion" (see Bausch[33)] for the case of tricritical points). It is in the latter that the origin of the borderline dimensionality is clearest. We shall outline here, for general q, a form of this argument that is suggested by the renormalization-group theory.[44)]

We know from the theory given in sections 3 and 4 that the ordinary critical point will be classical, with mean-field-theory critical-point exponents, or non-classical, with d-dependent exponents, according, respectively, as the s^4 term in $Q_n(s)$ becomes negligible or important as n increases. More generally, for a critical point of order $q/2$ it is the s^q term in $Q_n(s)$ that determines the nature of the result in this way. The appropriate extension[42-43)] of (4.2) to general q contains all even powers of x up to and including x^q, while $\epsilon = d^* - d$. After the nth iteration of the renormalization-group transformation, the effective blocks of spins that act as single spins in the re-scaled model are of linear dimension L, which increases with n by the formula (2.10). The s^q term in $Q_n(s)$ is then important or not according as $\int s(\vec{r})^q d\tau$, extended over a volume of magnitude L^d, is large or small compared to $\int |\nabla s(\vec{r})|^2 d\tau$ extended over the same volume; for these integrals are measures of the long-wavelength (i.e., wavelength > L) contributions of the terms $s(\vec{r})^q$ and $|\nabla s(\vec{r})|^2$ to the Hamiltonian density, hence measures of the importance of these terms in the n-times transformed Hamiltonian density. But if s is the magnitude of the mean spin in a block of linear dimension L, then, in order of magnitude,

$$\int_{|\vec{r}| \le L} s(\vec{r})^q d\tau \approx L^d s^q \tag{9.3}$$

$$\int_{|\vec{r}|\leq L} |\nabla s(\vec{r})|^2 d\tau \approx L^{d-2}\, s^2 \quad . \tag{9.4}$$

These are now to be compared under circumstances where the second is of order unity, i.e., where $s \approx L^{-(d-2)/2}$; for, as we saw in (3.2) and (3.3), there is at each stage of the transformation a spin-rescaling factor $\ell^{(d-2)/2d}$, and so, by (2.10), a cumulative spin-rescaling factor, after n iterations, of $L^{(d-2)/2}$, designed precisely to make the integral in (9.4) remain of order unity for all n or L. On this scale, the integral (9.3) is $L^{d-q(d-2)/2}$; so the s^q term in $Q_n(s)$ is important or not according as $d > q(d-2)/2$ or $d < q(d-2)/2$, respectively; i.e., according as $d < 2q/(q-2)$ or $d > 2q/(q-2)$, respectively. The borderline dimensionality is then $d^* = 2q/(q-2)$, which is (9.2).

To be interpreted as twice the order of a critical point, q must be an even integer, but formally (9.2) relates d^* to q even when q is more general. It was observed by Baker[20] that if the $Q_0(s)$ in the Wilson theory had been essentially $v_0 s^2 + u_0|s|^3$ instead of $v_0 s^2 + u_0 s^4$ — so $q = 3$ instead of $q = 4$ — the borderline between classical and non-classical behaviour would have been at $d = 6$. This is in accord with (9.2). Indeed, the hyperbolic relation (9.2) yields dual pairs of values of d^* and q. The Wilson $q = 4$, $d^* = 4$ is its own dual, while Baker's $q = 3$, $d^* = 6$ is the dual of the Riedel-Wegner $q = 6$, $d^* = 3$. Another dual pair is $q = 2$, $d^* = \infty$ and $q = \infty$, $d^* = 2$; the former says that when the highest power of s in $Q_0(s)$ is the second, the properties of the model are just those of the Gaussian model at every d, while the latter says that in two dimensions every critical point, however high its order, is non-classical. (We refer here only to systems with short-range forces.)

Because the idea of the borderline dimensionality is at the foundation of our present understanding of critical phenomena, experimental verification or refutation of the theoretical prediction that tricritical-point exponents in three-dimensional systems will have their classical values is of great importance. It seems so far to be borne out in the He^3-He^4 system[45]; we await with interest the results of quantitative studies of the classical fluid mixtures.

REFERENCES

1) P.W. Kasteleyn, in Fundamental Problems in Statistical Mechanics II, E.G.D. Cohen, editor (North Holland, 1968), pp. 30-70.
2) L.P. Kadanoff, Physics 2(1966)263.
3) B. Widom, J.Chem.Phys. 43(1965)3892.
4) B. Widom, J.Chem.Phys. 43(1965)3898.
5) J.W. Essam and M.E. Fisher, J.Chem.Phys. 38(1963)802.
6) M.E. Fisher, J.Math.Phys. 5(1964)944.

7) K.G. Wilson, Phys.Rev. B 4(1971)3174.

8) K.G. Wilson, Phys.Rev. B 4(1971)3184.

9) T.H. Berlin and M. Kac, Phys.Rev. 86(1952)821.

10) H.W. Lewis and G.H. Wannier, Phys.Rev. 88(1952)682.

11) J.S. Langer, Phys.Rev. 137(1965)A 1531.

12) K.G. Wilson and M.E. Fisher, Phys.Rev.Lett. 28(1972)240.

13) K.G. Wilson, Phys.Rev.Lett. 28(1972)548.

14) E. Brézin, J.C. le Guillou, J. Zinn-Justin, and B.G. Nickel, Phys.Lett. A 44(1973)227.

15) R. Abe and S. Hikami, Prog.Theor.Phys. 49(1973)442.

16) H.E. Stanley, Phys.Rev. 176(1968)718.

17) Th. Niemeijer and J.M.J. van Leeuwen, Phys.Rev.Lett. 31(1973)1411.

18) Th. Niemeijer and J.M.J. van Leeuwen, Physica 71(1974)17.

19) M. Nauenberg and B. Nienhuis (to be published). See also K.G. Wilson, ref. 8; F.J. Wegner, Phys.Rev. B 5(1972)4529; D.R. Nelson and M.E. Fisher (submitted to Ann.Phys.); D.R. Nelson (submitted to Phys.Rev.); and M.P. Nightingale and A.H. 't Hooft (to be published).

20) G.A. Baker, Jr., Phys.Rev. B 5(1972)2622.

21) F.J. Dyson, Commun.Math.Phys. 12(1969)91.

22) R.B. Griffiths, Phys.Rev.Lett. 24(1970)715.

23) R.B. Griffiths, Phys.Rev. B 7(1973)545.

24) J.D. van der Waals and Ph. Kohnstamm, Lehrbuch der Thermodynamik (Barth, Leipzig, 1912), 2[er] Teil, pp. 39-40.

25) Ph. Kohnstamm, Handbuch der Physik (Springer, 1926), volume 10, chapter 4, section 45.

26) J. Zernike, Rec.Trav.Chim. Pays-Bas 68(1949)585.

27) B. Widom, J.Phys.Chem. 77(1973)2196.

28) A.V. Shvarts and G.D. Efremova, Russ.J.Phys.Chem. 44(1970)615.

29) G.S. Radyshevskaya, N.I. Nikurashina, and R.V. Mertslin, J.Gen.Chem. USSR 32(1962)673.

30) R.B. Griffiths, J.Chem.Phys. 60(1974)195.

31) L.D. Landau and E.M. Lifshitz, Statistical Physics (Pergamon, 1958), chapter XIV, section 138.

32) R.B. Griffiths and B. Widom, Phys.Rev. A 8(1973)2173.

33) R. Bausch, Z. Physik 254(1972)81.

34) J.T. Bartis, J.Chem.Phys. 59(1973)5423.

35) M. Papoular, Phys. Fluids 17(1974)1038.

36) B. Widom, in Phase Transitions and Critical Phenomena, C. Domb and M.S. Green, editors (Academic Press, 1972), volume 2, chapter 3.

37) B. Widom, Physica 73(1974)107.

38) B. Widom, submitted to J.Chem.Phys.

7) K.G. Wilson, Phys.Rev. B 4(1971)3174.
8) K.G. Wilson, Phys.Rev. B 4(1971)3184.
9) T.H. Berlin and M. Kac, Phys.Rev. 86(1952)821.
0) H.W. Lewis and G.H. Wannier, Phys.Rev. 88(1952)682.
1) J.S. Langer, Phys.Rev. 137(1965)A 1531.
2) K.G. Wilson and M.E. Fisher, Phys.Rev.Lett. 28(1972)240.
3) K.G. Wilson, Phys.Rev.Lett. 28(1972)548.
4) E. Brézin, J.C. le Guillou, J. Zinn-Justin, and B.G. Nickel, Phys.Lett. A 44(1973)227.
5) R. Abe and S. Hikami, Prog.Theor.Phys. 49(1973)442.
6) H.E. Stanley, Phys.Rev. 176(1968)718.
7) Th. Niemeijer and J.M.J. van Leeuwen, Phys.Rev.Lett. 31(1973)1411.
8) Th. Niemeijer and J.M.J. van Leeuwen, Physica 71(1974)17.
9) M. Nauenberg and B. Nienhuis (to be published). See also K.G. Wilson, ref. 8; F.J. Wegner, Phys.Rev. B 5(1972)4529; D.R. Nelson and M.E. Fisher (submitted to Ann.Phys.); D.R. Nelson (submitted to Phys.Rev.); and M.P. Nightingale and A.H. 't Hooft (to be published).
0) G.A. Baker, Jr., Phys.Rev. B 5(1972)2622.
1) F.J. Dyson, Commun.Math.Phys. 12(1969)91.
2) R.B. Griffiths, Phys.Rev.Lett. 24(1970)715.
3) R.B. Griffiths, Phys.Rev. B 7(1973)545.
4) J.D. van der Waals and Ph. Kohnstamm, Lehrbuch der Thermodynamik (Barth, Leipzig, 1912), 2er Teil, pp. 39-40.
5) Ph. Kohnstamm, Handbuch der Physik (Springer, 1926), volume 10, chapter 4, section 45.
6) J. Zernike, Rec.Trav.Chim. Pays-Bas 68(1949)585.
7) B. Widom, J.Phys.Chem. 77(1973)2196.
8) A.V. Shvarts and G.D. Efremova, Russ.J.Phys.Chem. 44(1970)615.
9) G.S. Radyshevskaya, N.I. Nikurashina, and R.V. Mertslin, J.Gen.Chem. USSR 32(1962)673.
0) R.B. Griffiths, J.Chem.Phys. 60(1974)195.
1) L.D. Landau and E.M. Lifshitz, Statistical Physics (Pergamon, 1958), chapter XIV, section 138.
2) R.B. Griffiths and B. Widom, Phys.Rev. A 8(1973)2173.
3) R. Bausch, Z. Physik 254(1972)81.
4) J.T. Bartis, J.Chem.Phys. 59(1973)5423.
5) M. Papoular, Phys. Fluids 17(1974)1038.
6) B. Widom, in Phase Transitions and Critical Phenomena, C. Domb and M.S. Green, editors (Academic Press, 1972), volume 2, chapter 3.
7) B. Widom, Physica 73(1974)107.
8) B. Widom, submitted to J.Chem.Phys.

TRICRITICAL POINTS IN METAMAGNETS AND HELIUM MIXTURES

E.G.D. COHEN

The Rockefeller University, New York, N.Y. 10021, U.S.A.

1. INTRODUCTION - EXPERIMENTAL DATA

According to the phase rule not more than 3 distinct phases of a pure substance can be in equilibrium with each other. The existence of a triple point, however, does not mean that there is a point where 3 phases can become identical. In fact, for a pure substance there is only a critical point — the gas - liquid critical point — where 2 phases become identical. Van der Waals and Kohnstamm already noticed that in the van der Waals theory of phase equilibrium, this can be reconciled with the phase rule by the notion of a critical phase, that must be counted as 3 phases[1]: the unstable phase is included, with the gas - and the liquid phase, in the counting of phases that become identical at the critical point. Similarly in a 2-component mixture the number of phases that become identical at a critical point cannot exceed 2 either, since 3 phases that become identical should, according to the van der Waals theory, be counted as 5 phases, if one includes 2 unstable phases as well. Such a tricritical point can occur, however, in a multicomponent mixture consisting of 3 or more components as Professor Widom has mentioned and as recently has been observed.

Since for a binary mixture such a tricritical point is not possible in general, it is of interest that in at least 2 systems, that can be considered as binary mixtures, points have been observed in the phase diagram, that have partially the character of a critical point and partially of a triple point. These points are nowadays also called tricritical points. The 2 cases are:

1. a binary liquid mixture of the two helium isotopes: He^3 and He^4 at low temperatures;
2. a number of anisotropic antiferromagnetic compounds[2] such as $FeCl_2$, $FeBr_2$, $Ni(NO_3)_2 \cdot 2H_2O$ etc., called metamagnets by Kramers because of their unusual magnetic behavior.

Before going into a theoretical discussion, let me first summarise briefly some of the relevant experimental data for these systems.

1. He^3-He^4 mixtures - In 1932, Keesom discovered[3] that under its vapor pressure, He^4 shows at a temperature $T_\lambda = 2.2^oK$ (the lambda temperature) a phase transition from a high temperature liquid phase, that he called HeI, to a low temperature liquid phase, that was called HeII. Later it was discovered that the HeII phase showed superfluid properties. Therefore, as is customary now, I shall refer to a phase in which the He^4 occurs as HeI, as a normal phase, while a phase in which He^4 occurs as HeII will be called a superfluid phase.

The transition differed from the usual — first order — phase transitions in

Fundamental Problems in Statistical Mechanics, Vol. 3, Editor, E.D.G. Cohen.

that not only the temperature T, the pressure p and the chemical potential μ were the same in the 2 coexisting liquid phases but that also the first derivatives: $s = -\frac{\partial\mu}{\partial T}$ and $v = \frac{\partial\mu}{\partial p}$ were continuous. Higher order derivatives of μ, such as $C_V = T\frac{\partial^2\mu}{\partial T^2}$ were singular at T_λ, and showed a jump, thus indicating that a phase transition did occur. Ehrenfest[4)] called such a transition a second order phase transition, but a better name is perhaps the one proposed by Landau[5)]: a continuous transition, since $C_V(T)$ does actually not have a jump discontinuity but rather a logarithmic behavior near $T = T_\lambda$.

In mixtures of liquid He^3 and He^4, Abraham, Weinstock and Osborne found in 1949[6)] that under saturated vapor pressure T_λ becomes a decreasing function of the He^3-concentration x: $T_\lambda(x)$: the lambda-line. In 1956, Walters and Fairbank[7)] discovered that the lambda-line ends in the T-x-plane at the point $T_t = 0.87^\circ K$ and $x_t = 0.67$ where the homogeneous mixture separates into 2 coexisting liquid phases with different concentrations $x_\ell(T)$ and $x_u(T)$ $(x_\ell(T)<x_u(T))$. The He^4 in the x_u-phase is HeI, and in the x_ℓ-phase HeII. That the critical point (T_t, x_t) for the phase separation lies on the λ-line, has been clearly demonstrated by Graf, Lee and Reppy in 1967[8)] by using the dependence of the dielectric constant on the density (i.e. on x). At $T = 0^\circ K$ Edwards found in 1965[9)] that the phase separation is incomplete, in that a phase of pure He^3 $(x_u(0) = 1)$ coexists with a 6.4% mixture of He^3 and He^4 $(x_\ell(0) = 0.064)$ (cf. fig. 1). From fig. 1 it will be clear that the critical mixing point C is a different kind of critical point than in a classical binary mixture. Not only do 3 lines meet and 2 phases become identical in C, but the approach of the lower - and upper branches of the coexistence curve towards C is linear, rather than cubic, as in the case at a normal critical point. Thus, as was found already by Graf, Lee and Reppy[8)] and confirmed by Alvesalo c.s.[10)]:

$$x_\ell(T) - x_t \sim (T_t - T)^{\beta_{u-}} \quad , \quad T < T_t \tag{1.1}$$

and

$$x_u(T) - x_t \sim (T - T_t)^{\beta_{u+}} \quad , \quad T > T_t \tag{1.2}$$

with

$$\beta_{u-} = \beta_{u+} = 1 \tag{1.3}$$

in the neighborhood of the critical point C[11)]. Note that the slopes in (T_t, x_t) at the λ-line and at the upper branch $x_u(T)$ are unequal.

We shall call the critical point C, a tricritical point.

The behavior of the mixture in the immediate neighborhood of the λ-line and the tricritical point C, that I shall report, has mainly been obtained by 2 groups:

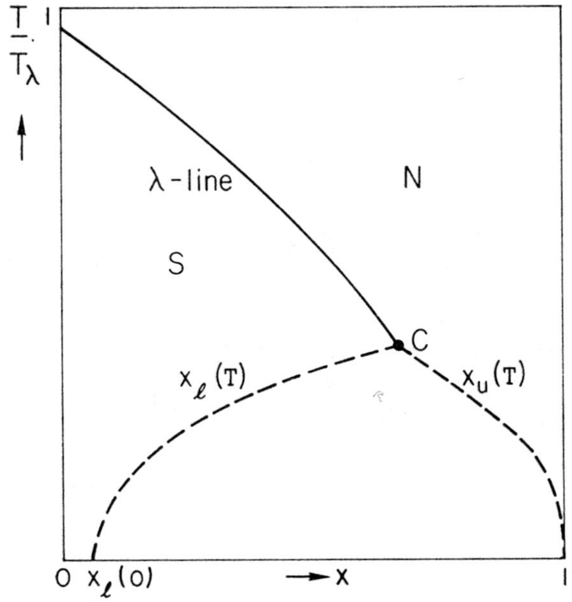

Fig. 1. Phase diagram of He^3-He^4 mixtures in the T-x-plane under saturated vapor pressure. The λ-line separates phases of the mixture that contain He^4 as HeI and HeII, which are denoted by N (normal) and S (superfluid) respectively. The tricritical point C, the critical point for the phase separation into 2 coexisting phases, is located at $T_t/T_\lambda = 0.40$ and $x_t = 0.67$. The lower branch of the coexistence curve ($x_\ell(T)$) and the upper branch of the coexistence curve ($x_u(T)$) meet the λ-line at C. The slopes of the λ-line and of $x_u(T)$ in C are <u>un</u>equal. The residual solubility of He^3 in He^4 at $T = 0^{\circ}K$, $x_\ell(0) = 0.064$.

Meyer c.s. at Duke University[12] and Zimmerman c.s. at the University of Minnesota[10,13]. Zimmerman c.s. measured the specific heat at saturated vapor pressure along the λ-line and near the tricritical point. From this he could, by thermodynamic arguments, discuss C_{px}, the specific heat at constant p and x; $C_{p\Delta}$, the specific heat at constant p and $\Delta = \mu_3 - \mu_4$ (where μ_i is the chemical potential of He^i (i = 3,4)); $\Delta(x,T)$ and $(\frac{\partial x}{\partial \Delta})_{T,p}$.

Meyer c.s. made vapor pressure measurements from which he derived $\Delta(x,T)$ and $(\frac{\partial x}{\partial \Delta})_{T,p}$.

a) C_{px} does not show a logarithmic behavior at $T = T_\lambda(x)$ when $x>0$, but instead a cusp-like behavior. At $x = x_t$, C_{px} remains finite and continuous, while $\frac{dC_{px}}{dT}$ is discontinuous. Thus along the λ-line one has:

$$C_{px} \sim (T_\lambda - T)^{-\alpha'_\lambda} \quad , \quad T < T_\lambda \tag{1.4}$$

$$C_{px} \sim (T - T_\lambda)^{-\alpha_\lambda} \quad , \quad T > T_\lambda \tag{1.5}$$

where

$$\alpha'_\lambda = \alpha_\lambda \approx 0 \tag{1.6}$$

and near the tricritical point one has

$$C_{px} \sim (T_t - T)^{-\alpha'_u} \quad , \quad x = x_t \quad , \quad T < T_t \tag{1.7}$$

$$C_{px} \sim (T - T_t)^{-\alpha_u} \quad , \quad x = x_t \quad , \quad T > T_t \tag{1.8}$$

where

$$\alpha'_u = \alpha_u = 0 \tag{1.9}$$

b) $C_{p\Delta}$ diverges at the tricritical point for $\Delta = \Delta_t$ and may be divergent along the λ-line. Thus along the λ-line one has:

$$C_{p\Delta} \sim (T_\lambda - T)^{-\alpha'} \quad , \quad T < T_\lambda \tag{1.10}$$

$$C_{p\Delta} \sim (T - T_\lambda)^{-\alpha} \quad , \quad T > T_\lambda \tag{1.11}$$

where

$$\alpha' = \alpha \cong 0 \ (?) \tag{1.12}$$

while near the tricritical point one has:

$$C_{p\Delta} \sim (T_t - T)^{-\alpha'_t} \quad , \quad \Delta = \Delta_t \quad , \quad T < T_t \tag{1.13}$$

$$C_{p\Delta} \sim (T - T_t)^{-\alpha_t} \quad , \quad \Delta = \Delta_t \quad , \quad T > T_t \tag{1.14}$$

where

$$\alpha'_t = \alpha_t = 1/2 \quad . \tag{1.15}$$

c) $(\frac{\partial x}{\partial \Delta})_{T,p}$ along the lower (-), and upper (+) branches of the coexistence curve, behaves like:

$$(\frac{\partial x}{\partial \Delta})_{T,p} \sim (T_t - T)^{\gamma'_{u\pm}} \quad , \quad x = x_t \quad , \quad T < T_t \quad , \tag{1.16}$$

$$(\frac{\partial x}{\partial \Delta})_{T,p} \sim (T - T_t)^{\gamma_u} \quad , \quad x = x_t \quad , \quad T > T_t \tag{1.17}$$

where

$$\gamma'_{u+} = \gamma'_{u-} = 1 \tag{1.18}$$

$$\gamma_u = 1 \quad . \tag{1.19}$$

d) Similarly, $\Delta = \mu_3 - \mu_4$ behaves in the neighborhood of x_t as:

$$\Delta(x) - \Delta(x_t) \sim |x - x_t|^{\delta_{u\pm}} \quad , \quad T = T_t \quad , \quad x \gtrless x_t \tag{1.20}$$

where

$$\delta_{u+} = \delta_{u-} = 2 \tag{1.21}$$

e) Johnson and Lai[14)] found that the tricritical point changes its location but not its nature as a function of pressure using pressures up to 20 atm.: it becomes a tricritical line.

It is interesting to remark that Watson c.s.[15)] found that the limiting solubility of He^3 in the He^4 at $T = 0^o K$, $x_\ell(0)$, also changes with pressure. Johnson[14)] has pointed out that there is a similarity in the change of T_t/T_λ and $x_\ell(0)$ as a function of pressure in that both first increase to a maximum and then decrease.

It would be interesting if the measurements of Meyer c.s. and Zimmerman c.s. could also be extended from vapor pressure to higher pressures.

2. Metamagnets - In 1932 Néel[16)] realised, from susceptibility measurements, that Mn, Cr etc. show a phase transition in an external magnetic field at a temperature T_N (the Néel-temperature) from a high temperature paramagnetic (P) phase, with a relatively large magnetic moment, to a low temperature antiferromagnetic (AF) phase, with a relatively small magnetic moment. This transition is similar to that in He^4 in that it is a continuous transition, with no latent heat. As a function of the external magnetic field strength B, it was realised later[17)] that T_N becomes a decreasing function of B: $T_N(B)$ — or as a function of magnetisation: $T_N(m)$ — : the Néel-line.

In 1940, Star, Bitter and Kaufmann[18)] observed "a field-induced transition" in the antiferromagnet $FeCl_2$, which was of a different nature than the continuous

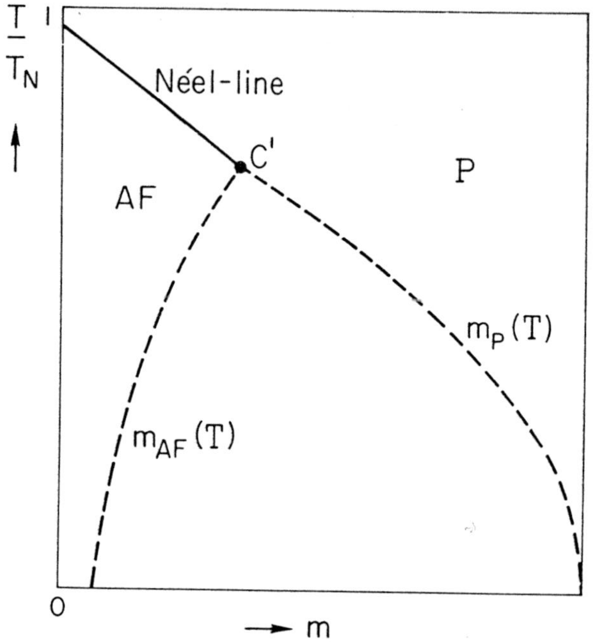

Fig. 2. Schematic phase diagram in the T-m-plane of a metamagnet. The Néel-line separates paramagnetic (P) and antiferromagnetic phases (AF). The tricritical point C', is the critical point for the phase separation into 2 coexisting phases. The lower branch of the coexistence curve (m_{AF}(T)) and the upper branch of the coexistence curve (m_P(T)) probably meet the Néel-line at C' and almost certainly go to pure AF- and P-phases at $T = 0^{\circ}K$. The slopes of the Néel-line and of m_P(T) at C' are unequal.

paramagnetic - antiferromagnetic transition discussed above. For, below a certain temperature T_t and for sufficiently strong fields, the transition became a first order transition, where a mixed phase appeared in which paramagnetic domains, with a high magnetic moment, coexisted with antiferromagnetic domains, with a low magnetic moment (cf. fig. 2). Following Kramers[19] we shall call such antiferromagnets, with this unorthodox magnetic behavior, metamagnets.

The precise way in which the Néel-line ends at the tricritical point (T_t,m_t) and goes over into the two branches of the coexistence curve in the T-m-plane is not entirely clear. There are, as yet, no measurements of comparable accuracy to those of Graf c.s. for the helium mixtures. It is generally expected that the behavior is similar to that of the helium mixtures: the 2 coexisting branches meet the Néel-line at the tricritical point C'. The detailed behavior in the immediate neighborhood of the Néel-line and the tricritical point has been investigated mainly by Wolf c.s. for DAG[20], using magnetic resonance and by Birgenau c.s.[21] for $FeCl_2$, using neutron scattering. The magnetic resonance can reveal the existence of 2 different internal fields in the P - and the AF - domains, while the neutron scattering is determined by the sublattice magnetisation (see below).

There are far fewer as well as less accurate data for the metamagnets available than for the Helium mixtures.

a) The behavior of the lower (AF) - and upper (P) branches near C' is linear:

$$|m_{AF} - m_t| \sim (T_t - T)^{\beta_{u-}} \quad , \quad T < T_t \tag{1.22}$$

$$m_P - m_t \sim (T_t - T)^{\beta_{u+}} \quad , \quad T < T_t \tag{1.23}$$

where

$$\beta_{u-} = ? \quad , \quad \beta_{u+} = 1 \ . \tag{1.24}$$

The coefficient β_{u-}, that characterizes the approach to the tricritical point along the lower (AF) branch of the coexistence curve, has not yet been determined reliably.

The slopes in (T_t, m_t) at the Néel-line and at the upper branch $m_P(T)$ seem to be unequal, like in the helium mixtures.[22)]

b) Birgenau c.a.[21a)] determined the staggered magnetisation $m_s(T)$ (cf. II eq. (2.12)) along the Néel-line:

$$m_s(T) \sim (T_N - T)^{\beta} \quad , \quad T < T_N \tag{1.25}$$

where

$$\beta = 0.29 \quad . \tag{1.26}$$

c) The behavior under pressure has recently been investigated by Vettier, Alberts and Bloch for $FeCl_2$ and $FeBr_2$.[23)] They notice a change in the location but not in the nature of the tricritical point with pressure in $FeCl_2$: it becomes a tricritical line.

The behavior of $FeBr_2$ may well be qualitatively different from that of $FeCl_2$ and not show a tricritical point at all[24)].

d) All present data are consistent with the assumption, that the phase separation into coexisting P - and AF phases becomes "complete" at $T = 0^{\circ}K$, i.e. that a pure P - and a pure AF - phase are in equilibrium with each other at that temperature.

In both cases — the helium mixtures as well as the metamagnets — one finds that upon lowering T a continuous transition goes over, at a tricritical point, into a first order transition (cf. figs. 3 and 4). Corresponding thermodynamic quantities for the helium mixtures and the metamagnets are summarised in table I:

TABLE I

Helium mixtures	Metamagnets
T	T
P	P
$\Delta = \mu_3 - \mu_4$	B
x	m
T_λ	T_N
T_t	T_t

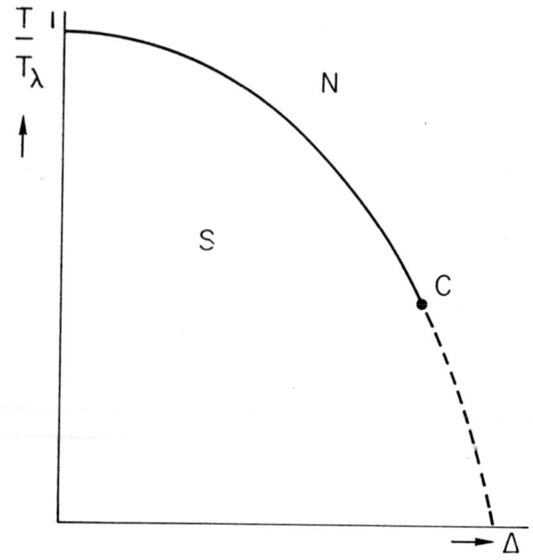

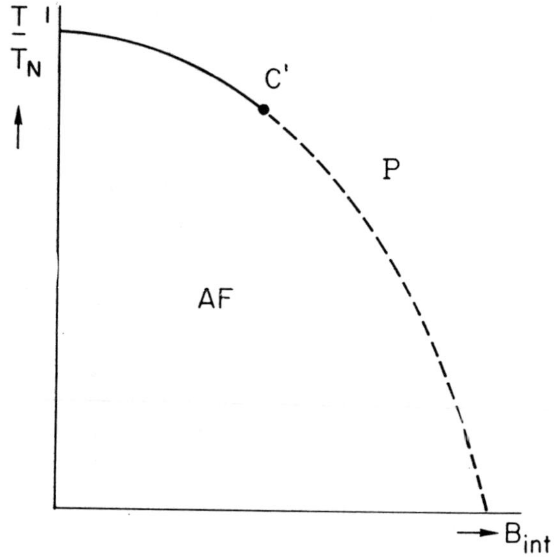

Fig. 3. Schematic phase diagram in the T-Δ plane for He^3-He^4 mixtures. For $T>T_t$, the N-S transition is a continuous transition, while for $T<T_t$ it is a first order transition. The two branches of the coexistence curve ($x_\ell(T)$ and $x_u(T)$) in fig. 1 have collapsed here into the dotted line below the tricritical point C.

Fig. 4. Schematic phase diagram in the T-B plane for a metamagnet. B_{int} is the "internal" magnetic field, the external field B corrected for demagnetisation effects. For $T>T_t$, the P-AF transition is continuous, while for $T<T_t$ it is a first order transition. The two branches of the coexistence curve ($m_{AF}(T)$ and $m_P(T)$) in fig. 2 have collapsed here into the dotted line below the tricritical point C'.

In the following two lectures I want to discuss to what extent the above mentioned behavior of the helium mixtures and the metamagnets can be understood. To that purpose 2 very simplified models are introduced: a hard-sphere model for the helium mixtures and an Ising-type model for the metamagnets.

2. SPIN 1/2 ISING MODEL FOR THE METAMAGNETS

The metamagnets we consider are all highly anisotropic, uniaxial antiferromagnets, where the magnetic moments of the atoms or ions can only be directed up or down. Therefore we shall use as a model for such a system an Ising-like spin ½ model. It will appear that such a model, when treated in the mean field approximation, shows qualitatively many of the properties of the metamagnets described in the previous lecture.

Let me make the model more precise. The magnetic moments or spins are arranged on a regular lattice of N sites that consists of 2 equivalent interpenetrating sublattices 1 and 2. The spins can only point up or down. The interaction energy between the spins is assumed to consist of an antiferromagnetic nearest neighbor (n.n.) interaction $\gamma > 0$, and a next nearest-neighbor (n.n.n.) exchange interaction γ', whose sign we leave open for the moment.

The Hamiltonian of the system is then:

$$H = \gamma \sum_{\text{n.n.}} \sigma_i \sigma_j - \gamma' \sum_{\text{n.n.n.}} \sigma_i \sigma_j - \mu B \sum_{i=1}^{N} \sigma_i \quad . \tag{2.1}$$

Here $\sum_{\text{n.n.}} \left(\sum_{\text{n.n.n.}} \right)$ is a sum over all nearest (next nearest) neighbor lattice sites; μ is the magnetic moment per spin; B the external magnetic field; the spin variable σ_i has values ± 1 according to whether the spin on lattice site i is up or down respectively. The free energy of such a system in the mean field approximation can be derived in a variety of ways. The simplest and for our purpose the most convenient is perhaps the Bragg-Williams method.

Distinguishing two sublattice magnetizations s_1 and s_2, where s_i is the normalized magnetization of sublattice i $(i = 1,2)$[25], the free energy per spin in the presence of an outside magnetic field B, can be written in the form:

$$f(T,B;s_1 s_2) = e(T,B;s_1 s_2) - T\sigma(T,B;s_1 s_2) \tag{2.2}$$

where

$$e(T,B;s_1 s_2) = \tfrac{1}{2}\left[J s_1 s_2 - J' \frac{s_1^2 + s_2^2}{2} - \mu B(s_1 + s_2)\right] \tag{2.3}$$

and

$$\sigma(T,B;s_1,s_2)/k = -\ln 2 + \frac{1}{4}[(1+s_1)\ln(1+s_1) + (1-s_1)\ln(1-s_1)$$

$$+ (1+s_2)\ln(1+s_2) + (1-s_2)\ln(1-s_2)] \quad . \tag{2.4}$$

Then s_1 and s_2 are determined from the conditions that f is a minimum:

$$\frac{\partial f}{\partial s_1} = 0 \quad ; \quad \frac{\partial f}{\partial s_2} = 0 \tag{2.5}$$

or with (2.2)-(2.4), by the two transcendental equations:

$$s_1 = \text{tgh}\,\frac{\mu B_1}{kT} \tag{2.6a}$$

$$s_2 = \text{tgh}\,\frac{\mu B_2}{kT} \tag{2.6b}$$

where the internal fields B_1 and B_2 are given by:

$$\mu B_1 = \mu B - Js_2 + J's_1 \tag{2.7}$$

$$\mu B_2 = \mu B - Js_1 + J's_2 \quad . \tag{2.8}$$

In these equations $J = z\gamma$ and $J' = z'\gamma'$, where z and z' are the number of n.n.'s and n.n.n.'s of a site respectively. For ferromagnetic n.n.n. interactions $J'>0$, while for antiferromagnetic n.n.n. interactions $J'<0$. Eq. (2.3) is simply the energy of the system at given sublattice magnetizations s_1 and s_2; the first term gives the interaction energy between the 2 sublattices 1 and 2, the second term gives the energy of each of the sublattices, while the third term gives the energy of the spins in the magnetic field. The right hand side of eq. (2.4) is proportional to the logarithm of the number of possible configurations of the spins on the two sublattices, with given s_1 and s_2, assuming a random distribution of the spins. The equations (2.6)-(2.8) are easy to understand on the basis of the Weiss-Néel theory of magnetism. For, the Langevin theory gives for the magnetization of a paramagnet the equation[26]:

$$M = N\mu\, L\left(\frac{B}{kT}\right) \quad , \tag{2.9}$$

where L is the Langevin function. For spin ½ particles $L(x) = \text{tgh}\,x$ so that eq. (2.9) becomes:

$$M = N\mu\,\text{tgh}\,\frac{\mu B}{kT}$$

or with $s = M/N\mu$:

$$s = \text{tgh}\,\frac{\mu B}{kT} \tag{2.10}$$

Following Weiss and Néel, the external field B on the right-hand side of eq. (2.10) must now be replaced for our antiferromagnet by the total field acting on a spin. This field is the sum of the external field plus the internal fields due to the two sublattice magnetizations s_1 and s_2. The magnetization on sublattices 1, s_1, is then found by substituting in eq. (2.10) for μB, μB_1 from eq. (2.7), leading to eq. (2.6a), while the magnetization on sublattice 2, s_2, is obtained by substituting in eq. (2.10) for μB, μB_2 from eq. (2.8) leading to eq. (2.6b). The equations (2.6)-(2.8) are two coupled transcendental equations for s_1 and s_2.

For later use we introduce still: the (total) normalised magnetization m:

$$m = \frac{1}{2}(s_1 + s_2) \tag{2.11}$$

and the normalised staggered magnetization m_s i.e. the difference between the magnetization of sublattice 1 and 2:

$$m_s = \frac{1}{2}(s_1 - s_2) \quad . \tag{2.12}$$

The staggered magnetization, m_s, is the important quantity for antiferromagnetic ordering: when there is no antiferromagnetic ordering, as in the paramagnetic phase, $m_s = 0$, while in the antiferromagnetically ordered phase, $0 < |m_s| \leqslant i$.

The thermodynamic properties of the metamagnet and its critical behavior in particular can be discussed on the basis of the equations (2.2)-(2.8).

These equations have been discussed before by a number of authors.[27] I shall summarize the results. One can solve the equations (2.2)-(2.8) for s_1 and s_2 at given J, J', for each T and B graphically (as Gorter and Van Peski-Tinbergen did) or numerically (as Bidaux and Kincaid did). Then, with the equations (2.1), (2.11) and (2.12), f, m and m_s can be obtained. We use reduced quantities $t = kT/(J+J')$ and $b = \mu B/(J+J')$ and plot m and m_s versus b, at given t. The graphs depend parametrically on the ratio $\varepsilon = J'/J$ (cf. fig. 5). Since the Néel-temperature T_N is given by the equation:

$$kT_N = J + J' \tag{2.13}$$

the reduction by $(J+J')$ can also be considered as a reduction by kT_N.

Thus it is clear that for some values of J'/J, m is not always a single-valued function of b. In fact, for small t and $J'/J > 0$, the magnetization isotherms have a wiggle. That part of the wiggle on which $\left(\frac{\partial m}{\partial b}\right)_t < 0$ is unstable, because m increases when b decreases. This wiggle is a consequence of the mean field approximation and, like in the case of a van der Waals gas, it can be eliminated by making the free energy a minimum or equivalently by making a

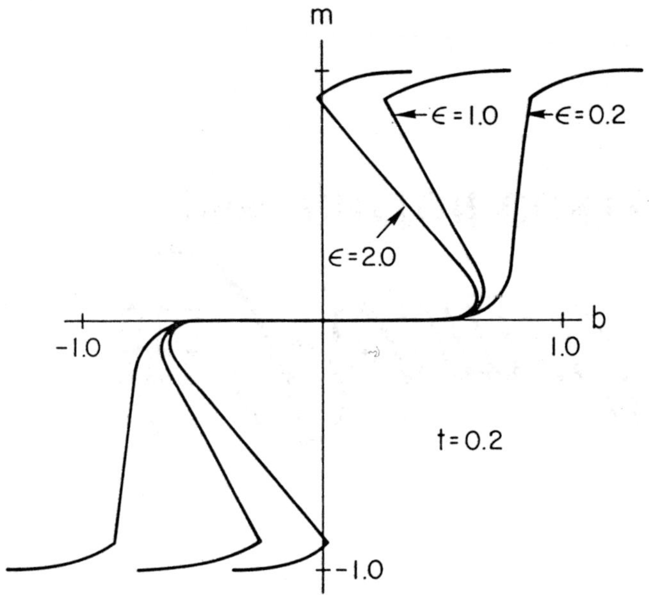

Fig. 5. The reduced magnetization m as a function of the reduced magnetic field b at the reduced temperature t = 0.2 for various values of $\varepsilon = J'/J$.

Maxwell-like equal area construction on the m-b isotherms (fig. 6). There is a unique value of b, b_1, such that an antiferromagnetic state ($|m_s| \neq 0$ or m small) and a paramagnetic state ($m_s = 0$ or m large) are in equilibrium with each other.[28] The corrected isotherms are given in fig. 7. With these m versus b isotherms, the t-m phase diagram can be constructed.

The nature of the phase diagram depends qualitatively on $\varepsilon = J'/J$. Only for certain values of ε does one obtain a phase diagram with a tricritical point.

(i) If $-1 \leqslant \varepsilon \leqslant 0$ (i.e. $J' < 0$) there is only a Néel-line that separates the paramagnetic ($m_s = 0$) and antiferromagnetic ($|m_s| \neq 0$) phases (cf. fig. 8). The equation in the Néel-line is: $m = \sqrt{1 - t_N}$ or $t_N(m) = 1 - m^2$.

(ii) If $0 < \varepsilon < \frac{3}{5}$, a phase separation between an antiferromagnetic and a paramagnetic phase occurs below a certain critical temperature — the bicritical endpoint — which is not located on the Néel-line. The Néel-line ends then in a critical endpoint (cf. fig. 9). The bicritical endpoint (BCE) as well as the critical endpoint (CE) as a function of ε cannot be found in analytic form and have to be computed numerically.

(iii) Only when $\varepsilon > \frac{3}{5}$ does the critical point for the phase separation into an antiferromagnetic and a paramagnetic phase lie on the Néel-line, thus creating a tricritical point (cf. fig. 10). The equation for the tricritical point as a function of ε is: $t_C = 1 - \frac{1}{3\varepsilon}$.

In fig. 11 the critical temperatures t_C, t_{BCE} and t_{CE} are plotted as a

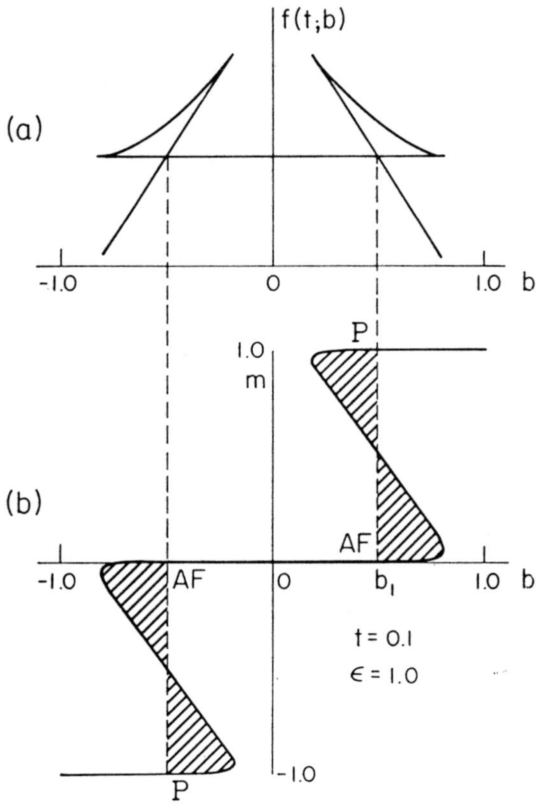

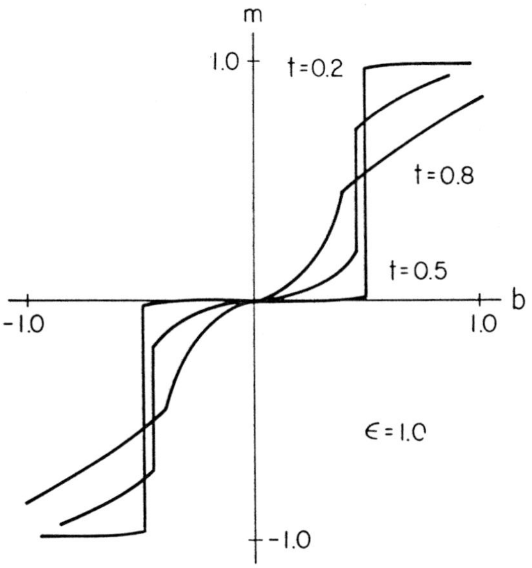

Fig. 6. The free energy per spin $f(t, b)$ as a function of the reduced field b at $t = 0.1$ for $\varepsilon = 1.0$. Minimizing f is equivalent to applying an equal area construction to the m-b isotherm of $t = 0.1$. b_1 is that value of b where an AF-phase $(m_s \neq 0)$ and a P-phase $(m_s = 0)$ are in equilibrium with each other.

Fig. 7. Corrected isotherms for m versus b at $\varepsilon = 1.0$. Note the similarity with V versus p isotherms in the case of the van der Waals equation for fluids.

function of ε.

(iv) When $\varepsilon = 3/5$ a new type of critical point occurs. For this value of ε the behavior sketched under (ii) goes over into that of (iii).

I remark that only the phase diagram in the t-m plane obtained from the equations (2.2)-(2.8) for case (iii), resembles qualitatively the one found for metamagnets with a tricritical point (cf. figs. 2 and 10). A difference seems to be that the slopes at the tricritical point along the Néel-line and the paramagnetic branch of the coexistence curve are equal in the mean field theory, while they appear to be unequal in actual metamagnets.

Almost exclusive attention has been paid to case (iii), when a tricritical

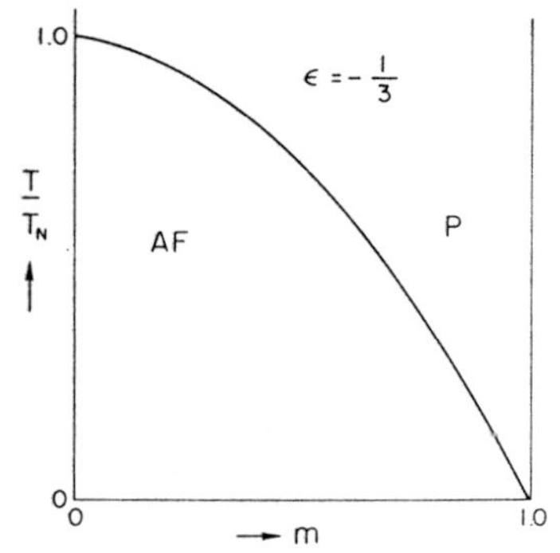

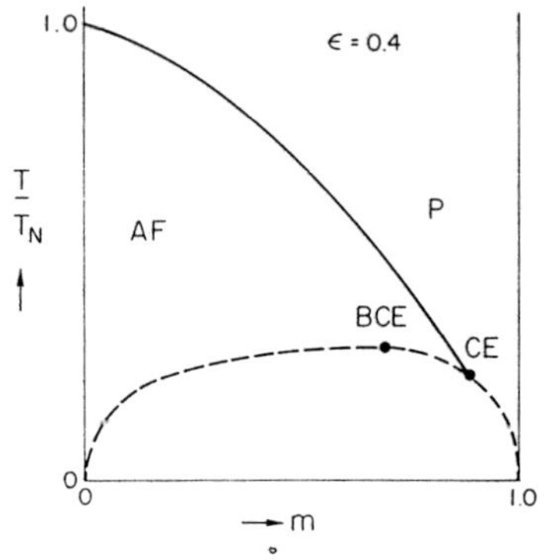

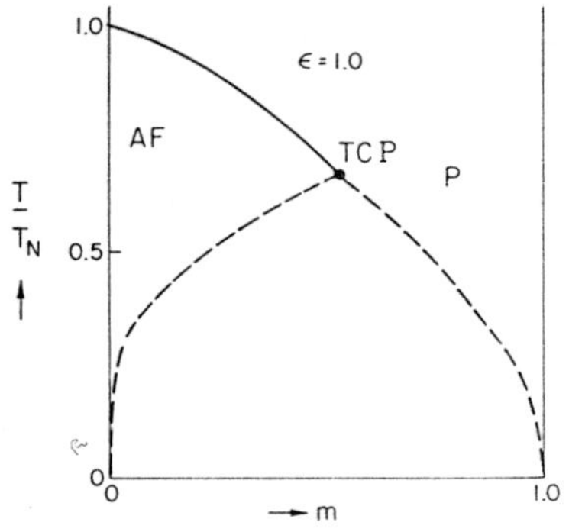

Fig. 8. t-m phase diagram for $-1 \leqslant \varepsilon \leqslant 0$. The drawn line is the Néel-line, which separates a P-phase from an AF-phase.

Fig. 9. t-m phase diagram for $0 < \varepsilon < 3/5$. The phase-separation starts at t_{BCE}, the bicritical endpoint (BCE), which is not on the Néel-line. The Néel-line ends in a critical endpoint (CE) at a temperature t_{CE}. The phase-separation is complete at $T = 0^{\circ}K$.

Fig. 10. t-m phase diagram for $\varepsilon > 3/5$. The phase-separation starts at t_{TCP}, the tricritical point, which is on the Néel-line. The phase-separation is complete at $T = 0^{\circ}K$.

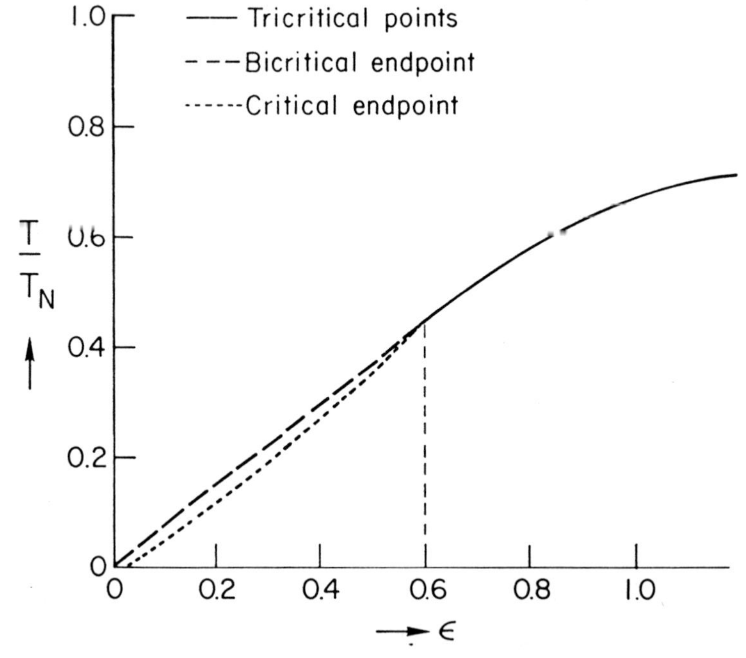

Fig. 11. The reduced temperatures of the tricritical point (t_{TCP}), the bicritical endpoint (t_{BCE}) and the critical endpoint (t_{CE}) as a function of ε. The point at $\varepsilon = 0.6$ represents a new critical point. The slopes in $\varepsilon = 0.6$ along all three curves is the same.

point is present. One should bear in mind, however, that to the extent one can believe the results of mean field theory, the other cases may well be found in nature also; in fact a critical end point may have been seen already, although not recognized as such, in $FeBr_2$.[23,24] After this general discussion, I shall now discuss the critical behavior in case (iii) i.e., when there is a tricritical point, in more detail.

The critical exponents that describe the behavior near the Néel-line and the tricritical point can be subdivided into two classes: those that describe the critical behavior near the Néel-line and the critical point C' with respect to 1) the field B: α', α, β and α_t', α_t, β_t and 2) the magnetization m: α_u', α_u, $\beta_{u\pm}$, γ_u, $\gamma_{u\pm}'$ and $\delta_{u\pm}$. The sub-u exponents describe the behavior along the coexistence curve in the t-m-plane. Of all the ways in which the critical exponents can be calculated, I only mention two.

1. By computing the thermodynamic quantities concerned directly from the basic equations (2.2)-(2.8) and expanding them in terms of the relevant variables around the Néel-line or the tricritical point C'. This method has been followed by Motizuki and Bidaux, who determined a number of them this way. In particular, expanding $b(t,m_s)$ in a power series of m_s yields the equation for the tricritical point C'.

2. One constructs, from the free energy (2.2), using the equations (2.11) and (2.12), a free energy $f(T,B;m,m_s)$. Then with the equation $\frac{\partial f}{\partial m} = 0$, which corresponds to one of the equations (2.5), one obtains a free energy $g(T,B;m_s)$, where the second of the equations (2.5) requires that $\frac{\partial g}{\partial m_s} = 0$. One can now study — as was first done by Landau[5] — the behavior near the Néel-line and the tricritical point C' by expanding $g(T,B;m_s)$ in powers of m_s, since $m_s = 0$ on the Néel-line and at the point C':

$$g(T,B,m_s) = g^0(T,B) + a(T,B)m_s^2 + b(T,B)m_s^4 + C(T,B)m_s^6 + \dots \quad (2.14)$$

In this expansion only even powers of m_s occur, since the free energy is invariant for an interchange of the two sublattices 1 and 2, i.e., for $m_s \to -m_s$. The critical behavior of the system, in which we are interested, is determined by the coefficients $a(T,B)$, $b(T,B)$ etc., which follow from the basic equations (2.2)-(2.8) and depend on ε. A study of $g(T,B;m_s)$ yields for the equation of the Néel-line (in the T-B-plane):

$$a(T,B) = 0 \quad (2.15)$$

with

$$b(T,B) > 0 \quad . \quad (2.16)$$

For the tricritical point C', one finds the two equations:

$$a(T,B) = 0 \tag{2.17}$$

$$b(T,B) = 0 \tag{2.18}$$

with

$$c(T,B) > 0 \tag{2.19}$$

which shows that this point is <u>on</u> the Néel-line. The behavior in the neighborhood of the Néel-line and the point C' can be found by expanding $g^0(T,B)$, $a(T,B)$, $b(T,B)$ etc. in the neighborhood of the Néel-line and the point C'. For details I refer to the literature.[5, 27e)] In table II, I have listed the results obtained not only for those exponents mentioned in the previous lecture, and which have therefore been measured, but also of others.[29)] A definition of all these exponents follows.[30)]

<u>List of exponents</u>

<u>Critical</u>

$C_B \sim (T_N - T)^{-\alpha'}$; $B = B_N$* ; $T < T_N$

$C_B \sim (T - T_N)^{-\alpha}$; $B = B_N$; $T > T_N$

$m_s(T) \sim (T_N - T)^{\beta}$; $B = B_N$; $T < T_N$

* B_N is the value of the (critical) magnetic field along the Néel-line.

<u>Tricritical</u>

<u>sub-t</u>

$C_B \sim (T_t - T)^{-\alpha'_t}$; $B = B_t$; $T < T_t$

$C_B \sim (T - T_t)^{-\alpha_t}$; $B = B_t$; $T > T_t$

$m_s(T) \sim (T_t - T)^{\beta_t}$; $B = B_t$; $T < T_t$

<u>sub-u</u>

$C_m \sim (T_t - T)^{-\alpha'_u}$; $m = m_t$; $T < T_t$

$C_m \sim (T_t - T)^{-\alpha_u}$; $m = m_t$; $T > T_t$

$|m_{AF}(T) - m_t| \sim (T_t - T)^{\beta_{u-}}$; $T < T_t$

$m_P(T) - m_t \sim (T_t - T)^{\beta_{u+}}$; $T < T_t$

$\chi \sim (T - T_t)^{-\gamma_u}$* ; $m = m_t$; $T > T_t$ *χ is the susceptibility.

$\chi \sim (T_t - T)^{-\gamma'_{u-}}$; $m = m_{AF}(T)$; $T < T_t$

$\chi \sim (T_t - T)^{-\gamma'_{u+}}$; $m = m_P(T)$; $T < T_t$

$B - B_t \sim (m_t - m)^{\delta_{u-}}$; $T = T_t$; $m < m_t$

$B - B_t \sim (m - m_t)^{\delta_{u+}}$; $T = T_t$; $m > m_t$

The usual scaling relations hold between these exponents. One should note, however, that in the mean field theory presented here primed and unprimed exponents — and in general exponents referring to the behavior of a quantity approaching the critical (or tricritical) point from the paramagnetic or the antiferromagnetic side — are not necessarily equal. This is related to the fact that in the expansion (2.14), $m_s \equiv 0$ on the P-side, so that then $g(T,B,m_s) \equiv g^0(T,B)$, while $m_s \neq 0$ on the AF-side, where $g(T,B,m_s)$ is given by the full expansion (2.14).

In the last column of table II are given the values for the tricritical exponents computed by Riedel and Wegner on the basis of renormalization group considerations. As one can see, these exponents do exhibit the usual equality of primed and unprimed exponents and agree well with experiment.

3. HARD SPHERE MODEL FOR THE HELIUM MIXTURES

The behavior of the helium mixtures at temperatures below T_λ, will be studied here on the basis of a very much simplified model, which is a generalization to binary mixtures of a hard sphere model that was considered by Yang, Lee and Huang[31] in connection with the behavior of He^4. We consider[32] an isotopic mixture of N_B hard spheres with mass m_B and diameter a, that follow Bose-Einstein statistics and N_F hard spheres with mass m_F and diameter a, that follow Fermi-Dirac statistics in a volume V at temperature T. This model for He^3-He^4 mixtures idealizes the interatomic repulsion to that between hard spheres and it ignores the interatomic attraction. If one takes the view — as I shall do — that the effects due to the quantum statistics are dominant in the behavior of the helium mixtures — as they are for the pure components — then the hard sphere mixtures should be considered at densities comparable to those of the helium mixtures, in order to show a similar behavior. We will therefore be interested in hard sphere mixtures not only for T-values but also for values of $n = N/V = (N_F+N_B)/V$ comparable to those present in actual helium mixtures. The calculation of the thermodynamic properties of the hard sphere mixtures will be

TABLE II

Exponent	Metamagnet		Helium Mixtures		Riedel and Wegner
	theory	exper	theory	exper	theory
Critical					
α'	0	0 ?	0	0*	0*
α	0	0 ?	0	0*	0*
β	1/2	0.29	1/2		1/3
Tricritical					
α'_t	0		0	1/2	1/2
α_t	1/2		1/2	1/2	1/2
β_t	1/4		1/4		1/4
α'_u	0		0	0*	0
α_u	0		0	0*	0
β_{u-}	1	1 ?	1	1	1
β_{u+}	1	1	1	1	1
γ_u	0		0	1	1
γ'_{u-}	1		1	1	1
γ'_{u+}	0		0	1	1
δ_{u-}	1		1	2	2
δ_{u+}	2		2	2	2

*Close to logarithmic behavior.

based on a computation of the free energy:

$$F(T,V,N_F,N_B) = -kT\,\ell n Q_N \tag{3.1}$$

where

$$Q_N = \sum_{E_n} e^{-E_n/kT} \tag{3.2}$$

with E_n the energy eigenvalues of the system, using periodic boundary conditions.

The difficulty is, of course, to compute the E_n and I shall use approximate eigenvalues, that are computed by perturbation theory from the known eigenvalues of a binary mixture of an ideal Bose-Einstein and an ideal Fermi-Dirac gas. Since a straightforward perturbation theory with a hard sphere potential is not possible, the pseudo-potential method of Huang, Yang and Lee will be used to obtain approximate eigenvalues E_n. The pseudo-potential method is introduced in 2 steps. Firstly, one replaces in the 2-body problem — a boson and a fermion say — the actual hard-sphere interaction potential between the 2 particles, by a pseudo-potential, which is constructed in such a way that — in principle at least — for the 2-body problem at hand the exact eigenvalues are obtained. Such a pseudo-potential is constructed successively, using the hard-sphere diameter a as an expansion parameter, so that the above construction is carried out in successive orders in a. Secondly, this 2-body pseudo-potential is used to construct a pseudo-potential for the N-body system. I shall only use the N-body pseudo-potential to lowest order in a i.e. giving the energy eigenvalues E_n correctly to first order in a. The Hamiltonian for the hard-sphere mixture reads then:

$$H = -\sum_{i=1}^{N_F} \frac{\hbar^2}{2m_F} \nabla_i^2 - \sum_{j=1}^{N_B} \frac{\hbar^2}{2m_B} \nabla_j^2 +$$

$$+ \frac{1}{2} \sum_{i \neq i'}^{N_F} {}_1\, \phi_{FF}(\vec{r}_i - \vec{r}_{i'}) + \sum_{i=1}^{N_F} \sum_{j=1}^{N_B} \phi_{FB}(\vec{r}_i - \vec{r}_{j'}) +$$

$$+ \frac{1}{2} \sum_{j \neq j'}^{N_B} {}_1\, \phi_{BB}(\vec{r}_j - \vec{r}_{j'}) \qquad (3.3)$$

where the pseudo-potentials $\phi_{IJ}(\vec{r})$ are given by:

$$\phi_{IJ}(\vec{r}) = \phi_{IJ}\delta(\vec{r}) \quad , \qquad (I, J = F, B) \qquad (3.4)$$

with

$$\phi_{IJ} = 2\pi a\hbar^2\left(\frac{1}{m_I} + \frac{1}{m_J}\right) \quad , \qquad (I, J = F, B) \quad . \qquad (3.5)$$

The first two terms in (3.3) represent the kinetic energy of the fermions and bosons respectively, while the last three terms give the fermion-fermion, fermion-boson and boson-boson interaction energies respectively. Note that the fact that we deal with an isotopic mixture is reflected in that only one a appears in equation (3.5). The Hamiltonian (3.3) only gives the eigenvalues E_n correct to

$\mathcal{O}(a)$. We shall denote these by E'_n. The E'_n can be determined using the last three terms in (3.3) — which are proportional to a — as a perturbation, since the unperturbed problem, characterized by the first two terms in (3.3), can be solved exactly. Substituting these E'_n into the partition function (3.2), one keeps, for consistency, in the resulting expression for F only terms that are independent of a or are of $\mathcal{O}(a)$.[33)]

The following expression for the Helmholtz free energy F as a function of T, V and $x = N_F/N$ the fermion concentration, is then obtained:

$$F(T,V,x) = F_F^o + F_B^o + F_{int} \tag{3.6}$$

where

$$F_F^o(T,V,x) = N_F\mu_F^o + 2VkT\,\lambda_F^{-3} g_{5/2}(-e^{\mu_F^o/kT}) \tag{3.7}$$

$$F_B^o(T,V,x) = N_B\mu_B^o - VkT\,\lambda_B^{-3} g_{5/2}(e^{\mu_B^o/kT}) \tag{3.8}$$

$$F_{int}(T,V,x) = \frac{1}{2V}\left[\frac{1}{2}\,\phi_{FF}N_F^2 + 2\phi_{FB}N_FN_B + \phi_{BB}N_B^2(2-\bar{\xi}^2)\right] \tag{3.9}$$

Here F_F^o is the free energy of an ideal fermi gas, F_B^o that of an ideal Bose gas, while F_{int} is the contribution of $\mathcal{O}(a)$ of the hard sphere interaction to the free energy. Since the perturbation theory has only been carried out to first order in a, the equations (3.6)-(3.9) are strictly speaking only valid for $na^3 \ll 1$ and $na\lambda_B^2 \ll 1$. We shall use them, however, outside this domain (cf. ref. 33).
$\lambda_I^2 = h^2/2\pi m_I kT$ $(I = F, B)$, while the function $g_\alpha(z)$ defined by the integral:

$$g_\alpha(z) = \frac{1}{\Gamma(\alpha)}\int_0^\infty dt\, t^{\alpha-1}\,\frac{ze^{-t}}{1-ze^{-t}}$$

is well-known from the theory of the ideal Bose gas.

The expressions (3.7)-(3.9) contain further the chemical potentials of the ideal Fermi and Bose gas μ_F^o and μ_B^o respectively, as well as the fraction of bose particles, $\bar{\xi}$, that are condensed in the zero momentum single particle state. The equation that determines μ_F^o is:

$$xn = 2\lambda_F^{-3} g_{3/2}(-e^{\mu_F^o/kT}) \tag{3.10}$$

The equations that determine μ_B^o and $\bar{\xi}$ differ according to whether the Bose-Einstein gas is condensed or not i.e. whether $\bar{\xi}$ is different from zero or not.

To lowest order in a, the temperature in the hard sphere mixture at which Bose condensation starts to occur, that is the lambda temperature of the hard sphere mixture, is the same as that of an ideal Fermi-Bose mixture. We identify the lambda transition in the hard sphere mixture with the normal-superfluid transition in helium mixtures. The λ-line of the hard sphere mixture, $T_\lambda(x,p)$, that gives, at a given p, the locus of the points at which the Bose-Einstein condensation starts as a function of the concentration x, follows from the condition that $\mu_B^o = 0$ or:

$$(1-x)\, n\,(x, T_\lambda(x,p), p) = \lambda_B^{-3} g_{3/2}(1) = 2.612\ \lambda_B^{-3} \tag{3.11}$$

which is an obvious modification of the usual condition for the onset of Bose-Einstein condensation in a pure Bose gas: $n\lambda^{-3} = 2.612$, where in (3.11) the number density n has been replaced by the He^4 number density: $n(1-x)$. Although the precise dependence of $T_\lambda(x,p)$ on x and p is rather complicated, because n is a complicated function of T, p and x, $T_\lambda(x,p)$ behaves roughly as

$$T_\lambda(x,p) \cong T_\lambda(0,p)(1-x)^{2/3} \tag{3.12}$$

i.e. as in an ideal gas Bose-Fermi mixture at constant density. While $\mu_B^o = 0$ for $T < T_\lambda(x,p)$, it is given by

$$(1-x)n = \lambda_B^{-3} g_{3/2}(e^{\mu_B^o/kT}) \quad \text{for} \quad T > T_\lambda(x,p) \quad . \tag{3.13}$$

Finally for $T < T_\lambda(x,p)$, $\bar{\xi}$, the fraction of condensed particles, that minimizes F, is determined by the equation

$$(1-x)n(1-\bar{\xi}) = \lambda_B^{-3} g_{3/2}(1) = 2.612\ \lambda_B^{-3} \quad \text{for} \quad T < T_\lambda(x,p) \tag{3.14}$$

which is related to (3.13) by setting $\mu_B^o = 0$ on the right hand side and replacing $(1-x)$ by the concentration of non-condensed He^4 particles: $(1-x)(1-\bar{\xi})$. Roughly, $\bar{\xi} = 1 - (T/T_\lambda(x,p))^{3/2}$, which is similar to the variation of $\bar{\xi}$ in an ideal Bose gas at constant density.

In formulae involving $\bar{\xi}$ or μ_B^o it is always understood that $\mu_B^o = 0$ for $T < T_\lambda(x,p)$ while $\bar{\xi} = 0$ for $T > T_\lambda(x,p)$.

The expression (3.12) can easily be understood on the basis of an argument due to Daunt and Heer.[34)]

Bose-Einstein statistics will become important in a Bose gas when the average distance d between particles is of the same order of magnitude as the de Broglie wave length λ_B, that is characteristic for the wave packets that describe the particles. Since the average distance $d \sim n_B^{-1/3}$, where n_B is the number density of the Bose particles, this condition becomes: $n_B^{-1/3} \approx \lambda_B$ or $n_B\lambda_B^3 \approx 1$. Since in the Bose-Fermi mixture $n_B = n(1-x)$ and $\lambda_B \sim T^{-1/2}$ the result (3.12) follows immediately.

I remark that the free energy (3.8) reduces, for $x = 0$, to that of a hard-sphere Bose gas to $\mathcal{O}(a)$ and that it exhibits in this case — as it does in the mixture — a second order transition in the Ehrenfest sense at T_λ, with no horizontal piece in the p-V isotherms below T_λ.[33)] This in contradistinction to the ideal Bose gas that exhibits a first order transition at T_λ, since the pressure is constant below T_λ.

Since we want to investigate the hard sphere mixtures at a given T and pressure p, we are interested in the Gibbs free energy G rather than in the Helmholtz free energy F. One can obtain G from F by using the relation:

$$G = Ng(T,x,p) = N[x\mu_F(T,p) + (1-x)\mu_B(T,p,x)] \tag{3.15}$$

with

$$\mu_I = \left(\frac{\partial F}{\partial N_I}\right)_{T,V} \qquad (I = F,\ B) \tag{3.16a}$$

and

$$p = -\left(\frac{\partial F}{\partial V}\right)_{T,N_F,N_B} \tag{3.16b}$$

where $g = G/N$ is the Gibbs free energy per particle.

I now discuss the thermodynamic properties of the hard-sphere mixture on the basis of the Gibbs free energy per particle $g(T,p,x)$.

To investigate, in particular, the stability of the mixture one computes $\left(\frac{\partial^2 g}{\partial x^2}\right)_{T,p}$. Above the λ-line, i.e. for $T > T_\lambda(x,p)$, the mixture is stable for all values of na^3 in which we are interested, since one can show that then $\left(\frac{\partial^2 g}{\partial x^2}\right)_{T,p} > 0$. Below the λ-line, however, i.e. for $T < T_\lambda(x,p)$, one obtains the following condition for $\frac{\partial^2 g}{\partial x^2} > 0$:

$$\left(\frac{\partial \mu_F^o}{\partial (nx)}\right)_T > \frac{\phi_{FB}^2 - \frac{1}{2}\phi_{FF}\phi_{BB}}{\phi_{BB}} = \frac{ah^2}{4\pi m_F}\left(\nu + \frac{1}{\nu}\right) \tag{3.17}$$

where $\nu = m_F/m_B$.

Since

$$\left(\frac{\partial \mu_F^o}{\partial (nx)}\right)_T \geq \left(\frac{\partial \mu_F^o}{\partial (nx)}\right)_{T=0}$$

the condition (3.17) is most difficult to satisfy at $T = 0^\circ K$, where using that

$$\left(\frac{\partial \mu_F^o}{\partial (nx)}\right)_{T=0} = h^2/4m_F(3\pi^2 xn)^{1/3}$$

it reduces to:

$$xna^3 < \frac{\pi}{3}\left(\nu + \frac{1}{\nu}\right)^{-3} \quad . \tag{3.18}$$

Now (3.18) implies, since $x = 1$ at best, that at $T = 0^{o}K$ there is a maximum density n_c, or a maximum pressure p_c, such that only for $p < p_c$ the condition (3.18) can be satisfied for all x. For $p > p_c$ — or $n > n_c$ — there is a certain range of x-values for which (3.18) can still be satisfied, but for x too large it will be violated and the hard sphere mixture becomes unstable.

In fact, for $p > p_c$ one finds for the mixture an instability domain in the T,x-plane that is bordered on the upper side (i.e. for large x) by the λ-line and on the lower side (i.e. for small x) by the solution of the equation

$$\left(\frac{\partial \mu_F^o}{\partial (nx)}\right)_T = \frac{ah^2}{4\pi m_F}\left(\nu + \frac{1}{\nu}\right) \tag{3.19}$$

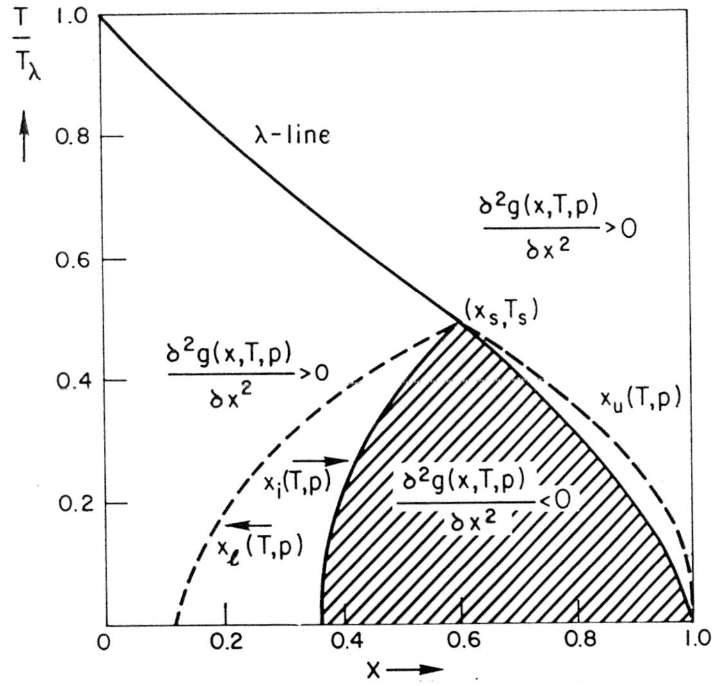

Fig. 12. Instability domain (shaded area) and λ-line in the T-x-phase diagram at constant $p > p_c$ for hard sphere mixtures. On the upper side, the instability domain is bounded by the λ-line and on the lower side by the solution of eq. (3.19). The lower branch $x_\ell(T)$ and the upper branch $x_u(T)$ of the coexistence curve are found by a bitangent construction on $g(T,x,p)$ and run <u>outside</u> the instability domain. They meet the λ-line at the tricritical point C. Thus $x_u(T)$ is in the normal (N) and $x_\ell(T)$ in the superfluid (S) phase. T_λ is the lambda temperature of the pure bosons.

(cf. fig. 12). The equation for the top of the instability region, the tricritical point T_t, x_t is obtained from the 2 equations (3.11) and (3.19). T_t/T_λ increases as a function of p, while x_t decreases as a function of p. For $T < T_t$ the instability of the homogeneous mixture leads to a separation into 2 coexisting phases. The concentrations $x_\ell(T,p)$ and $x_u(T,p)$ can be found, as a function of T and p, from a bitangent construction on $g(T,p,x)$ or equivalently from the conditions that the chemical potentials of the fermions and bosons in the 2 coexisting phases must be equal:

$$\mu_F(T,p,x_\ell(T,p)) = \mu_F(T,p,x_u(T,p)) \tag{3.20a}$$

$$\mu_B(T,p,x_\ell(T,p)) = \mu_B(T,p,x_u(T,p)) \tag{3.20b}$$

The coexistence curve $x_\ell(T)$, $x_u(T)$, at a given p, is the locus of all coexisting points (x_ℓ, x_u) for varying T (cf. fig. 13). The upper branch $x_u(T)$ runs above the λ-line and is therefore normal, while the lower branch $x_\ell(T)$ runs below the λ-line and is therefore superfluid.

At $T = 0^\circ K$, the condition (3.19) reduces to:

$$xna^3 = \frac{\pi}{3}\left(\nu + \frac{1}{\nu}\right)^{-3} \tag{3.21}$$

which leads for $n > n_c$ to an incomplete phase separation with a limiting solubility $x_\ell(0)$ that decreases as a function of p.

It is clear, from fig. 12, that the top of the phase separation curve C is a tricritical point and that in general this diagram shows a great similarity with the corresponding one for the helium mixtures (cf. fig. 1); in fact, for corresponding temperatures and densities, corresponding quantities are of the same order of magnitude.[35)]

Like in the case of the metamagnets, the theoretical phase diagram exhibits a continuity of slope at the tricritical point when going from the λ-line to the upper branch of the coexistence curve. This is due to mean field-like approximations, that make the λ-transition a second order transition in the Ehrenfest sense. In contrast, in He^3-He^4 solutions the λ-transition is a continuous transition and a discontinuity of slope at the tricritical point occurs.

I remark that when $\phi_{IJ} = 0$ (I, J = F, B) — and one has a binary mixture of an ideal Bose and an ideal Fermi gas — the mixture is stable for all x. There is then only a λ-line (cf. fig. 13).

The critical exponents that describe the behavior near the λ-line and the tricritical point can again be subdivided into 2 classes: those that describe the critical behavior near the λ-line and the critical point C with respect to 1) Δ : α', α and α'_t, α_t and 2) the concentration x: α'_u, α_u, $\beta_{u\pm}$, γ_u, $\gamma'_{u\pm}$ and $\delta_{u\pm}$. The sub-u exponents describe the behavior along the phase-separation (coexistence) curve in the T-x plane. These exponents are defined below. Since the pressure is always constant, it is not indicated explicitly.

List of exponents

Critical

$C_\Delta \sim (T_\lambda - T)^{-\alpha'}$; $\Delta = \Delta_\lambda$* ; $T < T_\lambda$

$C_\Delta \sim (T - T_\lambda)^{-\alpha}$; $\Delta = \Delta_\lambda$; $T > T_\lambda$

* Δ_λ is the value of Δ along the λ-line.

Tricritical

sub-t

$C_\Delta \sim (T_t - T)^{-\alpha'_t}$; $\Delta = \Delta_t$; $T < T_t$

$C_\Delta \sim (T - T_t)^{-\alpha_t}$; $\Delta = \Delta_t$; $T > T_t$

sub-u

$C_x \sim (T_t - T)^{-\alpha'_u}$; $x = x_t$; $T < T_t$

$C_x \sim (T - T_t)^{-\alpha_u}$; $x = x_t$; $T > T_t$

$x_t - x_\ell(T) \sim (T_t - T)^{\beta_{u-}}$; $T < T_t$

$x_u(T) - x_t \sim (T_t - T)^{\beta_{u+}}$; $T < T_t$

$\frac{\partial x}{\partial \Delta} \sim (T - T_t)^{\gamma_u}$; $x = x_t$; $T > T_t$

$\frac{\partial x}{\partial \Delta} \sim (T_t - T)^{\gamma'_{u-}}$; $x = x_\ell(T)$; $T < T_t$

$\frac{\partial x}{\partial \Delta} \sim (T_t - T)^{\gamma'_{u+}}$; $x = x_u(T)$; $T < T_t$

$\Delta - \Delta_t \sim (x_t - x)^{\delta_{u-}}$; $T = T_t$; $x < x_t$

$\Delta - \Delta_t \sim (x - x_t)^{\delta_{u+}}$; $T = T_t$; $x > x_t$

These exponents can be computed in a similar fashion as was done for the metamagnet: 1) either by direct expansion or 2) by using a new free energy $g(T,p,\Delta,\xi)$, where $\Delta = \mu_3 - \mu_4$ again. This free energy contains one more variable

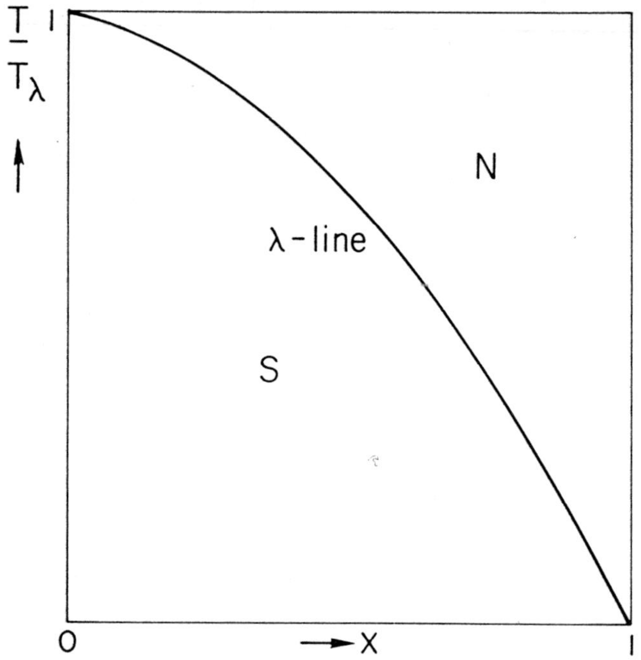

Fig. 13. Schematic representation of the λ-line in a binary mixture of an ideal Bose and an ideal Fermi gas.

than the corresponding one in the case of the metamagnets, since there p was not introduced as a thermodynamic variable. Table I of corresponding quantities can be extended to include:

TABLE I A

Helium mixtures	Metamagnets
ξ	m_s
normal phase	paramagnetic phase
superfluid phase	antiferromagnetic phase

The critical exponents for the hard sphere mixtures are identical with those for the metamagnet and are listed in Table II.

Johnson[14a)] has remarked that, although the variation of T_t/T_λ and $x_\ell(0)$ with pressure in the hard sphere mixtures differs from that found in helium mixtures, the ratio of the two quantities behaves very similarly.

There are indications that this difference in behavior of T_t/T_λ and $x_\ell(0)$

individually could be related to the extremely schematic way in which the attractive forces in the helium mixtures have been incorporated into the hard sphere model.

Let me end with two remarks.

1. The incomplete phase-separation at $T = 0^{\circ}K$ is due to the fermions. If one considers a mixture of 2 hard sphere Bose gases or of a hard sphere Bose- and Boltzmann gas, a complete phase separation would occur. In this respect the phase diagram of the metamagnets resembles that of a Bose-Boltzmann mixture more than of a Bose-Fermi mixture[27e].

2. The dependence of the phase diagram on the mass ratio ν is small, the dominant feature of the phase separation being the Bose-Einstein statistics.

Thus the influence of both quantum statistics is apparent in the behavior of the He^3-He^4 mixtures: the Bose-Einstein statistics causes the phase-separation, the Fermi-Dirac statistics makes it incomplete at $T = 0^{\circ}K$.

4. DISCUSSION

1. From the foregoing it will be clear that there is a certain analogy between metamagnets with $\varepsilon > 3/5$[36] and liquid helium mixtures, in that both show similar phase diagrams, that contain a tricritical point. One can well ask: can one understand this analogy, since the 2 systems are, at first sight, very different. I shall attempt to comment on this question in 2 ways: a) by a physical argument and b) by a formal extension of the thermodynamical treatment of both systems.

a. 1) Metamagnet. I consider only the case that there is a tricritical point and that $J > J' > 0$. There are 4 relevant energies: kT, J, J' and μB. In field $B = 0$, upon lowering the temperature, AF-ordering will take place when $kT_N \approx J$. Increasing B from zero will lower T_N, since the field opposes — like the temperature — the AF-ordering: it tries to put the spins parallel instead of antiparallel. When the field is sufficiently large, the tendency to parallel (or paramagnetic) ordering starts to compete with the AF-ordering. Crucial is that J' helps both equally. Therefore, when in addition to a large B, also T is sufficiently low, so that $kT = kT_t \approx J'$, J' can stabilize both phases against the thermal motion and 2 coexisting phases, one AF and the other paramagnetic can appear.

2) Hard sphere mixture. Here the relevant quantities are: kT, kT_λ, ϕ, a typical hard sphere interaction energy and $\Delta = \mu_3 - \mu_4$ or more conveniently x. For a pure Bose gas, upon lowering the temperature, Bose-Einstein condensation will take place when $kT = kT_\lambda$. Increasing x from zero, will lower T_λ, as argued above. When x is sufficiently large, coexistence may occur of regions with small x, that show Bose condensation and regions with large x, that do not show Bose

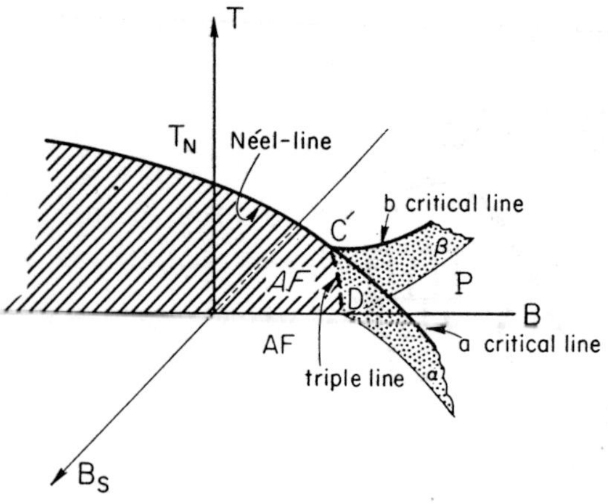

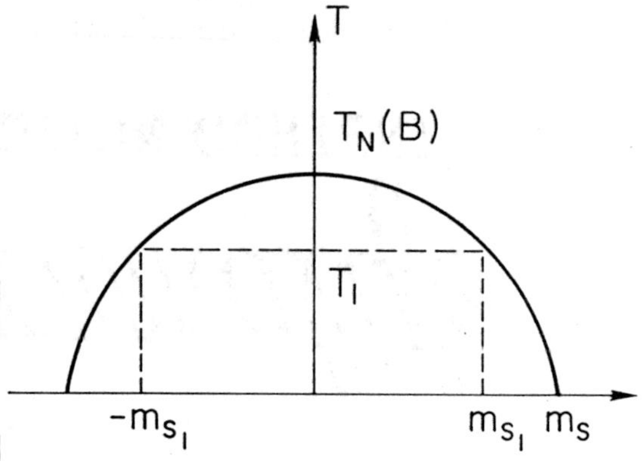

Fig. 14. Schematic phase diagram for metamagnet in TBB_s-space, where B_s is a staggered magnetic field, that has opposite directions on the 2 sub-lattices. The Néel-line (T_NC') is a critical line at which 2 coexisting AF-phases (with $m_s > 0$ and $m_s < 0$ respectively) become identical. C' is the tricritical point, where 3 phases (2 AF and 1 P) become identical, but also 3 critical lines meet: T_NC', a and b. The wings α and β separate AF- and P-regions: the wing α an AF-region with $m_s > 0$ and the P-region, the wing β an AF-region with $m_s < 0$ and the P-region. Above the 3 critical lines the system is in a P-state. The line C'D is a triple line, where 3 phases (2 AF and one P) are in equilibrium. The coexistence surface of the 2 AF phases is shaded.

Fig. 15. When traversing the coexistence region in fig. 14 (shaded area) parallel to the B_s-axis at a given field B, the staggered magnetization m_s jumps discontinuously from a value $-m_{s_1}$ to $+m_{s_1}$ for instance, as long as $T_1 < T_N(B)$, the Néel-temperature for field B.

The Néel-line is now a critical line for a <u>first</u> order transition, at which 2 coexisting antiferromagnetic phases (with $m_s \gtrless 0$ respectively) become identical. The shaded region in the T-B-plane is a coexistence surface, where 2 antiferromagnetic phases with staggered magnetization $m_s > 0$ and $m_s < 0$ respectively, coexist. m_s jumps discontinuously when one traverses the coexistence surface parallel to the B_s-axis (cf. fig. 15). At a temperature $T_1 < T_N(B)$, m_s jumps, upon traversing the coexistence surface, from $-m_{s_1}$ to m_{s_1}.

The point C' is a point where not only 3 phases become identical, but also a point where 3 critical lines meet. For, jutting out of the (physical) T-B-plane, condensation. Crucial is that the hard sphere interaction ϕ stabilizes the presence of 2 phases and, at that, equally, since $\phi_{33} + \phi_{44} - 2\phi_{34} = 0$. Therefore, when in addition to a large x, also T is sufficiently low, so that $kT = kT_t \approx \phi$, ϕ can maintain both phases against the thermal motion and 2 coexisting phases, one with Bose-Einstein condensation and the other without Bose-Einstein condensation can exist.

In this analogy ϕ plays the role of J'. For $\phi = 0$ and $J' = 0$, no phase separation into 2 coexisting phases occurs and only a λ-line and Néel-line appear. The presence of $\phi \neq 0$ and $J' \neq 0$ is therefore necessary for a tricritical point to occur (cf. fig. 8 and fig. 13).

b. The analogy between metamagnets and helium mixtures has also been discussed by Griffiths[37], following ideas of Landau.[5] I shall illustrate the argument on the metamagnet first, since this appears to be simpler.

1) Metamagnet. Let me first discuss the ferromagnet. When one lowers the temperature below the Curie temperature T_c in field $B = 0$, no net magnetization will appear; although regions with a magnetization $m(T) \neq 0$ will be present, their magnetizations precisely cancel due to their random orientations. To obtain a spontaneous magnetization $m(T) \neq 0$, one first lowers T in a field $B \neq 0$ and then, when $T < T_c$, lets $B \to 0$, thus producing a magnetization parallel to B. This procedure produces, so to say, one of the ∞ phases with $m(T) \neq 0$, that lay "dormant" in the ferromagnet when it was cooled down below T_c in the field $B = 0$. Similarly in an anisotropic 2 sublattice antiferromagnet, upon lowering the temperature (with or without an external field B) below the Néel-temperature T_N, no net staggered magnetization m_s will appear; although regions with $m_s(T) \neq 0$ will be present, they precisely cancel each other due to the fact that the 2 sublattices 1 and 2 are completely equivalent and that therefore there are as many regions with $m_s(T) > 0$ as with $m_s(T) < 0$. To obtain a staggered magnetization $m_s(T) \neq 0$, one should introduce a staggered external field B_s, that has opposite directions on the sublattices 1 and 2: say up on sublattice 1 and down on sublattice 2. Then, with $B_s \neq 0$, when $T < T_c$, let $B_s \to 0$, thus producing a staggered magnetization in the direction of B_s. This procedure produces, so to say, one of the 2 phases with $m_s(T) \neq 0$, that lay "dormant" in the antiferromagnet when it was cooled down below T_N.

Looking at the metamagnet this way, the antiferromagnetic regions below the Néel-line, can be considered as to consist of 2 coexisting ("dormant") phases: one with $m_s(T) > 0$ and the other one of equal magnitude but opposite sign, with $m_s(T) < 0$. Then, one could say that at the tricritical point really 3 phases become identical: 2 antiferromagnetic phases (with $m_s \neq 0$) and one paramagnetic phase (with $m_s = 0$). Or, if one extends the thermodynamic description, and formally introduces the staggered field B_s in addition to the field B, one obtains the following 3 dimensional phase-diagram in T, B, B_s space (cf. fig. 14).

where $B_s = 0$, are now 2 infinite "wings" α and β, that meet along the coexistence line C'D. The region in the phase diagram, where $m_s > 0$, ends at the wing α, since for B too large, or for T too high, the antiferromagnetic ordering disappears and the system becomes paramagnetic. The lines a and b that end in C', are therefore critical lines for a first order transition and m_s will jump discontinuously when one passes through the wings. A paramagnetic phase is found above and between the wings, as well as above the Néel-line: $T_N C'$. In this picture the (collapsed) coexistence curve C'D is a triple line (a line of triple points) since 3 phases coexist along this line: a paramagnetic phase and 2 antiferromagnetic phases.

2) Helium mixtures. A similar formal thermodynamic extension as for the metamagnet can be made for the helium mixtures. It is less obvious here what "phases" lie "dormant" and what the field should be that couples to them. Since in the models m_s and ξ are analogues[38)], one might somehow introduce a field H that couples to ξ i.e. to the He^4 particles in the single particle zero momentum state. Such a field has indeed been introduced by Bogolubov[39)] and it is even more fictitious than the staggered magnetic field B_s. Using this field Kincaid[27e)] has shown, as Griffiths[37)] had surmised, that a phase diagram similar to fig. 14 can be constructed, but where the field H plays the role of B_s and Δ the role of B. In this TΔH-space a tricritical point C appears again. Strictly speaking in this case an ∞ number of phases (with $\xi \neq 0$)[40)] and one normal phase (with $\xi = 0$) become identical, but still 3 critical lines, the analogues of the Néel-line and the lines a and b, meet. For details I refer to the literature.

One must say, that although this treatment may elucidate the analogy between the two systems and also make the connection with classical ternary mixtures clearer, it does so at the expense of introducing the unphysical fields B_s and H. It is not clear, whether this is a consequence of the fact that these fields couple to quantities like m_s or ξ, which are not true thermodynamic quantities, but rather refer already to a more microscopic description of the system than is customary in thermodynamics.

2. Using the picture of Landau and Griffiths, the notion of "a phase" can be extended to include "dormant" phases. One can now again raise the question, discussed at the beginning of these lectures, as to the connection with the phase rule of Gibbs:

Can one, just as in the van der Waals theory the critical phenomena could be incorporated in the phase rule by using the notion of a critical phase, reconcile the tricritical phenomena with the phase rule, by introducing the notion of "dormant" phases? Or, does one have to extend the phase rule, since for continuous transitions, which are involved here, a more microscopic description is required?

ACKNOWLEDGEMENT

It is a pleasure to thank Dr. J.M. Kincaid for many helpful discussions.

REFERENCES

1) See "Lehrbuch der Thermodynamik" by J.D. van der Waals and Ph. Kohnstamm, J.A. Berth, Leipzig (1912) p. 37.

2) The analogy between the anisotropic antiferromagnets discussed here and binary mixtures can be appreciated by realizing that both can be described by a spin 1/2 Ising model.

3) W.H. Keesom, Helium, Elsevier, Amsterdam (1942) p. 211.

4) P. Ehrenfest, Proc.Kon.Ned.Ak.Wet. Amsterdam, 36(1933)153; Leiden Comm.Suppl. no. 75b.

5) a. L.D. Landau, JETP 7(1937)19, 627;
   b. L.D. Landau and E.M. Lifshitz, Statistical Physics, 2nd edition, Addison-Wesley, Reading, Mass. (1969), Chapter XIV.
   c. M.E. Fisher, Rep.Progr.Phys. 30(1967)615.

6) B.M. Abraham, B. Weinstock and D.W. Osborne, Phys.Rev. 76(1949)864.

7) G.K. Walters and W.M. Fairbank, Phys.Rev. 103(1956)262.

8) E.H. Graf, D.M. Lee and J.D. Reppy, Phys.Rev.Letters 19(1967)417.

9) D.O. Edwards, D.F. Brewer, P. Seligman, M. Skertic and M. Jaqub, Phys.Rev. Letters 15(1965)773.

10) T.A. Alvesalo, P.M. Berglund, S.T. Islander, G.R. Pickett, W. Zimmerman Jr., Phys.Rev.Letters 22(1969)1281; Phys.Rev. 4(1971)2354.

11) The symbol $\sim$ should be interpreted in the usual way: $f(x) \sim x^p$ if $p = \lim_{x \to 0+} \frac{\ln f(x)}{\ln x}$.

12) a. G. Goellner and H. Meyer, Phys.Rev.Letters 26(1971)1534;
   b. G. Goellner, R. Behringer and H. Meyer, J. Low Temp.Phys. 13(1973)113.

13) S.T. Islander and W. Zimmerman Jr., Phys.Rev. A 7 (1973)188.

14) a. R.L. Johnson, Ph.D. Thesis, SUNY at Stonybrook (1973);
   b. Ching-Ming Lai, Ph.D. Thesis, SUNY at Stonybrook (1973).

15) G.E. Watson, J.D. Reppy and R.C. Richardson, Phys.Rev. 188(1969)384.

16) L. Néel, Ann.Physique (10) 18(1932)5; (11) 5(1936)232; C.R.Acad.Sci. Paris, 203(1936)304.

17) C.J. Gorter and Tineke van Peski-Tinbergen, Physica 22(1956)273.

18) C. Starr, F. Bitter and A.R. Kaufman, Phys.Rev. 58(1940)977.

19) See: J.S. Jacobs and P.E. Lawrence, Phys.Rev. 164(1967)866, reference 3.

20) a. M. Ball, W.P. Wolf and A.F.G. Wyatt, Phys.Lett. 10(1964)1, 7;
   b. B.E. Keen, D.P. Landau, B. Schneider and W.P. Wolf, J.Appl.Phys. 37(1966) 1120; 38(1967)967;

c. D.P. Landau, B.E. Keen, B. Schneider and W.P. Wolf, Phys.Rev. B 3 (1971) 2310;

d. W.P. Wolf, B. Schneider, D.P. Landau and B.E. Keen, Phys.Rev. B 5 (1972) 4472;

e. See also: M. Blume, L.M. Corliss, J.M. Hastings and E. Schiller, Phys.Rev. Letters 32 (1974) 544.

21) a. R.J. Birgenau, W.B. Yelon, E. Cohen and J. Makovsky, Phys.Rev. B 5 (1972) 2607;

b. W.B. Yelon and R.J. Birgenau, Phys.Rev. B 5 (1972) 2615.

22) V.A. Schmidt and S.A. Friedberg, Phys.Rev. B 1 (1970) 2250.

23) C. Vetter, H.L. Alberts and D. Bloch, Phys.Rev. Letters 31 (1973) 1414.

24) J.M. Kincaid and E.G.D. Cohen, to be published.

25) The normalized sublattice magnetization s_1 is defined by: $s_1 = 2m_1/N\mu$, where m_1 is the magnetization of sublattice 1. Similarly for s_2.

26) See e.g. R. Kubo, Statistical Mechanics, North-Holland Publ. Cy, Amsterdam, (1967).

27) a. K. Motizuki, J.Phys.Soc.Japan 14 (1959) 759;

b. C.J. Gorter and J. Haantjes, Physica 18 (1952) 285; Commun.Suppl. 104b (1952);

c. C.J. Gorter and Tineke van Peski-Tinbergen, Physica 22 (1956) 273; Commun. Suppl. 110b (1956);

d. R. Bidaux, P. Carrara and B. Vivet, J.Phys.Chem.Solids 28 (1967) 2453;

e. J.M. Kincaid, Thesis, The Rockefeller University, New York (1974).

28) The sign of m_s is not determined by this procedure since there is no distinction between the 2 sublattices, so that sublattice 1 and sublattice 2 are equivalent (cf. eq. (2.12)).

29) The notation for the tricritical exponents in Table II is that proposed by R.B. Griffiths, Phys.Rev. 7 (1973) 545. In addition to those listed, exponents γ, γ', γ_t and γ_t' can be defined (see ref. 27e) that might be measured by neutron diffraction methods.

30) The formulae below are all at a given pressure, which I have not indicated explicitly. I remark that the behavior under pressure cannot be studied directly in the theory presented in this section, since the volume of the system enters only indirectly through the constants J and J'. One can, however, assume that $\varepsilon = J'/J$ is a certain (for instance decreasing) function of p and then study the behavior as a function of p via the behavior as a function of ε.

31) a. K. Huang and C.N. Yang, Phys.Rev. 105 (1957) 767;

b. T.D. Lee and C.N. Yang, Phys.Rev. 105 (1957) 1119;

c. T.D. Lee, K. Huang and C.N. Yang, Phys.Rev. 106 (1957) 1135;

d. C.N. Yang and T.D. Lee, Phys.Rev. 112 (1958) 1419.

32) a. E.G.D. Cohen and J.M.J. van Leeuwen, Physica 26 (1960) 1171;

b. E.G.D. Cohen and J.M.J. van Leeuwen, Physica 27 (1961) 1157;

c. J.M.J. van Leeuwen and E.G.D. Cohen, Phys.Rev. 176 (1968) 385.

33) a. Cf. K. Huang, Statistical Mechanics, J. Wiley, New York (1963) p. 289;

b. K. Huang in "Studies in Statistical Mechanics" (G.E. Uhlenbeck and J. de Boer eds), North-Holland Publ.Cy, Amsterdam (1964) p. 35.

34) J.G. Daunt and C.V. Heer, Phys.Rev. 79(1950)46.

35) A density of the mixture of the correct order of magnitude is, for example, obtained by applying an outside pressure such that the density of the bosons equals that of pure He^4 at $T = 0^oK$. For this density $na^3 = 0.365$ i.e. na^3 is not $\leqslant 1$, so that it is not clear that one can restrict oneself to the first order perturbation theory, as was done in the equations (3.6)-(3.9). The only indication, at present, that the results obtained may persist when higher order perturbation theory is applied and that they constitute a genuine property of the hard sphere mixture is a higher order calculation carried out at $T = 0^oK$, which indeed showed that, at this temperature at least, the incomplete phase separation remains[32b)].

36) One might wonder why there are no ferromagnets whose phase diagram exhibit a tricritical point. The reason is that for this to occur, an external staggered magnetic field, which points up, say, on sublattice 1 and down on sublattice 2, must be applied[27e)].

37) R.B. Griffiths, Phys.Rev.Letters 24(1970)715.

38) In fact, m_s^2 and ξ correspond.

39) a. N.N. Bogolubov, Physica 26(1960)51;

b. P.C. Hohenberg and P.C. Martin, Annals of Physics 34(1965)291.

40) Actually one considers a complex particle source field $H(\vec{r})$, that creates or destroys a particle at the point $\vec{r}$ and couples to the boson operator field $\phi(\vec{r})$. If the source field has a phase Θ, then $\langle\phi\rangle$, the thermal expectation of $\phi(\vec{r})$, will also have a phase Θ $(0 \leqslant \Theta \leqslant 2\pi)$. Thus we have introduced an external field, that can produce one of the ∞ thermodynamic phases — namely the one with phase Θ — that lie "dormant" in the helium mixtures, when it is cooled down below the lambda-temperature.

J.M.J. van Leeuwen
Laboratorium voor Technische Natuurkunde
Technological University, Delft
The Netherlands

The application of Wilson's ideas on renormalization[1] to critical phenomena has been mostly concentrated on rather general systems in which the dimensionality d of the lattice or the dimensionality n of the order parameter are varying parameters. In fact one takes advantage of this generality by expanding in powers of 4-d or 1/n, which leaves the 2-dimensional Ising spin system (d=2, n=1) as the most difficult corner to discuss.

In these lectures we will explore very specific and more restricted realizations of renormalization transformations for 1-component discrete spin systems, which allow not only to study the locus of the critical point and the nature of the critical singularities but also a determination of the amplitudes of the singularities, the homogeneous scaling function and the behavior of the magnetization below the critical temperature.

The reader will have noticed that the commonly accepted terminology as "the renormalization group approach" is avoided. The reason is that in this work no (semi-)group of transformations is constructed which depends on a continuously varying scaling parameter ℓ. Instead all the properties are derived from one single transformation, involving a fixed scaling length ℓ.

We start with an outline of the method at the hand of an example for the triangular lattice. The transformation properties of the free energy and the definition of the scaling fields follow in section 2. Then we derive the expressions for the amplitudes of the singularities and the determination of the homogeneous scaling function (section 3) with a separate discussion for the behavior of the spontaneous magnetization below the critical point (section 4). We close with a number of remarks on various alternative attempts and failures and some problems left open.

1. RENORMALIZATION TRANSFORMATION FOR A TRIANGULAR LATTICE

A renormalization transformation is a map of the spin hamiltonian space of the original (= site) lattice onto the (effective) hamiltonian space for "cells" of sites. For a triangular lattice one may construct cells by uniting sites in groups of three neighboring sites in such a way that the lattice of cells has again a triangular structure[2]. We will denote the spin of site i as

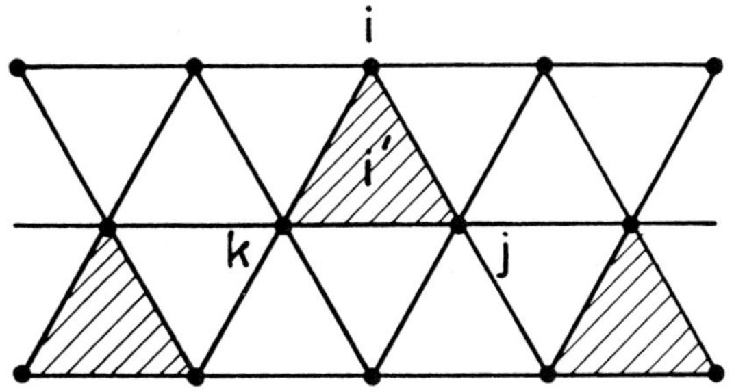

Fundamental Problems in Statistical Mechanics, Vol. 3, Editor, E.D.G. Cohen.

s_i (= ±1) and define the spin $s'_{i'}$ of cell i' as

$$s'_{i'} = \text{sign}\left(\sum_{i \in i'} s_i \right) \tag{1.1}$$

Cell variables generally have primes. Note that in order to make the definition (1.1) unambiguous one should have cells with an odd number of sites. The cell spin $s'_{i'}$ = ±1 is telling whether the majority of site spins in the cell is up or down. This leaves for a given cell spin in our case still 4 possible site spin configurations, labeled by the variable $\sigma_{i'}$:

$$\begin{cases} \sigma_{i'} = 0 & s_i = s_j = s_k = s'_{i'} \\ \sigma_{i'} = 1 & -s_i = s_j = s_k = s'_{i'} \\ \sigma_{i'} = 2 & s_i = -s_j = s_k = s'_{i'} \\ \sigma_{i'} = 3 & s_i = s_j = -s_k = s'_{i'} \end{cases} \tag{1.2}$$

where i, j and k are the sites of cell i'. The pair $(s'_{i'}, \sigma_{i'})$ completely specifies the site configuration in cell i'.

Let H(s) be the site spin hamiltonian (the usual factor $-1/k_B T$ included). We shift the energy eventually such that

$$\sum_{\{s\}} H(s) = 0 \tag{1.3}$$

where the sum runs over all site spin configurations. Then we define a renormalization transformation as

$$\exp\left[G + H'(s') \right] \equiv \sum_{\{\sigma\}} \exp H(s) \tag{1.4}$$

The right hand side is a partial sum over states, summing only over the internal configurations $\{\sigma\}$ and keeping the cell spin configuration $\{s'\}$ fixed. G + H'(s') may be viewed as the free energy for such a constrained system and in that sense is H'(s') the effective hamiltonian for the cell system. G is chosen such that

$$\sum_{\{s'\}} H'(s') = 0 \tag{1.5}$$

The transformation (1.4) is much too general for practical use (not even the lattice structure plays a role for general hamiltonians) and we will restrict our hamiltonian space to hamiltonians which reflect the symmetry of the lattice. One may write a general hamiltonian as

$$H(s) = \sum_a k_a s_a \tag{1.6}$$

where a is a subset of sites and $s_a = \prod_{i\in a} s_i$. The interaction parameters k_a follow formally from H(s) as

$$k_a = 2^{-N} \sum_{\{s\}} s_a H(s) \tag{1.7}$$

where N is the number of sites in the lattice. A hamiltonian reflecting the symmetry of the lattice will have the same k_a for equivalent sets a i.e. one value (say h) for single sites, one value (k) for pairs of neighboring sites etc. such that (1.6) takes the form

$$H(s) = h \sum_i s_i + k \sum_{<i,j>} s_i s_j + \dots . \tag{1.8}$$

The transformation (1.4) yields renormalised values h',k' etc. which are functions of h, k .... We will abbreviate the transformation (1.4) as

$$k'_\alpha = k'_\alpha(k) \tag{1.9}$$

where α stands for "single site", "neighboring pair" etc. and view the transformation as a map in the interaction parameter space k_α.

Except from some corners of the parameter space k_α, the exact form of the function $k'_\alpha(k)$ is harder to establish than the solution of the Ising model. Thus one has to be satisfied with an approximation to (1.9).
Various approximation methods are possible, of which we will mention here the cumulant method as the simplest. The starting point is a separation of the hamiltonian in a manageable zero order part H_o and a perturbation V. Then rewrite (1.4) as

$$\exp [G + H'(s')] = \exp [G_o + H'_o(s')] . <\exp V>_o \tag{1.10}$$

where the zero order part is given by

$$\exp [G_o + H'_o(s')] = \sum_{\{\sigma\}} \exp H_o(s) \tag{1.11}$$

and the zero order average $< >_o$ defined as:

$$<A>_o = [\exp -[G_o + H'_o(s')]] \sum_{\{\sigma\}} A(s) \exp H_o(s) \tag{1.12}$$

H_o should be chosen such that the evaluation of G_o and H'_o presents no problem and the perturbation V has to handled by the cumulant method as:

$$\langle \exp V \rangle_o = \exp \langle V \rangle_o + \frac{1}{2} [\langle V^2 \rangle_o - \langle V \rangle_o^2] + \ldots . \tag{1.13}$$

A separation of H in $H_o + V$ which suggests itself is to include in H_o all intracell interactions and in V all intercell interactions. To lowest order we thus find [2)] for example:

$$\begin{aligned} G_o &= (N/6) \log(z_o^+ z_o^-) \\ h' &= (1/2) \log(z_o^+/z_o^-) \\ k' &= (1/2)[n^+/z_o^+ + n^-/z_o^-]^2 k \end{aligned} \qquad \begin{cases} z_o^{\pm} = e^{3k \pm 3h} + 3e^{-k \pm h} \\ n^{\pm} = e^{3k \pm h} + e^{-k \pm h} \end{cases} \tag{1.14}$$

2. TRANSFORMATION OF THE FREE ENERGY AND THE SCALING FIELDS

The usefulness of a transformation (1.4) stems from the fact that it leads to the following relation for the free energy

$$\begin{aligned} F(k) &= \log \sum_{\{s\}} \exp H(s) = \log \sum_{\{s'\}} \sum_{\{\sigma\}} \exp H(s) = \\ &= G + \log \sum_{\{s'\}} \exp H'(s') = G(k) + F'(k') \end{aligned} \tag{2.1}$$

connecting the free energy at the points k_α and k'_α in the interaction parameter space. Using that the free energy is an extensive quantity $F(k) = Nf(k)$, $F'(k') = N'f(k')$ and that also $G(k) = Ng(k)$ we have the relation

$$f(k) = g(k) + \ell^{-d} f(k') \tag{2.2}$$

where the volume ℓ^d of the cell equals the ratio of sites to cells N/N'. ℓ is the lattice spacing of the cells in units of the site spacing or the linear scale on which the system is contracted.

It is one of the basic assumptions of the renormalization approach that the k'_α are regular functions of the k_α. $g(k)$ is also assumed to be a regular function of the k_α. One can in fact consider $g(k)$ as a special k'_α with α corresponding to the empty set. In the next section we show how the singularities in $f(k)$ can be expressed in terms of $g(k)$ alone on the basis of (2.2). Here we shall prepare this discussion by introducing some notions related to a fixed point of the transformation (1.4).

A fixed point k^* is a set k^*_α such that

$$k'_\alpha(k^*) = k^*_\alpha \tag{2.3}$$

One trivial fixed point is obviously $k^*_\alpha = 0$ which corresponds to the infinite temperature limit of any spin system.

Because of the regularity assumptions a neighborhood of a fixed point maps onto a neighborhood of that fixed point. In linear approximation the transformation can be written in the neighborhood of k^* as

$$k'_\alpha - k^*_\alpha = \sum_\beta T_{\alpha\beta} (k_\beta - k^*_\beta) \tag{2.4}$$

with $T_{\alpha\beta} = (\partial k'_\alpha/\partial k_\beta)_{k=k^*}$. The matrix $T_{\alpha\beta}$ is not symmetric in α and β. It is convenient to introduce a type of normal coordinates in which the transformation takes a simple form. Let $T_{\alpha\beta}$ have eigenvalues λ_i with associated left eigenvectors $\varphi^{(i)}_\alpha$ and right eigenvectors $\psi^{(i)}_\alpha$:

$$\sum_\alpha \varphi^{(i)}_\alpha T_{\alpha\beta} = \lambda_i \varphi^{(i)}_\beta , \qquad \sum_\beta T_{\alpha\beta} \psi^{(i)}_\beta = \lambda_i \psi^{(i)}_\alpha \tag{2.5}$$

Then construct a normal coordinate u_i as

$$u_i = \sum_\alpha \varphi^{(i)}_\alpha (k_\alpha - k^*_\alpha) \tag{2.6}$$

such that u_i according to (2.4) and (2.5) transforms as

$$u'_i = \sum_\alpha \varphi^{(i)}_\alpha (k'_\alpha - k^*_\alpha) = \lambda_i \sum_\beta \varphi^{(i)}_\beta (k_\beta - k^*_\beta) = \lambda_i u_i \tag{2.7}$$

One may extend the definition of u_i beyond the linear regime in such a way that (2.7) holds also for finite u_i. For that purpose expand (2.4) further as

$$k'_\alpha - k^*_\alpha = \sum_\alpha T_{\alpha\beta} (k_\beta - k^*_\beta) + \frac{1}{2!} \sum_{\beta\gamma} T_{\alpha,\beta\gamma} (k_\beta - k^*_\beta)(k_\gamma - k^*_\gamma) + \dots \tag{2.8}$$

as well as (2.6)

$$u_i = \sum_\alpha \varphi^{(i)}_\alpha (k_\alpha - k^*_\alpha) + \frac{1}{2!} \sum_{\alpha\beta} \varphi^{(i)}_{\alpha\beta} (k_\alpha - k^*_\alpha)(k_\beta - k^*_\beta) + \dots \tag{2.9}$$

In order to ensure that also to second order holds

$$u'_i = \lambda_i u_i \tag{2.10}$$

one should relate $\varphi^{(i)}_{\alpha\beta}$ to $T_{\alpha,\beta\gamma}$ as the solutions of the set of linear equations

$$\sum_{\gamma,\delta} \varphi^{(i)}_{\gamma\delta} \{\lambda_i \delta_{\gamma\alpha} \delta_{\delta\beta} - T_{\gamma\alpha} T_{\delta\beta}\} = \sum_\gamma \varphi^{(i)}_\gamma T_{\gamma,\alpha\beta} \tag{2.11}$$

To find the u_i as function of k it is for practical purposes more convenient to use the relation

$$\lambda_i u_i(k) = u_i' = u_i(k') \quad \text{or} \quad \lambda_i^n u_i(k) = u_i(k^{(n)}) \qquad (2.12)$$

in which $k^{(n)}$ is the n-times transformed point k. By choosing k or $k^{(n)}$ in the neighborhood of the fixed point one finds values of $u_i(k^{(n)})$ or $u_i(k)$ further away. The $u_i(k)$ may be considered as curvilinear coordinates adapted to the transformation (Wegners scaling fields [3]). Note that the u_i are defined up to a factor since the eigenvectors are only defined up to a factor.

For a number of properties it is very convenient to view the free energy as a function of the scaling fields $u_i(k)$. Then (2.2) takes the simple form

$$f(u_1,u_2,\ldots) = g(u_1,u_2,\ldots) + \ell^{-d}\, f(\lambda_1 u_1,\lambda_2 u_2,\ldots) \qquad (2.12)$$

We assume (2.12) to hold in a finite domain of u_i values.

The eigenvalues determine the nature of the singularities. Consider (2.12) along a line $u_2 = u_3 = \ldots = 0$ and assume that f has a powerlike singularity Au_1^{a1} along this line. Inserting this into (2.12) yields

$$Au_1^{a_1} = \ell^{-d}\, A\, [\lambda_1 u_1]^{a_1} \qquad (2.13)$$

from which the exponent a_1 follows as

$$a_1 = d \log \ell/\log \lambda_1 \qquad (2.14)$$

A powerlike singularity is only acceptable from a physical viewpoint if $a_1 > 0$ otherwise the free energy would become infinite at the fixed point which suggests that singularities can only be associated with eigenvalues $\lambda_i > 1$. We note that the comparison (2.13) gives no information about the amplitude A. Also (2.14) shows that the eigenvalues λ_i will depend on the transformation chosen. Following Wegner [3] we write

$$\lambda_i = \ell^{y_i} \qquad (2.15)$$

such that $a_i = d/y_i$ and since the exponents a_i are physical quantities the y_i may be assumed to be independent of the transformation. From the known singularities of the Ising model it is then expected that the transformation (1.4) has two $y_i > 0$ with the values $y_1 = 15/8$ and $y_2 = 1$ (corresponding to a logarithmic singularity; see next section). This picture is confirmed [2] by the numerical determination of the fixed point in the neighborhood of the point where the Ising system (only nearest neighbor interaction) is critical ($k_c = 0.2744$). The approximation (1.14) has a fixed point at $k^* = 0.3356$, $h^* = 0$ with two eigenvalues with $y_1 = 1.461$ and $y_2 = 0.892$.

3. AMPLITUDES OF THE SINGULARITIES[4)]

The approximation (1.14) shows the general property that the subspace of interaction parameters of even interactions (here k) is invariant under the transformation (1.4). Thus of the two scaling fields u_1 and u_2 of (1.14) one (say u_1) will be field-like ($u_1 \sim h$) and the other (u_2) will be temperature-like ($u_2 \sim k-k^*$). If we start out with a point with $u_1 = 0$ and $u_2 < 0$ and small (corresponding to a point with $h = 0$ and T slightly above T_c) the value of u_2 will grow under transformation with a factor λ_2 (<1). After a certain number (n) of steps the corresponding point in k-space $k^{(n)}$ will have moved away from the fixed point k^* (=0.3356) towards the trivial fixed point $k = 0$. It is easy to show (from (1.14)) that near $k = 0$ the point $k^{(n)}$ approaches $k = 0$ by reducing the distance each time with a factor 1/2. (Note that (1.14) is exact near $k = 0$). Thus the point $k = 0$ will correspond to $k^{(\infty)}$ and have a value $u_2 = \infty$ for the second scaling field associated with the non trivial fixed point.

We will now investigate this process on the basis of (2.12) which we simplify to

$$f(u) = g(u) + \ell^{-d} f(\lambda u) \qquad (3.1)$$

since only one scaling field (u_2) is involved.

Iteration of (3.1) yields for f(u) the series

$$f(u) = \sum_{j=0}^{\infty} \ell^{-jd} g(\lambda^j u) \qquad (3.2)$$

where we have used the fact that $\lim_{n\to\infty} \ell^{-nd} f(\lambda^n u) = 0$ in the example given ($f(u = \infty) = \log 2$). The problem is now to show that the series (3.2) exhibits a singularity $A\, u^{d/y}$ and to compute A.

First we construct the regular part of f(u) on the basis of the power series for g(u)

$$g(u) = \sum_{m=0}^{\infty} g_m u^m \qquad (3.3)$$

which g(u) will have as a regular function. Inserting this into (3.1) and a similar power series for f(u):

$$f_{reg}(u) = \sum_{m=0}^{\infty} f_m u^m \qquad (3.4)$$

one fulfils (3.1) by chosing

$$f_m = g_m/(1 - \ell^{-d}\lambda^m) \tag{3.5}$$

We must exclude here the case that an m with $\lambda^m = \ell^d$ occurs, leading to a logarithmic singularity, which will be discussed at the end of this section. From (3.5) one sees that $f_{reg}(u)$ has a convergence radius which is a factor λ larger than that of $g(u)$. Now we call m_o the first power for which $\lambda^m > \ell^d$. (In our example $m_o = 3$) and write

$$g(u) = \sum_{m=0}^{m_o-1} g_m u^m + g_{rem}(u) \tag{3.6}$$

Note that for $\lambda < 1$, $m_o = \infty$ and g_{rem} will vanish. Inserting this into (3.2) one observes that the sum over j for the first m_o powers may be carried out and leads to the first m_o powers of $f_{reg}(u)$. For the remainder we rewrite the sum (3.3) as

$$\sum_{j=0}^{\infty} \ell^{-jd} g_{rem}(\lambda^j u) = \sum_{j=-\infty}^{\infty} \ell^{-jd} g_{rem}(\lambda^j u) - \sum_{j=-\infty}^{-1} \ell^{-jd} g_{rem}(\lambda^j u) \tag{3.7}$$

The part that is added and subtracted can be evaluated by the power series expansion of $g_{rem}(u)$:

$$\sum_{m=m_o}^{+\infty} -\sum_{j=-\infty}^{-1} \ell^{-jd} g_m \lambda^{jm} u^m = \sum_{m=m_o}^{\infty} u^m g_m/(1 - \ell^{-d}\lambda^m) \tag{3.8}$$

and furnishes the other part of f_{reg}. Thus we have

$$f(u) = f_{reg}(u) + \sum_{j=-\infty}^{\infty} \ell^{-jd} g_{rem}(\lambda^j u) \tag{3.9}$$

The whole procedure was meant to subtract from g(u) the powers which forbid to extend the summation (3.2) inwardly to $j = -\infty$. $g_{rem}(\lambda^j u)$ behaves for $j \to -\infty$ as $\lambda^{jm_o} u^{m_o}$ which decreases sufficiently fast to compensate the increasing factor ℓ^{-jd} and for $j \to \infty$ $g_{rem}(\lambda^j u)$ is bounded by the larger of $g(\lambda^j u)$ and the strongest subtracted power $(\lambda^j u)^{m_o-1}$. When g(u) is well behaved the factor ℓ^{-jd} garantuees convergence at the upper side $j \to \infty$.

The sum in (3.9) represents the singular part of the free energy, fulfilling the homogeneous part of (3.1). If we define an amplitude A(u) as:

$$A(u) = |u|^{-d/y} \sum_{j=-\infty}^{\infty} \ell^{-jd} g_{rem}(\lambda^j u) \tag{3.10}$$

then A(u) will fulfil the relation $A(\lambda u) = A(u)$. Thus A(u) is equal for all the points ... $\lambda^{-2}u$, $\lambda^{-1}u$, u, λu, $\lambda^2 u$ which accumulate to u=0. This is however not sufficient to garantuee that A(u) is a constant (depending only on the sign of u) as

(3.10) still allows for a periodic function[5] in $\log|u|$ with period $\log \lambda$. It is however quite likely that only the zeroth fourier component of $A(u)$ has a meaning since the period $\log \lambda = y \log \ell$ depends on the (arbitrary) scaling length ℓ[6]. So it is concluded that (3.9) has the form

$$f(u) = f_{reg}(u) + A_{\pm}|u|^{d/y} \tag{3.11}$$

where $A_{\pm}$ follows from (3.10) as zeroth fourier component:

$$A_{\pm} = (\log \lambda)^{-1} \int_0^{\infty} dt\, t^{-1-d/y}\, g_{rem}(\pm\, t) \tag{3.12}$$

The situation for more than one scaling field present is similar. The solution of (2.12) in terms of a sum over g reads

$$f(u_1,u_2,u_3,\ldots) = \sum_{j=0}^{\infty} \ell^{-jd} g(\lambda_1^j u_1,\ \lambda_2^j u_2,\ \lambda_3^j u_3,\ldots) \tag{3.13}$$

Again g is splitt into two parts: one containing the powers for which the sum (3.13) converges and a remainder. The first part leads to a piece of the regular free energy $f_{reg}(u_1,u_2,\ldots)$ which is constructed as in (3.5) on the basis of the power series expansion of $g(u_1,u_2,\ldots)$. By adding and subtracting in the remainder the sum over $j = -\infty$ to -1 and evaluating this sum by expansion one recovers the second piece of the $f_{reg}(u_1,u_2,\ldots)$ and one arrives at

$$f(u_1,u_2,u_3,\ldots) = f_{reg}(u_1,u_2,u_3,\ldots) + \\ + \sum_{j=-\infty}^{\infty} \ell^{-jd} g_{rem}(\lambda_1^j u_1, \lambda_2^j u_2, \lambda_3^j u_3,\ldots) \tag{3.14}$$

The sum in (3.14) fulfils the homogeneous equation (2.12). We define an amplitude as in (3.10) (ignoring the possible oscillating dependence on $\log|u_1|$)

$$A_{1\pm}(v_2,v_3,\ldots) = \\ = |u_1|^{-d/y_1} \sum_{j=-\infty}^{\infty} \ell^{-jd}\, g_{rem}(\lambda_1^j u_1, \lambda_2^j v_2 |u_1|^{y_2/y_1}, \lambda_3^j v_3 |u_1|^{y_3/y_1},\ldots) \tag{3.15}$$

(The precise definition of $A_{1\pm}$ follows in (3.20).) Using (3.15) in (3.14) gives for $f(u_1,u_2,\ldots)$

$$f(u_1,u_2,u_3,\ldots) = f_{reg}(u_1,u_2,u_3,\ldots) + \\ + |u_1|^{d/y_1} A_{1\pm}(u_2/|u_1|^{y_2/y_1}, u_3/|u_1|^{y_3/y_1},\ldots) \tag{3.16}$$

In order to appreciate this result we note that for the eigenvalues $\lambda_i < 1$ the exponents $y_i < 0$ and therefore expansion in (3.16) of the $u_3, \ldots$ dependence, corresponding to $y_3 < 0, \ldots$, leads to less singular terms. The most singular part is

$$f_{sing}(u_1, u_2) = |u_1|^{d/y_1} A_{1\pm}(u_2/|u_1|^{y_2/y_1}, 0, 0 \ldots) \qquad (3.17)$$

The next singular part (due to the u_3 dependence) behaves as:

$$f_{sing}^{next}(u_1, u_2, u_3) = u_3 |u_1|^{(d-y_3)/y_1} \frac{\partial A_1}{\partial v_3}(u_2/|u_1|^{y_2/y_1}, 0, 0, \ldots) \qquad (3.18)$$

where $\partial A_1/\partial v_3$ follows from (3.15) as:

$$\frac{\partial A_1}{\partial v_3}(v_2, 0, \ldots) =$$

$$|u_1|^{-(d-y_3)/y_1} \sum_{j=-\infty}^{\infty} \ell^{-jd} \lambda_3^j \frac{\partial g_{rem}}{\partial u_3}(\lambda_1^j u_1, \lambda_2^j v_2 |u_1|^{y_2/y_1}, 0, \ldots) \qquad (3.19)$$

The independence of the most singular part of the irrelevant variables ($y_i < 0$) is a form of universality. The corrections to the scaling behavior as given by (3.18) have been discussed by Wegner [3].

For the scaling function $A_1(v_2, v_3, \ldots)$ an integral representation analogous to (3.12) can be derived as:

$$A_{1\pm}(v_2, v_3, \ldots) =$$

$$= [\log \lambda_1]^{-1} \int_0^\infty dt\, t^{-1-d/y} g_{rem}(\pm t, v_2 t^{y_2/y_1}, v_3 t^{y_3/y_1}, \ldots) \qquad (3.20)$$

We have given the scaling function A_1 the index 1 because we have singled out the (largest) eigenvalue λ_1. Similar expressions can derived by letting the other eigenvalue $\lambda_2 > 1$ play a special role.

Finally we have to look into the case that a power λ^m equals ℓ^d or more generally that a combination $\lambda_1^{m_1} \lambda_2^{m_2} \ldots = \ell^d$. One can follow two procedures: treating the dangerous power combination separately from the start or taking the limit in the final formulae by treating (one of) the eigenvalue(s) as a continuous parameter. The result is the appearance of a logarithmic term. For example instead of the combination (3.11) and (3.12) one obtains for $d/y = m$:

$$f(u) = \bar{f}_{reg}(u) + A_\pm |u|^m - g_m |u|^m \log|u| / \log\lambda \qquad (3.21)$$

where $\bar{f}_{reg}(u)$ is defined as before except that the power $f_m u^m$ (which would be undefined) is missing. The amplitude $A_\pm$ is given by

$$A_\pm = \frac{g_m}{2} + \frac{1}{\log\lambda}\left\{\int_0^1 \frac{g_{rem}(\pm t)}{t^{m+1}}\,dt + \int_0^1 \frac{g_{rem}(\pm t) + g_m(\pm t)^m}{t^{m+1}}\,dt\right\} \quad (3.22)$$

4. THE SPONTANEOUS MAGNETIZATION

In the previous section the origin of the critical singularities has been discussed. From such an analysis does not follow the appearance of a spontaneous magnetization below T_c. In terms of the free energy the problem is to understand why for $h = 0$ the derivative $\partial f/\partial h$ vanishes for $T > T_c$ and has a non zero value for $T < T_c$. In order to be specific let us turn to the approximate renormalization equations (1.14) and take the small h limit of these equations.

$$g(h,k) = \frac{1}{3}\log(e^{3k} + 3e^{-k}) + O(h^2)$$

$$\begin{cases} h' = 3\mu(k)h + O(h^3) \\ k' = 2\mu^2(k)k + O(h^2) \end{cases} \qquad \mu(k) = \frac{e^{3k} + e^{-k}}{e^{3k} + 3e^{-k}} \quad (4.1)$$

These equations together with the relation

$$f(h,k) = g(h,k) + \ell^{-d} f(h',k') \quad (4.2)$$

determines supposedly the small h behavior of $f(h,k)$.

As $g(h,k)$ and k' are even functions of h and h' an odd function of h, the relation (4.2) implies for the magnetization at $h = 0$:

$$m(k) = \left(\frac{\partial f(h,k)}{\partial h}\right)_{h=0} = 0 + \ell^{-d} m(k') \left(\frac{\partial h'}{\partial h}\right)_{h=0} \quad (4.3)$$

or explicitly

$$m(k') = m(k)/\mu(k) \quad (4.4)$$

using that $\ell^d = 3$. The relation (4.4) enables us to compute the magnetization at "temperature" k' when it is known at k.
Using (4.4) n times yields

$$m(k^{(n)}) = \left\{\prod_{j=0}^{n-1} [\mu(k^{(j)})]^{-1}\right\} m(k) \quad (4.5)$$

This formula displays already a markedly different behavior for $T > T_c$ ($k < k^*$) and $T < T_c$ ($k > k^*$). From (4.1) it follows that for $k < k^*$ the value of $k^{(n)}$

decreases at a rate $2\mu^2(k)$ which approaches the value $2\mu^2(0) = 1/2$ when $k^{(n)}$ approaches zero. If m(k) would be different from zero for $k \lesssim k^*$, $m(k^{(n)})$ would become infinite for $n \to \infty$ since $\mu(k^{(n)})$ approaches 1/2 for $n \to \infty$ and the product in (4.5) increases by a factor 2 at each step. On the other hand for $k > k^*$ the value of $k^{(n)}$ increases, finally by a factor 2 at each step, since $\mu(\infty) = 1$, and the infinite product in (4.5) for $n \to \infty$ will reach a finite value relating the magnetization at $T = 0$ ($k = \infty$) with that for k. Thus one observes that the behavior above and below T_c are completely dictated by the behavior near the fixed point.

In the neighborhood of k^* the relation (4.4) implies the powerlike behavior

$$m(k) = A[k - k^*]^{\beta} \tag{4.6}$$

with β given by

$$[\partial k'/\partial k]^{\beta}_{k^*} = \lambda_2^{\beta} = [\mu(k^*)]^{-1} = \ell^d \lambda_1^{-1} \quad \text{or} \quad \beta = (d-y_1)/y_2 \tag{4.7}$$

which is nothing else than the scaling relation for the exponent β.

The amplitude A remains undetermined by (4.4) and should follow from the analysis of the previous section. In fact it is easier to turn the argument around and determine the critical behavior below and above T_c from the behavior at $T = 0$ and $T = \infty$. Before we start this calculation on the basis of the renormalization theory we mention that from elementary considerations it follows that $m(k{=}0) = 0$ and $m(k{=}\infty) = \pm 1$ but it is curious to see how this result follows even from such a simpleminded approximation as (1.14).

The infinite temperature case is easy to obtain. We start with a situation in which $k = 0$ and a small magnetic field h is present. Quite generally, but also from (1.14) follows, that a system with only a magnetic field present leads upon renormalization only to a new magnetic field according to the formulae

$$\begin{aligned} h' &= (1/2)\log[\exp 3h + 3\exp h]/[\exp - 3h + 3\exp - h] \\ g(h) &= (1/6)\log[\exp 3h + 3\exp h][\exp - 3h + 3\exp -h] \end{aligned} \tag{4.8}$$

It follows upon substitution that $f(h) = \log[\exp h + \exp -h]$ fulfils the relation

$$f(h) = g(h) + \ell^{-d} f(h') \tag{4.9}$$

and that therefore $[\partial f(h)/\partial h]_{h=0} = 0$, but the game is to show that also the series

$$f(h) = \sum_{j=0}^{\infty} \ell^{-jd} g(h^{(j)}) \tag{4.10}$$

yields this result. This can be seen as follows. Starting from a small h, $h^{(j)}$ will grow initially as

$$h^{(j)} = [3/2]^j \, h \tag{4.11}$$

Once $h^{(j)}$ has reached a finite value it pretty soon grows according to (4.8) by a factor 2 at each step. The switch occurs when j equals t given by

$$t = -\log|h|/\log(3/2) \tag{4.12}$$

For the terms in (4.10) with $j < t$, $g(h^{(j)})$ may be expanded in powers of $h^{(j)}$ and no linear power in h results from this part. The second part is a little more delicate since there the asymptotic behavior of g(h) for large h starts out as $|h|/3$. For the terms $j > t$ one estimates the contribution to (4.10) as ($\ell^d = 3$)

$$(1/3) \sum_{j=t}^{\infty} \ell^{-j} \, 2^{j-t} (3/2)^t |h| = 2^{-t}|h| \tag{4.13}$$

Inserting (4.12) one has again no linear term in h and thus also (4.10) implies a zero magnetization at $h = 0$.

The magnetization at zero temperature ($k = \infty$) is calculated in the same spirit. However, one cannot start right away with $k = \infty$ and therefore the free energy is studied for k very large and h very small. According to (4.1) the h and k transform as ($\mu(k) \simeq 1$)

$$\begin{cases} h^{(j)} = 3^j \, h \\ k^{(j)} = 2^j \, k \end{cases} \tag{4.14}$$

We note that the factor 3 by which h grows is not accidentally equal to ℓ^d, for in a strongly interacting system every site in the cell gives a contribution $\mu(k) \simeq 1$ to the effective cell field. Since $h^{(j)}$ grows faster than $k^{(j)}$ at a certain value of j, $h^{(j)}$ will exceed $2k^{(j)}$. Then the approximation (4.1) fails and $h^{(j)}$ and $k^{(j)}$ start to grow at different rates. The turning point is determined by the value

$$t = [\log 2k/|h|]/\log(3/2) \tag{4.15}$$

One should realize that for $k >> 1$ and $h << 1$, t will be large and $h^{(j)}$ and $k^{(j)}$ extremely large. If j_t is the first integer larger than t, then the next h, k will no longer be given by (4.14) but rather by the corresponding formulae for large h which imply that $h^{(j)}$ grows with a factor 2 at each step and $k^{(j)}$ decreases by a factor 8/9. The larger initial value of k the sharper the transition from the initial behavior (4.14) to the large h behavior. Again the initial terms do not lead to a magnetization and the remainder now contributes to dominant order to the free energy:

$$1/3 \sum_{j=j_t}^{\infty} 3^{-j} 2^{j-j_t} 3^{jt}|h| = |h| \tag{4.16}$$

This leads to $m(k = \infty) = \pm 1$ as expected.

In this derivation we have been relying heavily on the properties of the approximation (1.14) but the outcome suggests that the argument is much more general and indeed one can extend the proof.

Once the asymptotic behavior of $m(k)$ for $k = 0$ and $k = \infty$ has been established the practical calculation of $m(k)$ can be performed with (4.5).

Finally we note that for all $k_\alpha = 0$ we have a fixed point with an eigenvalue $\lambda = 3/2$ (see (4.11)); the other non zero eigenvalues are $\lambda = 1/2$ and $\lambda = 1/8$). The eigenvalue $\lambda = 3/2$ suggests on the basis of the previous section that a powerlike behavior in h will occur of the type

$$f(h) \simeq A|h|^{\log 3/[\log 3-\log 2]}$$

which also follows from the estimate (4.13). However an actual calculation of the amplitude A according to (3.12) leads to $A = 0$.

5. ALTERNATIVES, FAILURES AND PROBLEMS

So far everything has been illustrated at the hand of only one realization of a renormalization transformation, given in the first section. In this section we will discuss some alternatives displaying at same time certain difficulties associated with renormalization transformations. In order to see what possibilities are open we first generalize the transformation (1.4).

a.) General renormalization transformations.

Let $P(s',s)$ be a weight factor depending on both the cell- and site spinconfiguration $\{s'\}$ and $\{s\}$ with the properties

$$P(s',s) \geq 0, \qquad \sum_{\{s'\}} P(s',s) = 1 \tag{5.1}$$

Then define a renormalization transformation

$$\exp[G + H'(s')] = \sum_{\{s\}} P(s',s) \exp H(s) \tag{5.2}$$

Because of (5.1) one recovers the same transformation law for the free energy as (2.2), viz.

$$f(k) = g(k) + \ell^{-d} f(k') \qquad (5.3)$$

The earlier treated transformation for the triangular lattice follows from (5.2) by taking P as a product over weightfunctions for the cells $P = \prod_{i'} P_{i'}$ of the following form

$$P_{i'}(s'_{i'}, s_i s_j s_k) = \frac{1}{2}\{1 + s'_{i'}[p(s_i+s_j+s_k) + b\, s_i s_j s_k]\} \qquad (5.4)$$

with $p = -b = 1/2$. The more general form (5.4) is chosen for later convenience and to show in which directions generalizations are possible. Any p and b complying with the first relation (5.1) seem at first sight equally good. Yet there must be practical limitations as $p = b = 0$ (which satisfy (5.1)) leads to a P independent of s' thus to $H'(s') = 0$. Such a transformation maps every H into $H' = 0$ and little can be learned from it. In fact then (5.2) yields nothing else than a direct calculation of the free energy G of the system.

b.) Checkerboard transformation.

A very attractive idea, followed by many people, is to design the following transformation for a square lattice[7]. Divide the lattice in black and white sites as on a checkerboard. Associate with every black site a cell spin variable $s'_{i'}$ and define $P(s',s) = 1$ when the cell spins are all equal to the black site spin and take $P = 0$ otherwise. In other words the sum in (5.2) runs only over the white spins, whereas the black spins are kept fixed. In order to get an idea about this transformation one can carry out the sum over the white spinconfigurations by ignoring their mutual coupling. For zero magnetic field this leads to the following transformation

$$\begin{aligned} k'_1 &= (1/4)\log(\cosh 4\,k_1) + k_2 \\ k'_2 &= (1/8)\log(\cosh 4\,k_1) \end{aligned} \qquad (5.5)$$

where k_1 and k_2 are the nearest and next nearest coupling constants.

This transformation shows an interesting structure for the critical properties as shown in Fig. 2. A fixed point appears at $k_1^* = 0.51$, $k_2^* = 0.17$through which a line of critical point passes, intersecting the k axis at $k_1 = k_c = 0.63$ and the k_2 axis at the same value $k_2 = k_c$. (k_c is substantial larger than the exact Ising value $k_c = 0.44$, but in view of the crudeness of the approximation this is not surprising). The critical line continues into the other quadrants and so passes through areas where different magnetic orderings are present. E.g. for $k_1 = -k_c, k_2 = 0$ antiferromagnetic ordering appears. Interesting is to observe that the piece $k_1 < 0$, $k_2 > 0$ maps on the part $k_1 > 0$, $k_2 > 0$ and that also a point $k_1 = -k_1^*, k_2 = k_2^*$

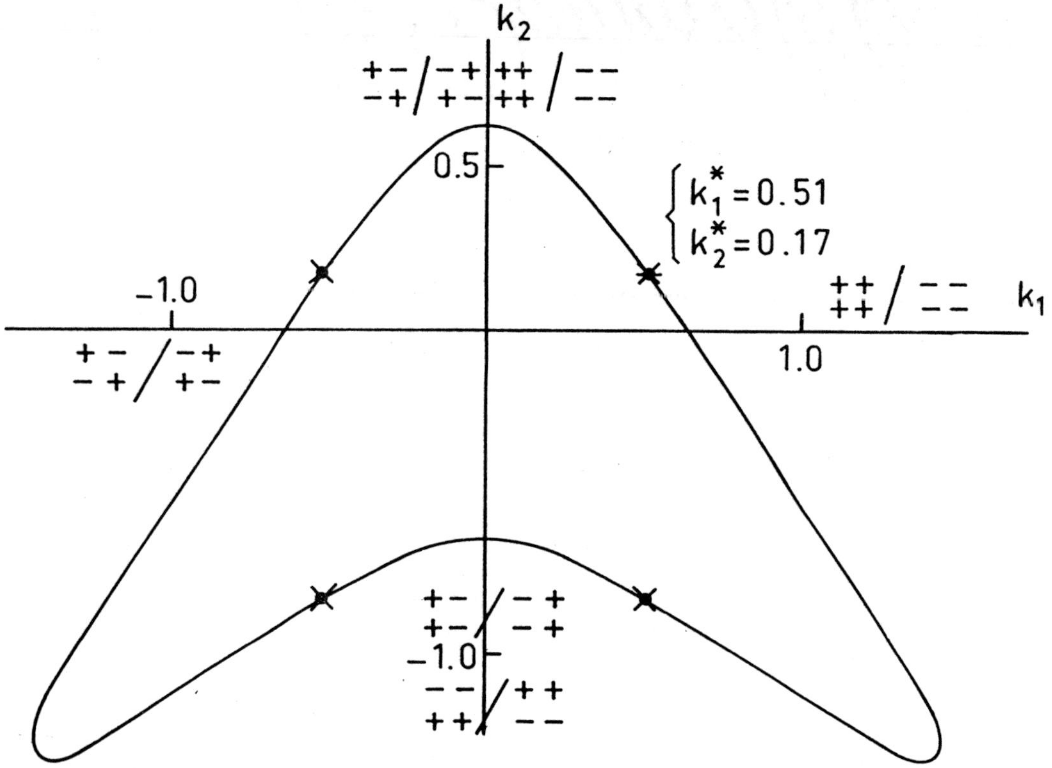

Fig. 2. Critical line of transformation (5.5) with the different magnetic orderings indicated.

exist, which maps directly on the fixed point, showing that the transformation has no inverse. The lower part of the curve corresponds to a layered antiferromagnetic ordering, (mapping on the antiferromagnetic line). The picture is qualitative as expected except for the connection of the layered antiferromagnetic line to the (anti)ferromagnetic line(s) in the lower corner(s), but again the approximation (5.1) is particularly poor there (large k_2).

One encounters however the following difficulty. Let i and j be two black sites on a large distance $|i-j|$. From the standard theory one knows that the spin correlation function $g(|i-j|)$ behaves as

$$g(|i-j|) = \langle s_i s_j \rangle \simeq A|i-j|^{-\eta} \text{ with } \eta = 1/4 \quad (d = 2) \tag{5.6}$$

From the renormalization transformation one derives the relation

$$g(|i-j|) = \sum_{\{s_{\text{black}}\}} \sum_{\{s_{\text{white}}\}} s_i s_j \exp H(s) \Big/ \sum_{\{s_{\text{black}}\}} \sum_{\{s_{\text{white}}\}} \exp H(s)$$

$$= \sum_{\{s_{\text{black}}\}} s_i s_j \exp H'(s) \Big/ \sum_{\{s_{\text{black}}\}} \exp H'(s) = g'(|i-j|/\ell) \tag{5.7}$$

with the scaling length $\ell = \sqrt{2}$ and g' the correlation function for parameters k'_α. At the fixed point (5.3) implies

$$g(|i-j|) = g(|i-j|/\ell) \tag{5.8}$$

which is only compatible with (5.2) when $\eta = 0$. Note that for this contradiction no approximation is involved. A similar objection cannot be raised against the previous triangular lattice renormalization transformation since (5.7) follows only if the cell (black) spin are at the same time site spins.
To meet this difficulty one may use Legendre type transformations.

c.) Legendre transformations.

These transformations are not of the scaling type but concern a map of the site spin hamiltonian space onto itself. Define H_q as the image of H by the following transformation

$$\exp[G_q + H_q(t)] = \sum_{\{s\}} [\prod_j \frac{1}{2} (1 + q\, t_j s_j)] \exp H(s) \tag{5.9}$$

where the product runs over all sites. Again G_q is defined such that $\sum_{\{t\}} H_q(t) = 0$. The name Legendre transformation is chosen because one may write (5.9) in the form

$$\exp[G - Na + H_q(t)] = \sum_{\{s\}} \exp[b \sum_j t_j s_j + H(s)] \tag{5.10}$$

with

$$\begin{cases} a = (1/2) \log[(1 - q^2)/4] \\ b = (1/2) \log[(1 + q)/(1 - q)] \end{cases} \tag{5.11}$$

using that

$$\frac{1}{2} [1 + q\, t_j s_j] = \exp(a + b\, t_j s_j) \tag{5.12}$$

For varying q on has a one dimensional set of transformations with the property

$$(H_q)_p = H_{qp} = (H_p)_q \tag{5.13}$$

indicating that the transformations form an abelian semigroup. Considering the factor $(1/2)(1+q\, t_j s_j)$ as a weight factor one sees that for $q = 1$ the sum over $\{s\}$ only contributes when $\{s\} = \{t\}$ and thus (5.9) is for $q = 1$ the identity transformation. It should be noted that for a proper definition of H_q, q should be restricted to the interval $-1 \leq q \leq 1$ otherwise negative terms will appear on the right hand side of (5.9) and a real H_q is then not garantueed. For $q = 0$, $H_{q=0} = 0$.

Therefore the line of H_q associated with H passes through H and 0.

The interesting property of the Legendre transformations is that the correlation functions of system with hamiltonian H_q are easily related to these with hamiltonian H. One finds analoguous to (5.7)

$$g_q(|i-j|) = \langle t_i t_j \rangle_q = q^2 \langle s_i s_j \rangle = q^2\ g(|i-j|) \qquad (5.14)$$

Taking the long rangedness of the correlation functions as the most fundamental property of critical systems one concludes from (5.14) that by (5.9) critical systems are mapped into each other. By the time that q approaches zero H_q must have developed curious long range forces in order to understand that $H_{q\to 0} = 0$ and that still H_q remains critical.

d.) Linear weightfactors.

A special class of weightfactors are those which are linear in the cell and site variables. For example let $S_{i'}$ be the total spin of cell i' then consider the transformation

$$\exp[G + H'(s)] = \sum_{\{s\}} \left\{ \prod_{\text{cells } i'} \frac{1}{2}(1 + p\ s'_{i'} S_{i'}) \right\} \exp H(s) \qquad (5.15)$$

One may consider this as the product of a transformation in which one sums all configuration at fixed total spin $S_{i'}$ of the cell, followed by a Legendre transformation of the $S_{i'}$ to cell spins $s'_i = \pm 1$. The important property of these transformations (somewhat misleadingly called "linear transformations") is that they lead to a simple transformation property for the spin-spin correlation. By a similar calculation as in (5.7) one finds for sufficiently large $|i-j|$

$$g'(|i-j|/\ell) = p^2\ \ell^{2d}\ g(|i-j|) \qquad (5.16)$$

The value of η is then, curiously enough, determined by the arbitrary parameter p according to

$$\ell^{\eta} = p^2\ \ell^{2d} \qquad (5.17)$$

One argues then, however that, in order to find an Ising like fixed point p has to be chosen carefully and in fact such as to fulfil (5.17). In this way also the checkerboard transformation can be reconciled with a non-vanishing η. One should then take for $S_{i'}$ instead of the total spin of the cell, the value s_i of the site spin at a black site i and carry out the product in (5.15) over all black sites. In that case the relation (5.17) would follow without the factor ℓ^{2d}. An unsettling feature of this procedure is that for a positive η one has to chose $p > \ell^{-d}$ implying that in (5.15) negative terms occur as S_i ranges from ℓ^d to $-\ell^d$. (In the adapted checkerboard case $p = \ell^{\eta/2} > 1$ which also leads to negative terms.)

Also the use of linear weightfactors implies the following curiosity. As Wilson notes[9] the existence of a fixed point leads to a line of fixed points of the same transformation (5.15). Let H_q be the Legendre transform of H and $(H_q)'$ the result of the transformation (5.15) applied to H_q. $(H')_q$ is the result of applying the transformations in the reversed order, but a straight forward calculation tells that

$$(H')_q = (H_q)' \tag{5.18}$$

So if (5.15) exhibits a fixed point $H' = H$ we have $(H')_q = H_q$ and by (5.18) also that $(H_q)' = H_q$ i.e. the whole line H_q is a fixed line of (5.15). Every fixed point has the same η given by (5.17). Whether this richness in fixed points, some of them corresponding to strange systems for $q \to 0$, will be an advantage or a disadvantage for practical calculations is not clear.

e.) Different phase transitions.

The checkerboard transformation as sketched in Fig. 2 maps the antiferromagnetic critical line into the ferromagnetic critical line. Leaving the magnetic field out of consideration it is acceptable that the free energies of the antiferromagnetic and ferromagnetic systems are declared to be of similar singular behavior by this transformation. However one knows that for an antiferromagnet the staggered magnetic field plays the role of the magnetic field for the ferromagnet. Now constricting the transformation to translational invariant fields as done here, the staggered magnetic field does not come into picture at all. So if the transformation will do its proper job in connecting the singularities of ferro- and antiferromagnetic systems it has to be singular itself. But this goes against the grain of the renormalization theory since one wants to explain singularities in terms of regular transformations.

The remedy is to construct a transformation such that antiferromagnetic hamiltonians map into themselves. An obvious example is taking on the quadratic lattice square cells of 9 sites and defining the cell spin again as the sign of the majority of the site spins in the cell. The dominant antiferromagnetic state will then lead also the alternating cell spins. Then the ferromagnetic and the antiferromagnetic systems will each have their own fixed point. However, when two attracting fixed points appear on the same critical surface they have to be separated from each other by at least one (partly) repulsive fixed point which should be located near $k_1 = 0$ and $k_2 \neq 0$. The hope is that upon inclusion of a 4-spin interaction k_4 a whole line of such fixed points will appear as deviding line between ferro- and antiferromagnetic behavior which then would explain the anomalous critical behavior of the symmetric 8 vertex model, as this model is characterized by $k_1 = 0$ and $k_2, k_4 \neq 0$.

Generally the safe strategy seems to be to design the renormalization transformation such that the ground states of the original and renormalized hamiltonian are the same. This is presumably the explanation why the triangular lattice transformation (1.4) fails to describe properly the critical behavior of a triangular lattice with pure triple spin interaction which has been solved recently by Baxter and Wu[10]. In the case of pure triple spin interaction one has at zero temperature a coexistence of a ferromagnetic state (all spins up) and a state where a sublattice of next nearest neighbor spins with spin up is surrounded by down spins. The transformation (1.4) maps the latter state into a ferromagnetic state with all the spins down. So the transformation (1.4) is likely to be singular itself when it maps the critical point found by Baxter and Wu into an Ising type critical point.

ACKNOWLEDGEMENT

The work described here has been carried in collaboration with Dr. Th. Niemeijer, M.den Nijs and R.W. Kooy of the Delft Technological University. Numerous discussions with them and with Dr. H.F. Knops, M. Nauenberg and A. Weijland helped to shape these lectures as well as most illuminating conversations during the summerschool with D. Nelson, B. Widom, P.C. Hemmer, E.H. Hauge and J.C. Wheeler.

REFERENCES

1) K.G. Wilson, Phys. Rev. B4 (1971) 3174, 3184.
K.G. Wilson and M.E. Fisher, Phys. Rev. Letters 28 (1972) 240.
K.G. Wilson and J. Kogut, Physics Reports, to be published.
2) Th. Niemeijer and J.M.J. van Leeuwen, Phys. Rev. Letters 31 (1973) 1411.
Th. Niemeijer and J.M.J. van Leeuwen, Physica 71 (1974) 17-40.
3) F.J. Wegner, Phys. Rev. B5 (1972) 4529.
4) The treatment of this section is based on the work performed in Delft in collaboration with M.den Nijs. Similar treatments have been given by
M. Nauenberg and G. Nienhuis, preprint Univ. of Utrecht,
D. Nelson and M.E. Fisher, preprint Cornell Univ.,
M.P. Nightingale and A.H. 't Hooft, preprint Univ. of Amsterdam.
5) The possibility of oscillatory terms was pointed out to me by M. Nauenberg.
6) At this point one would have much pleasure from a continuous group of renormalization transformation of varying scaling length ℓ, having the same scaling fields, to exclude the oscillatory terms, as was noted by D. Nelson. In fact two transformations with log ℓ_1 and log ℓ_2 incommensurate and asymptotic ($u \to 0$) equivalent scaling fields are sufficient to rule out the oscillations.
7) L.P. Kadanoff , See e.g. Conference on Renormalization Group Application to Statistical Mechanics and Field Theory 1973, Temple Univ., Philadelphia (Pa) 19122, U.S.A., M.S. Green and J.D. Gunton, editors.

Th. Niemeijer and J.M.J. van Leeuwen, Phys. Lett. 41A (1972) 211.

D. Nelson and M.E. Fisher, preprint Cornell Univ.

8) T.L. Bell and K.G. Wilson, preprint Cornell Univ.

9) K.G. Wilson, private communication.

10) R.J. Baxter and F.Y. Wu, Phys. Rev. Letters 31 (1973) 1294.

EXACTLY SOLVABLE LATTICE MODELS

P.W. KASTELEYN

Instituut-Lorentz, Rijksuniversiteit Leiden

Leiden, Netherlands.

INTRODUCTION

One of the main branches of the theory of phase transitions is the theory of exactly solvable lattice models (lattice models, usually with nearest-neighbour interactions, for which one or more physical quantities have been calculated exactly). This theory began in 1925 with a paper by Ising on what is now called the one-dimensional Ising model. Up to now, its development has been largely determined by three major break-throughs, each of which consisted in the calculation of the free energy (and a few other quantities) of a certain model defined on the two-dimensional square lattice, viz.

A. the zero-field Ising model, by Onsager (1944),

B. the symmetric six-vertex model, by Lieb (1967),

C. the symmetric eight-vertex model, by Baxter (1971).

In these lectures we shall discuss these models as special cases of a single class of classical lattice models on the square lattice. The emphasis will be on relations between these models, relations with certain one-dimensional quantum lattice models, and the basic ideas of the solution methods, rather than on specific properties of the solutions. We shall further restrict ourselves to one thermodynamic property, the free energy per lattice site in the thermodynamic limit $f(\beta) = \lim_{\mathcal{N}\to\infty} F(\beta,\mathcal{N})/\mathcal{N}$; $\mathcal{N}$ is the number of lattice sites, β = (Boltzmann's constant $\cdot$ temperature)$^{-1}$, and $F(\beta,\mathcal{N})$ is the total free energy, related to the partition function by $F(\beta,\mathcal{N}) = -\beta^{-1} \log Z(\beta,\mathcal{N})$. For some models we shall only discuss the ground-state energy per site in the thermodynamic limit $e_0 = \lim_{\mathcal{N}\to\infty} E_0(\mathcal{N})/\mathcal{N}$, with $E_0(\mathcal{N}) = \lim_{\beta\to\infty} F(\beta,\mathcal{N})$. For a discussion of other aspects of the models (other physical quantities, analytic properties, other two-dimensional lattices etc.) the reader is referred to the review articles and monographs listed as refs. 1-7 and the references given therein.

Two types of methods have been developed for finding the partition function, and thereby the free energy, of a classical lattice model with nearest-neighbour interactions:

a. "Single-stroke methods". These methods had their origin in an attempt to find a matrix, expressing the topological structure of the lattice, with the property that the non-vanishing terms of its determinant correspond one-to-one to the terms in the partition function when this is expressed as a power series in an appropriate variable. This idea turned out to be very fruitful, and led

Fundamental Problems in Statistical Mechanics, Vol. 3, Editor, E.D.G. Cohen.

to methods that became known as the combinatorial method, the Pfaffian method and the S-matrix method (see ref. 1, pp. 254-266; ref. 2, pp. 101-123, 148-156, 169-181; ref. 3, pp. 202-211; ref. 4, chaps. 3,4,6; ref. 6).

We shall not enter into these methods, however useful they are, because for the models to be discussed in these lectures their applicability is too restricted.

b. "Rolling-up methods" (transfer-matrix methods). In these methods one divides the model mentally into a large number of identical subsystems. One then writes the statistical weight of a state of the model as a product of factors each of which represents the effect of adding one subsystem to the model; the resulting expression for the partition function is then "rolled up" to a formally very simple expression. In many applications the model consists of units (to be called atoms for convenience), situated at lattice sites, which can be in two different states (described by a variable taking the values ±1), and the subsystems are layers, labelled $k=1, \ldots, M$, say, of $N = \mathcal{N}/M$ atoms each, chosen in such a way that the atoms in layer k interact only with atoms in the layers k-1, k and k+1. The variable describing the state of the jth atom in layer k is denoted by μ_{jk}, the state of the entire layer k by $\mu^{(k)} \equiv (\mu_{1k}, \ldots, \mu_{Nk})$; there are 2^N possible states for a layer. The energy E of the system is split as follows: $E = \Sigma_{k=1}^{M} E_L(\mu^{(k)}, \mu^{(k+1)})$, where $E_L(\mu^{(k)}, \mu^{(k+1)})$ contains the interactions of the atoms in layer k with those in layer k+1 as well as the mutual interactions between the atoms in layer k; in extending the summation to k=M we have included interactions between the Mth layer and the first one (periodic boundary condition). Homogeneity of the system requires that $E_L(\mu,\mu')$ depend only on the states μ and μ' of two successive layers, and not on their labels. In the partition function we can now factorize the Boltzmann factor $\exp(-\beta E)$ into factors of the type $\exp\{-\beta E_L(\mu,\mu')\}$, which we denote by $T(\mu,\mu')$ henceforth. Thus we write

$$Z = \sum_{\mu^{(1)}} \sum_{\mu^{(2)}} \cdots \sum_{\mu^{(M)}} T(\mu^{(1)},\mu^{(2)})T(\mu^{(2)},\mu^{(3)})\ldots T(\mu^{(M)},\mu^{(1)}), \qquad (1)$$

thereby explicitly exhibiting the layer structure of the system. We shall also encounter examples where not all units are grouped to layers, and where, accordingly, $T(\mu,\mu')$ is not defined as a single exponential, but as a sum of exponentials. However, also in those cases eq. (1) is valid.

If we now arrange the factors $T(\mu,\mu')$ into a matrix T of 2^N rows, labelled μ, and 2^N columns, labelled μ', the summations over $\mu^{(2)},\ldots,\mu^{(M)}$ can be considered as matrix multiplications. Denoting the (μ,μ') element of the matrix T^k by $T^k(\mu,\mu')$ and the trace of a matrix by Tr we can "roll up" the expression (1) for Z as follows:

$$Z = \sum_{\mu^{(1)}} \sum_{\mu^{(3)}} \cdots \sum_{\mu^{(M)}} T^2(\mu^{(1)},\mu^{(3)})T(\mu^{(3)}, \mu^{(4)}) \ldots T(\mu^{(M)}, \mu^{(1)}) =$$

$$= \ldots = \sum_{\mu^{(1)}} T^M(\mu^{(1)}, \mu^{(1)}) = \mathrm{Tr}\, T^M. \tag{2}$$

The matrix T is called the <u>transfer matrix</u> of the system. Note that different ways of choosing layers in a system lead, in general, to different transfer matrices. Since the trace of a matrix is equal to the sum of its eigenvalues, we can rewrite eq. (2) as

$$Z = \sum_{i=1}^{2^N} \Lambda_i^M , \tag{3}$$

where the Λ_i are the eigenvalues of T. If one is interested in the thermodynamic limit, the next step is to let the number of layers go to infinity, and to define the free energy per layer in this limit by

$$F_L(\beta,N) = -\beta^{-1} \lim_{M\to\infty}\{M^{-1} \log Z(\beta,MN)\}. \tag{4}$$

It follows from (3) and (4) that if Λ_0 is the (possibly degenerate) eigenvalue of largest absolute value of T, we have $F_L(\beta,N) = -\beta^{-1} \log \Lambda_0$. If one then takes the limit $N\to\infty$, which affects T, and hence Λ_0, one finds:

$$f(\beta) = \lim_{N\to\infty} \frac{1}{N} F_L(\beta,N) = \lim_{N\to\infty} \{- \frac{1}{\beta N} \log \Lambda_0(N)\} . \tag{5}$$

The two states of an atom can be interpreted as the "spin up" and "spin down" states, with respect to a certain axis, of a spin-½ particle, the 2^N states of a layer as the products of N such spin states, and T as the matrix representation of a linear operator in the vector space spanned by these product states (the state space of a system of N spins). Thus the eigenvalue problem for T is of the same nature as that for a Hamiltonian $\mathcal{H}_L$ of a single layer of N spins. In particular, the problem of determining the largest eigenvalue Λ_0 of T is similar to that of finding the lowest eigenvalue of $\mathcal{H}_L$, the ground-state energy E_0. It is this similarity which was stressed by the authors who introduced, more or less simultaneously, the transfer matrix method, Montroll[8], Kramers and Wannier[9], Lassettre and Howe[10], and Kubo[11]. They suggested in particular the possibility of applying techniques developed for solving eigenvalue problems in quantum mechanics to the statistical theory of lattice models. Note that if the original lattice model is d-dimensional, its layers and the corresponding quantum spin system are (d-1)-dimensional.

It has gradually become clear that the analogy between the transfer matrix of a classical lattice model and the Hamiltonian of a quantum lattice model is, in a sense, not accidental: we shall show that there exists a very close mathematical relationship between certain transfer matrices and certain spin Hamiltonians. Before doing so we shall first introduce the specific models to be discussed.

1. SPIN MODELS AND VERTEX MODELS

1.1. Spin models

Consider a lattice of $\mathcal{N}$ sites with periodic boundary conditions for all directions, and at each site a spin-$\frac{1}{2}$ particle. There are four linearly independent operators acting on a given spin. As such we choose the Pauli spin operators σ^x, σ^y, σ^z together with the unit operator, to be denoted by $\sigma^0 \equiv I$. The spin operators acting on the ith spin are then $\sigma_i^\alpha = I \otimes I \otimes \ldots \otimes \sigma^\alpha \otimes \ldots \otimes I$, where σ^α $(\alpha = x,y,z,0)$ is the ith factor in the direct product; for each i, σ_i^0 is the unit operator in the space of $\mathcal{N}$-spin states, which we shall often omit, or denote by 1 (writing $1 + \sigma_i^z$ etc., as usual). Alternatively, we can work with the spin raising and lowering operators $\sigma_i^\pm = \frac{1}{2}(\sigma_i^x \pm i\sigma_i^y)$ and their products $\sigma_i^+\sigma_i^-$ and $\sigma_i^-\sigma_i^+$. We shall always use the standard representation in which σ^x, σ^y, σ^z are represented by the Pauli matrices, and not distinguish between an operator and its matrix representation. The basis of this representation is formed by the common eigenvectors of the operators σ_i^z, to be denoted by $|\mu_1,\ldots,\mu_{\mathcal{N}}\rangle$ with $\mu_i = \pm 1$:

$$\sigma_i^z|\mu_1,\ldots,\mu_{\mathcal{N}}\rangle = \mu_i|\mu_1,\ldots,\mu_{\mathcal{N}}\rangle \qquad (i = 1,\ldots,\mathcal{N}). \tag{1.1}$$

An arbitrary state vector will be denoted by Ψ.

An operator that we shall frequently encounter is the spin parity operator $U^z = \Pi_i\sigma_i^z$. Its eigenvalues are ± 1; an eigenstate of U^z belonging to the eigenvalue $1(-1)$ is called a state of parity $1(-1)$ or even (odd) state. An even (odd) state is a linear combination of basis states with an even (odd) number of down spins ($\mu_i = -1$).

We consider Hamiltonians of the form $\mathcal{H} = \Sigma_{i=1}^{\mathcal{N}}\mathcal{H}_i$, where $\mathcal{H}_i$ contains only the spin operators acting on the ith spin and on one or more neighbouring spins. Two types of spin models will be discussed: two-dimensional Ising models and one-dimensional generalized Heisenberg models.

1.1.1. Two-dimensional Ising models

Here the lattice is two-dimensional, and $\mathcal{H}$ contains only the operators σ_i^z. Since these commute, the eigenvectors of $\mathcal{H}$ are just the basis vectors, and the eigenvalues $E(\mu_1,\ldots,\mu_{\mathcal{N}})$ are found by replacing in $\mathcal{H}$ each σ_i^z by μ_i. The system can therefore be treated as a classical system. The partition function is

$$Z = \sum_{\mu_1}\ldots\sum_{\mu_{\mathcal{N}}} \exp\{-\beta E(\mu_1,\ldots,\mu_{\mathcal{N}})\},$$

and the whole problem lies in the calculation of this sum.

The prototype is the Ising model with nearest-neighbour interactions on an $M \times N$ square lattice ($MN = \mathcal{N}$). If the sites are labelled by a column index $j = 1, \ldots, N$ and a row index $k = 1, \ldots, M$, the Hamiltonian is

$$\mathcal{H}^I = -\sum_{j=1}^{N}\sum_{k=1}^{M} (J_1\sigma^z_{jk}\sigma^z_{j+1,k} + J_2\sigma^z_{jk}\sigma^z_{j,k+1} + H\sigma^z_{jk}) , \tag{1.2}$$

where $\sigma^z_{N+1,k} = \sigma^z_{1k}$, $\sigma^z_{j,M+1} = \sigma^z_{j1}$. It was the calculation by Onsager[12), in 1944, of the free energy of this model for $H = 0$ that opened the door to an exact treatment of two-dimensional lattice models.

More complicated Ising models are obtained by adding to $\mathcal{H}^I$ terms representing interactions between next-nearest neighbours, three-spin or four-spin interactions etc.

1.1.2. One-dimensional generalized Heisenberg models

For these models the lattice is a linear chain of N spins, and the Hamiltonian is of the form

$$\mathcal{H} = \sum_j \mathcal{H}_{j,j+1}; \quad \mathcal{H}_{j,j+1} = - \sum_{\alpha,\beta=x,y,z,0} J^{\alpha\beta}\sigma^\alpha_j\sigma^\beta_{j+1} ; \tag{1.3}$$

here, and in what follows, $\Sigma_j = \Sigma_{j=1}^N$. We call a Hamiltonian of the form (1.3) a generalized Heisenberg Hamiltonian. In general, it contains 16 independent coefficients, including magnetic fields and a constant, J^{00}. Because of the summation over j the coefficients $J^{\alpha 0}$ and $J^{0\alpha}$ (a = x, y, z) occur in $\mathcal{H}$ only in the combination $J^{\alpha 0} + J^{0\alpha}$, so that we can take $J^{0x} = J^{0y} = J^{0z} = 0$ without lack of generality.

In these lectures we shall restrict ourselves to models with a Hamiltonian conserving the parity of spins, i.e. having zero matrix elements between states of opposite parity, or, equivalently, commuting with the parity operator U^z. We then have $J^{x0} = J^{y0} = J^{xz} = J^{zx} = J^{yz} = J^{zy} = 0$, so that at most 7 non-vanishing $J^{\alpha\beta}$ remain.

Besides the Ising model, which is trivially included in this class of models, the following special cases have been extensively studied:

A. The XY model. The Hamiltonian of this model is

$$\mathcal{H}^{XY} = -\Sigma_j (J_x\sigma^x_j\sigma^x_{j+1} + J_y\sigma^y_j\sigma^y_{j+1} + H\sigma^z_j) . \tag{1.4}$$

The case $J_x = J_y$ was first studied by Nambu[13). For $H = 0$ the free energy was calculated in 1961 by Lieb et al.[14), for arbitrary H in 1962 by Katsura[15).

B. The (zero-field) XXZ model (semi-anisotropic Heisenberg model). The

Hamiltonian is

$$\mathcal{H}^{XXZ} = -\Sigma_j (J(\sigma_j^x\sigma_{j+1}^x + \sigma_j^y\sigma_{j+1}^y) + J_z\sigma_j^z\sigma_{j+1}^z). \tag{1.5}$$

With $J_z = J$ this is the original, isotropic Heisenberg model [16]. For $J > 0$ its ground state is trivial: it is the (N+1)-fold degenerate state with all spins parallel. Bethe [17] proposed a specific form for all eigenvectors, and from this "Ansatz" derived a set of equations from which the eigenvectors and eigenvalues can in principle be found, but he gave only a few, comparatively simple explicit results. The ground-state energy e_0 for $J < 0$ was evaluated by Hulthén [18].

The ground-state energy of the XXZ model with $J_z < -|J|$ was calculated by Orbach [19], that for general J_z and J by Yang and Yang [20], and by Des Cloizeaux and Gaudin [21].

This model has a well-known interpretation as a one-dimensional quantum lattice gas (ref. 1, p. 20).

C. The (zero-field) <u>XYZ model</u> (anisotropic Heisenberg model). The Hamiltonian is

$$\mathcal{H}^{XYZ} = -\Sigma_j (J_x\sigma_j^x\sigma_{j+1}^x + J_y\sigma_j^y\sigma_{j+1}^y + J_z\sigma_j^z\sigma_{j+1}^z). \tag{1.6}$$

An expression for the ground-state energy for arbitrary J_x, J_y, J_z was recently derived by Baxter [22]. We mention the XXZ model and the XYZ model separately, in spite of the fact that the latter includes the former as a special case, first because Baxter's method for solving the XYZ model does not for $J_x = J_y$ reduce to the method by which the XXZ model was solved, secondly because we shall see later on that it is natural to consider an extension of the XXZ model that is not a special case of the XYZ model.

The Hamiltonians (1.4), (1.5) and (1.6) will be referred to as the XY Hamiltonian, the XXZ Hamiltonian and the XYZ Hamiltonian.

1.2. Vertex models

Consider a finite square lattice L of M rows and N columns with periodic boundary conditions. We now draw edges between neighbouring sites, and we allow each edge (rather than each site, or atom) to be in two different states; we distinguish these states by orienting the edge, i.e. by placing an arrow on it in one of the two directions (see for other representations ref. 1, p. 338). The possible states of the lattice are then all configurations of arrows on the lattice. The set of four oriented edges meeting at a lattice site is called a vertex configuration, or, briefly, a <u>vertex.</u> There are sixteen different vertices, represented in fig. 1; there is no generally accepted convention for their numbering, except for the first six vertices.

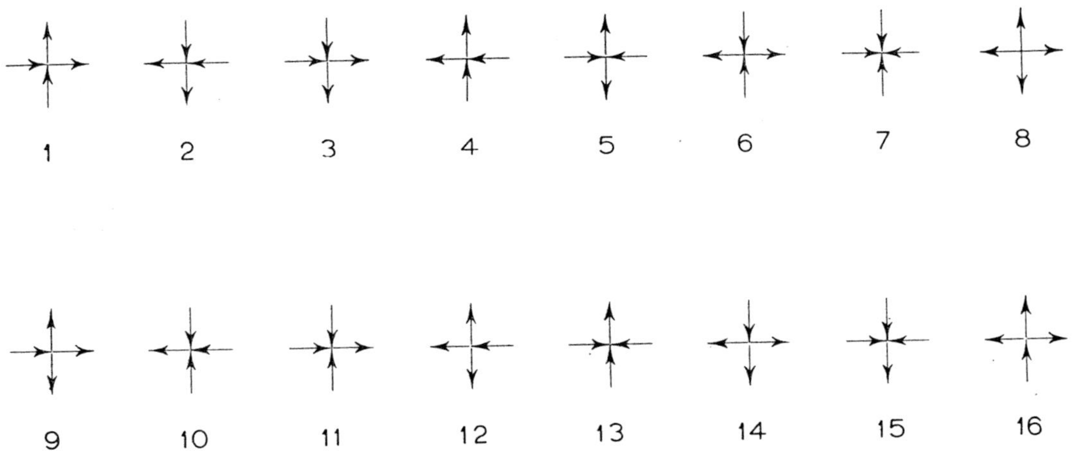

Fig. 1. The vertex configurations of the sixteen-vertex model on a square lattice.

If we associate with each vertex configuration r (r = 1,..., 16) an energy e_r and a corresponding statistical weight $\omega_r = \exp(-\beta e_r)$, we obtain a system called the <u>sixteen-vertex model</u>; for a reason to be explained below it is sometimes called the general ferroelectric model. It was first considered by Wu[23]. The partition function of the sixteen-vertex model is, by definition,

$$Z = \sum_C \prod_{i=1}^{MN} \omega_{r(i)} \quad , \tag{1.7}$$

where r(i) is the vertex configuration at the site i, and the sum is over all configurations C of arrows. One often considers the weights, rather than the energies, as the basic parameters of the model; if we do so, we shall always take $\omega_r \geq 0$ for all r. By the definition of the states and their energies, the model is a classical lattice model. A sixteen-vertex model is called <u>symmetric</u> if it is invariant under the reversal of all arrows, i.e. if $\omega_{2p-1} = \omega_{2p}$ (p = 1, ..., 8).

The sixteen-vertex model has thus far not been extensively studied except in the case where all vertices with an odd number of incoming arrows have zero weight: $\omega_9 = \omega_{10} = \ldots = \omega_{16} = 0$. We shall therefore discuss only the model obtained by this restriction. It is called the (general) <u>eight-vertex model</u>, because it contains at most eight different vertices with non-zero weight.

The eight-vertex model on L is equivalent to a spin model (generalized Ising model) on the dual lattice L^*. This lattice is obtained by placing a site in the middle of each of the faces (elementary squares) formed by the edges of L: it is itself also a square lattice. With each spin configuration on L^*

(described by spin variables $\mu_{jk} = \pm 1$, when the spins are labelled as in eq. (1.2)) we associate an arrow configuration on L by drawing an up (down) arrow between any two like (unlike) nearest neighbours in a row, and a right-pointing (left-pointing) arrow between any two like (unlike) nearest neighbours in a column. By inspection, or by a simple proof, one may convince oneself that the only vertices constructed in this way are those numbered 1,...,8 . Reversing all spins on L^* leads to the same arrow configuration on L. Conversely, for each arrow configuration of the eight-vertex model on L we can construct two spin configurations on L^*, which are related by a reversal of all spins (fig. 2).

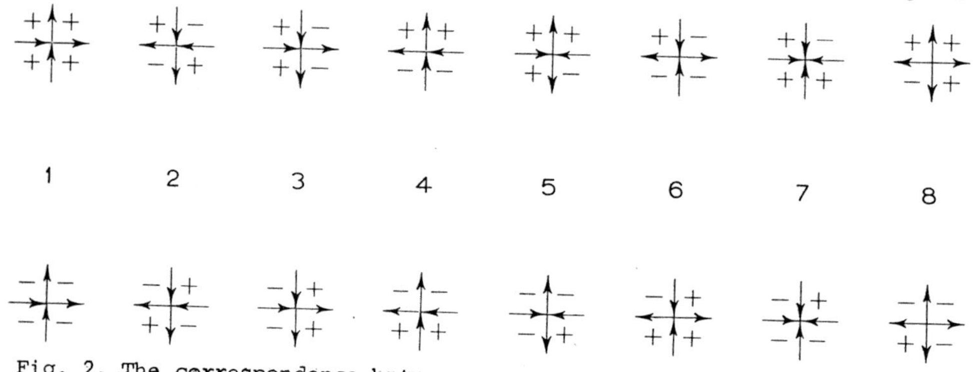

Fig. 2. The correspondence between vertex configurations on L and local spin configurations on L^*; +(−) stands for $\mu = 1(-1)$.

To match the energies we associate with the spin system the following energy:

$$E = -\sum_j \sum_k (J_0 + J_1\mu_{jk}\mu_{j+1,k} + J_2\mu_{jk}\mu_{j,k+1} + J_3\mu_{jk}\mu_{j+1,k+1} + J_3'\mu_{j+1,k}\mu_{j,k+1} + J_4\mu_{jk}\mu_{j+1,k}\mu_{j,k+1}\mu_{j+1,k+1}) \quad . \tag{1.8}$$

The terms with J_3 and J_3' represent interactions between two next-nearest (diagonal) neighbours, the last term a four-spin interaction between the spins surrounding a site of L. E is even in the μ_{jk}; in particular, it does not contain a magnetic-field term. To complete the correspondence, the terms in eq. (1.8) are associated with the sites of L as indicated in fig.3, with $J_{1a}+J_{1b}=J_1$, $J_{2a}+J_{2b}=J_2$.

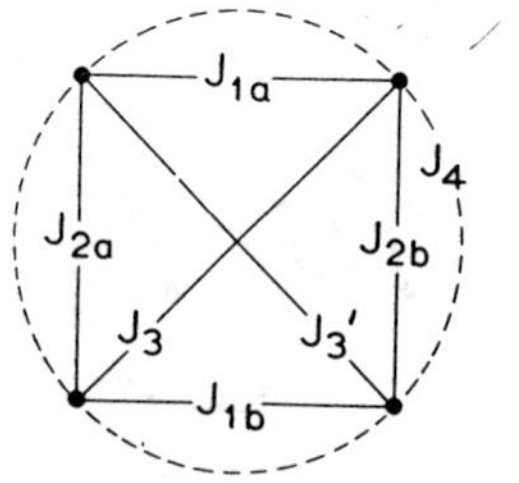

Fig. 3. The interactions between the spins on the four sites of L (black circles) surrounding a site of L^* (situated at the intersection of the diagonals) that are associated with the latter site. The drawn lines represent two-spin interactions, the dotted circle the four-spin interaction.

Notice that each horizontal and vertical interaction is split into two parts, associated with two neighbouring sites of L. Identifying the vertex energies with the associated spin energies we find

$$\begin{aligned}
e_1 &= -J_0 - J_{1a} - J_{1b} - J_{2a} - J_{2b} - J_3 - J_3' - J_4 ,\\
e_2 &= -J_0 + J_{1a} + J_{1b} + J_{2a} + J_{2b} - J_3 - J_3' - J_4 ,\\
e_3 &= -J_0 + J_{1a} + J_{1b} - J_{2a} - J_{2b} + J_3 + J_3' - J_4 ,\\
e_4 &= -J_0 - J_{1a} - J_{1b} + J_{2a} + J_{2b} + J_3 + J_3' - J_4 ,\\
e_5 &= -J_0 + J_{1a} - J_{1b} - J_{2a} + J_{2b} - J_3 + J_3' + J_4 ,\\
e_6 &= -J_0 - J_{1a} + J_{1b} + J_{2a} - J_{2b} - J_3 + J_3' + J_4 ,\\
e_7 &= -J_0 - J_{1a} + J_{1b} - J_{2a} + J_{2b} + J_3 - J_3' + J_4 ,\\
e_8 &= -J_0 + J_{1a} - J_{1b} + J_{2a} - J_{2b} + J_3 - J_3' + J_4 ;
\end{aligned} \qquad (1.9)$$

these equations can be inverted to give the J's in terms of the e_r.

The above equivalence enables us to represent a spin model with Hamiltonian (1.8) by a vertex model; such a representation will be called the dual or edge representation of the spin model, to be distinguished from its original or site representation. Note that this representation depends on how we split J_1 and J_2.

The following special cases of the eight-vertex model have been extensively studied:

A. The free-fermion model. For $J_3 = J_3' = J_4 = 0$ the spin equivalent of the eight-vertex model reduces to the Ising model (1.2) with $H = 0$; the corresponding condition on the vertex weights is $\omega_1\omega_2 = \omega_3\omega_4 = \omega_5\omega_6 = \omega_7\omega_8$. The solution of this model by Onsager was mentioned in section 1.1.1.

If we require only $J_3 = J_4 = 0$, or $J_3' = J_4 = 0$, we obtain an Ising model in which each spin has an additional interaction with two diagonal neighbours, or, equivalently, the Ising model on a (deformed) triangular lattice. This model was solved in 1950 by various authors (see ref. 1, p. 322). The corresponding restrictions on the ω_r are: $\omega_1\omega_2 = \omega_7\omega_8$, $\omega_3\omega_4 = \omega_5\omega_6$, and $\omega_1\omega_2 = \omega_5\omega_6$, $\omega_3\omega_4 = \omega_7\omega_8$, respectively.

If the restrictions on the weights are further relaxed to the single condition

$$\omega_1\omega_2 + \omega_3\omega_4 = \omega_5\omega_6 + \omega_7\omega_8 \quad , \qquad (1.10)$$

one obtains a more general model, for which the free energy f was first calculated by Fan and Wu[24)] by means of the S-matrix method. Since in this method the model is formally equivalent to a system of non-interacting fermions, they called it the <u>free-fermion model</u>, and the condition (1.10) the free-fermion condition. Recently, Felderhof[25)] rederived Fan and Wu's expression for f by means of the transfer-matrix method.

B. The six-vertex model. If we put $\omega_7 = \omega_8 = 0$, the eight-vertex model reduces to what is called the six-vertex model. In this model the vertices 7 and 8, which are "sinks" and "sources" of arrows, do not occur. Hence every vertex has two incoming and two outgoing arrows. There are a few special cases that have been studied for several decades:

B1. $\omega_1 = \omega_2 = \omega_3 = \omega_4 = \omega_5 = \omega_6 = 1$ (ice model). This model is called after a similar three-dimensional model proposed by Pauling [26)] in 1935 in a (successful) attempt to explain the experimental fact that ice has a residual entropy at very low temperatures (see ref. 1, p. 334). According to Pauling, the oxygen ions occupy the sites of a lattice in which each site has four nearest neighbours. Each pair of neighbouring oxygen ions is separated (and chemically bonded) by a hydrogen ion which sits closer to one oxygen than to the other. The hydrogen ions are distributed according to the following constraint ("ice rule"): each O ion is surrounded by two H ions close to it and two H ions farther away, so that local H_2O groups are formed. If the position of each H ion with respect to the midpoint of the O-O bond is indicated by an arrow (fig. 4a), the ice rule implies that at each site there are two incoming and two outgoing arrows. If the ice rule is applied to "square ice", the two-dimensional analogue of ice (fig. 4b), one obtains the six-vertex model with $e_r = 0$, i.e. $\omega_r = 1$, for all r. The partition function of this model, which reduces to the number of arrow configurations obeying the ice rule, was calculated by Lieb [27)] in 1967.

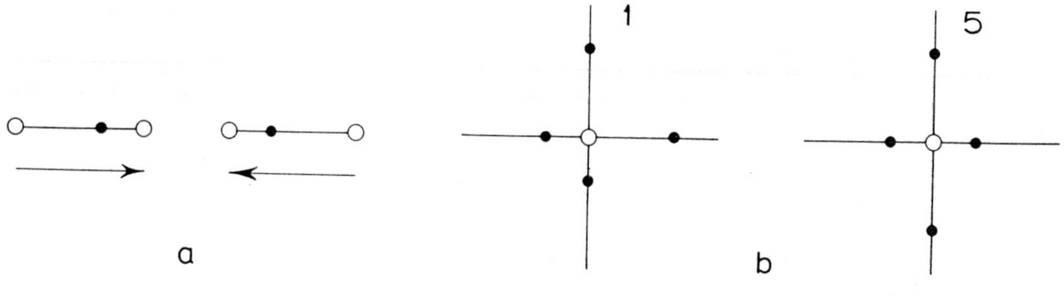

Fig. 4. (a) The two possible positions of a H ion (black circle) between two O ions (open circles) in ice, and their arrow representation; (b) local configurations on L of H ions around an O ion corresponding to the vertices 1 and 5.

B2. $\omega_1 = \omega_2 = 1$, $\omega_3 = \omega_4 = \omega_5 = \omega_6 = \exp(-\beta\varepsilon) < 1$. This is the Slater model or KDP model, the two-dimensional version of the model proposed by Slater [28)] in 1941 to account for the ferroelectric properties of the compound KH_2PO_4 (potassium (K) dihydrogen phosphate, or KDP); for details on this behaviour see ref. 1, p. 332, and the references given there. **The Slater model is similar to Pauling's model for ice:** the phosphate groups are situated at the sites of a lattice with co-ordination number four; they are pairwise separated and chemically bonded by asymmetrically placed hydrogen ions. The asymmetric position of the hydrogen ions gives rise to local electric dipoles; the net electric dipole moment of the vertices 1, 2, 3, 4 is non-zero, that of the vertices 5 and 6 is zero (see fig. 4b). Since the vertices 1 and 2 are favoured by the above choice of weights, the ground state consists solely of vertices 1 or solely of vertices 2, and thereby has a spontaneous electric polarization. The partition function of the Slater model was calculated by Lieb [29].

B3. $\omega_1 = \omega_2 = \omega_3 = \omega_4 = \exp(-\beta\varepsilon') < 1$, $\omega_5 = \omega_6 = 1$. This is the F model, introduced in 1963 by Rys [30], who did not mention the origin of the name. The ground state consists of alternating vertices 5 and 6, and so has no spontaneous polarization; it is called antiferroelectric. Again, it was Lieb [31] who calculated the partition function.

The models B1-B3 are special cases of the symmetric six-vertex model ($\omega_1 = \omega_2$, $\omega_3 = \omega_4$, $\omega_5 = \omega_6$). The general six-vertex model (with six different non-zero weights) was solved by Sutherland, Yang and Yang [32,33].

Because of their application to hydrogen-bonded crystals six-vertex models are often called ferroelectric models. Since in these applications differences between the energies e_1 and e_2 and between e_3 and e_4 can be described in terms of an external electric field with suitably chosen horizontal and vertical components (see ref. 1, p. 344), a model with $\omega_1 = \omega_2$, $\omega_3 = \omega_4$ is called a zero-field ferroelectric model, and the general model: the ferroelectric model in an arbitrary electric field. The eight-vertex model and, a fortiori, the sixteen-vertex model are called general(ized) ferroelectric models; the vertices 7 and 8 represent doubly charged ion groups, the vertices 9 through 16 singly charged ion groups.

C. The symmetric eight-vertex model. This is the eight-vertex model with $\omega_1 = \omega_2$, $\omega_3 = \omega_4$, $\omega_5 = \omega_6$, $\omega_7 = \omega_8$. The equivalent spin model has $J_{1a} = J_{1b} = J_{2a} = J_{2b} = 0$, i.e. all interactions between neighbours in a row and in a column vanish. Yet, the model does include the zero-field Ising model on a square lattice, viz. as the special case $\omega_1\omega_2\omega_3\omega_4 = \omega_5\omega_6\omega_7\omega_8$. In this case the equivalent spin model has no four-spin interactions ($J_4 = 0$), and thus decomposes into two non-interacting spin models, each one identical with an Ising model on a square lattice which is rotated over 45° with respect to the lattice L.

Obviously, the symmetric eight-vertex model also includes the symmetric six-vertex model, and hence the ice, KDP and F models. However, it does not, as is sometimes said, include all previously solved lattice models: the general (non-symmetric) free-fermion and six-vertex models are not included, at least not in an obvious way.

The partition function of this model was calculated by Baxter [34,35] in 1971.

Returning to the general eight-vertex model we make a slight simplification. Since in a lattice with periodic boundary conditions there must be equal numbers of sinks and sources of arrows, the vertices 7 and 8 always occur in equal numbers. We may therefore take $e_7 = e_8$ without lack of generality. Similarly, there are equal numbers of sinks and sources of horizontal arrows, i.e., the total number of vertices 5 and 7 equals the total number of vertices 6 and 8. Hence the vertices 5 and 6 also occur in equal numbers, and we may take $e_5 = e_6$. Henceforth we shall write $\omega_5 = \omega_6 = \omega_c$, $\omega_7 = \omega_8 = \omega_d$. With this simplification, the zero-field eight-vertex model ($\omega_1 = \omega_2$, $\omega_3 = \omega_4$) is identical with the symmetric eight-vertex model. By (1.9), our choice implies $J_{1a}=J_{1b}=\frac{1}{2}J_1$, $J_{2a}=J_{2b}=\frac{1}{2}J_2$.

Two eight-vertex models with weights ω_r and $\overline{\omega}_r = c\omega_r$ ($r = 1,\ldots, 8$), i.e. with energies which are shifted by a constant amount with respect to each other, will sometimes be considered as essentially the same model.

The set of weights $(\omega_1, \ldots, \omega_8)$ will be denoted by ω, the corresponding transfer matrix by $T(\omega)$, and the set of all weight sets ω with $\omega_r \geq 0$ for all r, to be called the weight space, by Ω. For brevity we shall often refer to the eight-vertex model with the set of weights $\omega\in\Omega$ as "the vertex model $\omega\in\Omega$ ".

2. THE TRANSFER MATRIX IN OPERATOR FORM

2.1. Introduction

In the study of the eigenvalue problem for the transfer matrix of a lattice model it is convenient to have an explicit expression for the transfer matrix in terms of simple operators with well-known properties. Since in the models we are discussing the elementary units (spins or edges) can be in two different states, the natural operators to work with are the spin-$\frac{1}{2}$ operators σ_j^α.

2.2. The transfer matrix of the zero-field Ising model

We consider an Ising model with nearest-neighbour interactions on a square lattice of M rows and N columns in the site representation, i.e. with the spins on the lattice sites. For the transfer-matrix method we have first to define layers in the system. As such we choose the rows of spins. The elements of the transfer matrix are denoted by $T(\mu,\mu')$, where $\mu = (\mu_1, \ldots, \mu_N)$ and $\mu' = (\mu_1', \ldots, \mu_N')$ label the spin states of two successive rows of the lattice. Where necessary, we shall refer to μ' as the state of the upper row, and to μ as the state of the lower row; for vertex models we shall follow the same convention (which is widely, but not generally, accepted: see e.g. ref. 1, p.362). Since by convention one always studies the right eigenvectors of T, a factor $T(\mu,\mu')$ in a term of $\mathrm{Tr}\, T^M$ can be considered as the number by which the Boltzmann factor of a model with its lowest row in the state μ' is multiplied when the model is extended downwards by a row in the state μ.

If the external magnetic field is zero it follows from eq. (1.2) that we can write

$$T(\mu,\mu') = T_2(\mu,\mu)T_1(\mu,\mu') \quad , \tag{2.1}$$

$$T_1(\mu,\mu') = e^{K_2\Sigma_j\mu_j\mu_j'} \quad , \tag{2.2}$$

$$T_2(\mu,\mu) = e^{K_1\Sigma_j\mu_j\mu_{j+1}} \quad , \tag{2.3}$$

with $K_1 = \beta J_1$, $K_2 = \beta J_2$. $T_1(\mu,\mu')$ is the Boltzmann factor for the interactions between the "old" and the "new" row, $T_2(\mu,\mu)$ that for the interactions within the new row. If we extend the definition of $T_2(\mu,\mu)$ to

$$T_2(\mu,\mu') = e^{K_1\Sigma_j\mu_j\mu_{j+1}} \prod_j \delta(\mu_j,\mu_j') \quad , \tag{2.4}$$

where $\delta(\mu,\mu') \equiv \delta_{\mu\mu'}$ is the Kronecker symbol, we can write $T = T_2T_1$. The diagonal matrix T_2 is readily expressed in terms of spin operators:

$$T_2 = e^{K_1\Sigma_j\sigma_j^z\sigma_{j+1}^z} \quad . \tag{2.5}$$

To find an expression for T_1 in terms of spin operators we observe that we can write

$$e^{K_2\mu_j\mu_j'} = e^{K_2}\delta(\mu_j,\mu_j') + e^{-K_2}\delta(\mu_j, -\mu_j') \quad . \tag{2.6}$$

We further observe that the matrix elements of I and σ^x are

$$\left.\begin{aligned} \langle \mu_j|I|\mu_j'\rangle &= \langle \mu_j|\mu_j'\rangle = \delta(\mu_j,\mu_j') \quad , \\ \langle \mu_j|\sigma^x|\mu_j'\rangle &= \langle \mu_j|-\mu_j'\rangle = \delta(\mu_j,-\mu_j') \quad , \end{aligned}\right\} \tag{2.7}$$

so that eq. (2.6) can be rewritten:

$$e^{K_2\mu_j\mu_j'} = \langle \mu_j|e^{K_2}I + e^{-K_2}\sigma^x|\mu_j'\rangle \quad . \tag{2.8}$$

From eqs. (2.2) and (2.8) we see that we can write

$$T_1(\mu,\mu') = \prod_j \langle \mu_j|e^{K_2}I + e^{-K_2}\sigma^x|\mu_j'\rangle = \langle \mu|T_1|\mu'\rangle \quad , \tag{2.9}$$

$$T_1 = (e^{K_2}I + e^{-K_2}\sigma^x) \otimes (e^{K_2}I + e^{-K_2}\sigma^x) \otimes \ldots \otimes (e^{K_2}I + e^{-K_2}\sigma^x) =$$

$$= \prod_j (e^{K_2} + e^{-K_2}\sigma_j^x) \quad , \tag{2.10}$$

where the unit operator $I \otimes \ldots \otimes I$ is omitted, as usual. The factors $e^{K_2} + e^{-K_2}\sigma_j^x$ can be written in the form $C\, e^{K_2^*\sigma_j^x}$, because $(\sigma_j^x)^n = 1$ for n even, $(\sigma_j^x)^n = \sigma_j^x$ for n odd, and hence

$$C\, e^{K_2^* \sigma_j^x} = C \sum_{n=0}^{\infty} \frac{(K_2^*)^n}{n!} (\sigma_j^x)^n = (C \cosh K_2^*) + (C \sinh K_2^*)\sigma_j^x \quad . \tag{2.11}$$

Identifying $C \cosh K_2^*$ with e^{K_2} and $C \sinh K_2^*$ with e^{-K_2} we find

$$K_2^* = -\tfrac{1}{2} \log \tanh K_2 ; \quad C = (2 \sinh 2K_2)^{\frac{1}{2}} \tag{2.12}$$

Since furthermore all σ_j^x commute, we obtain from eq. (2.10)

$$T_1 = C^N e^{K_2^* \Sigma_j \sigma_j^x} \quad . \tag{2.13}$$

Combining eqs. (2.5) and (2.13) we finally obtain the following expression for T in terms of spin operators:

$$T = C^N e^{K_1 \Sigma_j \sigma_j^z \sigma_{j+1}^z} e^{K_2^* \Sigma_j \sigma_j^x} \quad . \tag{2.14}$$

If T were of the form $C^N e^{K_1 \Sigma_j \sigma_j^z \sigma_{j+1}^z + K_2^* \Sigma_j \sigma_j^x}$, its eigenvalue problem would reduce to that of the exponent, which is a Hamiltonian of the general type (1.3). However, the two exponents in (2.14) do not commute, and if two operators A and B do not commute, we have in general $e^A e^B \neq e^{A+B}$.

Note that the operator (2.14) commutes with the spin-reversal operator $U^x = \Pi_j \sigma_j^x$: for each value of j we have $\sigma_j^x U^x = U^x \sigma_j^x$, $\sigma_j^z U^x = -U^x \sigma_j^z$, and hence $\sigma_j^z \sigma_{j+1}^z U^x = U^x \sigma_j^z \sigma_{j+1}^z$. Physically, this means that the contribution $T(\mu,\mu')$ to the Boltzmann factor from two successive rows does not change if in both rows all spins are reversed.

2.3. The transfer matrix of the eight-vertex model

We consider an eight-vertex model $\omega \in \Omega$. As the layers of the model we choose the rows of vertical edges; the edges in a row are labelled $j = 1, \ldots, N$. The state of the edge j is described by a "spin variable" $\mu_j = \pm 1$: $\mu_j = 1$ for an up arrow, $\mu_j = -1$ for a down arrow. The states of a layer are denoted by $\mu = (\mu_1, \ldots, \mu_N)$. The rows of horizontal edges will not be considered explicitly, but we shall form the elements $T(\mu,\mu')$ of the transfer matrix by summing at once over all arrangements of horizontal arrows between the layers in the states μ and μ'.

We observe that if in a vertex the two horizontal arrows are opposite, the two vertical arrows are also opposite. Since the periodic boundary condition requires that each row contain an even number of vertices with opposite horizontal arrows (viz. an arbitrary number of sources and an equal number of sinks, cf. section 1.2), the number of vertices with opposite vertical arrows must also be even. It follows that T conserves the parity of the number of down arrows, i.e. T commutes with the parity operator $U^z = \Pi_j \sigma_j^z$.

The horizontal edge connecting the ends of two vertical arrows j-1 and j is labelled j. We describe the state of the horizontal edge j by a variable λ_j which can take the "values" R and L: λ_j = R for a right-pointing arrow, λ_j = L for a left-pointing arrow. We could have denoted these states by $\lambda_j = 1$ and $\lambda_j = -1$, but we shall not do so, because we are not going to introduce explicitly spin operators acting on these states, and a simple label is perhaps less confusing than another spin variable would be. Fig. 5 illustrates the notation used.

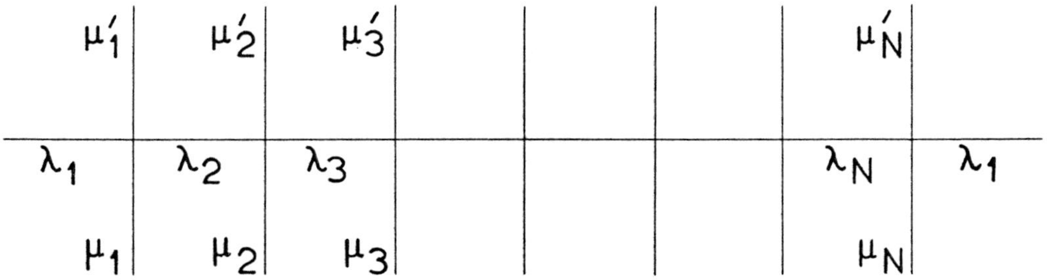

Fig. 5. The state of two successive rows of vertical edges and of the intervening row of horizontal edges.

Consider an arbitrary configuration of horizontal arrows $\lambda_1, \lambda_2, \ldots, \lambda_N$. Let $T^{\lambda_1 \ldots \lambda_N}$ be the transfer matrix when this configuration is fixed, and $T^{\lambda_1 \ldots \lambda_N}(\mu,\mu')$ its matrix elements. In the sixteen-vertex model every site j contributes a factor $\omega_{r(j)}$ to the matrix. In the eight-vertex model some factors are zero, viz. those for sites where the given values of μ_j and μ_j' together with λ_j and λ_{j+1} would form one of the vertices 9, ..., 16. Let $T^{\lambda_j \lambda_{j+1}}(\mu_j,\mu_j')$ be the factor, possibly zero, contributed by the site j. Consider first $T^{RR}(\mu_j,\mu_j')$. We have (see fig. 1)

$$T^{RR}(\mu_j,\mu_j') = \begin{cases} \omega_1 \text{ if } \mu_j = \mu_j' = 1 \quad , \\ \omega_3 \text{ if } \mu_j = \mu_j' = -1 \quad , \\ 0 \text{ if } \mu_j \neq \mu_j' \quad . \end{cases} \tag{2.15}$$

We observe that $\langle \mu_j | \sigma^+ \sigma^- | \mu_j' \rangle = \delta(\mu_j,1)\delta(\mu_j',1)$, $\langle \mu_j | \sigma^- \sigma^+ | \mu_j' \rangle = \delta(\mu_j,-1)\delta(\mu_j',-1)$, and conclude that $T^{RR}(\mu_j,\mu_j')$ is the matrix element $\langle \mu_j | T_j^{RR} | \mu_j' \rangle$ of an operator T^{RR}, acting on the "spin" j alone:

$$T^{RR} = \omega_1 \sigma^+ \sigma^- + \omega_3 \sigma^- \sigma^+ \quad . \tag{2.16}$$

Similarly, the other local weight factors $T^{\lambda_j \lambda_{j+1}}(\mu_j,\mu_j')$ are found to be the matrix elements of operators $T^{\lambda_j \lambda_{j+1}}$. Since $T^{\lambda_1 \ldots \lambda_N}(\mu,\mu') = \Pi_j \langle \mu_j | T^{\lambda_j \lambda_{j+1}} | \mu_j' \rangle$ we may write

$$T^{\lambda_1 \ldots \lambda_N} = T^{\lambda_1 \lambda_2} \otimes T^{\lambda_2 \lambda_3} \otimes \ldots \otimes T^{\lambda_N \lambda_1} = \prod_{j=1}^{N} T_j^{\lambda_j \lambda_{j+1}} \quad , \tag{2.17}$$

$$T_j^{\lambda_j \lambda_{j+1}} = I \otimes I \otimes \ldots \otimes T^{\lambda_j \lambda_{j+1}} \otimes \ldots \otimes I \quad . \tag{2.18}$$

Now T is the sum of $T^{\lambda_1 \ldots \lambda_N}$ over all configurations $\lambda_1, \ldots, \lambda_N$:

$$T = \sum_{\lambda_1} \ldots \sum_{\lambda_N} T^{\lambda_1 \ldots \lambda_N} = \sum_{\lambda_1} \ldots \sum_{\lambda_N} T_1^{\lambda_1 \lambda_2} T_2^{\lambda_2 \lambda_3} \ldots T_N^{\lambda_N \lambda_1} \quad . \tag{2.19}$$

If we arrange the operators $T_j^{\lambda_j \lambda_{j+1}}$ to an operator matrix A_j :

$$A_j = \begin{pmatrix} T_j^{RR} & T_j^{RL} \\ T_j^{LR} & T_j^{LL} \end{pmatrix} \quad , \tag{2.20}$$

we can write

$$T = \mathrm{Tr}_2 \, \Pi_j A_j = \mathrm{Tr}_2 \, A, \tag{2.21}$$

where $A = \Pi_j A_j$ is the ordered matrix product $A_1 A_2 \ldots A_N$, and Tr_2 is the trace over the 2 ×2 "RL matrix", not over the spin operators occurring in the matrix elements. The explicit form of A_j is found to be

$$A_j = \begin{pmatrix} \omega_1 \sigma_j^+ \sigma_j^- + \omega_3 \sigma_j^- \sigma_j^+ & \omega_d \sigma_j^+ + \omega_c \sigma_j^- \\ \omega_c \sigma_j^+ + \omega_d \sigma_j^- & \omega_4 \sigma_j^+ \sigma_j^- + \omega_2 \sigma_j^- \sigma_j^+ \end{pmatrix} \quad . \tag{2.22}$$

We shall say that A_j is a universal 2 × 2 operator matrix with elements acting on the spin j alone.

The difference between (2.14) and (2.21) is striking: whereas the transfer matrix (2.14) for the Ising model in the site representation is a product of <u>two</u> N-fold products of <u>spin operators</u>, the transfer matrix (2.21) of the eight-vertex model (and of the equivalent spin model in the dual representation) is the <u>trace</u> of a <u>single</u> N-fold product of 2 × 2 <u>spin-operator matrices.</u>

3. RELATIONS BETWEEN TRANSFER MATRICES AND SPIN HAMILTONIANS

3.1. Introduction

In the course of years it has become increasingly clear that there exist close, non-trivial relations between transfer matrices of two-dimensional classical lattice models and certain Hamiltonians of one-dimensional spin models.

To begin with, mathematical similarities between the two classes of operators were discovered or stressed. In 1950, Nambu [13] introduced an operator method for solving eigenvalue problems which is similar to, but more transparent than, the one developed by Onsager [12], and pointed out that it can be applied both to a certain spin operator (in our nomenclature: the zero-field isotropic XY Hamiltonian) and to the transfer matrix of the Ising model on a square lattice. In 1964, Schultz, Mattis and Lieb [36] showed that Onsager's method can be cast into a form in which it runs completely parallel to their own method [14] for solving the XY model. Shortly after, Lieb [27,29,31] observed that Bethe's method for treating the Hamiltonian of a one-dimensional Heisenberg model [17], as extended by Yang and Yang [20], can also be used to solve the eigenvalue problem for the transfer matrix of six-vertex models.

In 1968, McCoy and Wu [37] made an important discovery: they showed that, given an arbitrary six-vertex model, there exists a generalized Heisenberg Hamiltonian $\mathcal{H}$ which commutes with the transfer matrix T of the model. The Hamiltonian is a (non-Hermitian) generalization of the XXZ Hamiltonian, with interaction constants $J^{\alpha\beta}$ depending on the weights ω_r of the vertex model, but not on N; the latter fact we express by saying that "$[T,\mathcal{H}] = 0$ for all N". The importance of this discovery lies in the fact that $[T,\mathcal{H}] = 0$ implies the existence of a common set of eigenvectors of T and $\mathcal{H}$. If there were no degeneracy, the problem of finding the eigenvectors of T would thus be reduced to the analogous problem for $\mathcal{H}$, which is probably simpler, because $\mathcal{H}$ is the sum of N terms bilinear in the spin operators, whereas T is the trace of an N-fold product of operator matrices.

McCoy and Wu's result inspired further research into the possible existence of commuting transfer matrices and Hamiltonians. In 1970, Sutherland [38] found that for the symmetric eight-vertex model there is also a Hamiltonian commuting, for all N, with the transfer matrix. It is a (Hermitian) XYZ Hamiltonian with coefficients $J^{\alpha\beta}$ depending on the weights ω_r. In 1971, Suzuki [39] showed that for the Ising model on a square lattice, too, there exists a Hamiltonian commuting, for all N, with the transfer matrix in the site representation (provided the latter is first subjected to two similarity transformations, see section 4.1); it is an XY Hamiltonian. Finally, Krinsky [40], and independently Felderhof and Rae [41], proved that also for the transfer matrix of the free-fermion model in the edge representation there exists an XY Hamiltonian commuting with it for all N.

At about the same time Onsager [42] revealed that not only did he know, as far back as 1942, that there is a Hamiltonian (which he called "linear operator") commuting with the transfer matrix of the Ising model on a square lattice with "diagonal" rows of spins chosen as layers, but this very fact had inspired him to, and formed the starting point of, his solution of the Ising model!

A second significant step was the proof, by Baxter [34], that, given a symmetric eight-vertex model ω, there exist other eight-vertex models, $\bar{\omega}$, say, such that $[T(\omega), T(\bar{\omega})] = 0$. If the weights are properly parametrized (see ref. 34 and section 4.3.2, eq. (4.102)): $\omega_r = \omega_r(v,\eta,k)$, then

$$[T(v,\eta,k), T(\bar{v},\bar{\eta},\bar{k})] = 0 \qquad \text{if } \bar{\eta} = \eta,\ \bar{k} = k \quad . \tag{3.1}$$

This means that there exist one-parameter families of symmetric eight-vertex models with commuting transfer-matrices, each allowed combination of η and k characterizing one family. It is this fact which played a crucial role in Baxter's original solution of this model. It is worth noting that the families consist of all transfer matrices commuting with one and the same Hamiltonian.

Finally, Baxter [22] derived a third important relation. He showed that the logarithmic derivative of $T(v,\eta,k)$ with respect to v at the value $v = \eta$, $(\partial \log T(v,\eta,k)/\partial v)_{v=\eta}$, is just the XYZ Hamiltonian which commutes with the transfer matrix of any member of the family labelled (η,k). Note that if T were of the form $T = \exp(-\beta\mathcal{H})$, differentiation of $\log T$ with respect to $-\beta$ would already give such a result. However, the situation is, in general, not so simple!

In view of these results it is natural to ask the following questions:

a. Given an eight-vertex model $\omega\in\Omega$, is there a generalized Heisenberg Hamiltonian $\mathcal{H}$ such that $[T(\omega),\mathcal{H}] = 0$ for all N, and if so, is it unique?

b. Given an eight-vertex model $\omega\in\Omega$, are there other eight-vertex models $\bar{\omega}\in\Omega$ such that $[T(\omega),T(\bar{\omega})] = 0$ for all N?

c. Given a family of eight-vertex models with pairwise commuting transfer matrices, is there a, possibly unique, generalized Heisenberg Hamiltonian which is obtained from the transfer matrix by logarithmic differentiation in a suitable direction at a suitable point in Ω?

Thus far, only the first question has received some attention in the literature (see ref. 1, p. 367). A systematic analysis of all three problems has recently been undertaken [43]; although a complete answer has not yet been obtained, it is expected that the picture that has emerged will not undergo essential changes. We shall here review the results. Note that we consider only $\mathcal{H}$ of the type (1.3).

3.2. Transfer matrices and associated Hamiltonians

We shall work along two lines: given a vertex model ω, we first derive sufficient conditions for the existence of a Hamiltonian such that $[T(\omega),\mathcal{H}] = 0$ for all N, and then derive necessary conditions; if such a Hamiltonian exists, we call it an associated Hamiltonian of the vertex model.

The quantity we want to study is the commutator

$$[\mathrm{Tr}_2 A,\mathcal{H}] = [A^{RR} + A^{LL},\mathcal{H}] = [A^{RR},\mathcal{H}] + [A^{LL},\mathcal{H}] = \mathrm{Tr}_2[A,\mathcal{H}] \quad . \tag{3.2}$$

Note that $A = \Pi_j A_j$ is an operator matrix, whereas $Tr_2 A$ and $\mathcal{H} = \Sigma_j \mathcal{H}_{j,j+1}$ are single operators; $A\mathcal{H}$ and $\mathcal{H}A$ are the operator matrices with elements $A^{\lambda\lambda'}\mathcal{H}$ and $\mathcal{H}A^{\lambda\lambda'}$, respectively.

To find sufficient conditions for the existence of an associated Hamiltonian we first define

$$C_j = [A, \mathcal{H}_{j,j+1}] \; ; \qquad C = [A, \mathcal{H}] = \sum_j C_j \quad . \tag{3.3}$$

Since $\mathcal{H}_{j,j+1}$ commutes with the elements of $A_{j'}$, for $j' \neq j$, $j+1$, we have

$$\left.\begin{aligned} C_j &= A_1 A_2 \dots A_{j-1} [A_j A_{j+1}, \mathcal{H}_{j,j+1}] A_{j+2} \dots A_N, \qquad (j = 1, \dots, N-1) \\ C_N &= A_1 A_2 \dots A_N \mathcal{H}_{N1} - \mathcal{H}_{N1} A_1 \dots A_N \quad . \end{aligned}\right\} \tag{3.4}$$

Instead of C_N we consider a slightly different operator matrix

$$C'_N = A_2 \dots A_{N-1} [A_N A_1, \mathcal{H}_{N1}] \quad . \tag{3.5}$$

Since the elements of matrices A_j with different indices are operators acting on different spins, and hence commute, we may use the cyclicity of the trace to show that $Tr_2 C'_N = Tr_2 C_N$. We further define $C' = \Sigma_{j=1}^{N-1} C_j + C'_N$.

The question is now: is there a Hamiltonian $\mathcal{H}$ such that $Tr_2 C' = Tr_2 C = 0$? Following Sutherland [38)] we observe that if the commutators $[A_j A_{j+1}, \mathcal{H}_{j,j+1}]$ are of the form

$$[A_j A_{j+1}, \mathcal{H}_{j,j+1}] = B_j A_{j+1} - A_j B_{j+1} \qquad (j = 1, \dots, N) \; , \tag{3.6}$$

where the B_j $(j = 1, \dots, N)$ are operator matrices of the same type as the A_j, i.e. universal 2×2 matrices with operator elements acting on the spin j alone, then summation over j will make all terms in C' cancel pairwise:

$$\begin{aligned} C' = {} & (B_1 A_2) A_3 \dots A_N & & - (A_1 B_2) A_3 \dots A_N & + \\ & + A_1 (B_2 A_3) \dots A_N & & - A_1 (A_2 B_3) \dots A_N & + \\ & + A_1 A_2 (B_3 A_4) \dots A_N & & - \dots & \\ & + \dots & & - \dots & \\ & + \dots & & - A_1 \dots A_{N-2} (A_{N-1} B_N) & + \\ & + A_2 \dots A_{N-1} (B_N A_1) & & - A_2 \dots A_{N-1} (A_N B_1) & , \end{aligned} \tag{3.7}$$

except the first term and the last three terms; these terms cancel, however, if we take the trace. This reduces the problem to ascertaining whether or not there exists a Hamiltonian of the form $\Sigma_j \mathcal{H}_{j,j+1}$, together with a set of auxiliary operator matrices B_j, such that eq. (3.6) is satisfied. Since T conserves parity, we restrict ourselves to parity conserving Hamiltonians; we further look for matrices B_j of the same type (2.22) as A_j, with coefficients β_r where A_j has ω_r ($r = 1, \ldots, 8$). The matrix equation (3.6) represents 4 equations, linear in the unknowns β_r, the unknown interaction constants $J^{\alpha\beta}$ and the operators $\sigma_j^\alpha \sigma_{j+1}^\beta$. These equations must be satisfied identically in the 16 spin operators. In principle, this leads to 64 homogeneous linear equations in the unknowns β_r and $J^{\alpha\beta}$. Many of these equations are identical, or automatically satisfied, and some of the variables do not appear, so that ultimately only 12 equations in 11 unknowns remain.

For a general weight set ω these equations have no solution except the trivial one: $\mathcal{H} = c$, $B_j = c'A_j$, where c and c' are arbitrary constants. Non-trivial solutions exist only if the ω_r satisfy one of the following conditions (A), (B), (C), (D).

A. $\omega_1\omega_2 + \omega_3\omega_4 = \omega_c^2 + \omega_d^2$. (A)

This is just the free-fermion condition (1.10). The associated Hamiltonian is of the form

$$\mathcal{H} = -\sum_j \{J_x\sigma_j^x\sigma_{j+1}^x + J_y\sigma_j^y\sigma_{j+1}^y + J_z\sigma_j^z\sigma_{j+1}^z + J_s(\sigma_j^x\sigma_{j+1}^y - \sigma_j^y\sigma_{j+1}^x) + H\sigma_j^z\} \qquad (3.8)$$

with

$$\begin{aligned} J_x &= \omega_1\omega_4 + \omega_2\omega_3 + 2\omega_c\omega_d , \\ J_y &= \omega_1\omega_4 + \omega_2\omega_3 - 2\omega_c\omega_d , \\ J_z &= 0 , \\ J_s &= \text{arbitrary}, \\ H &= \omega_1^2 + \omega_4^2 - \omega_2^2 - \omega_3^2 . \end{aligned} \qquad (3.9)$$

With $J_s = 0$ this is the associated XY Hamiltonian found by Krinsky [40]. The freedom in the choice of J_s shows that $\mathcal{H}$ is not uniquely determined by eq. (3.6): there is a one-parameter family of associated Hamiltonians; in addition, we could multiply $\mathcal{H}$ by a constant and add a constant term, but this freedom we shall not use. Alternatively, we can say that, in addition to the trivial solution (a constant), there are two linearly independent solutions for $\mathcal{H}$. We shall denote the subspace of the weight space Ω determined by the conditon (A) by Ω^A.

B. $\omega_c\omega_d = 0$. (B)

If we put $\omega_d = 0$ we obtain the six-vertex model. If instead we put $\omega_c = 0$, we obtain a model for which the transfer matrix can, by a similarity transformation with U^x (reversing all vertical arrows), be transformed into that of the six-vertex model, so it has essentially the same properties as the latter. The associated Hamiltonian is in both cases of the form (3.8) with the following coefficients, where the upper and lower signs in the expression for J_s refer to the cases $\omega_d = 0$ and $\omega_c = 0$, respectively:

$$\begin{aligned} J_x &= J_y = \omega_1\omega_3 + \omega_2\omega_4 , \\ J_z &= \omega_1\omega_2 + \omega_3\omega_4 - \omega_c^2 - \omega_d^2 , \\ J_s &= \mp i(\omega_1\omega_3 - \omega_2\omega_4) , \\ H &= \text{arbitrary}. \end{aligned} \tag{3.10}$$

With $H = 0$ and the + sign for J_s this is McCoy and Wu's Hamiltonian [37]. Again, there is a one-parameter family of associated Hamiltonians. Note that the factor i in the expression for the coefficient J_s of the skewsymmetric term makes $\mathcal{H}$ non-Hermitian. We shall denote the subspace of Ω determined by eq. (B) by Ω^B, and the subspace of Ω^B determined by $\omega_d = 0$ ($\omega_c = 0$) by $\Omega^{B'}$ ($\Omega^{B''}$).

C. $\omega_1 = \omega_2 = \omega_a$, $\omega_3 = \omega_4 = \omega_b$. (C)

This double condition defines the symmetric eight-vertex model solved by Baxter [34,35] (who writes a, b, c, d where we have ω_a, ω_b, ω_c, ω_d). The associated Hamiltonian is of the form (3.8) with

$$\begin{aligned} J_x &= 2\omega_a\omega_b + 2\omega_c\omega_d , \\ J_y &= 2\omega_a\omega_b - 2\omega_c\omega_d , \\ J_z &= \omega_a^2 + \omega_b^2 - \omega_c^2 - \omega_d^2 , \\ J_s &= H = 0 . \end{aligned} \tag{3.11}$$

This Hamiltonian is uniquely determined, so it must be, and is, identical with the associated Hamiltonian found by Sutherland [38]. We shall denote the subspace of Ω determined by the condition (C) by Ω^C.

D. There turns out to be a fourth possibility, or rather two equivalent possibilities, for an eight-vertex model to have an associated Hamiltonian:

$$\omega_1 = \omega_4 , \ \omega_2 = \omega_3 , \ \omega_c = \omega_d , \tag{D'}$$

$$\omega_1 = \omega_3 , \ \omega_2 = \omega_4 , \ \omega_c = \omega_d . \tag{D''}$$

The models satisfying either of the triple conditions (D') and (D") are trivial in the sense that they can, by a simple change of variables, be reduced to a set of independent one-dimensional models. Consider a model satisfying (D'). Its spin equivalent has only two non-vanishing interaction constants, J_1 and J_4. The energy E, given by eq. (1.8), then contains the spin variables μ_{jk} only in the combination $\mu_{jk}\mu_{j+1,k}$. Denoting this product by $\tilde{\mu}_{jk}$ we have $E = \Sigma_j E_j$ with $E_j = -\Sigma_k (J_0 + J_1\tilde{\mu}_{jk} + J_4\tilde{\mu}_{jk}\tilde{\mu}_{j,k+1})$. This is just the energy of a set of uncoupled vertical Ising chains with a nearest-neighbour interaction of strength J_4 in a magnetic field J_1. The essentially one-dimensional nature of this model, which makes it trivially solvable, was also discussed, from a different point of view, by Rae [44]. There is a unique associated Hamiltonian, viz. the isotropic Heisenberg Hamiltonian $\mathcal{H} = -\Sigma_j(\sigma_j^x\sigma_{j+1}^x + \sigma_j^y\sigma_{j+1}^y + \sigma_j^z\sigma_{j+1}^z)$.

The model defined by (D") is equivalent to a set of uncoupled horizontal Ising chains; the associated Hamiltonian is the Ising Hamiltonion $\mathcal{H} = -\Sigma_j \sigma_j^z \sigma_{j+1}^z$.

Let Ω^D be the subspace of Ω consisting of all ω satisfying (D') or (D").

If ω satisfies more than one of the conditions (A)-(D) there is a larger freedom in the choice of the associated Hamiltonian. For details we refer to ref. 43.

For a vertex model ω not lying in one of the subspaces Ω^A, Ω^B, Ω^C and Ω^D, Sutherland's method does not provide us with an associated Hamiltonian. It is conceivable, however, that there exists such a Hamiltonian which does not satisfy eq. (3.6). To investigate this possibility we study the cases N = 2,3,4 (cf. ref. 1, p. 370), because it is necessary that T and $\mathcal{H}$ commute for <u>all</u> N. We calculate the $(2^N)^2$ elements of $T\mathcal{H}$ and $\mathcal{H}T$ for a given $T(\omega)$ and an arbitrary $\mathcal{H}$, we put them equal and solve the resulting equations for the coefficients $J^{\alpha\beta}$ of $\mathcal{H}$. The algebra is straightforward but tedious. The result is that the equations have a solution only if ω lies in one or more of the subspaces Ω^A, ..., Ω^D, i.e., the necessary conditions for the existence of an associated Hamiltonian are identical with the sufficient conditions.

If an eight-vertex model has an associated Hamiltonian $\mathcal{H}$, its transfer matrix T has a complete set of eigenvectors in common with $\mathcal{H}$. This is of great help in solving the eigenvalue problem for T. Since we are mainly interested in the eigenvector belonging to the eigenvalue of largest absolute value Λ_0 (the principal eigenvector), it would be of even more value if we could show that this vector is also the vector belonging to an extreme eigenvalue of $\mathcal{H}$. To prove such a statement we can investigate if the well-known theorem of Perron and Frobenius can be applied. This theorem, in a generalisation due to Brauer (ref. 45, theorem 29), says that if a square matrix S with non-negative elements and at least one positive diagonal element is irreducible, i.e. cannot by a simultaneous permutation of rows and columns be brought into the form $\begin{pmatrix} S' & O \\ R & S'' \end{pmatrix}$ with S' and S" square matrices and O a zero matrix, then (a) the eigenvalue of largest absolute value of S is positive real, non-degenerate, and larger than the absolute value of all the other eigenvalues; (b) the elements of the corresponding eigenvector can be chosen as positive numbers. Moreover, there is no other eigenvector with property (b) [46]. If S is not irreducible, the theorem applies to its irreducible diagonal blocks.

Obviously, T and its associated Hamiltonian $\mathcal{H}$ are not irreducible since they have vanishing matrix elements between states of opposite parity. The diagonal blocks of T acting in the subspace of even states and the subspace of odd states, however, have all elements positive, and so are irreducible, provided all weights ω_r are positive; this is the case for general points in Ω^A and Ω^C. It can further be shown that the corresponding blocks of the associated Hamiltonians (with $J_s = 0$ for $\omega \in \Omega^A$), after multiplication by -1 and addition of a sufficiently large positive term, also satisfy the conditions for the Perron-Frobenius-Brauer theorem. Hence, the largest eigenvalue of $-\mathcal{H}$, i.e. the lowest eigenvalue of $\mathcal{H}$, in either subspace is non-degenerate, the corresponding eigenvector (to be called the even or odd ground state) is therefore also an eigenvector of T (in virtue of the relation $[T,\mathcal{H}] = 0$), it has positive elements, and is therefore identical with the unique positive eigenvector of T: the even or odd principal eigenvector. Therefore, once we have found the even and odd ground state of $\mathcal{H}$, we have only to evaluate the corresponding eigenvalues of T and see which one is largest.

For points in Ω^B the situation is more complicated because T and its associated Hamiltonian $\mathcal{H}$ conserve both the spin parity and the total spin, and thus have more, and smaller, irreducible blocks. The argument just given now applies to this set of blocks (even though $\mathcal{H}$ is not Hermitian).

3.3. Commuting transfer matrices

We now come to question (b) of section 3.1. Given a vertex model ω with transfer matrix $T = T(\omega)$, we shall first try to find sufficient conditions for the existence of a vertex model $\bar{\omega}$ with transfer matrix $\bar{T} = T(\bar{\omega})$ such that $[T,\bar{T}] = 0$ for all N. Following an idea of Baxter [34)], we express $T\bar{T}$ and $\bar{T}T$ in terms of the matrices $A_j = A_j(\omega)$ and $\bar{A}_j = A_j(\bar{\omega})$:

$$T\bar{T} = \sum_{\lambda_1} \dots \sum_{\lambda_N} \sum_{\lambda'_1} \dots \sum_{\lambda'_N} T_1^{\lambda_1\lambda_2} \dots T_N^{\lambda_N\lambda_1} \bar{T}_1^{\lambda'_1\lambda'_2} \dots \bar{T}_N^{\lambda'_N\lambda'_1} =$$

$$= \sum_{\lambda_1,\lambda'_1} \dots \sum_{\lambda_N,\lambda'_N} (T_1^{\lambda_1\lambda_2} \bar{T}_1^{\lambda'_1\lambda'_2}) \dots (T_N^{\lambda_N\lambda_1} \dots \bar{T}_N^{\lambda'_N\lambda'_1}) =$$

$$= \mathrm{Tr}_4 (A_1 \otimes \bar{A}_1) \dots (A_N \otimes \bar{A}_N) = \mathrm{Tr}_4 \Pi_j S_j \quad , \qquad (3.12)$$

where Tr_4 is the trace of the ordered product of the 4×4 matrices $S_j = A_j \otimes \bar{A}_j$ ($j=1, \dots, N$). Similarly, we write $\bar{T}T = \mathrm{Tr}_4 \Pi_j \bar{S}_j$, with $\bar{S}_j = \bar{A}_j \otimes A_j$. In order that $T\bar{T} = \bar{T}T$ it is not necessary that $S_j = \bar{S}_j$ for all j; it is sufficient that there exists a 4×4 matrix X (with complex numbers as elements) such that $\bar{S}_j = XS_jX^{-1}$ for all j, or

$$\bar{S}_j X = XS_j \quad \text{for all } j. \qquad (3.13)$$

The requirement (3.13) leads to 16 equations, linear in the unknown elements of the auxiliary matrix X and the 4 spin operators σ_j^+, σ_j^-, $\sigma_j^+\sigma_j^-$ and $\sigma_j^-\sigma_j^+$, but non-linear in the unknowns $\bar{\omega}_r$. To satisfy them identically in the spin operators we have to solve 32 equations in the $\bar{\omega}_r$ and the elements of X, which fortunately can be reduced to a smaller number. From the resulting equations X can be solved provided the ω_r and $\bar{\omega}_r$ satisfy a set of non-linear relations.

To simplify the problem we restrict question (b) as follows: given $\omega\in\Omega$, are there points $\bar{\omega}\in\Omega$ in an infinitesimally small neighbourhood of ω such that $[T(\omega),T(\bar{\omega})] = 0$? Evidently, $T(\omega)$ commutes with itself, so that $\bar{\omega} = \omega$ is always a solution; for the corresponding X we can then choose the 4×4 unit matrix $\underline{I}_4 = I \otimes I$. We now linearize eq. (3.13) around this trivial solution, putting $\bar{\omega}_r = \omega_r + \varepsilon\omega_r'$, $X = I_4 + \varepsilon X'$, inserting this into eq. (3.13), and neglecting terms of higher than first order in ε. The resulting linear equations can then be solved simultaneously for X' and the ω_r'. The result is that for general ω the equations have only one solution: $\omega_r' = c\omega_r$, $X' = c'I_4$ with arbitrary constants c and c'; this is a trivial solution, for the two vertex models ω and $\bar{\omega}$ do not differ essentially. Non-trivial solutions exist only if the ω_r satisfy certain conditions. There are three alternatives, coinciding with the conditions (A), (B) and (C) for the existence of an associated Hamiltonian! Condition (A) ensures the existence of two linearly independent solutions for ω' (and X); in other words: there is a two-dimensional neighbourhood of ω where $T(\omega+\varepsilon\omega')$ commutes with $T(\omega)$. The same is true if condition (B) is satisfied, but under condition (C) there is only one solution for ω', and hence a one-dimensional neighbourhood of ω where $[T(\omega+\varepsilon\omega'),T(\omega)] = 0$.

There is a fourth possibility for a vertex model to have a transfer matrix commuting with that of an infinitesimally different vertex model $\bar{\omega}$. It is found by starting again from the trivial solution $\bar{\omega} = \omega$, but taking $X = X_0 \neq I_4$. This is possible if for $\bar{\omega} = \omega$, i.e. $S_j = \bar{S}_j = A_j \otimes A_j$, we have

$$S_j X_0 = X_0 S_j \qquad \text{for all } j. \tag{3.14}$$

Outside the subspaces Ω^A, Ω^B and Ω^C of Ω this equation has a solution X_0 only if ω satisfies the condition (D') or (D"). If we linearize around this solution we find in both cases one more solution for ω', but from now on we shall disregard these pseudo-onedimensional models.

We now return to the full (non-linearized) equations (3.13). One can show that for every $\omega\in\Omega^B$ there are models $\bar{\omega}\in\Omega^B$, essentially different from ω, such that ω and $\bar{\omega}$ satisfy the conditions for solvability of these equations, i.e. such that $[T,\bar{T}] = 0$. There are two possibilities: (1) $\bar{\omega}$ lies in the same subspace, $\Omega^{B'}$ or $\Omega^{B''}$, of Ω^B as ω (i.e., $\bar{\omega}_d = 0$ if $\omega_d = 0$, or $\bar{\omega}_c = 0$ if $\omega_c = 0$) and satisfies the following relations (one with the upper and one with the lower sign):

$$\frac{\bar{\omega}_1\bar{\omega}_3 \pm \bar{\omega}_2\bar{\omega}_4}{\bar{\omega}_1\bar{\omega}_2 + \bar{\omega}_3\bar{\omega}_4 - \bar{\omega}_c^2 - \bar{\omega}_d^2} = \frac{\omega_1\omega_3 \pm \omega_2\omega_4}{\omega_1\omega_2 + \omega_3\omega_4 - \omega_c^2 - \omega_d^2} ; \tag{3.15}$$

(2) $\bar{\omega}$ lies in the other subspace of Ω^B ($\bar{\omega}_c = 0$ if $\omega_d = 0$, or $\bar{\omega}_d = 0$ if $\omega_c = 0$) and satisfies the relations

$$\frac{\bar{\omega}_1\bar{\omega}_3 \pm \bar{\omega}_2\bar{\omega}_4}{\bar{\omega}_1\bar{\omega}_2 + \bar{\omega}_3\bar{\omega}_4 - \bar{\omega}_c^2 - \bar{\omega}_d^2} = \frac{\omega_2\omega_4 \pm \omega_1\omega_3}{\omega_1\omega_2 + \omega_3\omega_4 - \omega_c^2 - \omega_d^2} \quad . \tag{3.16}$$

The two equations (3.15), or (3.16), relate the four ratios of the weights $\bar{\omega}_r$ ($\bar{\omega}_1 : \bar{\omega}_2 : \bar{\omega}_3 : \bar{\omega}_4 : \bar{\omega}_c$ or $\bar{\omega}_d$) to those of the weights ω_r; thus they determine a two-parameter family of eight-vertex models with commuting transfer matrices, or two-parameter CT family, for short.

Similarly, one can show that every $\omega \in \Omega^C$ belongs to a one-parameter CT family, which is determined by two relations for the three ratios $\bar{\omega}_a : \bar{\omega}_b : \bar{\omega}_c : \bar{\omega}_d$,

$$\frac{\bar{\omega}_a\bar{\omega}_b \pm \bar{\omega}_c\bar{\omega}_d}{\bar{\omega}_a^2 + \bar{\omega}_b^2 - \bar{\omega}_c^2 - \bar{\omega}_d^2} = \frac{\omega_a\omega_b \pm \omega_c\omega_d}{\omega_a^2 + \omega_b^2 - \omega_c^2 - \omega_d^2} \quad . \tag{3.17}$$

For $\omega \in \Omega^A$ the analogous proof has not yet been completed. From the explicit solution of the free-fermion model by Felderhof [25] it follows, however, that two models $\omega, \bar{\omega} \in \Omega^A$ have commuting transfer matrices if

$$\frac{\bar{\omega}_1\bar{\omega}_4 + \bar{\omega}_2\bar{\omega}_3 \pm 2\bar{\omega}_c\bar{\omega}_d}{\bar{\omega}_1^2 + \bar{\omega}_4^2 - \bar{\omega}_2^2 - \bar{\omega}_3^2} = \frac{\omega_1\omega_4 + \omega_2\omega_3 \pm 2\omega_c\omega_d}{\omega_1^2 + \omega_4^2 - \omega_2^2 - \omega_3^2} \quad ; \tag{3.18}$$

here, the models form two-parameter CT families.

In all three cases, the conditions for $[T, \bar{T}] = 0$ can, in view of eqs. (3.9), (3.10) and (3.11), be summarized to the single requirement that, up to a factor, ω and $\bar{\omega}$ have the same associated Hamiltonian, or family of associated Hamiltonians.

A derivation of necessary conditions for the existence of eight-vertex models with commuting transfer matrices is under way (see ref. 43).

3.4. The associated Hamiltonians of a CT family

The point $\omega = \omega^L \equiv (1,1,0,0,1,1,0,0)$ represents a special point in Ω: $T_L = T(\omega^L)$ is the left-shift operator, shifting every arrow one place to the left [22]. It lies in each of the subspaces Ω^A, $\Omega^{B'}$ and Ω^C (but not in $\Omega^{B''}$), and belongs to every CT family in these subspaces; it even commutes with $T(\omega)$ for every $\omega \in \Omega$. The latter property, which is easily proven, expresses the translation invariance of the eight-vertex model.

For a point $\bar{\omega} = \omega^L + \varepsilon\omega'$ in the immediate neighbourhood of ω^L we can expand $T(\bar{\omega})$ in powers of ε. Neglecting terms of higher than first order in ε we find

$$T(\bar{\omega}) \approx T(\omega^L) + \varepsilon T' = T_L(1 + \varepsilon\mathcal{H}) \quad , \tag{3.19}$$

$$\mathcal{H} = T_L^{-1}T' = \tfrac{1}{4}\sum_j \{(\omega_3'+\omega_4'+2\omega_d')\sigma_j^x\sigma_{j+1}^x + (\omega_3'+\omega_4'-2\omega_d')\sigma_j^y\sigma_{j+1}^y + (\omega_1'+\omega_2'-2\omega_c')\sigma_j^z\sigma_{j+1}^z - i(\omega_3'-\omega_4')(\sigma_j^x\sigma_{j+1}^y - \sigma_j^y\sigma_{j+1}^x) + 2(\omega_1'-\omega_2')\sigma_j^z + (\omega_1'+\omega_2'+2\omega_c')\} \quad . \tag{3.20}$$

We observe that $\mathcal{H}$ is a generalized Heisenberg Hamiltonian! By substituting $\bar{\omega} = \omega^L + \varepsilon\omega'$ into eqs.(3.15)-(3.18) and (A) - (C), and neglecting terms of higher than first order in ε we find under what conditions on ω' the matrix $T(\omega^L + \varepsilon\omega')$, and hence the Hamiltonian $\mathcal{H}$ given by eq. (3.20), commutes with $T(\omega)$ when ω is a given point in Ω^A, $\Omega^{B'}$, $\Omega^{B''}$ and Ω^C, respectively:

$$\omega_1' + \omega_2' = 2\omega_c' \quad , \quad \frac{\omega_3' + \omega_4' \pm 2\omega_d'}{2(\omega_1' - \omega_2')} = \frac{\omega_1\omega_4 + \omega_2\omega_3 \pm 2\omega_c\omega_d}{\omega_1^2 + \omega_4^2 - \omega_2^2 - \omega_3^2} \quad ; \tag{3.21}$$

$$\omega_d' = 0 \quad , \quad \frac{\omega_3' \pm \omega_4'}{\omega_1' + \omega_2' - 2\omega_c'} = \frac{\omega_1\omega_3 \pm \omega_2\omega_4}{\omega_1\omega_2 + \omega_3\omega_4 - \omega_c^2 - \omega_d^2} \quad ; \tag{3.22}$$

$$\omega_d' = 0 \quad , \quad \frac{\omega_3' \pm \omega_4'}{\omega_1' + \omega_2' - 2\omega_c'} = \frac{\omega_2\omega_4 \pm \omega_1\omega_3}{\omega_1\omega_2 + \omega_3\omega_4 - \omega_c^2 - \omega_d^2} \quad ; \tag{3.23}$$

$$\left.\begin{array}{l} \omega_1' = \omega_2' = \omega_a' \\ \omega_3' = \omega_4' = \omega_b' \end{array}\right\} \quad , \quad \frac{\omega_b' \pm \omega_d'}{2(\omega_a' - \omega_c')} = \frac{\omega_a\omega_b \pm \omega_c\omega_d}{\omega_a^2 + \omega_b^2 - \omega_c^2 - \omega_d^2} \quad . \tag{3.24}$$

The Hamiltonian (3.20) which is determined (up to a factor) by these relations turns out to be the associated Hamiltonian (3.8) with coefficients given by eq. (3.9), eq. (3.10) with the - sign for J_s, eq. (3.10) with the + sign for J_s, and eq. (3.11), respectively, as was to be expected. This answers question (c).

Similar results are obtained if $T(\omega)$ is expanded around the point $\omega = \omega_L \equiv (0,0,1,1,0,0,1,1)$, for which the transfer matrix is also the left-shift operator $(T(\omega_L) = T(\omega^L))$, but which lies in $\Omega^{D''}$ and not in $\Omega^{D'}$.

4. SOLUTION METHODS FOR SPIN AND VERTEX MODELS

4.1. The XY model and the Ising model

4.1.1. The XY model

In solving the eigenvalue problem of an operator O it is often useful to look for an operator O', commuting with O, for which the solution of the eigenvalue problem is known. The eigenvalues of O' can then be used to label the eigenvectors of O, and the eigenvalue problem for O is correspondingly reduced. In case O is a Hamiltonian or a transfer matrix we shall call O' a conserved quantity. For the XY Hamiltonian $\mathcal{H} = \mathcal{H}^{XY}$, given by eq. (1.4), the spin parity operator U^z is a conserved quantity; its eigenvalues are 1 and -1. We introduce the projection operators $P_\pm = \frac{1}{2}(1 \pm U^z)$ on the spaces of even and odd states, and write $\mathcal{H} = \mathcal{H}P_+ + \mathcal{H}P_-$.

In terms of the operators σ_j^+ and σ_j^-, $\mathcal{H}$ can be written as

$$\mathcal{H} = -2J \sum_{j=1}^{N} \{(\sigma_j^- \sigma_{j+1}^+ + \sigma_j^+ \sigma_{j+1}^-) + \Gamma(\sigma_j^- \sigma_{j+1}^- + \sigma_j^+ \sigma_{j+1}^+) + h(1 - 2\sigma_j^- \sigma_j^+)\} \quad (4.1)$$

with $J = \frac{1}{2}(J_x + J_y)$, $\Gamma = (J_x - J_y)/(J_x + J_y)$, $h = H/(J_x + J_y)$, $\sigma^{\pm}_{N+1} = \sigma^{\pm}_1$. Since $\mathcal{H}$ is quadratic in the $\sigma_j^{\pm}$, it could be brought into a formally diagonal form by introducing suitable linear combinations of the spin operators. However, since these operators obey a mixed set of commutation-anticommutation relations:

$$\left.\begin{aligned} &\{\sigma_j^+, \sigma_j^-\} \equiv \sigma_j^+ \sigma_j^- + \sigma_j^- \sigma_j^+ = 1, \qquad \{\sigma_j^+, \sigma_j^+\} = \{\sigma_j^-, \sigma_j^-\} = 0; \\ &[\sigma_j^+, \sigma_{j'}^+] = [\sigma_j^+, \sigma_{j'}^-] = [\sigma_j^-, \sigma_{j'}^-] = 0 \quad \text{for } j \neq j' , \end{aligned}\right\} \quad (4.2)$$

such a linear transformation would lead to forbiddingly complicated commutation relations for the new operators, and hence be of no use. Therefore one first applies a non-linear transformation, the so-called Jordan-Wigner transformation, to bring the commutation relations into line:

$$\left.\begin{aligned} a_j &= \left(\prod_{k=1}^{j-1} \sigma_k^z\right) \sigma_j^+ , \quad a_j^\dagger = \left(\prod_{k=1}^{j-1} \sigma_k^z\right) \sigma_j^- , \quad \text{with } \sigma_k^z = 1 - 2\sigma_k^- \sigma_k^+ = (-1)^{\sigma_k^- \sigma_k^+} , \\ \sigma_j^+ &= \left(\prod_{k=1}^{j-1} \sigma_k^z\right) a_j , \quad \sigma_j^- = \left(\prod_{k=1}^{j-1} \sigma_k^z\right) a_j^\dagger , \quad \text{with } \sigma_k^z = 1 - 2a_k^\dagger a_k = (-1)^{a_k^\dagger a_k} . \end{aligned}\right\} \quad (4.3)$$

The a_j and $a_j^\dagger$ obey fermion anticommutation relations

$$\{a_j, a_{j'}^\dagger\} = \delta_{jj'}, \{a_j, a_{j'}\} = \{a_j^\dagger, a_{j'}^\dagger\} = 0 \quad . \quad (4.4)$$

The "vacuum" for these operators is the state with all spins up ($\mu_j = 1$ for all j), which will be denoted by $|0\rangle$. Fortunately, the transformation (4.3) has a surprisingly slight effect on the form of $\mathcal{H}$, consisting in the appearance of two minus signs; in particular, $\mathcal{H}$ remains quadratic. The only complication lies in the periodic boundary condition to be applied. It is due to the fact that the terms with j = N in eq. (4.1) go over into terms containing a factor $\Pi_{k=1}^{N} \sigma_k^z = U^z$, so that it is necessary to consider even and odd eigenvectors of $\mathcal{H}$ separately. A convenient way of doing so is to write $\mathcal{H}$ in terms of two auxiliary Hamiltonians $\mathcal{H}^+$ and $\mathcal{H}^-$ not containing U^z:

$$\mathcal{H} = \mathcal{H}P_+ + \mathcal{H}P_- = \mathcal{H}^+ P_+ + \mathcal{H}^- P_- \quad , \quad (4.5)$$

$$\mathcal{H}^{\pm} = -2J \sum_{j=1}^{N} \{(a_j^\dagger a_{j+1} - a_j a_{j+1}^\dagger) + \Gamma(a_j^\dagger a_{j+1}^\dagger - a_j a_{j+1}) + h(1 - 2a_j^\dagger a_j)\}, \quad (4.6)$$

with $a_{N+1} = -a_1$ in $\mathcal{H}^+$, $a_{N+1} = a_1$ in $\mathcal{H}^-$ [15]. If Ψ is an even eigenvector of $\mathcal{H}^+$ ($\mathcal{H}^+\Psi = E\Psi$, $P_+\Psi = \Psi$), it is also an eigenvector of $\mathcal{H}$:

$$\mathcal{H}\Psi = \mathcal{H}P_+\Psi = \mathcal{H}^+P_+\Psi = \mathcal{H}^+\Psi = E\Psi \quad . \quad (4.7)$$

Similarly, an odd eigenvector of $\mathcal{H}^-$ is also an eigenvector of $\mathcal{H}$. Together, the even eigenvectors of $\mathcal{H}^+$ and the odd eigenvectors of $\mathcal{H}^-$ form all eigenvectors of $\mathcal{H}$. The other eigenvectors of $\mathcal{H}^+$ and $\mathcal{H}^-$ can be disregarded.

Now we can try to diagonalize $\mathcal{H}^+$ and $\mathcal{H}^-$. We first apply a Fourier transformation to running-wave operators, well known from solid-state theory. For simplicity we discuss only the case of even N:

$$A_q = N^{-\frac{1}{2}} e^{i\phi} \sum_{j=1}^{N} e^{-iqj} a_j ; \quad A_q^{\dagger} = N^{-\frac{1}{2}} e^{-i\phi} \sum_{j=1}^{N} e^{iqj} a_j^{\dagger} , \tag{4.8}$$

with $q = \pm(2\ell-1)\pi/N$ ($\ell = 1,\ldots,\frac{1}{2}N$) for $\mathcal{H}^+$, and $q = 0,\ \pi,\ \pm 2\ell\pi/N$ ($\ell = 1,\ \ldots,\frac{1}{2}N-1$) for $\mathcal{H}^-$; it is convenient to choose $\phi = -\frac{1}{4}\pi$. Under (4.8) eq. (4.6) goes over into

$$\mathcal{H}^{\pm} = \Sigma^{\pm}_{q\geq 0} \mathcal{H}_q , \tag{4.9}$$

$$\left.\begin{aligned} \mathcal{H}_q &= 4J[(h-\cos q)(A_q^{\dagger}A_q + A_{-q}^{\dagger}A_{-q} - 1) + \Gamma \sin q(A_{-q}^{\dagger}A_q^{\dagger} + A_q A_{-q})] \quad (q\neq 0,\pi), \\ \mathcal{H}_0 &= 4J(h-1)(A_0^{\dagger}A_0 - \tfrac{1}{2}), \qquad \mathcal{H}_{\pi} = 4J(h+1)(A_{\pi}^{\dagger}A_{\pi} - \tfrac{1}{2}) . \end{aligned}\right\} \tag{4.10}$$

The sums $\Sigma^{\pm}_{q\geq 0}$ run over the two sets of possible non-negative values of q; use has been made of the relation $\Sigma^{\pm}_{q\geq 0} \cos q = 0$. The A_q and $A_q^{\dagger}$ obey fermion anti-commutation relations; since the $\mathcal{H}_q$ are bilinear in these operators we have $[\mathcal{H}_q, \mathcal{H}_{q'}] = 0$ for all q and q', so that all $\mathcal{H}_q$ can be diagonalized simultaneously. Thus the eigenvalue problem reduces to $\frac{1}{2}N$ (for $\mathcal{H}^+$) or $\frac{1}{2}N+1$ (for $\mathcal{H}^-$) simpler eigenvalue problems.

$\mathcal{H}_0$ and $\mathcal{H}_{\pi}$ are diagonal in the occupation-number representation; their eigenvalues are $\pm 2J(h-1)$ and $\pm 2J(h+1)$, respectively. For $q \neq 0, \pi$, $\mathcal{H}_q$ acts essentially in a space of four dimensions, spanned by the vectors $|0\rangle$, $A_q^{\dagger}|0\rangle$, $A_{-q}^{\dagger}|0\rangle$ and $A_{-q}^{\dagger}A_q^{\dagger}|0\rangle$. For $\Gamma = 0$ (isotropic XY model) it is diagonal, for general Γ it can be made so by one more transformation, the Bogolubov-Valatin transformation, or quasi-particle transformation, well known from the theory of superconductivity:

$$B_q = (\cos\phi_q)A_q + (\sin\phi_q)A_{-q}^{\dagger} , \qquad B_{-q}^{\dagger} = -(\sin\phi_q)A_q + (\cos\phi_q)A_{-q}^{\dagger} , \tag{4.11}$$

with the angle ϕ_q determined by

$$\tan 2\phi_q = \frac{\Gamma \sin q}{\cos q - h} = \frac{(J_x - J_y)\sin q}{(J_x + J_y)\cos q - H} , \tag{4.12}$$

$$\left.\begin{aligned} -\tfrac{1}{2}\pi < \phi_q < 0 \quad & \text{if } (J_x - J_y)\sin q > 0 , \\ 0 < \phi_q < \tfrac{1}{2}\pi \quad & \text{if } (J_x - J_y)\sin q < 0 , \\ \phi_q = 0 \quad & \text{if } J_x = J_y = J \text{ and } H \geq 2J\cos q , \\ \phi_q = \tfrac{1}{2}\pi \quad & \text{if } J_x = J_y = J \text{ and } H < 2J\cos q . \end{aligned}\right\} \tag{4.13}$$

Under this transformation, eq. (4.10) for $\mathcal{H}_q$ $(q \neq 0,\pi)$ goes over into

$$\mathcal{H}_q = \varepsilon_q (B_q^\dagger B_q + B_{-q}^\dagger B_{-q} - 1) \qquad (q \neq 0,\pi) \quad , \tag{4.14}$$

$$\varepsilon_q = 4|J|\{(h - \cos q)^2 + \Gamma^2 \sin^2 q\}^{\frac{1}{2}} \quad (q \neq 0,\pi) \quad . \tag{4.15}$$

Eq. (4.12) determines ϕ_q up to $\frac{1}{2}\pi$; the choice of ϕ_q described in eqs. (4.13) is made so as to make $\varepsilon_q \geq 0$ for all $q \neq 0,\pi$.

The ground state $\Psi_0^{\pm}$ of $\mathcal{H}^{\pm}$ is easily derived:

$$\Psi_0^{\pm} = (\prod_{q \geq 0}^{\pm} Y_q)\ |0\rangle \quad , \tag{4.16}$$

where the operators Y_q are given by

$$Y_q = \cos\phi_q + \sin\phi_q\, A_{-q}^\dagger A_q^\dagger \qquad (q \neq 0,\pi) \quad ,$$

$$Y_0 = \begin{cases} 1 & \text{for } h > 1 \ , \\ A_0^\dagger & \text{for } h < 1 \ , \end{cases} \qquad Y_\pi = \begin{cases} 1 & \text{for } h > -1 \ , \\ A_\pi^\dagger & \text{for } h < -1 \ . \end{cases} \tag{4.17}$$

The corresponding eigenvalues $E_0^{\pm}$ of $\mathcal{H}^{\pm}$ are

$$E_0^{\pm} = - \Sigma_{q \geq 0}^{\pm}\ \varepsilon_q \ , \tag{4.18}$$

where $\varepsilon_0 = 2|J(h-1)|$, $\varepsilon_\pi = 2|J(h+1)|$. Since the state $|0\rangle$ has parity 1 and the operators Y_q for $q \neq 0,\pi$ do not change the parity of a state, Ψ_0^+ is an even eigenvector of $\mathcal{H}^+$, and hence also an eigenvector of $\mathcal{H}$. The vector Ψ_0^- is for $|h| < 1$ an odd eigenvector of $\mathcal{H}^-$, and hence also an eigenvector of $\mathcal{H}$; for $|h| > 1$ it is an even state, and we have to go to the lowest excited state of $\mathcal{H}^-$ (which is also of the form (4.16), but with $Y_0 = A_0^\dagger$, $Y_\pi = 1$) to obtain the state of lowest energy and parity -1. In the thermodynamic limit $(N \to \infty)$ Ψ_0^+ is the ground state of $\mathcal{H}$ for all values of h; for $|h| > 1$ it is non-degenerate, for $|h| < 1$ it is degenerate with Ψ_0^-. The ground-state energy per spin in this limit is

$$e_0 = \lim_{N\to\infty} \left(-\frac{1}{N} \sum_{q>0}^{+} \varepsilon_q\right) =$$

$$= -\frac{1}{\pi} \int_0^\pi dq\{J_x^2 + J_y^2 + 2J_xJ_y \cos 2q - 2(J_x + J_y)H \cos q + H^2\}^{\frac{1}{2}} . \tag{4.19}$$

The free energy $f(\beta)$ has also been determined [15], but we shall not discuss it.

4.1.2. The Ising model

In the light of section 3 it would be logical to discuss now the eigenvalue problem for the transfer matrix of the general free-fermion model, but we shall not do so. To be sure, Felderhof's method for diagonalizing this matrix[25] is quite interesting and worth discussing, but it is also lengthy and complicated, while the results can be more easily derived by other methods [24]. Therefore we shall restrict ourselves to one special case, the Ising model on a square lattice, which we shall treat in the original site representation, and not in the edge representation (for details see ref. 36).

An operator commuting with the transfer matrix T in this representation, given by eq. (2.14), is the spin-reversal operator U^x, not the spin-parity operator U^z, which, as we have seen, is a conserved quantity for $\mathcal{H}^{XY}$ and for the transfer matrix of the Ising model in the edge representation (as a special case of the free-fermion model). Another difference between T and $\mathcal{H}^{XY}$ is the fact that the exponents of the two factors of T, when expressed in terms of the $\sigma_j^{\pm}$, are quartic and linear rather than quadratic. Both differences disappear if we first rotate all spins over $\frac{1}{2}\pi$ around the y-axis; this is achieved by a unitary transformation with the operator $U = \exp(\frac{1}{4}\pi i\Sigma_j\sigma_j^y)$. We obtain

$$\left.\begin{aligned} &U\sigma_j^x U^{-1} = \sigma_j^z\,, \quad U\sigma_j^z U^{-1} = -\sigma_j^x\,, \quad T' \equiv UTU^{-1} = T_2'T_1'\,, \\ &T_1' \equiv UT_1U^{-1} = C^N e^{K_2^*\Sigma_j\sigma_j^z}\,, \quad T_2' \equiv UT_2U^{-1} = e^{K_1\Sigma_j\sigma_j^x\sigma_{j+1}^x}\,. \end{aligned}\right\} \tag{4.20}$$

Following Suzuki [39] we further introduce $\tilde{T} = (T_1')^{\frac{1}{2}}T_2'(T_1')^{\frac{1}{2}} = (T_1')^{\frac{1}{2}}T'(T_1')^{-\frac{1}{2}}$, because it is $\tilde{T}$, and not T', that has an associated Hamiltonian of the form (3.8). This Hamiltonian is an XY Hamiltonian with $J_x : J_y : H = \exp(2K_2):\exp(-2K_2) : 2\coth 2K_1$, i.e.

$$\Gamma = \tanh 2K_2 = (\cosh 2K_2^*)^{-1}, \; h = \coth 2K_1 \tanh 2K_2^* \,. \tag{4.21}$$

These values of Γ and h differ from those following from eq. (3.9) in the case of the Ising model by the interchanges $K_1 \leftrightarrow K_2^*$, $K_2 \leftrightarrow K_1^*$, which constitute the well-known duality transformation for the Ising model (ref. 1, p. 278). This might have been anticipated because the edge representation is the dual of the site representation.

Obviously, $\tilde{T}$, T' and T are similar matrices, and thus have the same spectrum, and $\tilde{T}$ commutes with $U^z = UU^xU^{-1}$. We therefore write $\tilde{T} = \tilde{T}P_+ + \tilde{T}P_-$. The Perron-Frobenius-Brauer theorem tells us that the even (odd) principal eigenvector of $\tilde{T}$ is identical with the even (odd) ground state of $\mathcal{H}^{XY}$. To find the corresponding eigenvalues $\Lambda_0^{\pm}$ we must let T operate on these eigenvectors. To this end we submit T to the same transformations as $\mathcal{H}^{XY}$. Expressing σ_j^x and σ_j^z in σ_j^+ and σ_j^-, and these by the Jordan-Wigner transformation (4.3) and the Fourier transformation (4.8) in the running-wave operators A_q, $A_q^\dagger$, we find

$$\tilde{T}P_{\pm} = \tilde{T}^{\pm}P_{\pm}\,, \quad \tilde{T}^{\pm} = C^N \Pi^{\pm}_{q\geq 0}\, \tilde{T}_q\,, \tag{4.22}$$

$$\tilde{T}_q = (T_{1q}')^{\frac{1}{2}}\, T_{2q}'(T_{1q}')^{\frac{1}{2}} \qquad (q \neq 0,\pi)\,, \tag{4.23a}$$

$$T'_{1q} = e^{-2K_2^*(A_q^\dagger A_q + A_{-q}^\dagger A_{-q} - 1)} \quad , \tag{4.23b}$$

$$T'_{2q} = e^{2K_1\{\cos q(A_q^\dagger A_q + A_{-q}^\dagger A_{-q} - 1) + \sin q(A_{-q}^\dagger A_q^\dagger + A_q A_{-q})\}} \quad , \tag{4.23c}$$

$$\tilde{T}_0 = e^{2(K_1-K_2^*)(A_0^\dagger A_0 - \frac{1}{2})} \quad , \quad \tilde{T}_\pi = e^{-2(K_1+K_2^*)(A_\pi^\dagger A_\pi - \frac{1}{2})} \quad . \tag{4.23d}$$

Obviously, $[\tilde{T}_q, \tilde{T}_{q'}] = 0$ for all q,q'. $\tilde{T}_0$ and $\tilde{T}_\pi$ are diagonal in the occupation-number representation; their eigenvalues are $\exp \pm (K_1-K_2^*)$ and $\exp \pm (K_1+K_2^*)$, respectively. For $q \neq 0,\pi$, $\tilde{T}_q$ acts in the same space as $\mathcal{H}_q$ for the XY model. Like $\mathcal{H}_q$, it can be diagonalized by a Bogolubov-Valatin transformation (4.11); here, ϕ_q is given by eqs. (4.12) and (4.13) together with the "translation rule" (4.21). The result is

$$\tilde{T}_q = e^{-\tau_q(B_q^\dagger B_q + B_{-q}^\dagger B_{-q} - 1)} \qquad (q \neq 0,\pi) \quad , \tag{4.24}$$

$$\tau_q = \log\{\zeta_q + (\zeta_q^2 - 1)^{\frac{1}{2}}\}, \quad \zeta_q = \cosh 2K_1 \cosh 2K_2^* - \sinh 2K_1 \sinh 2K_2^* \cos q. \tag{4.25}$$

Since ζ_q is larger than 1, we can take the positive real square root and logarithm in (4.25). It is evident from the derivation that not only the principal eigenvectors but all eigenvectors of $\tilde{T}$ and $\mathcal{H}^{XY}$ (with parameters obeying eq. (4.21)) are identical.

The largest eigenvalue of $\tilde{T}$ in the space of even states is

$$\Lambda_0^+ = C^N \prod_{q>0}^+ \exp \tau_q \quad . \tag{4.26}$$

In the limit $N \to \infty$ it is also the largest eigenvalue of $\tilde{T}$ (called Λ_0 up to now); it is degenerate with Λ_0^- if $\coth 2K_1 < \coth 2K_2^*$, i.e. for $K_1 > K_2^*$, or $T < T_c$, where T_c is determined by $K_1 = K_2^*$, and non-degenerate for $T > T_c$. The free energy per spin in the limit $M \to \infty$, $N \to \infty$ is, by eq. (5),

$$f(\beta) = \lim_{N\to\infty} \{-(\beta N)^{-1} \log \Lambda_0^+\} = \lim_{N\to\infty} \{-(\beta N)^{-1}(N \log C + \sum_{q>0}^+ \tau_q)\} =$$

$$= -\tfrac{1}{2}\beta^{-1}\left[\log(2\sinh 2K_2) + \frac{1}{\pi}\int_0^\pi dq \log\{\zeta_q + (\zeta_q^2-1)^{\frac{1}{2}}\}\right] \quad , \tag{4.27}$$

which is Onsager's famous result [12)].

4.2. The XXZ model and the six-vertex model

4.2.1. The XXZ model

We write the XXZ Hamiltonian as

$$\mathcal{H} = -J\Sigma_j(\sigma_j^x\sigma_{j+1}^x + \sigma_j^y\sigma_{j+1}^y + \Delta\sigma_j^z\sigma_{j+1}^z) \quad , \tag{4.28}$$

with $\Delta = J_z/J$. When expressed in terms of the $\sigma_j^\pm$, $\mathcal{H}$ contains a quartic term, and this is not remedied by a rotation of the spins. The method used for diagonalizing $\mathcal{H}^{XY}$ can therefore not be applied. Instead we follow an entirely different method due to Bethe [17], which aims at a direct determination of the eigenvectors. The idea is to guess the form of the eigenvectors, and to show that there exist eigenvectors of this form and that the principal eigenvector is among them.

It is easily checked that for the Hamiltonian (4.28) the total spin $\Sigma_j \sigma_j^z$ is a conserved quantity. As its eigenvectors we can choose the basis states $|\mu_1, \ldots, \mu_N\rangle$; its eigenvalues are N-2n, where n is the number of down spins ($\mu_j = -1$). We can split the eigenvalue problem according to the values of n. It is convenient to introduce a change of notation, denoting the basis state with n down spins situated at the sites $j_1, j_2, \ldots, j_n$ (with $j_1 < j_2 < \ldots < j_n$) by $|j_1, \ldots, j_n\rangle$; $|0\rangle$ will denote the state with all spins up, as before. The eigenvectors of $\mathcal{H}$ labelled by the quantum number n are linear combinations of basis vectors with n down spins:

$$\Psi = \sum_{j_1 < \ldots < j_n} \psi(j_1, \ldots, j_n) |j_1, \ldots, j_n\rangle . \qquad (4.29)$$

Inserting (4.29) into the eigenvalue equation $\mathcal{H}\Psi = E\Psi$ we find the following relation between the coefficients $\psi(j_1, \ldots, j_n)$:

$$\sum_{j_1' < \ldots < j_n'} \{-\psi(j_1', \ldots, j_n') + \Delta\, \psi(j_1, \ldots, j_n)\} = E^* \psi(j_1, \ldots, j_n) \quad , \qquad (4.30)$$

where $E^* = (E + NJ\Delta)/2J$, and the sum runs over all arrangements $j_1', \ldots, j_n'$ of n down spins differing from the arrangement $j_1, \ldots, j_n$ by the interchange of two neighbouring antiparallel spins. Starting from n = 0 and proceeding to higher values of n we shall see the form to be guessed for $\psi(j_1, \ldots, j_n)$ emerge.

n = 0. There is only one basis vector with n = 0, viz. $|0\rangle$, so it must be an eigenvector of $\mathcal{H}$. The sum in eq. (4.30) is empty, so we have $E^* = 0$.

n = 1. The basis vectors with n = 1 are the vectors $|j\rangle$. Eq. (4.30) takes the form

$$-\psi(j - 1) - \psi(j + 1) + 2\Delta\psi(j) = E^* \psi(j) \quad , \qquad (4.31)$$

the solution of which is $\psi(j) = e^{ikj}$ (spin wave). Substitution into (4.31) gives the reduced energy eigenvalue $E^* = 2\Delta - 2 \cos k$. Finally, the periodic boundary condition $\psi(N+1) = \psi(1)$ restricts the possible values of the wave number to $k = 2\pi\ell/N$ ($\ell = 0, \ldots, N-1$).

n = 2. There are now two types of basis vectors, viz. those with $j_2 > j_1+1$ and those with $j_2 = j_1+1$. For the former, in which the two down spins are not nearest neighbours, eq. (4.30) takes the form

$$-\psi(j_1-1,j_2)-\psi(j_1+1,j_2)-\psi(j_1,j_2-1)-\psi(j_1,j_2+1)+4\Delta\psi(j_1,j_2) = E^*\psi(j_1,j_2), \quad (4.32)$$

and for the latter, where the down spins sit next to each other, it reads

$$-\psi(j_1-1,j_1+1) \qquad -\psi(j_1,j_1+2)+2\Delta\psi(j_1,j_1+1)=E^*\psi(j_1,j_1+1). \quad (4.33)$$

A solution of the "general" equation (4.32) alone is given by

$$\psi(j_1,j_2) = c_1\, e^{i(k_1j_1+k_2j_2)} + c_2\, e^{i(k_2j_1+k_1j_2)} \quad , \quad (4.34)$$

where c_1 and c_2 are arbitrary constants; substitution in (4.32) gives $E^* =$ $= 4\Delta - 2\cos k_1 - 2\cos k_2$. The function (4.34) also satisfies the equation obtained from eq. (4.32) by setting $j_2 = j_1+1$:

$$-\psi(j_1-1,\ j_1+1) - \psi(j_1+1,\ j_1+1) - \psi(j_1,j_1) - \psi(j_1,\ j_1+2) + 4\Delta\psi(j_1,\ j_1+1) =$$
$$= E^*\psi(j_1,\ j_1+1) \quad , \quad (4.35)$$

but it <u>should</u> satisfy eq. (4.33). The only way to achieve this is to choose the coefficients c_1 and c_2 so that the sum of the unwanted terms in eq. (4.35) vanishes:

$$-\psi(j_1+1,\ j_1+1) - \psi(j_1,j_1) + 2\Delta\psi(j_1,\ j_1+1) = 0 \quad . \quad (4.36)$$

Substituting (4.34) into eq. (4.36), which describes, so to speak, the "collision" of two down spins, yields a relation between c_1 and c_2 which is conventionally written as

$$c_1/c_2 = e^{-i\theta(k_1,k_2)} \quad ,$$

where the function $\theta(k,k')$ is defined by

$$\theta(k,\ k') = 2\arctan\frac{\Delta\sin\frac{1}{2}(k-k')}{\cos\frac{1}{2}(k+k') - \Delta\cos\frac{1}{2}(k-k')} \quad ; \quad (4.37)$$

note that $\theta(k,k')$ can be chosen so that $\theta(k',k) = -\theta(k,k')$. The periodic boundary condition is now: $\psi(j_1,\ N+1) = \psi(1,\ j_1)$. It leads to the following conditions on the wave numbers k_1 and k_2:

$$\left.\begin{aligned} Nk_1 &= (2\ell_1-1)\pi - \theta(k_1,k_2) \quad , \\ Nk_2 &= (2\ell_2-1)\pi - \theta(k_2,k_1) \quad , \end{aligned}\right\} \quad (\ell_1,\ \ell_2 = 0,\ 1,\ \ldots,\ N-1) \quad . \quad (4.38)$$

One can show that k_1 and k_2 are real for $\ell_2 \geq \ell_1+1$. The solution (4.34) then describes two spin waves, scattering from one another according to eq. (4.36), and $\theta(k,k')$ is a scattering phase shift. For $\ell_2 = \ell_1-1$, the wave numbers are complex conjugate; (4.34) then represents a bound state of two down spins travelling together through the lattice. For $\ell_2 = \ell_1$, the only remaining case one has to consider, both types of solution can appear.

General n. Guided by eq. (4.34) we try a solution of the following form:

$$\psi(j_1,\ldots,j_n) = \Sigma_P c(P)\, e^{i(k_{P1}j_1+\ldots+k_{Pn}j_n)} , \qquad (4.39)$$

where the sum is over all permutations P1, ..., Pn of 1, ..., n ("Bethe Ansatz"). Substitution of (4.39) into the general equations (4.30), i.e. those with $j_{r+1} > j_r+1$ for r = 1, ..., n-1, shows that it is indeed a solution, with

$$E^* = 2\Sigma_{r=1}^{n}(\Delta-\cos k_r) \quad . \qquad (4.40)$$

Substitution into the "collision equations" ($j_{r+1} = j_r+1$ for at least one r) puts restrictions on the coefficients c(P). It turns out that they can all be satisfied if we put

$$c(P) = (-1)^P \exp\{-\tfrac{1}{2}i\ \Sigma_{r<s}\ \theta(k_{Pr}, k_{Ps})\} , \qquad (4.41)$$

where $(-1)^P$ is the parity of P, and θ is the function defined by eq. (4.37). The periodic boundary condition $\psi(j_1, \ldots, j_{n-1}, N+1) = \psi(1, j_1, \ldots, j_{n-1})$ leads to the following restrictions for the k_r:

$$Nk_r = (2\ell_r - n+1)\pi - \Sigma_{s=1}^{n}\ \theta(k_r, k_s) \quad (\ell_r=0,1,\ldots,N-1;\ r=1,\ldots,n). \qquad (4.42)$$

These are transcendental equations for the k_r (or algebraic, highly non-linear equations in the unknowns $\exp(ik_r)$). It is a non-trivial question whether or not they have solutions leading to functions (4.39) that do not vanish identically.

It has been proven [20] that for even N and general Δ the ground state is the state with $n = \tfrac{1}{2}N$ and $\ell_r = r-1$; in this case eq. (4.42) reads

$$Nk_r = (2r - \tfrac{1}{2}N-1)\pi - \Sigma_{s=1}^{\frac{1}{2}N}\ \theta(k_r, k_s) \qquad (r = 1, \ldots, \tfrac{1}{2}N). \qquad (4.42a)$$

The corresponding wave numbers k_r turn out to be real for $\Delta < 1$, zero for $\Delta = 1$ and complex for $\Delta > 1$. We consider first the case $\underline{\Delta < 1}$.

In the limit $N\to\infty$ the set $\{k_r\}$ becomes dense on an interval $(-k_0, k_0)$ on the real axis with a density $N\rho(k)$ (i.e., $N\rho(k)dk$ = number of k_r values in (k,k+dk)); k_0 depends on Δ. Obviously, we must have $\int_{-k_0}^{k_0} \rho(k)dk = n/N = \tfrac{1}{2}$. The ground-state energy per spin in this limit is

$$e_0 = J\Delta - 4J \int_{-k_0}^{k_0} \rho(k) \cos k\ dk \quad . \qquad (4.43)$$

To determine $\rho(k)$ we take the difference of two equations (4.42a) with r+1 and r, multiply by $\rho(k_r)$, choose $k = k_r$ and $dk = k_{r+1} - k_r$ (so that $N\rho(k)dk = 1$), and convert the sum over k_s into an integral over k'. The result is an integral equation for $\rho(k)$:

$$1 = 2\pi\rho(k) - \int_{-k_0}^{k_0} \frac{\partial}{\partial k}\,\theta(k,k')\rho(k')dk' \quad . \tag{4.44}$$

If $\theta(k,k')$ were a difference kernel, i.e., a function of $k-k'$ alone, we could try to solve eq. (4.44) by means of Fourier transforms, but by its definition (4.37) it also depends on $k+k'$. It is possible, however, to remedy this defect by changing from k to an appropriate new variable α. The required transformation differs in the three cases $-1 < \Delta < 1$, $\Delta = -1$, $\Delta < -1$; we treat only the case $-1 < \Delta < 1$, referring to ref. 20 for a discussion of the other cases.

$|\Delta| < 1$. Putting $\Delta = -\cos\mu$ with $-\pi < \mu < \pi$ we define α and a density function $R(\alpha)$ by

$$e^{\alpha} = (e^{ik} + e^{i\mu})/(e^{i(k+\mu)} + 1) \quad , \tag{4.45}$$

$$R(\alpha)d\alpha = \rho(k)dk \quad . \tag{4.46}$$

In this case $k_0 = \pi-\mu$, so that $\alpha(k_0) = \infty$; hence we obtain

$$\int_{-\infty}^{+\infty} R(\alpha)d\alpha = \tfrac{1}{2} \quad , \tag{4.47}$$

$$e_0 = J\Delta - 4J \int_{-\infty}^{+\infty} R(\alpha)\,\frac{1 - \cos\mu\cosh\alpha}{\cosh\alpha - \cos\mu}\,d\alpha \quad . \tag{4.48}$$

From eqs. (4.37) and (4.45) we find, with $\alpha' = \alpha(k')$,

$$\theta(k,k') = \tilde{\theta}(\alpha,\alpha') = 2\arctan[\cot\mu\tanh\tfrac{1}{2}(\alpha'-\alpha)\} \quad , \tag{4.49}$$

which indeed depends only on $\alpha'-\alpha$. From eqs. (4.44)-(4.46) and (4.49) we obtain the following equation for $R(\alpha)$:

$$A(\alpha,\mu) = 2\pi R(\alpha) + \int_{-\infty}^{+\infty} A(\alpha-\alpha',\, 2\mu)R(\alpha')d\alpha' \quad , \tag{4.50}$$

where $A(\alpha,\mu) = dk/d\alpha = (\sin\mu)/(\cosh\alpha - \cos\mu)$. Introducing the Fourier transforms of $A(\alpha,\mu)$ and $R(\alpha)$:

$$\hat{A}(\omega,\mu) = \int_{-\infty}^{+\infty} e^{-i\omega\alpha} A(\alpha,\mu)d\alpha = 2\pi\{\sinh(\pi-\mu)\omega\}/\sinh\pi\omega \quad , \tag{4.51}$$

$$\hat{R}(\omega) = \int_{-\infty}^{+\infty} e^{-i\omega\alpha} R(\alpha)d\alpha \quad , \tag{4.52}$$

we obtain from eq. (4.50)

$$\hat{A}(\omega,\mu) = 2\pi\hat{R}(\omega) + \hat{A}(\omega,\, 2\mu)\hat{R}(\omega) \quad . \tag{4.53}$$

From (4.53) and (4.51) we find $\hat{R}(\omega) = (2 \cosh \mu\omega)^{-1}$, and hence, by inversion of eq. (4.52), $R(\alpha) = \{4\mu \cosh(\pi\alpha/2\mu)\}^{-1}$. Having found $R(\alpha)$ we insert the result into eq. (4.48), and obtain

$$e_0 = J\Delta - \frac{J}{\mu}\int_{-\infty}^{+\infty} \frac{(1 - \cos\mu \cosh\alpha)}{\cosh(\pi\alpha/2\mu)(\cosh\alpha - \cos\mu)}\, d\alpha =$$

$$= - J\Delta - 2J \sin^2\mu \int_{-\infty}^{+\infty} \frac{dx}{(\cosh \pi x)(\cosh 2\mu x - \cos\mu)} \qquad (-1 < \Delta < -1). (4.54)$$

$|\Delta| \geq 1$. In a similar way one finds for $\Delta < -1$ ($\Delta = -\cosh\lambda$ with $\lambda > 0$) and $\Delta = -1$:

$$e_0 = -J\Delta - 2J \sinh\lambda \left(1 + \sum_{m=1}^{\infty} \frac{4}{1 + e^{2m\lambda}}\right) \qquad (\Delta < -1) \quad , \qquad (4.55)$$

$$e_0 = J - 4J \log 2 \qquad (\Delta = -1) \quad . \qquad (4.56)$$

For $\Delta \geq 1$ it can be shown by a simple argument [20] that

$$e_0 = -J\Delta \qquad (\Delta \geq 1) \quad . \qquad (4.57)$$

It should be noted that (4.54)-(4.57) give e_0 for the Hamiltonian (4.28), which by eqs. (3.8) and (3.10) is the associated Hamiltonian (with H = 0) of a six-vertex model with $\omega_1\omega_3 = \omega_2\omega_4$. The eigenvalue problem for the associated Hamiltonian of the general six-vertex model, with $J_s \neq 0$, has thus far not been studied.

4.2.2. The symmetric six-vertex model

The solution of the eigenvalue problem for the transfer matrix of the six-vertex model follows the same lines as for the XXZ Hamiltonian, but the details are more complicated, and the application of the Perron-Frobenius theorem gives less information. Therefore we confine ourselves to a brief sketch; a detailed discussion is given in ref. 1, chapter 8, and ref. 7, second article. For simplicity, and because the general case has not been fully elucidated, we consider only the symmetric six-vertex model ($\omega_1 = \omega_2 = \omega_a$, $\omega_3 = \omega_4 = \omega_b$, $\omega_d = 0$).

It is convenient to introduce the notation $\alpha = |1\rangle$, $\beta = |-1\rangle$. First consider the case n = 0. The only eigenvector is $|0\rangle = \alpha \otimes \alpha \otimes \ldots \otimes \alpha$. From eqs. (2.21) and (2.22) and the relations $\sigma^+\alpha = 0$, $\sigma^-\alpha = \beta$, $\sigma^+\beta = \alpha$ we derive

$$T|0\rangle = \mathrm{Tr}_2 \prod_j (A_j\alpha) = \mathrm{Tr}_2 \prod_j \begin{pmatrix} \omega_a\alpha & \omega_d\beta \\ 0 & \omega_b\alpha \end{pmatrix} \quad . \qquad (4.58)$$

The elements of the matrices $A_j\alpha$ are one-spin vectors; the product Π_j is an ordered matrix product in which products of matrix elements are direct products. Since the LR element of each matrix in the product is zero, the matrix multiplication is trivial (the RL elements being irrelevant):

$$T\,|0\rangle = \mathrm{Tr}_2 \begin{pmatrix} (\omega_a\alpha)\otimes\dots\otimes(\omega_a\alpha) & \dots\dots\dots \\ 0 & (\omega_b\alpha)\otimes\dots\otimes(\omega_b\alpha) \end{pmatrix} =$$

$$= \mathrm{Tr}_2 \begin{pmatrix} \omega_a^N\,|0\rangle & \dots \\ 0 & \omega_b^N\,|0\rangle \end{pmatrix} = (\omega_a^N + \omega_b^N)\,|0\rangle = \Lambda\,|0\rangle \quad . \tag{4.59}$$

The fact that the eigenvalue Λ consists of two terms is due to the fact that for a row of horizontal arrows between two successive rows of up arrows precisely two states are possible. This is a general feature of the six-vertex model: between any two successive rows of vertical arrows with the same number of down arrows two configurations of horizontal arrows are possible.

For general n, and Ψ given by eqs. (4.29), (4.39) and (4.41) one can show (cf. ref. 1, p. 373 ff, with H = V = 0) that the eigenvalues of T are

$$\Lambda = \omega_a^N \prod_{r=1}^{n} \frac{\omega_a\omega_b e^{ik_r} - \omega_b^2 + \omega_c^2}{\omega_a^2 e^{ik_r} - \omega_a\omega_b} + \omega_b^N \prod_{r=1}^{n} \frac{\omega_a\omega_b e^{-ik_r} - \omega_a^2 + \omega_c^2}{\omega_b^2 e^{-ik_r} - \omega_a\omega_b} \ , \tag{4.60}$$

where the k_r $(r = 1,\dots,n)$ are given by eqs. (4.42) and (4.37) with $\Delta =$ $= (\omega_a^2 + \omega_b^2 - \omega_c^2)/2\omega_a\omega_b$ (for the relation with $\Delta = J_z/J$, compare eq. (3.10)).

The largest eigenvalue of T turns out to lie in the subspace $n = \frac{1}{2}N$. In the thermodynamic limit one finds for $\Delta < 1$ (ref. 1, p. 384, with y = 0):

$$\Lambda_0 \sim \left[\omega_a^{\frac{1}{2}} \exp \tfrac{1}{2} \int_{-k_0}^{k_0} \rho(k) \log \frac{\omega_a^2\omega_b^2 + (\omega_b^2-\omega_c^2)^2 - 2\omega_a\omega_b(\omega_b^2-\omega_c^2)\cos k}{\omega_a^2 + \omega_b^2 - 2\omega_a\omega_b \cos k}\, dk \right]^N , \tag{4.61}$$

if $\omega_a \geq \omega_b$; for $\omega_a < \omega_b$, ω_a and ω_b should be interchanged in (4.61). Henceforth we consider only the case $\omega_a \geq \omega_b$. The evaluation of Λ_0 is performed by applying the change of variables discussed above (for $|\Delta| < 1$ see eq. (4.45)), and a subsequent Fourier transformation. Again we have to distinguish between the various domains of Δ .

$|\Delta| < 1$, or $|\omega_a - \omega_b| < \omega_c < \omega_a + \omega_b$. In this case ω_a, ω_b and ω_c can be considered as the lengths of the sides of a triangle; if the opposite angles are denoted by $\frac{1}{2}(\mu+\phi)$, $\frac{1}{2}(\mu-\phi)$ and $(\pi-\mu)$, respectively, a convenient parametrization of the weights, consistent with $\Delta = -\cos\mu$, is

$$\omega_a = \rho \sin \tfrac{1}{2}(\mu+\phi) \ , \quad \omega_b = \rho \sin \tfrac{1}{2}(\mu-\phi) \ , \quad \omega_c = \rho \sin \mu . \tag{4.62}$$

For the free energy per spin one ultimately finds

$$f(\beta) = -\beta^{-1} \left[\log \omega_a + \frac{1}{8\mu} \int_{-\infty}^{+\infty} \frac{d\alpha}{\cosh(\pi\alpha/2\mu)} \log \frac{\cosh\alpha - \cos(2\mu-\phi)}{\cosh\alpha - \cos\phi} \right] . \tag{4.63}$$

An interesting special case is the ice model, where $\Delta = \frac{1}{2}$, $\mu = 2\pi/3$, $\rho = 2/\sqrt{3}$,

$\phi = 0$; there, eq. (4.63) reduces to

$$f(\beta) = -\beta^{-1}\left[\frac{3}{16\pi}\int_{-\infty}^{+\infty}\frac{d\alpha}{\cosh(3\alpha/4)}\log\frac{\cosh\alpha+\frac{1}{2}}{\cosh\alpha-1}\right] = -\beta^{-1}(\tfrac{3}{2}\log\tfrac{4}{3}) . \tag{4.64}$$

Equivalently, the partition function = the number of ice configurations is

$$Z \sim \left(\frac{4}{3}\right)^{\frac{3}{2}N} = (1.5396007\ \ldots)^N \qquad (N\to\infty) , \tag{4.65}$$

which is Lieb's well-known result[27)], the first exact result obtained for a six-vertex model.

$\Delta < -1$, or $\omega_c > \omega_a+\omega_b$. Setting

$$\omega_a = \rho\sinh\tfrac{1}{2}(\lambda+\theta) , \quad \omega_b = \rho\sinh\tfrac{1}{2}(\lambda-\theta) , \quad \omega_c = \rho\sinh\lambda, \tag{4.66}$$

which is consistent with $\Delta = -\cosh\lambda$, one finds

$$f(\beta) = -\beta^{-1}\left[\log\omega_a + \tfrac{1}{2}(\lambda-\theta) + \sum_{m=1}^{\infty}\frac{e^{-m\lambda}\sinh m(\lambda-\theta)}{m\cosh m\lambda}\right] . \tag{4.67}$$

$\Delta = -1$, or $\omega_c = \omega_a+\omega_b$. Setting

$$\omega_a = \rho(1+\gamma) , \quad \omega_b = \rho(1-\gamma) , \quad \omega_c = 2\rho , \tag{4.68}$$

one finds

$$f(\beta) = -\beta^{-1}\left[\log\omega_a + \log\frac{\Gamma\left(\frac{5-\gamma}{4}\right)\Gamma\left(\frac{1+\gamma}{4}\right)}{\Gamma\left(\frac{3-\gamma}{4}\right)\Gamma\left(\frac{3+\gamma}{4}\right)}\right] . \tag{4.69}$$

$\Delta \geq 1$, or $\omega_c \leq |\omega_a-\omega_b|$. In this case one can show that $f(\beta)$ does not depend on the values of Δ and ω_a/ω_b:

$$f(\beta) = -\beta^{-1}\log\omega_a . \tag{4.70}$$

4.3. The XYZ model and the symmetric eight-vertex model

Baxter has developed two (related) methods for solving the symmetric eight-vertex model and the XYZ model. We follow the second method, in which the eigenvectors are explicitly constructed. Unlike Baxter, however, we first treat the XYZ model. For a discussion of the XY model and the XXZ model as special cases of the XYZ model see ref. 47.

4.3.1. The XYZ model

In treating the XXZ model the first, and simplest, eigenvector that was obtained was the vector $|0\rangle = \alpha\otimes\ldots\otimes\alpha$ describing the state with all spins up. This direct-product vector formed the starting point of the analysis. In the

"Bethe Ansatz" the other eigenvectors were described in terms of deviations from this vector: some of the factors α were replaced by β, i.e. by factors that can be considered as being taken from the only other direct-product eigenvector, $\beta \otimes \beta \otimes \ldots \otimes \beta$, and suitable linear combinations of such states with a given number of deviating factors were determined.

We now ask if $\mathcal{H}^{XYZ}$, too, has eigenvectors that are direct products of (not necessarily identical) one-spin vectors. If so, we can try to find more eigenvectors by mixing factors from these special states and forming linear combinations according to a kind of (generalized) Bethe Ansatz.

Thus we form a direct product

$$\Psi = \psi_1 \otimes \psi_2 \otimes \ldots \otimes \psi_N \equiv \psi_1\psi_2 \ldots \psi_N \ , \quad \text{or } \Psi(\mu_1, \ldots, \mu_N) = \Pi_j \psi_j(\mu_j), \tag{4.71}$$

where the ψ_j ($j = 1, \ldots, N$) are one-spin vectors with components $\psi_j(1)$ and $\psi_1(-1)$; we shall sometimes write $\psi_j = \begin{pmatrix} \psi_j(1) \\ \psi_j(-1) \end{pmatrix}$, and omit the symbols $\otimes$. If we express σ_j^x and σ_j^y in terms of $\sigma_j^\pm$, we can write

$$\left.\begin{aligned} \mathcal{H} &= \Sigma_j \mathcal{H}_{j,j+1} \ , \\ \mathcal{H}_{j,j+1} &= -\ 2J\{(\sigma_j^-\sigma_{j+1}^+ + \sigma_j^+\sigma_{j+1}^-) + \Gamma(\sigma_j^-\sigma_{j+1}^- + \sigma_j^+\sigma_{j+1}^+) + \tfrac{1}{2}\Delta\sigma_j^z\sigma_{j+1}^z\} \ , \end{aligned}\right\} \tag{4.72}$$

with $J = \frac{1}{2}(J_x+J_y)$, $\Gamma = (J_x-J_y)/(J_x+J_y)$, $\Delta = J_z/J$, as before. If we insert (4.72) into the equation $\mathcal{H}\Psi = E\Psi$, $\mathcal{H}_{j,j+1}$ will act only on the factors $\psi_j\psi_{j+1}$ of Ψ. Let for each j ψ_j' be a vector orthogonal to ψ_j. We can then write

$$\mathcal{H}_{j,j+1}\ \psi_j\psi_{j+1} = c_{1j}\psi_j\psi_{j+1} + c_{2j}\psi_j'\psi_{j+1} + c_{3j}\psi_j\psi_{j+1}' + c_{4j}\psi_j'\psi_{j+1}' \ , \tag{4.73}$$

with, e.g., $c_{2j} = \langle\, \psi_j'\psi_{j+1} | \mathcal{H}_{j,j+1} | \psi_j\psi_{j+1} \,\rangle$, in an obvious notation. If Ψ is to be an eigenvector, it is only the first term in the right-hand side of (4.73) that can contribute to $E\Psi$, so we must have $E = \Sigma_j c_{1j}$. The second and third terms in (4.73) contain one "wrong" factor, at the sites j and j+1, respectively, but they might cancel upon summation over j; the condition for this to happen is $c_{3j} = -c_{2,j+1}$. The fourth term, however, contains two wrong factors and cannot cancel. Hence we must require $c_{4j} = 0$. One can derive that

$$c_{4j} = \psi_j^2(-1)\psi_{j+1}^2(-1)\,[\Gamma r_j^2 r_{j+1}^2 - r_{j+1}^2 + 2\Delta r_j r_{j+1} - r_j^2 + \Gamma] \ , \tag{4.74}$$

where $r_j = \psi_j(1)/\psi_j(-1)$; we assume $\psi_j(-1) \neq 0$, which can be shown not to be a serious restriction. From $c_{4j} = 0$ it follows that

$$\Gamma r_j^2 r_{j+1}^2 - r_{j+1}^2 + 2\Delta r_j r_{j+1} - r_j^2 + \Gamma = 0 \ , \tag{4.75}$$

from which follows a recursion relation for r_j:

$$r_{j+1} = \frac{\Delta r_j \pm \{\Gamma - (\Gamma^2+1-\Delta^2)r_j^2 + \Gamma r_j^4\}^{\frac{1}{2}}}{1 - \Gamma r_j^2} \ . \tag{4.76}$$

If in a calculation one encounters expressions with terms of the type $w = (a - bz^2 + az^4)^{\frac{1}{2}}$, it is often useful to introduce a parametrization in terms of elliptic functions. The first step is to define a parameter k by $k+k^{-1} = b/a$, and to change variables from z to $y = k^{-\frac{1}{2}}z$, writing $w = a^{\frac{1}{2}}(1-y^2)^{\frac{1}{2}}(1-k^2y^2)^{\frac{1}{2}}$. Then y can be written as a Jacobian elliptic function (sine amplitude) of a new variable u: $y = \mathrm{sn}(u,k)$. This function can (if for simplicity we ignore the problem of the two-valuedness of square roots) be defined as the solution of the differential equation $dy/du = (1-y^2)^{\frac{1}{2}}(1-k^2y^2)^{\frac{1}{2}}$ under the initial condition $y(0) = 0$. One further defines the functions $\mathrm{cn}(u,k) = (1-y^2)^{\frac{1}{2}}$ (cosine amplitude) and $\mathrm{dn}(u,k) = (1-k^2y^2)^{\frac{1}{2}}$ (delta amplitude), so that we finally can write $w = a^{\frac{1}{2}}\mathrm{cn}(u,k)\,\mathrm{dn}(u,k)$. For precise definitions of elliptic functions and their properties see ref. 48. The functions sn(u,k), cn(u,k) and dn(u,k), which are usually denoted by sn u, cn u and dn u, are doubly periodic functions with periods 4K and 2iK', where $K \equiv K(k) = \int_0^{\pi/2}(1-k^2\sin^2\omega)^{-\frac{1}{2}}d\omega$, $K' = \int_0^{\pi/2}(1 - (1-k^2)\sin^2\omega)^{-\frac{1}{2}}d\omega$; k is called their modulus. For $k = 0$ we have $K = \frac{1}{2}\pi$, $K' = \infty$, and $\mathrm{sn}(u,0) = \sin u$, $\mathrm{cn}(u,0) = \cos u$, $\mathrm{dn}(u,0) = 1$. For $k = 1$ we have $K = \infty$, $K' = \frac{1}{2}\pi$, and $\mathrm{sn}(u,1) = \tanh u$, $\mathrm{cn}(u,1) = \mathrm{dn}(u,1) = (\cosh u)^{-1}$.

A useful representation of the function sn u is that in terms of the Jacobian theta functions H(u) and Θ(u), which are entire functions defined by

$$\left.\begin{aligned} H(u) &= 2\sum_{n=1}^{\infty}(-1)^{n+1}q^{(n-\frac{1}{2})^2}\sin((2n-1)\pi u/2K) \\ \Theta(u) &= 1 + 2\sum_{n=1}^{\infty}(-1)^n q^{n^2}\cos(n\pi u/K) \end{aligned}\right\} \tag{4.77}$$

with $q = \exp(-\pi K'/K) = q(k)$:

$$k^{\frac{1}{2}}\mathrm{sn}\,u = H(u)/\Theta(u). \tag{4.78}$$

The elliptic functions form a generalization of the trigonometric functions. They satisfy the relations $\mathrm{cn}^2u = 1-\mathrm{sn}^2u$, $\mathrm{dn}^2u = 1-k^2\mathrm{sn}^2u$, which are obvious from their definition, and many other relations generalizing relations between trigonometric functions. We shall use one of these, the addition formula for sn u:

$$\mathrm{sn}(u\pm v) = \frac{\mathrm{sn}\,u(\mathrm{cn}\,v\,\mathrm{dn}\,v) \pm (\mathrm{cn}\,u\,\mathrm{dn}\,u)\mathrm{sn}\,v}{1 - k^2\mathrm{sn}^2u\,\mathrm{sn}^2v}. \tag{4.79}$$

Practice must show whether or not it is useful to parametrize a function in terms of elliptic functions. In the present case, eq. (4.76), we have $a = \Gamma$, $b = \Gamma^2+1-\Delta^2$, and hence

$$k + k^{-1} = (\Gamma^2 + 1 - \Delta^2)/\Gamma. \tag{4.80}$$

Putting $r_j = k^{\frac{1}{2}}\mathrm{sn}\,u_j$ and substituting this into eq. (4.76) we obtain

$$k^{\frac{1}{2}}\text{sn } u_{j+1} = \frac{\Delta k^{\frac{1}{2}}\text{sn } u_j \pm \Gamma^{\frac{1}{2}}(\text{cn } u_j \text{ dn } u_j)}{1 - \Gamma k \text{ sn}^2 u_j} \tag{4.81}$$

Since the right-hand side resembles that of eq.(4.79) we tentatively put

$$\Gamma^{\frac{1}{2}} = k^{\frac{1}{2}}\text{sn } 2\eta. \tag{4.82}$$

If now Δ would be equal to cn 2η dn 2η, the resemblance would be complete, and we would have derived

$$\text{sn } u_{j+1} = \text{sn}(u_j \pm 2\eta) \quad . \tag{4.83}$$

Expressing Δ by (4.80) in terms of Γ and k, and substituting (4.82) we find indeed Δ = cn 2η dn 2η. It is the simplicity of the resulting recursion relation (4.83) that justifies the introduction of elliptic functions in this problem.

The simplest solution of eq. (4.83) is $u_{j+1} = u_j \pm 2\eta$. The question is if the resulting expression for r_j also makes the middle terms in eq. (4.73) cancel. This turns out to be the case only if we take either $u_{j+1} = u_j + 2\eta$ for all j, or $u_{j+1} = u_j - 2\eta$ for all j. Consider the first case. There we can write $u_j = u_0 + 2j\eta$, so that we have

$$r_j = k^{\frac{1}{2}}\text{sn}(u_0 + 2j\eta) \quad . \tag{4.84}$$

If we define a set of spin vectors

$$\phi^{(\ell)} = \begin{pmatrix} H(u+2\ell\eta) \\ \\ \Theta(u+2\ell\eta) \end{pmatrix} , \tag{4.85}$$

with u arbitrary and ℓ any integer, then by (4.78) the choice $\psi_j = \phi^{(j)}$ makes (4.71) an eigenvector of $\mathcal{H}$. However, choosing $\psi_j = \phi^{(\ell+j-1)}$, i.e. $\psi_1 = \phi^{(\ell)}$, $\psi_2 = \phi^{(\ell+1)}$, ..., we also obtain an eigenvector; moreover, we can choose u arbitrary. Fixing u we get a discrete set of eigenvectors of $\mathcal{H}$ which are direct-product vectors:

$$\Psi^{(\ell)} = \phi^{(\ell)}\phi^{(\ell+1)} \dots \phi^{(\ell+N-1)} \quad . \tag{4.86}$$

The periodic boundary condition requires that r_{N+1}, determined by eq. (4.84), is equal to r_1; so we must have $\text{sn}(u_0 + 2(N+1)\eta) = \text{sn}(u_0 + 2\eta)$. Now sn u is periodic with periods 4K and 2iK'. Therefore, if η is of the form

$$\eta = (2m_1K + m_2iK')/L \tag{4.87}$$

with m_1, m_2 and L integers, we have $\text{sn}(u + 2L\eta) = \text{sn } u$. If now N/L is an integer, the periodic boundary condition is satisfied. Note that, unlike the wave vectors k_r in the eigenvectors of the XXZ model, η is not a free parameter to be disposed of, since by eqs. (4.80) and (4.82) it is a function of the interaction constants in $\mathcal{H}$. Hence it is only for special choices of $\mathcal{H}$, and for corresponding special choices for N, that there exist product eigenvectors. Of course, arbitrary values of η can be approximated to any desired degree of accuracy by the values (4.87).

Having found the eigenvector, we can calculate E in the manner described above. There is, however, an alternative method for deriving E from the eigenvector, which leads to a simpler, but not obviously identical, result. For a discussion of these results and their interrelation we refer to ref. 35, II, p. 21 and 22. A striking feature of the second expression is that it is independent of u, and a fortiori of ℓ, so that all vectors of the type (4.86) belong to the same eigenvalue. On the other hand, it is not yet fully understood how many of these vectors are actually linearly independent.

If we take the second solution of the recursion relation (4.83), with $u_{j+1} = u_j - 2\eta$ for all j, we obtain another set of product eigenvectors of $\mathcal{H}$:

$$\overline{\Psi}^{(\ell)} = \overline{\phi}^{(\ell)}\overline{\phi}^{(\ell-1)} \dots \overline{\phi}^{(\ell-N+1)} , \qquad (4.88)$$

$$\overline{\phi}^{(\ell)} = \begin{pmatrix} H(\overline{u} + 2\ell\eta) \\ \\ \Theta(\overline{u} + 2\ell\eta) \end{pmatrix} , \qquad (4.89)$$

with the same restriction (4.87) on η. For the XYZ model the two vectors $\Psi^{(\ell)}$ and $\overline{\Psi}^{(\ell)}$ play the same role that for the XXZ model was played by the vectors $\alpha\alpha\dots\alpha$ and $\beta\beta\dots\beta$. There are, however, three differences: (a) the one-spin states ψ_j vary from site to site; in other words, the vectors $\phi^{(\ell+j-1)}$ represent spins that are "up" with respect to an axis that rotates in a regular fashion from site to site, and the vectors $\overline{\phi}^{(\ell-j+1)}$ represent spins that are "down" with respect to an axis that rotates "in the opposite sense"; (b) although by a proper choice of u and $\overline{u}$ the vectors $\phi^{(\ell+j-1)}$ and $\overline{\phi}^{(\ell-j+1)}$ can easily be made linearly independent for all j, they can in general not be made orthogonal for all j (like α and β), i.e. the two axes with respect to which the spins are up and down, respectively, cannot be made to coincide for all sites; (c) there is a degeneracy due to the freedom in the choice of u and ℓ.

The next question to be considered is the following: are there, in addition to the product vectors $\Psi^{(\ell)}$ and $\overline{\Psi}^{(\ell)}$, other eigenvectors of $\mathcal{H}$, differing from these by the presence of one deviating factor, e.g. one "down-spin vector" $\overline{\phi}^{(\ell)}$ among N-1 "up-spin vectors" $\phi^{(\ell)}$, or consisting of a linear combination of such vectors with one "wrong" factor each? Such eigenvectors would be the counterpart of the eigenvectors $\Sigma_j\psi(j)\,|j\rangle$ of the XXZ Hamiltonian.

A direct answer to this question in its generality, i.e. for the Hamiltonian (4.72) with Γ and Δ arbitrary, has not been given thus far; only the special cases $\Delta = 0$ (XY model) and $\Gamma = 0$ (XXZ model) have been discussed by Jones[47]. However, an indirect answer was provided by Baxter, whose analysis of the symmetric eight-vertex model together with the relation between the transfer matrix of this model and $\mathcal{H}$ shows that there exist eigenvectors of $\mathcal{H}$ that are linear combinations of product vectors consisting of a given (but arbitrary) number n of factors $\bar{\phi}^{(\ell)}$ and N-n factors $\phi^{(\ell)}$. Since this is the only road to this result that is accessible at present we shall not pursue the eigenvalue problem for $\mathcal{H}$ any further but turn at once to the symmetric eight-vertex model.

4.3.2. The symmetric eight-vertex model

Having found direct-product eigenvectors of $\mathcal{H}$ we now ask if they are also eigenvectors of $T(\omega)$ for $\omega\in\Omega^C$ under the correspondence (3.11). To answer this question we have to let the operator $T(\omega)$, given by eq. (2.21), act on the vector (4.86). We first study its action on an arbitrary product vector (4.71):

$$T\Psi = \mathrm{Tr}_2 \prod_j U_j \quad , \tag{4.90}$$

$$U_j = A_j\psi_j = \begin{pmatrix} U_j^{RR} & U_j^{RL} \\ U_j^{LR} & U_j^{LL} \end{pmatrix} \quad , \tag{4.91}$$

$$U_j^{RR} = \begin{pmatrix} \omega_a\psi_j(1) \\ \omega_b\psi_j(-1) \end{pmatrix}, \quad U_j^{RL} = \begin{pmatrix} \omega_d\psi_j(-1) \\ \omega_c\psi_j(1) \end{pmatrix}; \quad U_j^{LR} = \begin{pmatrix} \omega_c\psi_j(-1) \\ \omega_d\psi_j(1) \end{pmatrix}, \quad U_j^{LL} = \begin{pmatrix} \omega_b\psi_j(1) \\ \omega_a\psi_j(-1) \end{pmatrix}. \tag{4.92}$$

In general, the U_j are not "triangular" matrices (with $U_j^{LR} = 0$ or $U_j^{RL} = 0$), as in eq. (4.58), so that the multiplication is non-trivial. At first sight one might hope that a similarity transformation might help us to reduce the U_j to such a form, because we may obviously write

$$T\Psi = \mathrm{Tr}_2 \, \Pi_j (M^{-1}U_jM) \quad , \tag{4.93}$$

but it is easily seen that there is no 2×2 matrix M which simultaneously brings all U_j to a similar triangular form. Following Baxter we therefore try to find N matrices M_j such that all matrices $U_j^* = M_j^{-1}UM_{j+1}$ are of the same triangular form, e.g. with $(U_j^*)^{RL} = 0$. Then

$$T\,\Psi = \mathrm{Tr}_2 \prod_j (M_1^{-1}U_1M_2)(M_2^{-1}U_2M_3) \ldots (M_N^{-1}U_NM_{N+1}) = \mathrm{Tr}_2 \prod_j U_j^* \quad , \tag{4.94}$$

provided $M_{N+1} = M_1$. Denote the matrix elements of M_j by $x_j(\pm 1)$ and $y_j(\pm 1)$, as follows:

$$M_j = \begin{pmatrix} y_j(1) & x_j(1) \\ y_j(-1) & x_j(-1) \end{pmatrix} \quad , \tag{4.95}$$

and define $p_j = x_j(1)/x_j(-1)$. The condition $(U_j^*)^{RL} = 0$ can then be written as

$$x_j(-1)x_{j+1}(1)U_j^{RR} - x_j(1)x_{j+1}(1)U_j^{LR} + x_j(-1)x_{j+1}(-1)U_j^{RL} - x_j(1)x_{j+1}(-1)U_j^{LL} = 0. \quad (4.96)$$

Since the $U_j^{\lambda\lambda'}$ are two-component vectors, eq. (4.96) leads to two relations between p_j, p_{j+1} and $\psi_j(\pm 1)$:

$$\left.\begin{aligned} (\omega_a p_{j+1} - \omega_b p_j)\psi_j(1) + (\omega_d - \omega_c p_j p_{j+1})\psi_j(-1) &= 0 \quad , \\ (\omega_c - \omega_d p_j p_{j+1})\psi_j(1) + (\omega_b p_{j+1} - \omega_a p_j)\psi_j(-1) &= 0 \quad . \end{aligned}\right\} \quad (4.97)$$

These are two homogeneous linear equations for $\psi_j(1)$ and $\psi_j(-1)$, so the determinant of the coefficients must vanish. The resulting equation for p_j and p_{j+1} can be written as

$$\Gamma p_j^2 p_{j+1}^2 - p_{j+1}^2 + 2\Delta p_j p_{j+1} - p_j^2 + \Gamma = 0 \quad , \quad (4.98)$$

where

$$\Gamma = \frac{\omega_c \omega_d}{\omega_a \omega_b} \quad , \qquad \Delta = \frac{\omega_a^2 + \omega_b^2 - \omega_c^2 - \omega_d^2}{2\omega_a \omega_b} \quad ; \quad (4.99)$$

in virtue of eq. (3.11), the definitions (4.99) are consistent with the definitions of Γ and Δ in eq. (4.72). Equation (4.98) is identical in form to eq. (4.75) so that the solution is

$$p_j = k^{\frac{1}{2}} \mathrm{sn}\, s_j \quad \text{with } s_{j+1} = s_j + 2\sigma_j \eta \quad , \quad \sigma_j = \pm 1, \quad (4.100)$$

where k and η are again defined by eqs. (4.80) and (4.82). If we introduce

$$\Gamma_1 = \omega_a \omega_d \,/\, \omega_b \omega_c \quad , \qquad \Gamma_2 = \omega_b \omega_d \,/\, \omega_a \omega_c \quad , \quad (4.101)$$

and define $\Gamma_1^{\frac{1}{2}} = k^{\frac{1}{2}} \mathrm{sn}\, 2\eta_1$, $\Gamma_2^{\frac{1}{2}} = k^{\frac{1}{2}} \mathrm{sn}\, 2\eta_2$, we can show, using eq. (4.79), that $\eta_1 + \eta_2 = \eta$. Setting $\eta_1 - \eta_2 = v$ we find that we can parametrize the weights as follows

$$\left.\begin{aligned} \omega_a &= \rho\, \mathrm{sn}(v+\eta) \quad , & \omega_b &= \rho\, \mathrm{sn}(v-\eta) \; , \\ \omega_c &= \rho\, \mathrm{sn}\, 2\eta \quad , & \omega_d &= \rho k\, \mathrm{sn}\, 2\eta\, \mathrm{sn}(v+\eta)\mathrm{sn}(v-\eta) \quad . \end{aligned}\right\} \quad (4.102)$$

The parametrizations (4.62), (4.66) and (4.68) can, with a few modifications, be considered as special cases, with k = 0, of (4.102).

If we now substitute (4.100) and (4.102) into (4.97) and solve the ratio $r_j = \psi_j(1) \,/\, \psi_j(-1)$, we obtain

$$r_j = k^{\frac{1}{2}} \mathrm{sn}\, u_j \quad \text{with } u_j = s_j + \sigma_j(\eta - v) \quad . \quad (4.103)$$

In the derivation we use the following identity

$$\begin{aligned} &\mathrm{sn}(s-t)[\mathrm{sn}(r+s)\mathrm{sn}(r+t) - \mathrm{sn}(r-s)\mathrm{sn}(r-t)] = \\ &= \mathrm{sn}(s+t)[\mathrm{sn}(r+s)\mathrm{sn}(r-t) - \mathrm{sn}(r-s)\mathrm{sn}(r+t)] \quad , \end{aligned} \quad (4.104)$$

with $r = \frac{1}{2}\{s_j + \sigma_j(v+\eta)\}$, $s = \frac{1}{2}\{s_j + \sigma_j(3\eta-v)\}$, $t = \frac{1}{2}\{s_j - \sigma_j(\eta+v)\}$. The identity (4.104), which is related to Baxter's identities I(59)-(60) [35], follows from the fact that the left-hand side is an even function of t, which goes back to the relation sn(-t) = -sn t. Note that in this case, as contrasted with that of section 4.3.1, r_j itself does not satisfy a recursion relation. In the light of this section we restrict ourselves, however, to the cases where $\sigma_j = \sigma$ for all j (σ = 1 or -1); obviously, we then have $u_{j+1} = u_j + 2\sigma\eta$ for all j. It can be shown that only these solutions of eq. (4.97) yield vectors that behave simply under T.

Consider first the case $\sigma = 1$. We write

$$p_j = k^{\frac{1}{2}}\mathrm{sn}(s_0 + 2j\eta), \qquad r_j = k^{\frac{1}{2}}\mathrm{sn}(u_0 + 2j\eta) \qquad (j = 1, \ldots, n) \;, \tag{4.105}$$

with $u_0 = s_0 + \eta - v$. If we now take $s_0 = s + 2(\ell-1)\eta$, $u_0 = u + 2(\ell-1)\eta$, with s arbitrary and $u = s+\eta-v$, we can choose, as in section 4.3.1, $\psi_j = \phi^{(\ell+j-1)}$, and hence $\Psi = \Psi^{(\ell)}$, with $\phi^{(\ell)}$ and $\Psi^{(\ell)}$ defined by eqs. (4.85) and (4.86). If we further set $x_j(1) = H(s_0 + 2j\eta)$, $x_j(-1) = \Theta(s_0 + 2j\eta)$, in agreement with the first eq. (4.105), and we choose $y_j(\pm 1)$ so as to give det $M_j = 1$, the diagonal elements of U_j^* can be calculated. The result is

$$U_j^* = \begin{pmatrix} g(v-\eta)\phi^{(\ell+j-2)} & 0 \\ \cdots\cdots & g(v+\eta)\phi^{(\ell+j)} \end{pmatrix} \;, \tag{4.106}$$

with $g(u) = \rho\Theta(0)H(u)\Theta(-u)$. The periodic boundary condition now reads $M_{N+1} = M_1$, i.e., by (4.95), $x_{N+1}(\pm 1) = x_1(\pm 1)$, $y_{N+1}(\pm 1) = y_1(\pm 1)$. From (4.105) it follows that if we choose η of the form (4.87), and $N = L \times$ integer, we have $p_{N+1} = p_1$, i.e. $x_{N+1}(1) / x_{N+1}(-1) = x_1(1) / x_1(-1)$. According to Baxter, this is already sufficient to ensure the working of the procedure followed. In order to satisfy the full boundary condition, which is necessary if one wants to avoid complicating extra factors, the vectors x_j and ψ_j should be normalized in a slightly different way, viz. in terms of renormalized theta functions; for details we refer to ref. 35, I, p. 17-18).

The multiplication of the U_j^* can now be performed. The result is

$$T\Psi^{(\ell)} = \mathrm{Tr}_2 \begin{pmatrix} [g(v-\eta)]^N\Psi^{(\ell-1)} & 0 \\ \cdots & [g(v+\eta)]^N\Psi^{(\ell+1)} \end{pmatrix} =$$

$$= G_-\Psi^{(\ell-1)} + G_+\Psi^{(\ell+1)} \;, \quad \text{with } G_\pm = [g(v\pm\eta)]^N \;. \tag{4.107}$$

We see that, in contrast to what we found for $\mathcal{H}^{XXZ}$ and $T(\omega)$ for $\omega \in \Omega^B$, the product vector $\Psi^{(\ell)}$, which is an eigenvector of $\mathcal{H}^{XYZ}$, is not an eigenvector of T; in view of the freedom in the choice of u (and ℓ) in eqs. (4.85)-(4.86) this is not entirely surprising.

The choice (4.87) for η makes r_j, given by eq. (4.105), periodic in j with period L, because $\mathrm{sn}(u_0+2L\eta) = \mathrm{sn}\, u_0$. It is this fact that helps us to combine the $\Psi^{(\ell)}$ to eigenvectors of T. Again, the simplest result is obtained if one uses Baxter's final normalization of the $\phi^{(\ell)}$, which makes $\phi^{(\ell)}$ periodic in ℓ with period L, so that we have $\Psi^{(\ell+L)} = \Psi^{(\ell)}$. Hence, if we form

$$\Psi = \Sigma_{\ell=1}^{L} e^{i\kappa\ell}\, \Psi^{(\ell)} , \tag{4.108}$$

with $\kappa = 2\pi m/L$ $(m = 0,1,\ldots,L-1)$, Ψ is an eigenvector of T:

$$T\Psi = (e^{i\kappa} G_- + e^{-i\kappa} G_+)\Psi = \Lambda(\kappa)\Psi. \tag{4.109}$$

Different values of m give different eigenvalues $\Lambda(\kappa)$; part of the degeneracy found in the previous section is thus removed if we turn from $\mathcal{H}$ to T.

If we had chosen the M_j so that $(U_j^*)^{LR} = 0$, rather than $(U_j^*)^{RL} = 0$, we would have obtained essentially the same results.

We now consider the case $\sigma = -1$, i.e. $s_j = \bar{s}_0 - 2j\eta$, $u_j = \bar{u}_0 - 2j\eta$ $(j = 1,\ldots,n)$, with $\bar{u}_0 = \bar{s}_0 - \eta + v$. We now take $\bar{s}_0 = \bar{s} + 2(\ell-1)\eta$, $\bar{u}_0 = \bar{u} + 2(\ell-1)\eta$, with $\bar{s}$ arbitrary and $\bar{u} = \bar{s} - \eta + v$, and choose $\psi_j = \bar{\phi}^{(\ell-j+1)}$, $\Psi = \bar{\Psi}^{(\ell)}$, with $\bar{\phi}^{(\ell)}$ and $\bar{\Psi}^{(\ell)}$ defined by eqs. (4.88), (4.89). Like the $\Psi^{(\ell)}$, the $\bar{\Psi}^{(\ell)}$ can be linearly combined to eigenvectors of T; the eigenvalues are the same as in the case $\sigma = 1$. Again, essentially the same result is obtained if the M_j are chosen so as to make $(U_j^*)^{LR} = 0$.

We turn to the question of the existence of eigenvectors made up of product vectors with a given number of "deviating" factors. We shall at once discuss the case of an arbitrary number $n > 0$ of deviating factors, rather than first treat the case $n = 1$. We shall from now on restrict ourselves to a brief sketch of Baxter's analysis, omitting many details and almost all proofs.

Let F be the family of direct-product vectors consisting of factors of the types $\phi^{(\ell)}$ and $\bar{\phi}^{(\ell)}$, with arbitrarily given values of the parameters s and $\bar{s}$ (or u and $\bar{u}$), arranged in such a way that a factor $\phi^{(\ell)}$ is always followed by $\phi^{(\ell+1)}$ or $\bar{\phi}^{(\ell+1)}$, and $\bar{\phi}^{(\ell)}$ is always followed by $\phi^{(\ell-1)}$ or $\bar{\phi}^{(\ell-1)}$, e.g.

$$\phi^{(\ell)}\phi^{(\ell+1)}\ldots\phi^{(\ell+m)}\bar{\phi}^{(\ell+m+1)}\bar{\phi}^{(\ell+m)}\bar{\phi}^{(\ell+m-1)}\phi^{(\ell+m-2)}\phi^{(\ell+m-1)}\phi^{(\ell+m)}\ldots\ldots$$

If we change our notation by writing $\phi^{(\ell)} = \phi^{\ell,\ell+1}$, $\bar{\phi}^{(\ell)} = \phi^{\ell,\ell-1}$, the general member of F can be denoted by

$$\Psi^{\ell_1\ldots\ell_{N+1}} = \bigotimes_{j=1}^{N} \phi^{\ell_j,\ell_{j+1}} = \phi^{\ell_1,\ell_2}\phi^{\ell_2,\ell_3}\ldots\phi^{\ell_N,\ell_{N+1}} , \tag{4.110}$$

with $\ell_{j+1} = \ell_j \pm 1$ $(j = 1,\ldots, N)$. The action of T on $\Psi^{\ell_1\ldots\ell_{N+1}}$ is given by

$$T\Psi^{\ell_1\ldots\ell_{N+1}} = \sum_{m_1}\ldots\sum_{m_{N+1}} \{\prod_j W(m_j,m_{j+1}|\ell_j,\ell_{j+1})\}\Psi^{m_1\ldots m_{N+1}} , \tag{4.111}$$

where the sum is over all sets of integers $m_1,\dots,m_{N+1}$ such that

$$m_{j+1} = m_j \pm 1 \; (j=1,\dots,N), \quad m_j = \ell_j \pm 1 \; (j=1,\dots,N+1), \quad m_{N+1} - m_1 = \ell_{N+1} - \ell_1, \qquad (4.112)$$

(see fig. 6) and where the coefficients W are defined in ref. 35, II eq. (7.1). We see that T carries a vector of F into a linear combination of vectors of F.

A necessary condition for (4.111) to hold is the periodic boundary condition, which can be shown to be obeyed if $\ell_{N+1} - \ell_1 = L \times$ integer. Let F_n be the subfamily of F consisting of all vectors containing n factors of the type $\phi^{\ell,\ell-1}$ and N-n factors $\phi^{\ell,\ell+1}$. If $\Psi^{\ell_1\dots\ell_{N+1}} \in F_n$, there are n decreasing steps and N-n increasing steps in the sequence $\ell_1,\dots,\ell_{N+1}$; hence we have $\ell_{N+1} = \ell_1 + N - 2n$, and the periodic boundary condition becomes: $N-2n = L \times$ integer, or $N = 2n \pmod L$.

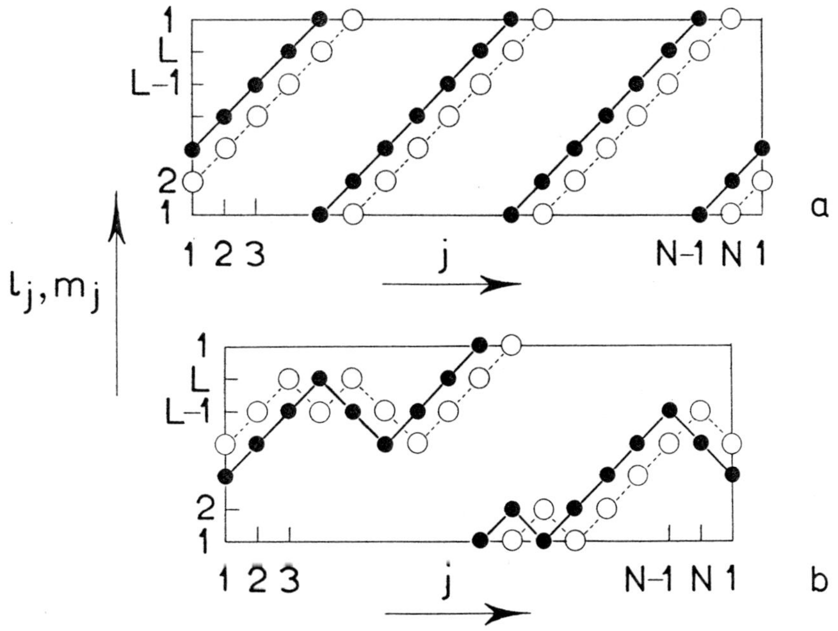

Fig. 6. Two examples of a set $\ell_1,\dots,\ell_{N+1}$ (black circles) characterizing a product vector $\Psi^{\ell_1\dots\ell_{N+1}}$ and a set $m_1,\dots,m_{N+1}$ (open circles) compatible with it by eq. (4.112) for: (a) N = 18, L = 6, n = 0; (b) N = 16, L = 6, n = 5. For ease of survey, ℓ_j and m_j are plotted modulo L; actually, they can take any value.

Since $m_{N+1} - m_1 = \ell_{N+1} - \ell_1 = N - 2n$, we see that all vectors $\Psi^{m_1\dots m_{N+1}}$ in (4.111) belong to F_n, i.e., T carries a vector of F_n into a linear combination of vectors of F_n. Obviously, n is a good quantum number with respect to the operator T, as was the number of down spins in the six-vertex model. However, a corresponding conserved quantity, which would be the analogue of the total spin $\Sigma_j \sigma_j^z$, has not been found (except for $\Delta = 0$, see ref. 47). Fig. 6 shows two examples of a set $\{m_j\}$ compatible with a given set $\{\ell_j\}$ by eq. (4.112).

We can give a graphical representation of T with respect to the new basis we have constructed. Given a vector $\Psi^{\ell_1 \ldots \ell_{N+1}}$ referring to a certain row of vertical edges, we place for each j the number ℓ_j ("face variable" or "generalized Ising variable") in the face between the edges j-1 and j of this row, and draw an up (down) arrow on the edge j if $\phi^{\ell_j, \ell_{j+1}}$ represents an up (down) "spin" in the new sense; these new arrows are to be well distinguished from the original arrows, which correspond to the basis states $|\mu_1, \ldots, \mu_N\rangle$. The interesting point is that if we represent two sets $\{\ell_j\}$ and $\{m_j\}$, compatible according to eq. (4.112), in two successive rows, the values of ℓ_j and m_j, which occur in adjacent faces of the lattice, also differ by ±1. Hence we can draw a right-pointing (left-pointing) arrow on the intervening horizontal edge labelled j if $m_j = \ell_j + 1$ ($m_j = \ell_j - 1$). As fig. 7 shows,

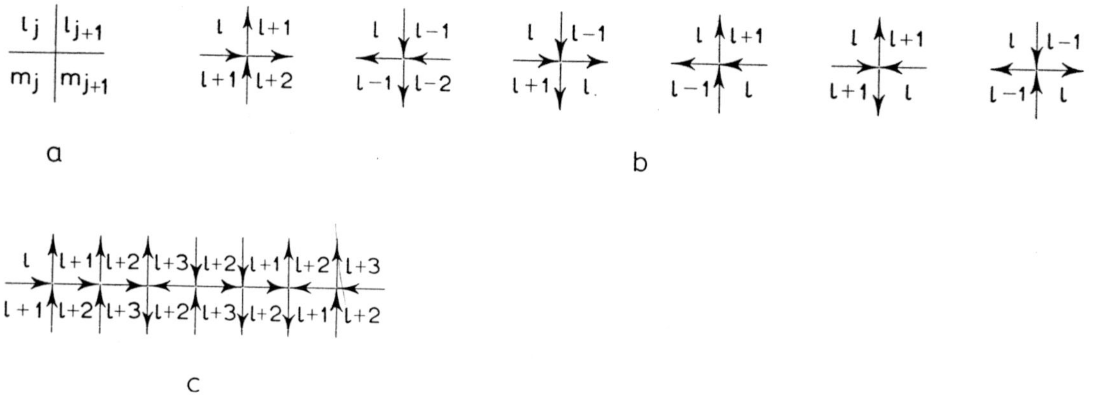

Fig. 7. Representation of two compatible sets $\{\ell_j\}$ and $\{m_j\}$ by face variables and vertices: (a) arrangement of the face variables ℓ_j, ℓ_{j+1}, m_j, m_{j+1} around a lattice site; (b) the vertices corresponding to the allowed types of sets $\{\ell_j, \ell_{j+1}, m_j, m_{j+1}\}$; (c) example of a representation of part of two compatible sets $\{\ell_j\}$ and $\{m_j\}$.

the only vertices that are formed in this way are the vertices 1, ..., 6. If the coefficients W are considered as the weights of these vertices, T is, with respect to the basis set of vectors $\Psi^{\ell_1 \ldots \ell_{N+1}}$, the transfer matrix of a generalized six-vertex model. That we do not find the proper six-vertex model is due to the fact that the correspondence we have established is many-to-one: the arrow configuration does not change if we increase all ℓ_j and m_j by 1. On the other hand, the coefficients W depend not only on ω (i.e. on ρ, v, η and k) but also on ℓ, so that increasing all ℓ by 1 changes the vertex weights. Hence the eigenvalue problem for T is essentially more complicated than in the case of the six-vertex model. Still, one can, in broad lines, follow the procedure developed in section 4.2.

If $\Psi^{\ell_1 \ldots \ell_{N+1}}$ is represented by n down arrows on the edges $j_1, \ldots, j_n$, with $j_1 < \ldots < j_n$, and N-n up arrows, we shall denote it by $\Psi^{\ell_1 | j_1, \ldots, j_n}$ henceforth (cf. the notation $|j_1, \ldots, j_n\rangle$ in section 4.2). The conservation of n tells us to look for eigenvectors of the form

$$\Psi = \sum_{j_1 < \ldots < j_n} \sum_{\ell=1}^{L} f(\ell | j_1, \ldots, j_n) \Psi^{\ell | j_1, \ldots, j_n} \tag{4.113}$$

The next, and crucial, step is a generalized "Bethe Ansatz": we assume that f is of the form

$$f(\ell | j_1, \ldots, j_n) = \sum_P c(P) g_{P1}(\ell, j_1) g_{P2}(\ell-2, j_2) \ldots g_{Pn}(\ell-2n+2, j_n) , \tag{4.114}$$

where $g_1(\ell,j)$, ..., $g_n(\ell,j)$ are "single-particle" functions of ℓ and j, comparable to the functions exp(ikj) in section 4.2; for a motivation of this assumption see ref. 35 III. The functions g_r and the coefficients c(P) are determined by substituting (4.113) with (4.114) into the equation $T\Psi = \Lambda\Psi$.

The solution can be characterized by n wave numbers $k_1, \ldots, k_n$, determined by the coupled equations

$$Nk_r = (2m_r - n + 1)\pi - \sum_{s=1}^{n} \zeta(k_r, k_s) \quad (m_r = 0, 1, \ldots, N-1; \quad r = 1, \ldots, n) , \tag{4.115}$$

where the function $\zeta(k,k')$ is not defined explicitly but only through the form it takes after a change of variable from k to u given by

$$e^{ik} = h(u+\eta) / h(u-\eta), \qquad h(u) = H(u)\Theta(-u) , \tag{4.116}$$

viz. by

$$\zeta(k,k') = \tilde{\zeta}(u,u'), \qquad e^{-i\tilde{\zeta}(u,u')} = -h(u-u'+2\eta) / h(u-u'-2\eta) . \tag{4.117}$$

Eqs. (4.115), (4.116) and (4.117) are the counterparts of eqs. (4.42), (4.45) (solved for e^{ik}), and (4.37), respectively. The functions g_r are given in terms of the u_r (and hence the k_r) by

$$g_r(\ell, j) = \left(\frac{h(u_r+\eta)}{h(u_r-\eta)} \right)^j \frac{h(w_{\ell+j-1} - \eta - u_r)}{h(w_{\ell+j-2}) h(w_{\ell+j-1})} , \tag{4.118}$$

$$w_\ell = \tfrac{1}{2}(s+\bar{s}) - K(k) + 2\ell\eta , \tag{4.119}$$

and the coefficients c(P) by the following counterpart of eq. (4.41):

$$c(P) = (-1)^P \exp\{-\tfrac{1}{2}i \sum_{r<s} \zeta(k_{Pr}, k_{Ps})\} = (-1)^P c^{-1} \prod_{r<s} h(u_{Pr} - u_{Ps} + 2\eta) , \tag{4.120}$$

$$c = \prod_{r<s} \{h(u_r - u_s + 2\eta)\}^{\frac{1}{2}} . \tag{4.121}$$

The eigenvalue Λ corresponding to the eigenvector thus obtained is

$$\Lambda = G_- \prod_{r=1}^{n} \frac{h(v-u_r+2\eta)}{h(v-u_r)} + G_+ \prod_{r=1}^{n} \frac{h(v-u_r-2\eta)}{h(v-u_r)} . \qquad (4.122)$$

So far, n has been arbitrary. The result (4.122) can be reformulated so as to allow a comparison with the result of Baxter's first method. In this method, which we have not discussed, the conserved quantities with respect to T (the operators U^x and U^z) play a role; in the present analysis their role is obscured. The comparison shows that the largest eigenvalue Λ_0 is obtained if one takes $n = \frac{1}{2}N$. Note that in this case the boundary condition is satisfied for any η!

For the last step of the analysis one can either follow Baxter [34], who used a new perturbation method, or follow the same procedure as for the six-vertex model [49]. In both cases one has to consider various regimes for the weights ω_r, like in the case of the six-vertex model ($\Delta \geq 1$, $|\Delta| < 1$, etc.). We give the result in the regime $\omega_a \geq \omega_b > 0$, $\omega_d > 0$, $\omega_c > \omega_a+\omega_b+\omega_d$ ("fundamental region", or FR). The partition function of the symmetric eight-vertex model, as opposed to that of the six-vertex model, satisfies a symmetry relation which makes it possible to reduce all cases governed by other inequalities to this case; cases where one or more inequalities are replaced by equalities are handled by taking appropriate limits [34].

It is convenient to change the definition of η and the parametrization (4.102) slightly by putting $\Gamma^{\frac{1}{2}} = ik^{\frac{1}{2}}\mathrm{sn}\, 2\eta$, $\Delta = -\mathrm{cn}\, 2\eta\, \mathrm{dn}\, 2\eta$, $\omega_b = -\rho\, \mathrm{sn}(v-\eta)$. In the FR k is then real ($0 < k < 1$), and η, v and ρ imaginary. We define

$$\tau = \pi K'/2K , \qquad \lambda = -i\pi\eta/K , \qquad \theta = -i\pi v/K . \qquad (4.123)$$

The free energy is then

$$f(\beta) = -\beta^{-1}\left[\log \omega_c + \sum_{m=1}^{\infty} \frac{\sinh^2[m(\tau-\lambda)]\{\cosh m\lambda - \cosh m\theta\}}{m \sinh 2m\tau \cosh m\lambda}\right] . \qquad (4.124)$$

According to section 3.4, the associated Hamiltonian of a given symmetric eight-vertex model is obtained from eqs. (3.19) and (3.20) with ω' satisfying eq. (3.24). A possible choice for ω' is: $\omega'_a = \Delta$, $\omega'_b = 1$, $\omega'_c = 0$, $\omega'_d = \Gamma$, with Γ and Δ given by eq. (4.99); in the FR we have $\Gamma > 0$, $\Delta < -1$. The resulting Hamiltonian is the one given by (4.72) with $J = -\frac{1}{2}$, with a constant term $\frac{1}{2}N\Delta$ added. Conversely, if J_x, J_y, J_z are given, we define J, Γ, Δ as in eq. (4.72), and choose ω' as above, but in terms of <u>these</u> Γ and Δ. The Hamiltonian (1.6) or (4.72) then satisfies the relation

$$\mathcal{H} = -2J(\partial \log T(\omega^L + \varepsilon\omega')/\partial\varepsilon)_{\varepsilon=0} + NJ_z ; \qquad (4.125)$$

this is, in different parameters, Baxter's equation I(125) [35]. Consequently, the ground-state energy is, in an obvious notation,

$$E_0 = -2J(\partial \log \Lambda_0(\omega^L + \varepsilon\omega')/\partial\varepsilon)_{\varepsilon=0} + NJ_z . \qquad (4.126)$$

To evaluate (4.126) we assume that we are in the FR of the Hamiltonian: $\Gamma > 0$, $\Delta < -1$, and we parametrize Γ and Δ: $\Gamma = ik^{\frac{1}{2}}\mathrm{sn}\ 2\eta$, $\Delta = -\mathrm{cn}\ 2\eta\ \mathrm{dn}\ 2\eta$. Given these values of k and η we then parametrize ω^L according to eq. (4.102) by choosing $v = \eta$, $\rho = (\mathrm{sn}\ 2\eta)^{-1}$. Similarly $\omega^L + \varepsilon\omega'$, with the given choice of ω', can be parametrized by choosing $v = \eta - \varepsilon\ \mathrm{sn}\ 2\eta$, $\rho = (\mathrm{sn}\ 2\eta)^{-1}$; remember the minus sign that we recently inserted into the second equation (4.102). The corresponding values of the parameters (4.123) are for ω^L: τ, λ, λ, and for $\omega^L + \varepsilon\omega'$: $\tau, \lambda, \lambda - i\varepsilon\pi K^{-1}\mathrm{sn}\ 2\eta$. Inserting these into (4.124) and differentiating at fixed τ and λ with respect to ε at $\varepsilon=0$, one ultimately finds

$$e_0 = \frac{4\pi i\ \mathrm{sn}\ 2\eta}{K}\ J \sum_{m=1}^{\infty} \frac{\sinh^2[m(\tau-\lambda)]\tanh m\lambda}{\sinh 2m\tau} + J_z \quad . \tag{4.127}$$

This is a real expression because η, and hence $\mathrm{sn}\ 2\eta$, is imaginary.

5. CONCLUDING REMARKS

The expressions for the free energy of the Ising model, eq. (4.27), of the (symmetric) six-vertex model, eqs. (4.63), (4.67), (4.69), (4.70), and of the symmetric eight-vertex model, eq. (4.124), together with the corresponding expressions for the ground-state energy of the associated Hamiltonians, form the final results of our calculations. It should be stressed that all these calculations, together with their extension to correlation functions, form only the first half of the theory of the lattice models we have considered. Once an explicit expression for a quantity has been derived, the next step is to study its analytic properties, in particular its behaviour near singularities. Only if this behaviour is known and well understood, the models are truly models for phase transitions. A discussion of these analytic properties, however, lies outside the scope of this review.

Note: Most of the subject matter of this review has been presented in regular lectures, part of it in special seminars.

REFERENCES

1) C. Domb and M.S. Green, Eds., Phase Transitions and Critical Phenomena, Vol. I, "Exact Results" (Academic Press, London, 1972), chaps. 5-8.
2) J.K. Percus, Combinatorial Methods (Springer-Verlag New York, New York, 1971).
3) C. Domb, Adv. in Phys. 9(1960)149.
4) H.S. Green and C.A. Hurst, Order-Disorder Phenomena (Wiley, New York, 1964).
5) D.C. Mattis, The Theory of Magnetism (Harper & Row, New York, 1965).
6) B.M. McCoy and T.T. Wu, The Two-dimensional Ising Model (Harvard University Press, Cambridge, Mass., 1973).
7) E.H. Lieb, "Exactly Soluble Models", in: Mathematical Methods in Solid State and Superfluid Theory (Scottish Universities Summer School, 1967),

R.C. Clark and G.H. Derrick, Eds. (Oliver & Boyd, Edinburgh, 1969); "Models in Statistical Mechanics" in: Statistical Mechanics and Quantum Field Theory (Ecole d'été de Physique Théorique, Les Houches, 1970), C. DeWitt and R. Stora, Eds. (Gordon and Breach, New York, 1971).

8) E.W. Montroll, J.Chem.Phys. 9(1941)706.

9) H.A. Kramers and G.H. Wannier, Phys.Rev. 60(1941)252.

10) E.N. Lassettre and J.P. Howe, J.Chem.Phys. 9(1941)747.

11) R. Kubo, Busseiron-kenkyu 1(1943)1.

12) L. Onsager, Phys.Rev. 65(1944)117.

13) Y. Nambu, Progr.Theor.Phys. 5(1950)1.

14) E.H. Lieb, T.D. Schultz and D.C. Mattis, Ann.Phys. 16(1961)407.

15) S. Katsura, Phys.Rev. 127(1962)1508.

16) W. Heisenberg, Z.Phys. 49(1928)619.

17) H.A. Bethe, Z.Phys. 71(1931)205.

18) L. Hulthén, Arkiv Mat.Astron.Fys. 26A(1938)1.

19) R. Orbach, Phys.Rev. 112(1958)309.

20) C.N. Yang and C.P. Yang, Phys.Rev. 147(1966)303; 150(1966)321,327.

21) J. des Cloizeaux and M. Gaudin, J.Math.Phys. 7(1966)1384.

22) R.J. Baxter, Ann.Phys. 70(1972)323.

23) F.Y. Wu, Phys.Rev.Letters 22(1969)1174.

24) C. Fan and F.Y. Wu, Phys.Rev. 179(1969)560.

25) B.U. Felderhof, Physica 65(1973)421; 66(1973)279,509.

26) L. Pauling, J.Am.Chem.Soc. 57(1935)2680.

27) E.H. Lieb, Phys.Rev.Letters 18(1967)692; Phys.Rev. 162(1967)162.

28) J.C. Slater, J.Chem.Phys. 9(1941)16.

29) E.H. Lieb, Phys.Rev.Letters 19(1967)108.

30) F. Rys, Helv.Phys.Acta 36(1963)537.

31) E.H. Lieb, Phys.Rev.Letters 18(1967)1046.

32) C.P. Yang, Phys.Rev.Letters 19(1967)586.

33) B. Sutherland, C.N. Yang and C.P. Yang, Phys.Rev.Letters 19(1967)588.

34) R.J. Baxter, Ann.Phys. 70(1972)193.

35) R.J. Baxter, Ann.Phys. 76(1973)1 (paper I), 25(paper II), 48(paper III).

36) T.D. Schultz, D.C. Mattis, E.H. Lieb, Rev.Mod.Phys. 36(1964)856.

37) B.M. McCoy and T.T. Wu, Nuovo Cimento 56B(1968)311.

38) B. Sutherland, J.Math.Phys. 11(1970)3183.

39) M. Suzuki, Progr.Theor.Phys. 46(1971)1337.

40) S. Krinsky, Phys.Letters 39A(1972)169.

41) B.U. Felderhof and J. Rae, private communication.

42) L. Onsager, "The Ising Model in Two Dimensions" in: Critical Phenomena in Alloys, Magnets and Superconductors, R.E. Mills, E. Ascher and R.I. Jaffee, Eds. (McGraw-Hill, New York, 1971), p. 3.

43) R.J. Boel and P.W. Kasteleyn, to be published.

44) J. Rae, J.Phys. A6(1973)L 140.

45) A. Brauer, "On the Characteristic Roots of Non-negative Matrices" in: Recent Advances in Matrix Theory, H. Schneider, Ed. (University of Wisconsin Press, Madison, 1964),p.3.

46) F.R. Gantmacher, Matrizenrechnung II (Deutscher Verlag der Wissenschaften, Berlin, 1966),p.56.

47) R.B. Jones, J.Phys. A6(1973)928; A7(1974)280, 495.

48) I.S. Gradshteyn and I.M. Ryzhik, Table of Integrals, Series and Products (Academic Press, New York, 1965),pp.909-925.

49) J.D. Johnson, S. Krinsky, B.M. McCoy, Phys.Rev. A8(1973)2526, in particular section IVB, p. 2535.

THE FUNCTIONAL INTEGRAL APPROACH TO QUANTUM STATISTICAL MECHANICS

J. HIJMANS

Institute for Theoretical Physics, University of Amsterdam,
Amsterdam, the Netherlands

1. INTRODUCTION

The concept of an integral over a function space goes back to 1923, when Norbert Wiener[1)] investigated the possibility of describing Brownian motion in terms of averages over the space of all possible trajectories of a Brownian particle. Wiener's work which was mainly concerned with the considerable mathematical difficulties associated with the proper definition of a probability measure in function space attracted little attention among physicists. The recognition of functional integral representations as a useful language for describing physical phenomena came only 25 years later with the publication in 1948 of Feynman's review paper[2)] on the so-called "space time approach" to quantum mechanics. From this formulation of quantum theory, in which the basic entity is a propagator represented by an integral over the space of all possible trajectories of the system, it took only a relatively small step to arrive at a corresponding reformulation of quantum statistical mechanics. This step, which consisted in recognizing the formal similarity between the role of time in quantum mechanics and the role of the reciprocal temperature in statistical mechanics, led Feynman to his path-integral representation of the partition function of a quantum system, which was published in his 1952 paper[3)] on liquid helium.

The next important contribution, which in my opinion was crucial in making functional integration techniques useful for solving statistical mechanical problems, came a few years later independently from M. Kac[4)], who was at that time a colleague of Feynman at Cornell, from A.J.F. Siegert[5)] at Evanston, and from R.L. Stratonovich [6)] in the Soviet Union. Their idea was to simulate the mutual interactions between different particles in a many-body system by a random external field acting on each particle separately, the field being characterized by an appropriate probability density in the space of all functions.

Application of this idea enabled Kac, Uhlenbeck and Hemmer[7)] in 1963 to determine the exact equation of state for the famous van der Waals model. In this case the attractive part of the potential, assumed to be exponential, could be simulated by a field behaving as a stationary Gaussian Markov "process", the "time" playing the role of the (one-dimensional) coordinate of the particle. However, the method of decoupling a many-body system by "parametrizing" its interaction potential is by no means restricted to the case of an exponential pair-potential (in fact not even to a pair-wise additive potential). The appreciation of the generality of the method of parametrization has led to applications in widely different areas such as condensation theory[8)], plasma physics[9)], solid

Fundamental Problems in Statistical Mechanics, Vol. 3, Editor, E.D.G. Cohen.

state physics[10], polymer statistics[11], etc.

The great variety of applications and the diversity of their formulations, makes it rather difficult to discuss functional integration techniques from a unified point of view. Therefore, rather than giving you a (necessarily incoherent and incomplete) survey of the problems where functional integrals have been or can be used, I prefer to give you an idea of the suggestive value of the language of functional integral representations for providing an explicit and "visual" picture of the various possible evolutions of a system and of their relative contributions to the observable behaviour. In doing so I shall more or less follow the historical development, starting from a single particle in a potential field and — by successively adding complications — arriving at a many Boson system in second quantization.

The material of these lectures is a "condensate" of part of the existing literature on functional integration, supplemented by some formulations and conclusions from our own work done in collaboration with F.W. Wiegel[12]. Good sources of information for further details are the books by Feynman and Hibbs[13], and by Rosen[14], the survey papers by Gelfand and Yaglom[15], and by Brush[16], conference reports by Siegert[17] and by Ginibre[18], and the papers by Casher, Lurié and Revzen[19] and by Edwards and Lenard[9]. Many applications of the method of random fields to problems in statistical mechanics are to be found in the work of Edwards and collaborators, published in an almost uninterrupted stream of papers in the Philosophical Magazine, the Proceedings of the Physical Society, London, and the Journal of Physics B and C, from about 1958 onwards.

2. A SINGLE PARTICLE IN CLASSICAL AND IN QUANTUM MECHANICS

Let us consider a single particle moving in a potential field $\phi(\vec{r})$. In classical mechanics one determines its trajectory in phase space by means of Hamilton's principle of least action. The trajectory is a curve in the 6-dimensional space of coordinates and velocity components. Along each trajectory, $(\vec{r}(t);\vec{v}(t))$ one defines the action-integral,

$$W([\vec{r}];[\vec{v}]) = \int_{t_i}^{t_f} dt\, L(\vec{r}(t);\vec{v}(t)) \quad , \tag{2.1}$$

which is a functional of the trajectory, determined by the Lagrangian of the particle

$$L(\vec{r},\vec{v}) = \frac{1}{2} m\vec{v}^2 - \phi(\vec{r}) \quad . \tag{2.2}$$

The <u>classical trajectory</u>, $(\vec{r}_c(t);\vec{v}_c(t))$ is by definition that trajectory for which the action functional, (2.1), is stationary with respect to all variations of the path, satisfying the restrictions,

$$\delta\vec{v}(t) = \frac{d}{dt}\,\delta\vec{r}(t) \quad , \tag{2.3a}$$

and

$$\delta\vec{r}(t_i) = \delta\vec{r}(t_f) = 0 \quad . \tag{2.3b}$$

From the stationarity condition, $\delta W_c = 0$, one finds, carrying out a partial integration, and using the restrictions (2.3), the condition

$$\delta W_c = \int_{t_i}^{t_f} dt \left(\frac{\partial L}{\partial\vec{r}} - \frac{d}{dt}\frac{\partial L}{\partial\vec{v}}\right)_c \delta\vec{r}(t) = 0 \quad , \tag{2.4}$$

which — because of the independence of the variations at different times — is equivalent with the Euler-Lagrange equation,

$$\frac{d}{dt}\frac{\partial L}{\partial\vec{v}_c} - \frac{\partial L}{\partial\vec{r}_c} = m\,\frac{d\vec{v}_c}{dt} + \frac{\partial\phi}{\partial\vec{r}_c} = 0 \quad , \tag{2.5}$$

i.e. with Newton's equation of motion.

Multiplication of this equation by $\vec{v}_c$ shows that the energy of the particle,

$$\varepsilon = \frac{1}{2}\,m\vec{v}_c^{\,2} + \phi(\vec{r}_c) \tag{2.6}$$

is a constant of the motion. This allows us to eliminate the potential from the action function (2.1) along the classical trajectory. Thus we may write

$$W_c = \int_{t_i}^{t_f} dt\left(m\vec{v}_c^{\,2}(t) - \varepsilon\right) \tag{2.7a}$$

$$= \int_{\vec{r}_i}^{\vec{r}_f} \vec{p}_c\cdot d\vec{r}_c - \varepsilon(t_f - t_i) \quad , \tag{2.7b}$$

where in the last expression we have introduced the momentum of the particle

$$\vec{p}_c = \frac{\partial L}{\partial\vec{v}_c} = m\vec{v}_c \quad . \tag{2.8}$$

In quantum mechanics one describes the time evolution of the system in a probabilistic way. The state of the particle is no longer characterized by a point $(\vec{r},\vec{v})$ in phase-space, but by a wave function $\psi(\vec{r},t)$, satisfying the Schrödinger equation

$$H\psi(\vec{r},t) = -\left\{\frac{\hbar^2}{2m}\Delta + \phi(\vec{r})\right\}\psi(\vec{r},t) = i\hbar\,\frac{\partial\psi(\vec{r},t)}{\partial t} , \qquad (2.9)$$

which determines a probability density

$$\rho(\vec{r},t) = |\psi(\vec{r},t)|^2 , \qquad (2.10a)$$

and a probability current density,

$$\vec{j}(\vec{r},t) = \mathrm{Re}\left(\frac{\hbar}{im}\,\psi^*(\vec{r},t)\vec{\nabla}\psi(\vec{r},t)\right) \qquad (2.10b)$$

in every point of the configuration space of the particle (i.e. not just along the classical trajectory).

What is the relation between the two formalisms? According to the correspondence principle the two descriptions must become equivalent in the classical limit, $h \to 0$. In order to see what this means, let us express the wave function in terms of an amplitude function and a phase function, writing

$$\psi(\vec{r},t) = A(\vec{r},t)\exp i\Phi(\vec{r},t) . \qquad (2.11)$$

Substitution into (2.9) and separation into real and imaginary parts, gives rise to two equations:

$$\hbar\frac{\partial\Phi}{\partial t} + \frac{\hbar^2}{2m}(\vec{\nabla}\Phi)^2 + \phi(\vec{r}) = \frac{\hbar^2}{2m}\frac{\Delta A}{A} , \qquad (2.12a)$$

$$\frac{\partial A}{\partial t} + \frac{\hbar}{m}(\vec{\nabla}A.\vec{\nabla}\Phi) + \frac{\hbar}{2m}A\Delta\Phi = 0 . \qquad (2.12b)$$

The physical significance of these equations can be made visible by introducing the probability density,

$$\rho(\vec{r},t) = \left(A(\vec{r},t)\right)^2 \qquad (2.13a)$$

and the current density

$$\vec{j}(\vec{r},t) = \frac{\hbar}{m}\left(A(\vec{r},t)\right)^2\vec{\nabla}\Phi(\vec{r},t) . \qquad (2.13b)$$

Multiplying eq. (2.12b) by $\frac{1}{2}A(\vec{r},t)$ it takes the form

$$\frac{\partial\rho(\vec{r},t)}{\partial t} + \vec{\nabla}.\vec{j}(\vec{r},t) = 0 \qquad (2.14)$$

of a continuity equation for a (probability) "fluid".

Taking the gradient of eq. (2.12a), and introducing the local velocity of the fluid,

$$\vec{v}(\vec{r},t) = \frac{\hbar}{m}\vec{\nabla}\Phi(\vec{r},t) \tag{2.15}$$

and its total time derivative,

$$\frac{d\vec{v}}{dt} = \frac{\partial\vec{v}}{\partial t} + (\vec{v}.\vec{\nabla})\vec{v} \quad , \tag{2.16}$$

we obtain the equation

$$m\frac{d\vec{v}(\vec{r},t)}{dt} + \vec{\nabla}\phi(\vec{r}) = \frac{\hbar^2}{2m}\vec{\nabla}\left(\frac{\Delta A(\vec{r},t)}{A(\vec{r},t)}\right) \quad , \tag{2.17}$$

which determines the "stream lines" of the probability flow. Comparing this equation with Newton's equation of motion, (2.5), we see that in the classical limit, when the quantummechanical force term on the right-hand side of (2.17) is absent, the stream-lines of the probability flow coincide with classical trajectories of the particle for various choices of the initial conditions (see fig. 1).

In order to stress the wave character of the function (2.11), we may also use an optical-, instead of a hydrodynamical picture, replacing the probability flow by the propagation of a wave through a medium, whose refractive index is determined by the local potential, $\phi(\vec{r})$. Then the stream-lines of the probability flow

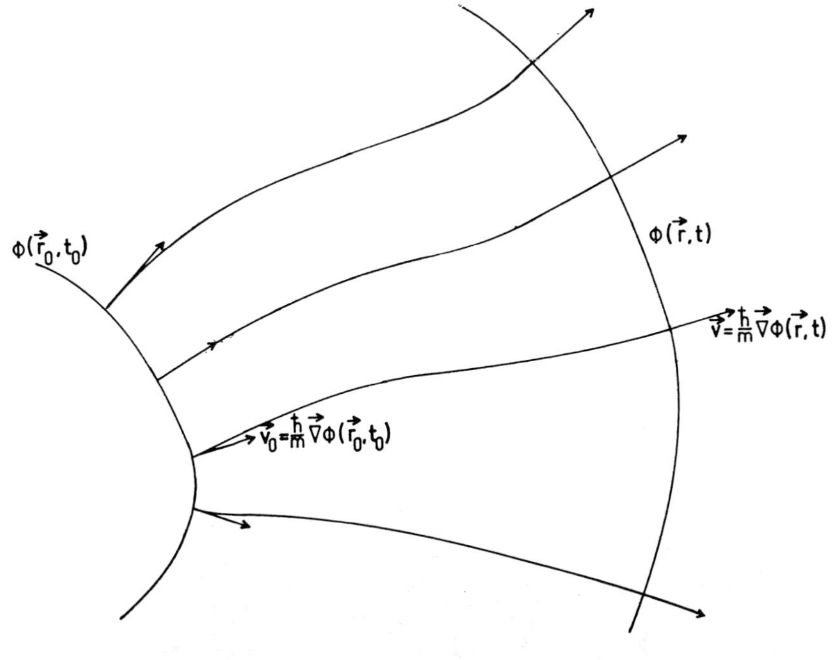

Fig. 1. Stream-lines and wave-fronts of the probability flow.

correspond to light-rays, propagating in the direction of the gradient of the phase function, i.e. orthogonal to the surfaces of constant phase

$$\Phi(\vec{r},t) = \text{const.} \tag{2.18}$$

These surfaces should therefore be identified with the wave-fronts.

Stationary state solutions of the Schrödinger equation are found by imposing in addition to (2.12) the conditions

$$\frac{\partial A}{\partial t} = 0 \quad ; \quad \frac{\partial \Phi}{\partial t} = -\omega = \text{const.} \tag{2.19a,b}$$

Combining the last condition with eq. (2.15), which fixes the gradient of Φ, we see that the phase-function must be of the form

$$\Phi(\vec{r},t) = \int_{\vec{r}_0}^{\vec{r}} \vec{k}(\vec{r}\,').d\vec{r}\,' - \omega(t-t_0) \quad , \tag{2.20}$$

with

$$\omega = \varepsilon/\hbar \quad , \quad \text{and} \quad \vec{k}(\vec{r}) = m\vec{v}(\vec{r})/\hbar \quad , \tag{2.21a,b}$$

representing a frequency and a local wave-number, respectively. The latter function, determined by the equation of motion (2.12a) and the stationarity condition (2.19b), is given by

$$\vec{k}(\vec{r}) = \left\{2m\left(\varepsilon-\phi(\vec{r})\right)/\hbar^2 + \Delta A(\vec{r})/A(\vec{r})\right\}^{1/2} \quad . \tag{2.22}$$

The classical limit, implying that in the last expression the second term on the right is negligible with respect to the first one, now corresponds to the approximation of geometrical optics, according to which the relative variation of the amplitude of the wave over the extent of one wave length, $\lambda = 2\pi/|\vec{k}|$, is everywhere negligible, i.e.:

$$\left(\lambda(\vec{r})\right)^2 \Delta A(\vec{r})/A(\vec{r}) \ll 1 \quad . \tag{2.23}$$

Multiplying eq. (2.20) by $\hbar$, and using (2.21), we see that the function

$$W(\vec{r},t) = \hbar\,\Phi(\vec{r},t) = \int_{\vec{r}_v}^{\vec{r}} m\vec{v}(\vec{r}\,').d\vec{r}\,' - \varepsilon(t-t_0) \tag{2.24}$$

has the general form of an action-function, which in the classical limit (2.23) reduces to the classical action of the particle, given by eq. (2.7).

Thus we see that the principle of least action of mechanics corresponds to Fermat's principle of geometrical optics, saying that waves in a medium propagate along "rays", i.e. trajectories along which the optical path-length is stationary with respect to arbitrary variations of the path.

3. PATH-INTEGRAL REPRESENTATION OF THE PROPAGATOR FOR A SINGLE PARTICLE

The analogy between classical mechanics and geometrical optics immediately suggests a correspondence between the quantum-effects associated with the non-classical term in the equation of motion, (2.17), and interference phenomena associated with the breakdown of the condition (2.23) in wave optics.

The fundamental idea underlying Feynman's approach to quantum mechanics is that the observable behaviour of a particle moving from an initial point $(\vec{r}_0, t_0)$ to a final point $(\vec{r}, t)$ in phase-space is not just determined by the classical trajectory between these points alone, but is the result of constructive interference of a bundle of "rays" close to the classical trajectory with a diameter of the order $\hbar$. The quality which singles out the classical path from among all conceivable paths is that its phase is stationary with respect to fluctuations to nearby paths. This local coherence stabilizes the contribution from the classical path, whereas the contributions from all other paths are washed out by destructive interference.

In order to put this idea on a quantitative basis, Feynman[2)] introduced a (complex) probability amplitude, or propagator, $K(\vec{r},t;\vec{r}_0,t_0)$, whose absolute square,

$$P(\vec{r},t;\vec{r}_0,t_0) = |K(\vec{r},t;\vec{r}_0,t_0)|^2 \tag{3.1}$$

represents the (conditional) probability density for the particle to arrive at time t at the position $\vec{r}$, given that it started at time t_0 from the position $\vec{r}_0$.

More specifically the propagator is defined as the integral operator transforming the initial wave-function at time t_0, into the wave function at time t, i.e. by the identity

$$\psi(\vec{r},t) = \int_\Omega d\vec{r}_0 K(\vec{r},t;\vec{r}_0,t_0)\psi(\vec{r}_0,t_0) \qquad (\text{for } t > t_0) \quad , \tag{3.2}$$

where Ω is the volume enclosing the particle.

From this identity, together with the wave-equation (2.9) it follows that $K(\vec{r},t;\vec{r}_0,t_0)$ is the Green-function of the Schrödinger equation, i.e. that it satisfies

$$\left\{\frac{\partial}{\partial t} - \frac{i\hbar}{2m}\Delta_r + \frac{i}{\hbar}\,\phi(\vec{r})\right\}K(\vec{r},t;\vec{r}_0,t_0) = \delta(\vec{r}-\vec{r}_0)\,\delta(t-t_0) \quad . \tag{3.3}$$

Now, in order to derive a path-integral representation for the propagator, we note that the kernel $K(\vec{r},t;\vec{r}_0,t_0)$ satisfies the so-called semi-group composition law

$$\begin{aligned}\int_\Omega d\vec{r}\,'K(\vec{r},t;\vec{r}\,',t')K(\vec{r}\,',t';\vec{r}_0,t_0) &= K(\vec{r},t;\vec{r}_0,t_0)\ , \quad \text{for} \quad t_0 < t' < t \\ &= 0\ , \quad \text{for} \quad t' \leqslant t_0;\ t' \geqslant t\ .\end{aligned} \tag{3.4}$$

This property, which can be verified immediately by iterating the transformation (3.2), is known in the theory of Brownian motion as the "Markov"-property and the integral equation (3.4) is called the Chapman-Kolmogorov (or sometimes Smoluchowsky) equation. From this integral equation one can derive a differential equation for $K(\vec{r},t;\vec{r}_0,t_0)$ in precisely the same way as one derives in the theory of Brownian motion the Fokker-Planck equation from the Chapman-Kolmogorov equation (see for instance ref. 20).

Writing

$$\frac{\partial K(\vec{r},t;\vec{r}_0,t_0)}{\partial t} = \lim_{\Delta t\to 0}\frac{1}{\Delta t}\left(K(\vec{r},t+\Delta t;\vec{r}_0,t_0) - K(\vec{r},t;\vec{r}_0,t_0)\right) \quad ,$$

and applying (3.4) to the first term on the right, one obtains

$$\begin{aligned}\frac{\partial K(\vec{r},t;\vec{r}_0,t_0)}{\partial t} = \lim_{\Delta t\to 0}\frac{1}{\Delta t}\Bigg(\int d\vec{r}\,'K(\vec{r},t+\Delta t;\vec{r}\,',t)K(\vec{r}\,',t;\vec{r}_0,t_0) - \\ - K(\vec{r},t;\vec{r}_0,t_0)\Bigg) \quad .\end{aligned}$$

Substituting for $K(\vec{r}\,',t;\vec{r}_0,t_0)$ the Taylor expansion,

$$K(\vec{r}\,',t;\vec{r}_0,t_0) = \sum_{n=0}^{\infty}\frac{1}{n!}\left((\vec{r}\,'-\vec{r})\cdot\vec{\nabla}_r\right)^n K(\vec{r},t;\vec{r}_0,t_0) \quad ,$$

and integrating term by term, one obtains the differential equation

$$\frac{\partial K(\vec{r},t;\vec{r}_0,t_0)}{\partial t} = \left(m_0(\vec{r}) + \left(\vec{m}_1(\vec{r})\cdot\vec{\nabla}\right) + \frac{1}{2!}\left(\vec{\vec{m}}_2(\vec{r}):\vec{\nabla}\vec{\nabla}\right) + \ldots\right)K(\vec{r},t;\vec{r}_0,t_0)\ , \tag{3.5}$$

where we have introduced the "moments" of the propagator,

$$m_0(\vec{r}) = \lim_{\Delta t\to 0}\frac{1}{\Delta t}\left(\int d\vec{r}\,'K(\vec{r},t+\Delta t;\vec{r}\,',t) - 1\right) \quad , \tag{3.6a}$$

$$\vec{m}_1(\vec{r}) = \lim_{\Delta t \to 0} \frac{1}{\Delta t} \int d\vec{r}\,'(\vec{r}\,'-\vec{r})K(\vec{r},t+\Delta t;\vec{r}\,',t) \quad , \tag{3.6b}$$

$$\vec{\vec{m}}_2(\vec{r}) = \lim_{\Delta t \to 0} \frac{1}{\Delta t} \int d\vec{r}\,'(\vec{r}\,'-\vec{r})(\vec{r}\,'-\vec{r})K(\vec{r},t+\Delta t;\vec{r},t) \quad , \tag{3.6c}$$

$$\ldots\ldots , \text{ etc.}$$

Thus, in order to achieve that the propagator satisfies the differential equation, (3.3), we have to ensure that the moments are given by

$$m_0(\vec{r}) = -(i/\hbar)\phi(\vec{r}) \tag{3.7a}$$

$$\vec{m}_1(\vec{r}) \equiv 0 \tag{3.7b}$$

$$\vec{\vec{m}}_2(\vec{r}) \equiv i\hbar/m \tag{3.7c}$$

$$m_n(\vec{r}) \equiv 0 \quad , \quad \text{for all} \quad n > 2 \quad . \tag{3.7d}$$

These requirements on the moments are sufficient to determine the short time behaviour of the propagator. This can be made plausible by first looking at the "free" propagator, i.e. the Green-function of the field-free equation

$$\left(\frac{\partial}{\partial t} - \frac{i\hbar}{2m}\Delta_r\right)K_0(\vec{r},t;\vec{r}_0,t_0) = \delta(t-t_0)\delta(\vec{r}-\vec{r}_0) \quad . \tag{3.8}$$

This free propagator is the well-known fundamental solution of the diffusion equation,

$$K_o(\vec{r},t;\vec{r}_0,t_0) = \left(4\pi D(t-t_0)\right)^{-3/2} \exp\left(-\frac{(\vec{r}-\vec{r}_0)^2}{4D(t-t_0)}\right) . \, \theta(t-t_0) \tag{3.9}$$

with "diffusion" constant given by

$$D = i\hbar/2m \quad , \tag{3.10}$$

and with

$$\theta(t-t_0) = \begin{cases} 0 & \text{for} \quad t \leqslant t_0 \\ 1 & \text{for} \quad t > t_0 \quad , \end{cases} \tag{3.11}$$

representing the unit step function.

The presence of the field, $\phi(\vec{r})$, affects only the zeroth "moment" of the propagator, (3.7a), characterizing its normalization. Accordingly, the short time behaviour of the propagator for a particle in a field,

$$K(\vec{r}+\Delta\vec{r},t+\Delta t;\vec{r},t) \underset{(\Delta t\to 0)}{\sim} \left(\frac{m}{2\pi i\hbar\Delta t}\right)^{3/2}.\exp\frac{i}{\hbar}\left(\frac{1}{2}m\left(\frac{\Delta\vec{r}}{\Delta t}\right)^2-\phi(\vec{r})\Delta t\right) , \qquad (3.12)$$

differs from the behaviour of the free propagator, (3.9), only in the presence of an extra factor $\exp\{-(i/\hbar)\phi(\vec{r})\Delta t\}$.

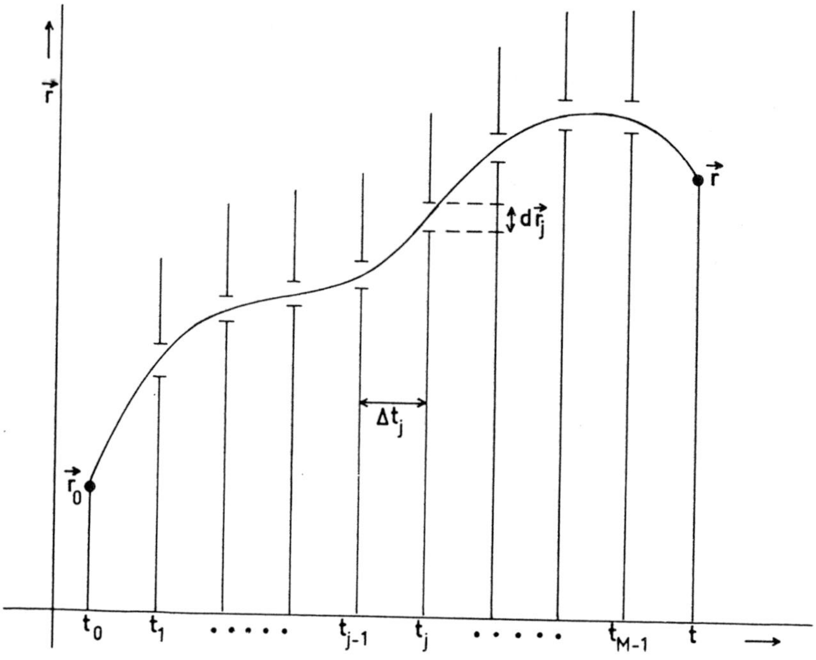

Fig. 2. Characterization of a trajectory, $\vec{r}(t)$ in function-space.

We can now construct a path-integral representation for the propagator, $K(\vec{r},t;\vec{r}_0,t_0)$, by subdividing the time interval $t-t_0$ into M subintervals of length Δt each (see fig. 2), applying the semi-group composition law (3.4) as many times as there are intermediate sample points (i.e. M-1 times), and taking the limit

$$\lim_{(M,\Delta t)} = \lim\left\{M\to\infty;\ \Delta t\to 0;\ \sum_{j=1}^{M}(t_j-t_{j-1}) = M\Delta t = t-t_0\right\} . \qquad (3.13)$$

Then, combining the (M-1)-fold integral, the normalizing factor, and the limit (3.13) into a single functional integration symbol,

$$\int_{(\vec{r}_0,t_0)}^{(\vec{r},t)} d[\vec{r}(t)] \equiv \lim_{(M,\Delta t)} \left(4\pi D\Delta t\right)^{-\frac{3M}{2}} \int_{\Omega} d\vec{r}_1 \cdots \int_{\Omega} d\vec{r}_{M-1} , \qquad (3.14)$$

we arrive at the expression

$$K(r,t;r_0,t_0) = \int_{(\vec{r}_0,t_0)}^{(\vec{r},t)} d[\vec{r}(t)] \exp\left(\frac{i}{\hbar}\int_{t_0}^{t} dt \left\{\frac{1}{2}m\left(\frac{d\vec{r}(t)}{dt}\right)^2 - \phi(\vec{r})\right\}\right) . \tag{3.15}$$

The integral in the exponent of (3.15) will be recognized as the classical action functional defined by equations (2.1) and (2.2).

The foregoing derivation shows that it is indeed possible to represent the propagator in the form of a path integral. The result that the solution of a second-order differential equation such as (3.3), can be always represented by a path-integral expression of the form (3.15) is due to M. Kac[4], who was the first to give a systematic proof of this relation between differential equations and path integrals.

In the quantum mechanical case the integrand of the path-integral expression, (3.15), is a complex functional of the trajectory. Therefore the contributions from different paths connecting the points $(\vec{r}_0,t_0)$ and $(\vec{r},t)$ will in general annihilate each other by destructive interference. Only near the classical trajectory, where the phase is stationary, the contributions will survive as a result of the local coherence of the contributions from nearby fluctuation paths.

It is tempting to associate the classical limit, $\hbar \to 0$, with the result of an evaluation of the functional integral, (3.15), by means of the "method of stationary phase" in function space. However, the applicability of this method, implying the approximation of the whole (functional) integral by the value of its (functional) integrand at the "point" (in function space) of stationary phase, is by no means straight forward in the case of function-space integrals. In fact this method (which for real integrals is called the method of steepest descent) may give rise to rather serious difficulties.

However, regardless of the method for evaluating the functional integral, the representation (3.15) of the propagator in terms of explicit contributions from well-defined trajectories, provides a much more visual picture of the behaviour of our system, than the customary Schrödinger formalism, embodied by the differential equation (2.9).

4. MANY PARTICLE SYSTEMS; THE GRAND PARTITION FUNCTION OF AN IDEAL GAS IN AN EXTERNAL FIELD

We now want to generalize our result for one particle to a many-particle system, and to establish a connection with quantum statistical mechanics. For this purpose it is convenient to start from the bilinear expansion of the propagator,

$$K(\vec{r},t;\vec{r}_0,t_0) = \sum_k u_k(\vec{r})u_k^*(\vec{r}_0)\, e^{-\frac{i}{\hbar}\varepsilon_k(t-t_0)} \tag{4.1}$$

where the $u_k(\vec{r})$ represent the eigenfunctions and ε_k the eigenvalues of the one particle Hamiltonian, satisfying

$$H\, u_k(\vec{r}) = \left\{ -\frac{\hbar^2}{2m} \Delta_r + \phi(\vec{r}) \right\} u_k(\vec{r}) = \varepsilon_k u_k(\vec{r}) \tag{4.2}$$

Just as the one-particle Green-function equation, (3.3), is satisfied identically by the expression (4.1) for the one particle propagator, the corresponding N-particle equation

$$\left\{ \frac{\partial}{\partial t'} + \frac{i}{\hbar} H_N\left(\{\vec{r}\,'\}\right) \right\} K_N\left(\{\vec{r}\,'\},t';\{\vec{r}\},t\right) = \delta(t'-t) \prod_{j=1}^{N} \delta(\vec{r}_j\,'-\vec{r}_j) \tag{4.3}$$

is satisfied identically by the expression

$$K_N\left(\{\vec{r}\,'\};\{\vec{r}\};t'-t\right) = \sum_{\{k\}} U_{\{k\}}\left(\{r'\}\right) U^*_{\{k\}}\left(\{\vec{r}\}\right) \exp\left(-\frac{i}{\hbar} E_{\{k\}}(t'-t)\right) \tag{4.4}$$

where

$$U_{\{k\}}\left(\{\vec{r}\}\right) \equiv U_{k_1,k_2,\ldots k_j\ldots}(\vec{r}_1,\vec{r}_2,\ldots\vec{r}_N) \tag{4.5a}$$

and

$$E_{\{k\}} \equiv E_{k_1,k_2,\ldots k_j\ldots} \tag{4.5b}$$

represent the set of eigenfunctions and the corresponding eigenvalues of the N-particle Hamiltonian, $H_N(\{\vec{r}\})$, labelled by the set of quantum numbers $\{k\} \equiv (k_1,k_2,\ldots k_j\ldots)$.

The generalization from a one- to a many-particle system is perfectly straightforward, except for the fact that we have to take into account the indistinguishability of the particles. This can be done by restricting the set of eigenfunctions (4.5a) to functions which are either symmetric or antisymmetric with respect to interchange of particle coordinates, depending on whether we are dealing with Bosons or Fermions respectively.

The link with quantum statistical mechanics is established by observing the formal similarity between the propagator, (4.4), which describes the evolution of a quantum mechanical N-particle system as a function of <u>time</u>, and the density matrix

$$\rho_N\left(\{\vec{r}\,'\};\{\vec{r}\};\beta\right) = \sum_{\{k\}} U_{\{k\}}\left(\{r'\}\right) U^*_{\{k\}}\left(\{\vec{r}\}\right) \exp\left(-\beta E_{\{k\}}\right) \quad , \tag{4.6}$$

which characterizes a quantum statistical equilibrium ensemble as a function of reciprocal <u>temperature</u>, $\beta = 1/kT$. Whereas the (unsymmetrized) propagator (4.4) is the fundamental solution of the N-particle wave equation, (4.3), the (unsymmetrized) density matrix, (4.6), satisfies the N-particle Bloch equation

$$\left\{\frac{\partial}{\partial\beta} + H_N\left(\{\vec{r}\,'\}\right)\right\} \rho_N\left(\{\vec{r}\,'\};\{\vec{r}\};\beta\right) = \delta(\beta) \cdot \prod_{j=1}^{N} \delta(\vec{r}\,'_j-\vec{r}_j) \quad , \tag{4.7}$$

which differs from eq. (4.3) only in the replacement of the time by $-i\hbar\beta$.

For the time being we shall restrict ourselves to a system of N non-interacting particles, moving in a common (in general inhomogeneous) external field $\phi(\vec{r})$. For such a system the N-particle Hamiltonian is a sum of one-particle Hamiltonians and the fundamental solution of the N-particle Bloch equation is simply the product of N one-particle propagators, i.e.

$$\rho_N\left(\{\vec{r}\,'\};\{\vec{r}\};\beta\right) = \prod_{j=1}^{N} \rho(\vec{r}\,'_j;\vec{r}_j;\beta) \quad . \tag{4.8}$$

Each of these can be represented by a functional integral of the form

$$\rho(\vec{r}\,';\vec{r};\beta) = \int_{(\vec{r},0)}^{(\vec{r}\,',\beta)} d[\vec{r}(\tau)] \exp\left(- \int_0^{\beta} d\tau \left\{\frac{m}{2\hbar^2} \left(\frac{d\vec{r}(\tau)}{d\tau}\right)^2 + \phi(\vec{r}(\tau))\right\} \right) \tag{4.9}$$

where the functional integration symbol is defined as in (3.14) with the diffusion coefficient (3.10) and with the time replaced by the thermodynamic 'time' variable

$$t = - i\hbar\tau \quad . \tag{4.10}$$

In order to account for the statistics of the particles we have to project the unsymmetrized density matrix, (4.8), on to the subspace of functions that are symmetric or antisymmetric in the labels of the particles. In this way we obtain the symmetrized density matrix

$$\rho_N^{(\varepsilon)}\left(\{\vec{r}\,'\};\{\vec{r}\};\beta\right) = \frac{1}{N!}\sum_P \varepsilon^P \rho_N\left(\{P\vec{r}\,'\};\{\vec{r}\};\beta\right) \tag{4.11}$$

where $\varepsilon = +1$ for Bosons and -1 for Fermions, and

$$\{P\vec{r}\,'\} \equiv \left(\vec{r}\,'_{P1},\vec{r}\,'_{P2},\ldots \vec{r}\,'_{PN}\right) \tag{4.12}$$

represents a permutation of the labels of the final coordinates of the particles, relative to those of the initial coordinates.

The bulk thermodynamic properties of the system are determined by the canonical partition function

$$Z_N(\beta,\Omega) = \mathrm{Tr}\, \rho_N^{(\varepsilon)}\left(\{\vec{r}\,'\};\{\vec{r}\};\beta\right) \quad , \tag{4.13}$$

which — on account of (4.8), (4.9) and (4.11) — can be written in functional integral form as

$$Z_N(\beta,\Omega) = \frac{1}{N!}\sum_P \varepsilon^P \int_\Omega d\vec{r}_1 \dots \int_\Omega d\vec{r}_N \int_{(\vec{r}_1,0)}^{(\vec{r}_{P1},\beta)} d[\vec{r}_1(\tau)] \dots \int_{(\vec{r}_N,0)}^{(\vec{r}_{PN},\beta)} d[\vec{r}_N(\tau)] \quad .$$

$$\cdot \exp\left(-\sum_{j=1}^{N}\int_0^\beta d\tau \left\{\frac{m}{2\hbar^2}\left(\frac{d\vec{r}_j(\tau)}{d\tau}\right)^2 + \phi(\vec{r}_j(\tau))\right\}\right) \quad . \tag{4.14}$$

In order to evaluate this functional integral, we decompose the permutations P into cycles. The contribution from permutations containing n_1 single elements, n_2 cycles of two elements, and in general n_s cycles of s elements consists of

$$N! \Big/ \prod_{s=1}^{\infty}\left(n_s!\, s^{n_s}\right) \tag{4.15a}$$

identical terms of magnitude

$$\prod_{s=1}^{\infty}\left(C_s(\beta,\Omega)\right)^{n_s} \quad , \tag{4.15b}$$

where each factor

$$C_s(\beta,\Omega) = \int_\Omega d\vec{r}_1 \dots \int_\Omega d\vec{r}_s\, \rho(\vec{r}_1;\vec{r}_s;\beta) \prod_{j=1}^{s-1} \rho(\vec{r}_j;\vec{r}_{j-1};\beta) \tag{4.16}$$

represents the contribution from a cycle of s elements.

Substituting (4.15) into (4.14), and using the fact that the parity of a permuation is odd (or even) accordingly as it contains an odd (or even) number of cycles of even length, we obtain for the partition function

$$Z_N(\beta,\Omega) = \sum_{\{n_s\}}{}' \varepsilon^{\sum_s (s-1)n_s} \prod_{s=1}^{\infty} \frac{1}{n_s!}\left\{\frac{1}{s} C_s(\beta,\Omega)\right\}^{n_s} \quad , \tag{4.17}$$

where the prime on the summation indicates the restriction, $\sum_{s=1}^{\infty} s\, n_s = N$.

This restriction can be removed by going over to the grand partition function

$$\Xi(z,\beta,\Omega) = \sum_{N=0}^{\infty} Z_N(\beta,\Omega)\, z^N \tag{4.18}$$

for which we find, substituting (4.17) and evaluating the multiple sum over $\{n_s\}$:

$$\Xi(z,\beta,\Omega) = \exp\left(\varepsilon^{-1}\sum_{s=1}^{\infty} c_s(\beta,\Omega)\ (\varepsilon z)^s/_s\right) . \tag{4.19}$$

In the absence of the field $\phi(\vec{r})$ the one-particle density matrix $\rho(\vec{r}_j;\vec{r}_{j-1};\beta)$ appearing in (4.16) reduces to the zero-field density matrix, which is given by the expression (3.9) for the free propagator, with D given by (3.10) and t replaced by (4.10), i.e.:

$$\rho_0(\vec{r};\vec{r}_0;\beta) = \left[\frac{m}{2\pi\hbar^2\beta}\right]^{-3/2} \exp\left(-\frac{2m(\vec{r}-\vec{r}_0)^2}{\hbar^2\beta}\right).\theta(\beta) . \tag{4.20}$$

As a consequence the coefficients (4.16) (which can be evaluated easily by Fourier transformation with respect to $\vec{r}-\vec{r}_0$) reduce to

$$c_s^{(0)}(\beta,\Omega) = \sum_{\vec{k}} \exp\left(-\beta\frac{\hbar^2k^2}{2m}.s\right) \tag{4.21}$$

and the grand partition function reduces to the familiar expression,

$$\Xi_0(z,\beta,\Omega) = \prod_{\vec{k}}\left\{1-\varepsilon z\, e^{-\beta\frac{\hbar^2k^2}{2m}}\right\}^{-1/\varepsilon} \tag{4.22}$$

for an ideal gas of Bosons ($\varepsilon = +1$) or Fermions ($\varepsilon = -1$). The case of Boltzmann statistics may also be obtained from (4.22) by letting ε go to zero. This implies that we restrict the cycle length of the permutations to $s = 1$ in eq. (4.19), i.e. that we suppress in (4.14) all permutations, except the identity.

5. FIELD DEPENDENCE OF THE GRAND PARTITION FUNCTION

The grand partition function for an ideal gas in a field $\phi(\vec{r})$ depends on the field via the coefficients (4.16), which are traces of powers of the one-particle density matrix. This function, which is defined as the fundamental solution of the one-particle Bloch equation

$$\left(\frac{\partial}{\partial\beta} - \frac{\hbar^2}{2m}\Delta_r + \phi(\vec{r})\right)\rho(\vec{r};\vec{r}_0;\beta) = \delta(\beta)\,\delta(\vec{r}-\vec{r}_0) \tag{5.1}$$

is related to the solution of the zero-field Bloch equation, given by (4.20), through the integral equation

$$\rho(\vec{r};\vec{r}_0;\beta) = \rho_0(\vec{r};\vec{r}_0;\beta) - \int_0^{\beta} d\tau \int_{\Omega} d\vec{r}_1\,\rho_0(\vec{r}-\vec{r}_1;\beta-\tau)\,\phi(\vec{r}_1)\,\rho(\vec{r};\vec{r}_0;\tau) . \tag{5.2}$$

This can be verified by applying the differential operator, $\partial/\partial\beta - (\hbar^2/2m)\Delta_r$, to both members of (5.2) and noting that the contribution from the second term on the right is just $-\phi(\vec{r})\rho(\vec{r};\vec{r}_0;\beta)$.

Iteration of the integral equation (5.2) leads to an explicit functional Taylor series of the one-particle density matrix in powers of the field, i.e.

$$\rho(\vec{r};\vec{r}_0;\beta) = \sum_{m=0}^{\infty} (-1)^m \int d\{\tau^m\} \int d\{\vec{r}^m\} \rho_0(\vec{r}-\vec{r}_m;\beta-\tau_m) \cdot$$

$$\cdot \sum_{j=1}^{m} \{ \phi(\vec{r}_j) \rho_0(\vec{r}_j-\vec{r}_{j-1};\tau_t-\tau_{j-1}) \} \quad . \tag{5.3}$$

Here we have introduced the abbreviated notation

$$\int d\{\tau^m\} \int d\{\vec{r}^{\,m}\} \equiv \int_0^\beta d\tau_1 \int_\Omega d\vec{r}_1 \ldots \int_0^\beta d\tau_m \int_\Omega d\vec{r}_m \quad , \tag{5.4}$$

and it is understood that $\tau_0 = 0$.

The explicit series (5.3) may now be used for evaluating the coefficients $c_s(\beta,\Omega)$ appearing in the grand partition function (4.19), as functionals of the field $\phi(\vec{r})$. Substituting (5.3) into (4.16) and making use of the semi-group composition law for the zero-field density matrix, i.e.

$$\int d\vec{r}_1 \rho_0(\vec{r}-\vec{r}_1;\tau-\tau_1)\rho_0(\vec{r}_1-\vec{r}_0;\tau_1-\tau_0) = \rho_0(\vec{r}-\vec{r}_0;\tau-\tau_0) \quad , \quad (\tau_0 < \tau_1 < \tau) \tag{5.5}$$

we obtain

$$c_s(\beta,\Omega) = \int_\Omega d\vec{r}_0 \sum_{M=0}^{\infty} (-1)^M \sum_{\{s_j\}}{}' \; d\{\tau^M\} \int d\{\vec{r}^M\} \rho_0(\vec{r}_0-\vec{r}_M;\beta s-\tau_M) \cdot$$

$$\cdot \prod_{j=1}^{M} \{ \phi(\vec{r}_j) \rho_0(\vec{r}_j-\vec{r}_{j-1};\tau_j-\tau_{j-1}+\beta s_j) \} \quad . \tag{5.6}$$

The procedure leading to this result is illustrated in fig. 3. The coordinates $\vec{r}_1,\vec{r}_2,\ldots\vec{r}_s$ appearing in eq. (4.16) have been indicated by crosses. The dots represent the intermediate points $\left(\{\vec{r}^M\},\{\tau^M\}\right)$ introduced as a result of the Taylor expansion (5.3) of each of the density matrices between adjacent crosses. Application of the semi-group composition law (5.5) eliminates all crosses except one, which is needed as a reference point, and whose coordinates have been relabelled $(\vec{r}_0,\tau_0)$. The coordinates of the dots have been renamed successively as $\left(\vec{r}_1,\beta s+\tau_1\right)$, $\left(\vec{r}_2,\beta(s_1+s_2)+\tau_2\right)$,... $\left(\vec{r}_M,\beta\sum_{j=1}^{M} s_j+\tau_M\right)$, where the s_j, ($j = 1,2,\ldots M$), represent the numbers of crosses between consecutive dots, that have been eliminated. The number of crosses between the last dot and the reference point is indicated by s_0 and has to be chosen so as to satisfy the

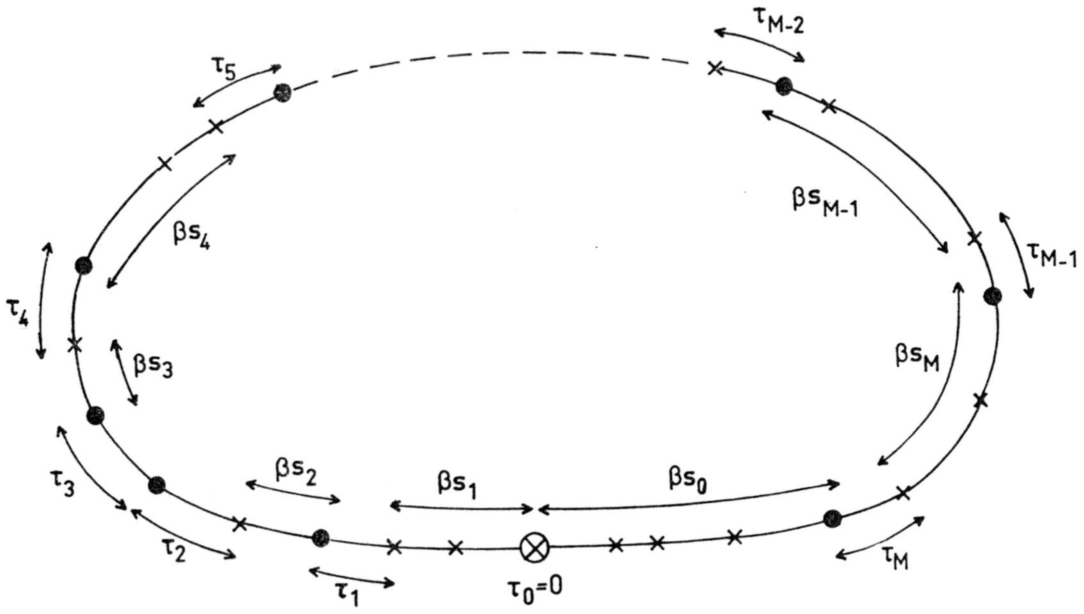

Fig. 3. Schematic representation of the terms in eqs (4.16) and (5.6). The crosses represent the 3-dimensional coordinate-points appearing in the terms of (4.16); the dots indicate intermediate 4-dimensional points, introduced by the Taylor-expansion (5.5).

restriction, $\sum_{j=0}^{M} s_j = s$, indicated by a prime on the second summation in eq. (5.6).

We are now ready to evaluate the grand partition function. Substituting (5.6) into (4.19), separating off the contribution from the terms with $M = 0$, and using the explicit form of the zero-field density matrix (5.2), we obtain an expression of the form

$$\Xi(z,\beta,\Omega) = \Xi_0(z,\beta,\Omega)\; J(z,\beta,[\phi]) \quad , \tag{5.7}$$

with

$$\Xi_0(z,\beta,\Omega) = \exp\left\{ \varepsilon^{-1}\Omega \left(\frac{m}{2\pi\hbar^2\beta}\right)^{3/2} \sum_{s=1}^{\infty} \frac{(\varepsilon z)^s}{s^{5/2}} \right\} \tag{5.8}$$

representing the grand partition function of an ideal Bose or Fermi-gas, and $J(z,\beta,[\phi])$ a functional of the field, which reduces to unity for $\phi(\vec{r}) \to 0$.

In order to determine the explicit form of this functional it is convenient to consider first its logarithmic derivative with respect to z. Introducing the grand-canonical form of the zero-field density matrix,

$$g_0\left(\vec{r}-\vec{r}_0;\tau-\tau_0;\beta;z\varepsilon\right) = \sum_{s=0}^{\infty} \rho_C\left(\vec{r}-\vec{r}_0;\tau-\tau_0+\beta s\right)\left(z\varepsilon\right)^s \quad , \tag{5.9}$$

we obtain from (4.19) and (5.6), omitting the $M = 0$ terms and differentiating,

$$\frac{\partial \ln J(z,\beta,[\phi])}{\partial z} = \sum_{M=1}^{\infty} (-1)^M \int_\Omega d\vec{r}_0 \int d\{\tau^M\} \int d\{\vec{r}^M\} g_0(\vec{r}-\vec{r}_M;\beta-\tau_M) \cdot$$

$$\cdot \prod_{j=1}^{M} \left\{ \phi(\vec{r}_j) g_0(\vec{r}_j-\vec{r}_{j-1};\tau_j-\tau_{j-1}) \right\} \quad . \tag{5.10}$$

By making use of the identity

$$\int_\Omega d\vec{r}_0 g_0(\vec{r}_1-\vec{r}_0;\tau_1) g_0(\vec{r}_0-\vec{r}_M;\beta-\tau_M) = \frac{\partial}{\partial(z\varepsilon)} g_0(\vec{r}_1-\vec{r}_M;\tau_1-\tau_M) \quad , \tag{5.11}$$

which follows from the definition (5.9) and the semi-group composition law, (5.5), we may perform the integration over the reference point in (5.10). Doing this, making use of the cyclic symmetry of the remaining integrals in (5.10), and integrating both sides with respect to z, we then obtain

$$J(z,\beta,\Omega) = \exp\left(-\varepsilon^{-1} \operatorname{Tr} \ln\left\{1 + \phi\, g_0\left(\beta, z\varepsilon\right)\right\}\right) \quad , \tag{5.12}$$

where the symbol Tr indicates a four-dimensional trace with respect to $\vec{r}$ in Ω and τ in the interval $0 \to \beta$.

6. THE GRAND PARTITION FUNCTION FOR A SYSTEM OF INTERACTING PARTICLES

We are now sufficiently prepared to consider a system of interacting particles. For convenience we shall restrict ourselves to a system of N particles interacting through a pair-potential, $V(\vec{r}_i-\vec{r}_j)$. For such a system the fundamental solution of the N-particle Bloch equation, (4.7), can no longer be represented by an integral over independent one-particle trajectories as in (4.8) with (4.9), but instead is given by

$$\rho_N\left(\{\vec{r}'\};\{\vec{r}\};\beta\right) = \int_{(\vec{r}_1,0)}^{(\vec{r}_1',\beta)} d[\vec{r}_1(\tau)] \int_{(\vec{r}_2,0)}^{(\vec{r}_2',\beta)} d[\vec{r}_2(\tau)] \ldots \int_{(\vec{r}_N,0)}^{(\vec{r}_N',\beta)} d[\vec{r}_N(\tau)] \cdot$$

$$\cdot \exp\left(-\int_0^\beta d\tau \left\{ \sum_{j=1}^{N} \frac{m}{2\hbar^2}\left(\frac{d\vec{r}_j(\tau)}{dt}\right)^2 + \sum_{i<j=1}^{N} V\left(\vec{r}_i(\tau)-\vec{r}_j(\tau)\right)\right\}\right) \quad . \tag{6.1}$$

We can, however, reduce the present problem to the problem of the last two sections, by introducing a parametrization of the interaction potential, i.e. by simulating the effect of the true interaction potential by means of a random external field, $\phi(\vec{r})$, acting on each particle separately. This we do by interpreting the value of the field at each point as a random variable, and choosing the probability distribution over the different possible field values to be such that for any set of N one-particle trajectories, $\vec{r}_1(\tau), \vec{r}_2(\tau), \ldots \vec{r}_N(\tau)$, we have

$$\left\langle \exp\left(-\sum_{j=1}^{N}\int_0^\beta d\tau\, \phi\left(\vec{r}_j(\tau)\right)\right)\right\rangle_\phi = \exp\left(-\sum_{i<j=1}^{N}\int_0^\beta d\tau\, V\left(\vec{r}_j(\tau)-\vec{r}_i(\tau)\right)\right) . \qquad (6.2)$$

Here the symbol $\langle\ \rangle_\phi$ indicates an average over the space of all functions $\phi(\vec{r})$, i.e. a functional integral in which the integrand is the functional inside the angular brackets, multiplied by a suitably chosen probability density in function space, $P[\phi(\vec{r})]$.

We shall leave aside questions concerning the existence and precise definition of this probability measure, which are discussed for instance in ref. 18), but concentrate on finding a formal definition of the average, which realizes the identity (6.2).

For this purpose we consider the <u>characteristic functional</u> of the distribution in function space (see for instance ref. 2)),

$$G_\phi[\xi] = \left\langle \exp\left\{ i \int_0^\beta d\tau \int_\Omega d\vec{r}\, \xi(\vec{r},\tau)\phi(\vec{r},\tau)\right\}\right\rangle_\phi . \qquad (6.3)$$

This functional of $\xi(\vec{r},\tau)$ represents the moment generating functional of the distribution in ϕ-space (see ref. 21)), by which we mean that the functional Taylor expansion of the expression inside the brackets of (6.3), with respect to $\phi(x)$,

$$G_\phi[\xi] = \sum_{n=0}^{\infty} \frac{i^n}{n!}\int d\{x^n\} m_n\left(\{x^n\}\right) \prod_{j=1}^{n} \xi(x_j) , \qquad (6.4)$$

generates the correlation functions (or "moments") of the distribution

$$m_n\left(\{x^n\}\right) = \langle \phi(x_1)\phi(x_2)\ldots\phi(x_n)\rangle_\phi \qquad (6.5)$$

Here we have introduced the abbreviated notation

$$\{x^n\} \equiv (x_1,x_2,\ldots x_n) \equiv (\vec{r}_1,\tau_1;\vec{r}_2,\tau_2;\ldots\vec{r}_n,\tau_n) \qquad (6.6)$$

From the complete set of correlation functions, (6.5), we now derive a unique set of so-called <u>cumulant</u> functions (ref. 21)), $\kappa_\ell\left(\{x^\ell\}\right)$, related to the correlation functions by the cluster expansion:

$$m_1(x_1) = \kappa_1(x_1) \quad ,$$

$$m_2(x_1,x_2) = \kappa_2(x_1,x_2) + \kappa_1(x_1)\kappa_1(x_2) \tag{6.6}$$

$$m_3(x_1,x_2,x_3) = \kappa_3(x_1,x_2,x_3) + \sum_P \kappa_1(x_{P1})\kappa_2(x_{P2},x_{P3}) + \kappa_1(x_1)\kappa_1(x_2)\kappa_1(x_3) \quad ,$$

$$\ldots\ldots, \text{ etc.}$$

Substituting this expansion and realizing that there are $n!/\prod_\ell \left(m_\ell!(\ell!)^{m_\ell}\right)$ ways of decomposing n coordinate points into m_1 single points, m_2 pairs, m_3 triples, etc., one obtains the following expression for the characteristic functional (6.4) in terms of cumulant functions:

$$G_\phi[\xi(x)] = \sum_{\{m_\ell\}} \prod_\ell \left(1/m_\ell!\right) \left\{ \frac{i^\ell}{\ell!} \int d\{x^\ell\}\kappa_\ell\left(\{x^\ell\}\right) \prod_{j=1}^{\ell} \xi(x_j) \right\}^{m_\ell}$$

$$= \exp\left\{ \sum_{\ell=1}^{\infty} \frac{i^\ell}{\ell!} \int d\{x^\ell\}\kappa_\ell\left(\{x^\ell\}\right) \prod_{j=1}^{\ell} \xi(x_j) \right\} \quad . \tag{6.7}$$

The expression in the exponent of (6.7) is called the cumulant generating functional.

In order to realize the parametrizing identity (6.2), we now specialize to a Gaussian distribution in function space, requiring all cumulant functions beyond $\ell = 2$ to vanish:

$$\kappa_\ell\left(\{x^\ell\}\right) \equiv 0 \quad \text{for} \quad \ell > 2 \quad . \tag{6.8}$$

In this case the equality of the two expressions (6.3) and (6.7) gives rise to the identity,

$$\left\langle \exp\left\{ i \int dx \xi(x)\phi(x) \right\} \right\rangle_\phi = \exp\Big(i \int dx \xi(x)\kappa_1(x) -$$

$$- \frac{1}{2}\int dx_1 \int dx_2 \xi(x_1)\kappa_2(x_1,x_2)\xi(x_2) \Big) \tag{6.9}$$

which reduces to (6.2) if we make the choices

$$\xi(x) = i\rho(x) = i\sum_{j=1}^{N} \delta\left(\vec{r}-\vec{r}_j(\tau)\right) \tag{6.10}$$

and

$$\kappa_1(x) = \langle\phi(x)\rangle_\phi = \frac{1}{2}\, V(0) \tag{6.11a}$$

$$\kappa_2(x_1,x_2) = \left\langle\left(\phi(x_1)-\langle\phi\rangle\right)\left(\phi(x_2)-\langle\phi\rangle\right)\right\rangle_\phi = -V(\vec{r}_1-\vec{r}_2)\,\delta(\tau_1-\tau_2) \quad , \qquad (6.11b)$$

for the "variable" $\xi(x)$, and for the first two cumulants, respectively.

When the potential cannot be represented as a sum of two-body contributions alone, we can still determine a random field $\phi(\vec{r},\vec{t})$ simulating the potential, but this field can no longer be chosen to be Gaussian, since cumulant functions beyond the second one are non-vanishing in this case.

As a result of our parametrization (6.2) we can now evaluate the partition function for a system of interacting particles by averaging the functional integral expression (4.14), for the partition function of an ideal gas in an external field $\phi(\vec{r})$, over a Gaussian distribution in function space, whose mean and variance are given by (6.11a) and (6.11b), respectively. Similarly, the grand partition function for a system of interacting particles is given by the function space average of the expression (5.7), i.e. by

$$\Xi(z,\beta,\Omega) = \Xi_0(z,\beta,\Omega)\,\langle J(z,\beta,[\phi])\rangle_\phi \qquad (6.12)$$

with Ξ_0 and J given by (5.8) and (5.12) respectively.

7. FIELD THEORETICAL FORMULATION

We shall now show that, in the case of Bose-statistics, the expression (6.12) for the grand partition function for a system of interacting particles, with $J(z,\beta,[\phi])$ given by (5.12), can be represented in the form of a double average over two Gaussian random field, $\phi(\vec{r},\tau)$ and $\psi(\vec{r},\tau)$, as

$$\Xi(z,\beta,\Omega) = \Xi_0(z,\beta,\Omega)\left\langle\left\langle\exp\left\{-\int dx\,\bar{\psi}(x)\psi(x)\phi(x)\right\}\right\rangle_\psi\right\rangle_\phi \qquad (7.1)$$

where as before we have used the abbreviations

$$x \equiv (\vec{r},\tau) \quad ; \quad \int dx \equiv \int_0^\beta d\tau \int_\Omega d\vec{r} \quad . \qquad (7.2)$$

The probability density of the field $\phi(x)$ is determined by the interaction potential via the conditions (6.11a) and (6.11b); the probability measure in the space of the functions $\psi(x)$ will be determined in terms of the grand canonical free propagator (5.9) by imposing the conditions

$$\langle\psi(x')\psi(x)\rangle_\psi = \langle\bar{\psi}(x')\bar{\psi}(x)\rangle_\psi = 0 \quad , \qquad (7.3a,b)$$

$$\langle\bar{\psi}(x')\psi(x)\rangle_\psi = g_0(x'-x;\beta;z) \quad , \qquad (7.3c)$$

where $\bar{\psi}(x)$ is the field, adjoint to $\psi(x)$, in a sense which is to be specified later.

The validity of (7.1) can be demonstrated by expanding the functional

$$J(z,\beta,[\phi]) = \left\langle \exp\left\{-\int dx \bar{\psi}(x)\psi(x)\phi(x)\right\}\right\rangle_{\psi} \tag{7.4}$$

in a functional Taylor series in powers of the field $\phi(x)$. Writing

$$J[\phi] = \sum_{n=0}^{\infty} \frac{(-1)^n}{n!} \int d\{x^n\} \left\langle \prod_{j=1}^{n} \{\bar{\psi}(x_j)\psi(x_j)\}\right\rangle_{\psi} \prod_{j=1}^{n} \phi(x_j) \tag{7.5}$$

and noting that, because of the Gaussian character of the ψ-field, we have

$$\left\langle \prod_{j=1}^{n} \{\bar{\psi}(x_j)\psi(x_j)\}\right\rangle_{\psi} = \sum_{P} \prod_{j=1}^{n} \langle\bar{\psi}(x_j)\psi(x_{Pj})\rangle_{\psi} \tag{7.6}$$

with the sum running over all permutations P of the second set of coordinates, relative to the first set.

Substituting (7.6) into (7.5), decomposing the permutations into cycles, and using the fact that there are

$$n!/\prod_{m}\left(n_m! m^{n_m}\right)$$

permutations with cycle structure $\{n_m\}$, we obtain after performing the summations over the n_m:

$$J[\phi] = \exp\left(\sum_{m=1}^{\infty} \frac{(-1)^m}{m} \int d\{x^m\} \prod_{j=1}^{m} \left\{\phi(x_j) \langle\bar{\psi}(x_j)\psi(x_{j-1})\rangle_{\psi}\right\}\right) \tag{7.7a}$$

$$= \exp\left(\operatorname{Tr} \ln\left\{1 + \phi g_0(\beta;z)\right\}\right) , \tag{7.7b}$$

which is just the expression (5.12) for the functional $J[\phi]$.

Apart from the factor Ξ_0, the expression (7.1) for the grand partition function is formally identical with the characteristic functional of the ϕ-field, defined by (6.3), where however the "variable" function $\xi(x)$ is now interpreted as i times a probability density

$$\rho(x) = \bar{\psi}(x)\psi(x) , \tag{7.8a}$$

which is determined stochastically by the distribution in ψ-space. The probability density (7.8a) may be looked upon as the field-theoretical counterpart of the "classical density of trajectories",

$$\rho(x) = \sum_{j=1}^{N} \delta\left(\vec{r}-\vec{r}_j(\tau)\right) \quad , \tag{7.8b}$$

which was used in deriving the parametrizing identity (6.2) for the pair-potential from eq. (6.9).

Now that we have introduced a parametrization of the function $g_0(x'-x)$, which characterizes the statistical properties of the system, the ϕ-parametrization of the pair-interaction is no longer needed and may be undone. Applying, in reverse, the identity (6.9) with $\xi(x)$ replaced by i times the probability density (7.8a), and substituting (6.11a) and (6.11b) for the first two cumulants of the ϕ-field, we obtain from (7.1)

$$\Xi(z,\beta,\Omega) = \Xi_0(z,\beta,\Omega)\left\langle \exp\left\{ \frac{1}{2} V(\vec{0}) \int dx \bar{\psi}(x)\psi(x) - \right.\right.$$
$$\left.\left. - \frac{1}{2}\int dx_1 \int dx_2 \bar{\psi}(x_1)\psi(x_1) V(\vec{r}_1-\vec{r}_2)\delta(\tau_1-\tau_2)\bar{\psi}(x_2)\psi(x_2)\right\}\right\rangle_{\psi} \quad . \tag{7.9}$$

The ψ-average in this representation of the grand partition function is by definition the functional integral over ψ-space of the expression between angular brackets in (7.9), multiplied by an appropriate probability density functional, $P[\psi,\bar{\psi}]$. The latter is determined by the characteristic functional of the ψ-distribution,

$$G_{\psi}[\chi,\bar{\chi}] = \left\langle \exp\left(i\int dx \{\chi(x)\bar{\psi}(x) + \bar{\chi}(x)\psi(x)\}\right)\right\rangle_{\psi} \quad , \tag{7.10a}$$

which on account of the Gaussian character of the field and the form (7.3) of its covariance is given by

$$G_{\psi}[\chi,\bar{\chi}] = \exp\left\{ -\int dx_1 \int dx_2 \chi(x_1) g_0(x_2-x_1)\bar{\chi}(x_2)\right\} \quad . \tag{7.10b}$$

Since the functional (7.10a) is formally the functional Fourier transform of the probability density, we can in principle evaluate $P[\psi,\bar{\psi}]$ by inverse Fourier transformation of the expression (7.10b) in the space of the functions $\chi,\bar{\chi}$. However, in view of the difficulties associated with defining Fourier integrals in a space of a continuously infinite number of dimensions, it is recommendable to go over to a discrete spectral representation.

For this purpose we introduce the right- and left-eigenfunctions of the grand canonical propagator, $g_0(x'-x)$, satisfying

$$\int dx\, g_0(x'-x)\chi_{\sigma}(x) = \lambda_{\sigma}\chi_{\sigma}(x') \quad , \tag{7.11a}$$

and

$$\int dx'\bar{\chi}_\sigma(x')g_0(x'-x) = \lambda_\sigma\bar{\chi}_\sigma(x) \quad , \qquad (7.11b)$$

respectively.

The distinction between right eigenfunctions, $\chi_\sigma(x)$ and left eigenfunctions, $\bar{\chi}_\sigma(x)$ is necessary because the kernel $g_0(x'-x)$ is not symmetric with respect to interchange of the variables $x \equiv (\vec{r},\tau)$ and $x' \equiv (\vec{r}',\tau)$. This is a consequence of the presence of a factor $\theta(\tau'-\tau+\beta s)$ in each of the terms on the right-hand side of equation (5.9) defining the grand canonical propagator. Because $g_0(x'-x)$ is a displacement-kernel the eigenfunctions are plane waves,

$$\chi_\sigma(x) = (\Omega\beta)^{-1/2}\exp i(\vec{k}.\vec{r} - \omega_\ell\tau) \quad , \qquad (7.12a)$$

$$\bar{\chi}_\sigma(x) = (\Omega\beta)^{-1/2}\exp -i(\vec{k}.\vec{r} - \omega_\ell\tau) \quad . \qquad (7.12b)$$

These are characterized by a real wave number, $\vec{k}$, and a "frequency", ω_ℓ, which is in general <u>complex</u> because of the non-hermitian character of $g_0(x'-x)$. Substituting the explicit form (5.9) of the kernel and solving the eigenvalue problem (7.11) for $\vec{r}$ in Ω and τ between 0 and β, one easily finds that the eigenvalues are given by

$$\lambda_\sigma = \left(\frac{\hbar^2 k^2}{2m} - i\omega_\ell\right)^{-1} \quad , \qquad (7.13a)$$

with

$$\omega_\ell = \frac{i}{\beta}\left(\ln z + 2\pi i\ell\right), \quad (\ell = 0,\pm 1,\pm 2,\ldots) \qquad (7.13b)$$

representing the allowed "frequency"-values.

The spectral representation is now obtained by expanding the functions $\psi(x)$, $\bar{\psi}(x)$, $\chi(x)$, and $\bar{\chi}(x)$ in terms of the eigenfunctions (7.12), i.e.

$$\psi(x) = \sum_\sigma a_\sigma\chi_\sigma(x) \quad ; \quad \bar{\psi}(x) = \sum_\sigma a^*_\sigma\bar{\chi}_\sigma(x) \qquad (7.14a,b)$$

$$\chi(x) = \sum_\sigma b_\sigma\chi_\sigma(x) \quad ; \quad \bar{\chi}(x) = \sum_\sigma b^*_\sigma\bar{\chi}_\sigma(x) \qquad (7.15a,b)$$

At this point we have finally completed the definition of the adjoint functions $\bar{\psi}(x)$, $\bar{\chi}(x)$, by requiring that the expansion coefficients $\bar{a}_\sigma$ and $\bar{b}_\sigma$ of the adjoint functions coincide with the complex conjugates of the corresponding coefficients in the expansions of the primary functions, a^*_σ, and b^*_σ, respectively.

Substituting the expansions (7.14) and (7.15), we may now express the characteristic functional (7.10) in spectral form, as

$$G(b,b^*) = \left\langle \exp\left\{ i \sum_\sigma (b_\sigma a_\sigma^* + b_\sigma^* a_\sigma) \right\} \right\rangle_a \tag{7.16a}$$

$$= \exp\left\{ - \sum_\sigma \lambda_\sigma b_\sigma b_\sigma^* \right\} . \tag{7.16b}$$

The inverse Fourier transform of this function with respect to the variables $|b_\sigma|$, i.e.

$$P(a,a^*) = \prod_\sigma \left\{ \frac{1}{\pi\lambda_\sigma} \exp - \left[\frac{a_\sigma a_\sigma^*}{\lambda_\sigma} \right] \right\} \tag{7.17}$$

represents the probability density in spectral form.

Substitution of the eigenvalues (7.13a) and re-introduction of the original fields by means of the inverse of the transformation (7.14), gives the probability density in function space

$$P[\psi,\bar{\psi}] = \mathcal{N}^{-1} \exp\left\{ - \int dx \bar{\psi}(x) \left(- \frac{\hbar^2}{2m} \Delta + \frac{\partial}{\partial\tau} \right) \psi(x) \right\} , \tag{7.18}$$

where $\mathcal{N}$ is the normalizing factor.

This result allows us to write the grand partition function (7.9) explicitly in the form of a (four-dimensional-) function space integral. Eliminating the imaginary part of the frequencies, (7.13b) by means of the transformation

$$\psi(x) = \Psi(x) e^{\mu\tau} \quad ; \quad \bar{\psi}(x) = \Psi^*(x) e^{-\mu\tau} \tag{7.19a,b}$$

with

$$\mu = \ln z + \frac{1}{2} V(0) \tag{7.20}$$

representing the chemical potential (relative to an appropriate zero point), we obtain from (7.9)

$$\Xi(z,\beta,\Omega) = \Xi_0(z,\beta,\Omega) \mathcal{N}^{-1} \int d[\Psi(x)] \cdot$$

$$\cdot \exp\left\{ - \int dx \Psi^*(x) \left(- \frac{\hbar^2}{2m} \Delta - \mu + \frac{\partial}{\partial\tau} \right) \Psi(x) - \frac{1}{2} \int dx_1 \int dx_2 |\Psi(x_1)|^2 V(x_1 - x_2) |\Psi(x_2)|^2 \right\} . \tag{7.21}$$

This result (see also ref. 12)), which has been derived in a different way by Casher, Lurié and Revzen[19)], has a formal resemblance with the well-known expression for the grand partition function of an interacting Bose gas in second quantized form. Its significance is, however, very different since the customary expression is a trace over a three dimensional operator field, whereas (7.21) represents a functional integral over a four dimensional c-number field, depending not only on the spatial coordinates but also on the thermodynamic "time" .

The expression (7.21) offers the advantage that the contributions from different fields to the functional integral can be compared. In particular, fields for which the contribution is a (local) maximum in function space, are seen to satisfy the so-called Landau-Ginzburg equation

$$\left\{ - \frac{\hbar^2}{2m} \Delta - \mu + \int d\vec{r}\,' V(\vec{r}-\vec{r}\,') \, |\Psi(\vec{r}\,')|^2 \right\} \Psi(\vec{r}) = 0 \quad . \tag{7.22}$$

Functional integral representations such as (7.21) provide a natural starting point for developing intuitively plausible approximations, based on the restriction of the functional integral to regions near stationary points in function space. These approximations, which can be considered as generalizations of the saddle point method to function space integrals, may give rise to rather subtle difficulties, arising from the coalescence of many stationary points in certain regions of function space. The resolution of these difficulties is in my opinion the main challenge facing the believers in functional integration methods.

REFERENCES

1) N. Wiener, J.Math. and Phys. 2(1923)131,
see also, M. Kac, Bull.Am.Math.Soc. 72(1966) part II, 52.
2) R.P. Feynman, Rev.Mod.Phys. 20(1948)367.
3) R.P. Feynman, Phys.Rev. 86(1952)621.
4) M. Kac, Proc. of the 2nd Berkeley Symposium on Probability and Statistics, Un. of Calif. Press, Berkeley, Cal. (1951) 189 ,
see also, M. Kac, "Probability and Related Topics in Physical Science", Interscience (1959) Ch. IV.
5) A.J.F. Siegert, Phys.Rev. 86(1952)621,
see also, A.J.F. Siegert, Physica 26(1960)S 30 (Utrecht conference on Many Particle Problems).
6) R.L. Stratonovich, Dokl.Akad.Nauk S.S.S.R. 115(1957)1097, transl. Soviet Phys. Doklady 2(1958)416.
7) M. Kac, G.E. Uhlenbeck and P.C. Hemmer, J.Math.Phys. 4(1963)216.
8) see for instance, J.S. Langer, Annals of Physics 41(1967)108.
9) see for instance, S.F. Edwards and A. Lenard, J.Math.Phys. 3(1962)778.
10) see for instance, S.F. Edwards, Phil.Mag. 6(1961)617, and
J. Zittartz and J.S. Langer, Phys.Rev. 148(1962)741.
11) see for instance, S.F. Edwards in: Proc. Washington Conf. on Critical Phenomena, M.S. Green and J.V. Sengers, editors, Nat.Bur.Stand. Misc.Publ. 273(1966)225.
12) F.W. Wiegel, Doct.Diss., Amsterdam (1973),

F.W. Wiegel and J. Hijmans, Proc.Kon.Ned.Akad.Wet. B 77(1974)177.

13) R.P. Feynman and A.R. Hibbs, "Quantum Mechanics and Path-Integrals", McGraw-Hill (1965).

14) G. Rosen, "Formulations of Classical and Quantum Dynamical Theory", Academic Press, New York (1969).

15) I.M. Gelfand and A.M. Yaglom, J.Math.Phys. 1(1960)48.

16) S.G. Brush, Rev.Mod.Phys. 33(1961)79.

17) A.J.F. Siegert in: "Statistical mechanics at the turn of the decade", E.G.D. Cohen editor, M. Dekker, New York (1971)145.

18) J. Ginibre in "Statistical Mechanics and Quantum Field Theory", Summerschool of Theoretical Physics, les Houches, C. deWitt and R. Stora, editors, Gordon and Breach (1970)327.

19) A. Casher, D. Lurié and M. Revzen, J.Math.Phys. 9(1968)1312.

20) see for instance: Ming Chen Wang and G.E. Uhlenbeck, Rev.Mod.Phys. 17(1945) 323.

21) R. Kubo, Proc.Phys.Soc. Japan 17(1962)1100.

ALMOST EQUILIBRIUM IN AN ALGEBRAIC APPROACH

MARINUS WINNINK

Institute for Theoretical Physics

University of Groningen

the Netherlands

INTRODUCTION

In these lectures we shall be concerned with the description of thermodynamic systems in the area that could be phrased as: "near equilibrium".

Since these lectures are the only ones that deal algebraically with thermodynamic systems we will firstly discuss some basic ideas of the algebraic approach. While doing so we shall ask, since we are going to discuss quantum mechanical systems, what in an axiomatized way ordinary quantum mechanics looks like. We shall then find that the structure of quantum mechanics, as we all know it, is precisely tailored for describing systems with a finite number of degrees of freedom or for describing a system in a box in which the probability for finding an infinite number of particles is zero. For systems with an infinite number of occupied degrees of freedom, i.e. systems consisting of an infinite number of particles, in an infinite volume and with finite density (thermodynamic systems!) the quantum mechanical description has to be modified. This then will lead us to consider a C^*-algebra of quasi-local observables, states thereupon, automorphisms thereof and all the structure that goes with it. Within this framework we shall discuss disturbances of equilibrium and return to equilibrium for some systems which in the jargon are called strongly clustering, i.e. systems which in a more traditional language would, loosely speaking, have vanishing pair correlations as the time tends to infinity.

Some of the disturbed systems, so-called dynamically disturbed systems, will be treated in a manner that resembles much the Raileigh-Schrödinger theory of perturbation in ordinary quantum mechanics. In this part we follow closely the work that recently has been done by R. Haag, D. Kastler and Ewa Trych-Pohlmeyer [1].

Fundamental Problems in Statistical Mechanics, Vol. 3, Editor, E.D.G. Cohen.

1. THE ALGEBRAIC STRUCTURE OF QUANTUM MECHANICS FOR FINITE SYSTEMS

The axiomatic approach towards quantum mechanics as given by Mackey [2] starts out with the following ingredients:

i) Observables (O);

ii) States (S);

iii) A positive function $p(A,\alpha,E)$, where $p(A,\alpha,E)$ is the probability that an observable A has the value in the Borel set E of the real line when the system is in the state α. (The Borel subsets $\mathcal{B}$ of the real line are the members of the smallest family, containing all semi-closed intervals $[a,b)$, of subsets of the real line that is closed under taking differences of pairs of sets and is also closed under taking countable unions of sets. It follows that $\mathcal{B}$ is also closed under taking countable intersections of sets. Some examples of Borel sets are R^1, (a,b), point sets $\{a\}$ and the empty set. A real function f defined on R^1 is a *Borel-function* when for every Borel set E, $f^{-1}(E) = \{x \in R^1: f(x) \in E\}$ is also a Borel set. An example of a Borel-function is the characteristic function of a Borel set.)

The ingredients summed up in i), ii) and iii) are required to satisfy a set of axioms from which the structure of quantum mechanics, as we all know it, follows.

Let us briefly indicate what the axioms look like and illustrate their degree of plausibility. While doing so we follow, for a large part, the treatment as given in [2].

Axiom I: $p(A,\alpha,R^1) = 1$, $p(A,\alpha,\emptyset) = 0$ ($\emptyset$ is the empty set).

$$p(A,\alpha,\bigcup_i E_i) = \sum_i p(A,\alpha,E_i) \qquad (E_i \cap E_j = \emptyset,\ i \neq j).$$

Axiom II: $p(A,\alpha,E) = p(A',\alpha,E)$, $\forall(\alpha \in S,\ E \in \mathcal{B})$, implies $A = A'$.

This part of axiom II gives the possibility of telling when two observables are equal. Similarly for states we have:

$$p(A,\alpha',E) = p(A,\alpha,E),\ \forall(A \in O,\ E \in \mathcal{B}),\ \text{implies } \alpha = \alpha'.$$

Axiom III: If $\{\alpha_i\}$ is a family of states, then their convex combinations shall also represent states (i.e. $\sum_i \gamma_i \alpha_i$ exists as a state for $\gamma_i \geq 0$, $\sum_i \gamma_i = 1$) with the property:

$$p(A, \sum_i \gamma_i \alpha_i, E) = \sum_i \gamma_i p(A, \alpha_i, E).$$

Axiom IV: By means of a Borel function f on the real line one requires the existence of the function f(A) of an observable A with the property

$$p(f(A), \alpha, E) = p(A, \alpha, f^{-1}(E)), \qquad \forall (A \in O,\ E \in \mathcal{B}).$$

Particular observables are those that admit either 0 (no) or 1 (yes) as outcomes of an experiment. Such an observable is called a question. Let Q be such an observable, then

$$p(Q, \alpha, \{0,1\}) = 1, \qquad \forall \alpha \in S.$$

With the help of axiom IV one then proves $p(Q^2, \alpha, E) = p(Q, \alpha, E)$ and from axiom II it then follows that $Q^2 = Q$.

Let Φ_E *be the characteristic function of the Borel set* E, then we can define an observable Q_E^A by means of axiom IV and the equation

$$p(Q_E^A, \alpha, F) = p(A, \alpha, \Phi_E^{-1}(F)), \forall F \in \mathcal{B}.$$

One proves: Q_E^A is a question that is affirmatively answered if the observable A has a value inside E. Indeed, it can be shown that

$$p(Q_E^A, \alpha, 1) = p(A, \alpha, E),$$
$$\forall \alpha \in S$$
$$p(Q_E^A, \alpha, 0) = p(A, \alpha, R^1 \setminus E).$$

Define: $m_\alpha(Q) = p(Q, \alpha, 1)$ for Q any question.

Knowing that Q is a question $m_\alpha(Q)$ determines, with the help of axiom II, Q uniquely.

One can also define a partial order on the set of questions $\underline{Q}$

$$Q_1 \leq Q_2 \iff m_\alpha(Q_1) \leq m_\alpha(Q_2), \qquad \forall\alpha \in S. \tag{1}$$

Two questions are said to be *disjoint* whenever

$$Q_1 \leq 1 - Q_2 \tag{2}$$

($1-Q_2$ is also a question!). We denote disjointness by $Q_1 \perp Q_2$.

Examples of two questions satisfying (1): $Q^A_{E_1} \leq Q^A_{E_2}$ if $E_1 \subseteq E_2$.
Examples of two questions satisfying (2): $Q^A_{E_1} \perp Q^A_{E_2}$ if $E_1 \cap E_2 = \emptyset$.

Axiom V: Given a family of mutually disjoint questions Q_i then there exists a question q denoted by $\sum_i Q_i$, such that

$$m_\alpha(q) = \sum_i m_\alpha(Q_i).$$

It can be shown that $\sum_i Q_i$ is the question that is answered with yes if one of the Q_i is answered with yes.

Let us come back to our questions Q^A_E and consider Q^A_E as the value of a function Q^A from $\mathcal{B}$ (the set of Borel sets of the real line) with values in the questions. Q^A has the properties:

i) $E \cap F = \emptyset \rightarrow Q^A_E \perp Q^A_F$;

ii) $E_i \cap E_j = \emptyset, \forall\, i \neq j \Rightarrow Q^A_{E_1 \cup E_2 \cup \ldots \cup E_n \ldots} = Q^A_{E_1} + Q^A_{E_2} + \ldots.$;

iii) $Q^A_{R^1} = 1$; $Q^A_\emptyset = 0$.

Axiom VI: Every function $E \in \mathcal{B} \rightarrow q_E$ satisfying i), ii) and iii) where $q_E \in \underline{Q}$ (the set of questions) gives rise to an observable A such that

$$Q^A_E = q_E.$$

Given objects that satisfy the axiomas I to V, we can arrange it in such a way that axiom VI is satisfied by a simple change of our set of observables O.

Until now no particular quantum structure has been introduced. For instance with the following identifications the axioms are satisfied for classical mechanics or classical statistical mechanics:

Observables: All real Borel functions on phase-space Γ.

States: All probability measures on Γ.

Let f be an observable, α a state, E a borel set in R^1, then

$$p(f,\alpha,E) = \alpha(f^{-1}(E)).$$

We know that all questions in classical physics are simultaneously answerable. Therefore we need a criterion which describes the fact that two questions are simultaneously answerable, that if we apply it to the above classical situation always is satisfied.

We define two questions Q_1, Q_2 as simultaneously answerable whenever R_1, R_2 and Q_3 exist, such that

$$Q_1 = R_1 + Q_3, \qquad Q_2 = R_2 + Q_3$$

with $R_1 \perp R_2$ and $R_i \perp Q_3$. (This definition is indeed always satisfied in the case of classical mechanics if we just realize that questions in classical mechanics are characteristic functions of Borel sets and can be identified with those sets.)

Now we come to the crucial axiom:

Axiom VII: The partially ordered set of questions in quantum mechanics is isomorphic with the partially ordered set of all projections on an infinite dimensional separable Hilbert space $\mathcal{H}$.

Once we have accepted this axiom two questions are simultaneously answerable iff they commute.

Looking at axiom V and axiom VII, we see that m_α is now a map of the projections of $\mathcal{H}$ into the positive real numbers with the properties:

$$\underset{i\neq j}{Q_i \perp Q_j} \rightarrow m_\alpha(\sum_i Q_i) = \sum_i m_\alpha(Q_i);\; m_\alpha(0) = 0,\; m_\alpha(1) = 1;\; 0 \leq m_\alpha(Q) \leq 1.$$

m_α is therefore a positive measure on the projection operators on $\mathcal{H}$. There is a very interesting theorem due to Gleason [3] saying:

Every positive measure on the projection operators has the form $m(Q) = Tr(\rho Q)$, *where* ρ *is a positive trace-class operator.*

If we now add:

Axiom VIII: With every projection Q there is a state α with $m_\alpha(Q) = 1$, i.e. we assume that for every question there is a state in which the answer to the question is yes.

Once this all is assumed we have the following theorem:

Every measure on the projection operators corresponds with a state.

From here on one can also find what the observables look like and one finds that the bounded observables correspond to all self-adjoint operators on $\mathcal{H}$. The expectation value $\langle A\rangle_\alpha$ for an observable A in the state α can be written as

$$\langle A\rangle_\alpha = \int x \, dp(A,\alpha,\{x\}).$$

(Indeed: $p(A,\alpha,E)$ is a measure on $\mathcal{B}$.)

If the state α is given by the operator $|\phi\rangle\langle\phi|$ then we find the usual expression

$$\langle A\rangle_\alpha = \int x \, d(\phi, P_x^A \phi),$$

where

$$P_x^A = Q^A_{(-\infty,x]}$$

(i.e. we have Von Neumann's spectral theorem).

The *spectrum* of the observable A is the set of values x where the function $(\phi, P_x^A\phi)$ varies, i.e. is equal to the spectrum of the operator A. For unbounded observables there are some modifications that we won't discuss now.

Let us now look at the algebra generated by all projections on $\mathcal{H}$, i.e. we take all finite polynomials in the projection operators with complex coefficients. We close this algebra in the so-called weak operator topology on $\mathcal{H}$ ($A_n \to A$ weakly when $(A_n\phi,\phi) \to (A\phi,\phi)$ $\forall\phi \in \mathcal{H}$). We then obtain all bounded operators on $\mathcal{H}$ denoted by $\mathcal{B}(\mathcal{H})$. This algebra is also uniformly closed (uniform convergence: $A_n \to A$: $\|A_n - A\| \to 0$), and is in fact a C^*-algebra namely $\|A^*A\| = \|A\|^2$. It is also a Von Neumann algebra, i.e. $\mathcal{B}(\mathcal{H}) = \mathcal{B}(\mathcal{H})''$ = bicommutant. (A Von Neumann algebra $\mathfrak{M}$ is a set of bounded operators on a Hilbert space that equals its *bicommutant*. The *commutant* $\mathfrak{M}'$ of a set $\mathfrak{M}$ is given by:

$$\mathfrak{M}' = \{x \in \mathcal{B}(\mathcal{H}) : [x,y] = 0 \ \forall y \in \mathcal{B}(\mathcal{H})\}.$$

The *bicommutant*

$$\mathfrak{M}'' = \{x \in \mathcal{B}(\mathcal{H}) : [x,y] = 0 \ \forall y \in \mathfrak{M}'\}.)$$

A state α gives rise to an expectation value $\langle A\rangle_\alpha$ for observables A. If we take for A a question Q then we find a *uniquely* defined positive trace-class operator ρ_α independent of Q such that

$$\langle Q\rangle_\alpha = m_\alpha(Q) = \mathrm{Tr}\ (\rho_\alpha Q).$$

One shows that

$$\langle A\rangle_\alpha = \mathrm{Tr}\ (\rho_\alpha A)$$

for all bounded self-adjoint operators on $\mathcal{H}$. It is clear that, by a trivial extension, one can define a linear functional on all of $\mathcal{B}(\mathcal{H})$ by the expression

$$\langle A\rangle_\alpha = \mathrm{Tr}\ (\rho_\alpha A).$$

Furthermore

$$\langle A^* A\rangle_\alpha = \mathrm{Tr}\ (\rho_\alpha A^* A) \geq 0,$$

it is a so-called *positive linear* functional on the Banach algebra $\mathcal{B}(\mathcal{H})$. *Not all positive linear functionals on $\mathcal{B}(\mathcal{H})$ are given by a trace-class operator.* The ones that are given by a trace-class operator are singled out by a *continuity* requirement. Indeed one can equip $\mathcal{B}(\mathcal{H})$ like any Von Neumann algebra with its so-called σ-weak topology [4], and the positive linear functionals that are continuous in the σ-weak topology are precisely the ones given by *density* operators.

The functionals (not necessarily positive) that are continuous in that topology are the so-called *normal* functionals on $\mathcal{B}(\mathcal{H})$.

What we have achieved now is the following algebraic structure for the kinematical part of the theory:

The questions generate a C^*-algebra, and a Von Neumann-algebra; the positive linear functionals that are continuous in the σ-weak topology give, when applied to the bounded self-adjoint operators, precisely the expectation-value of the observables that correspond to the self-adjoint operators.

One should ask the question whether axiom VII is not a little bit too restrictive, because it implies that every bounded self-adjoint operator is an observable (unbounded self-adjoint operators are unbounded observables).

Suppose that as an alternative to axiom VII one would take all projections in a Von Neumann algebra $\mathfrak{M}$ with

$$\mathfrak{M} \subsetneq \mathcal{B}(\mathcal{H}),$$

as the partially ordered set of projections. Then one can for certain choices of $\mathfrak{M}$ prove the following Gleason-like theorem: Every measure on the projection operators of $\mathfrak{M}$ is a σ-weakly continuous positive linear functional on $\mathfrak{M}$ [5].

Let us stick to the axioms as formulated above, i.e. axiom VII included, and try to see how the *dynamics* can be formulated in this framework.

Axiom IX: The dynamics is given by a one-parameter Abelian group of bijections V_t of S such that:

i) $V_t(\sum_i \gamma_i \alpha_i) = \sum_i \gamma_i V_t(\alpha_i), \qquad \alpha_i \in S, \qquad \gamma_i \geq 0, \qquad \sum_i \gamma_i = 1.$

ii) $p(Q, V_t(\alpha), 1)$ is continuous in t.

One can now proof by a reasoning which makes use of some highly non trivial theorems of R.V. Kadison [6], [7] and Bargmann [8] that there exists in $\mathcal{H}$ a *strongly continuous* unitary group

$$U_t \ (= \exp iHt)$$

such that

$$\rho_{V_t(\alpha)} = U_t \, \rho_\alpha \, U_{-t}.$$

The mapping

$$A \rightarrow A_t = U_t \, A \, U_{-t}, \qquad A \in \mathcal{B}(\mathcal{H})$$

is precisely the equation of motion in the Heisenberg picture we are all familiar with. The equation

$$\psi_t = U_t \psi_0$$

is precisely the solution of the Schrödinger equation

$$i \partial_t \psi_t = H \psi_t,$$

provided ψ_t is in the domain of H (the Hamiltonian!)

The map

$$A \to \alpha_t(A) = A_t$$

is an automorphism of the algebra $\mathcal{B}(\mathcal{H})$, i.e. it is one-to-one onto and preserves all algebraic relations. Indeed,

$$\alpha_t(\lambda A + \mu B) = \lambda \alpha_t(A) + \mu \alpha_t(B),$$

$$\alpha_t(AB) = \alpha_t(A) \alpha_t(B),$$

$$\alpha_t(A^*) = (\alpha_t(A))^* .$$

Furthermore

$$\alpha_{t_1+t_2} = \alpha_{t_1} \alpha_{t_2},$$

i.e. we have *a one-parameter abelian group of automorphisms of the C^*-algebra $\mathcal{B}(\mathcal{H})$, that happens to be a W^*-algebra at the same time, describing the dynamics.*

If we maintain, for a thermodynamic system, the description as given above we are always led to the existence of a Hamiltonian (the generator of time translation), that is an (unbounded) observable, if our C^*-algebra of observables is chosen to be all bounded operators on some Hilbert space. [The fact that the Hamiltonian is an unbounded *observable* is clear because it is a self-adjoint operator.]

For a thermodynamic system, however, there is no such thing as an observable total energy (it is infinite). Therefore we shall rather describe thermodynamic systems kinematically by means of a C^*-algebra that is *not* all bounded operators on some Hilbert space and dynamically we describe the system by means of a one-parameter Abelian group of automorphisms of the chosen C^*-algebra. This latter assumption may be too restrictive in certain cases, for quantum lattice systems [9], the free Fermi-gas [10] and the free Bose-gas [11] it is not.

The fact that for a finite system the dynamics is given by a one-parameter group of automorphisms of $\mathcal{B}(\mathcal{H})$ is *equivalent* with a description of the dynamics in terms of a one-parameter group of transformations acting upon the set of normal states with additional continuity properties (axiom IX). Suppose one agrees for thermodynamic systems upon the kinematical part of the theory, i.e. one agrees upon what the C^*-algebra of observables looks like. The dynamics can then also be described by means of a one-parameter group of transformations acting upon a set of states one considers to be of interest (for example in the finite case the *normal* states). Depending upon the requirements imposed on such transformations one may or may not end up with automorphisms of the algebra of observables. We shall not dwell on this point any longer, for more details on this point the reader is referred to [7][12][13].

For completeness we add the definition of a W^*-algebra:
A W^*-algebra is a C^*-algebra, i.e. its norm satisfies the C^*-property $\|A^*A\| = \|A\|^2$, which at the same time is a Banach-space dual of a Banach space. More precisely:
Let $\mathfrak{M}$ be a W^*-algebra, then there exists a Banach space $\mathfrak{M}_*$ such that for $A \in \mathfrak{M}$ and every $f \in \mathfrak{M}_*$ there exists a linear map of $\mathfrak{M}_*$ into the complex numbers $\mathbb{C}$

$$f \in \mathfrak{M}_* \to A(f) \in \mathbb{C},$$

such that

$$|A(f)| \leq \|A\|\,\|f\|.$$

$\mathfrak{M}_*$ is unique; for more details see [4].

2. KINEMATICS OF THERMODYNAMIC SYSTEMS

In the previous paragraph we argued the non-existence of an observable energy for a thermodynamic system.

Physical systems confined to a finite volume contain of course only a finite amount of energy, i.e. the probability to find an infinite number of particles in a finite volume is zero. Therefore, for a system enclosed in a finite box V, we assume that the algebra of observables is *all* bounded operators on a suitable Hilbert space $\mathcal{H}_V$ and we assume that the dynamics is described by a one parameter group of automorphisms.

For a system in a finite volume V, that is a subsystem of a larger system (in particular of an infinitely extended system), we assume that the algebra of observables is also all bounded operators on $\mathcal{H}_V$. The dynamics of such a system, however, is clearly not adequately described by a group of automorphisms of $\mathcal{B}(\mathcal{H}_V)$, since the dynamics is not governed by the observables in the finite system alone.

The observables for a thermodynamic system should somehow be built out of the sets of observables for all possible subsystems. Furthermore the observables of a subsystem in the volume V should be a subset of the observables for a subsystem in the volume V' whenever $V \subseteq V'$. Like in the preceding paragraph we rather discuss *the algebras generated by the observables* than the observables alone.

More precisely:

Let $\mathfrak{U}_V$ denote the W^*-algebra of observables for a system in a volume V. In view of what we said above we assume:

$$\mathfrak{U}_V \subseteq \mathfrak{U}_{V'} \qquad \text{for } V \subseteq V' \text{ (isotony);}$$

$$[\mathfrak{U}_V, \mathfrak{U}_{V'}] = 0 \qquad \text{for } V \cap V' = \emptyset.$$

The *C^*-algebra of quasi-local observables* $\mathfrak{U}$ is now defined by:

$$\mathfrak{U} = \overline{\bigcup_{V \subset R^3} \mathfrak{U}_V}^{n},$$

where $\overline{(\cdot)}^n$ means the normclosure in the C^*-norm that in a natural way can be defined on the *-algebra $\bigcup_{V \subset R^3} \mathfrak{U}_V$ starting from the C^*-norm defined on every $\mathfrak{U}_V$ [$\mathfrak{U}_V$ is a W^*-algebra isomorphic to $\mathcal{B}(\mathcal{H}_V)$ and $\mathfrak{U}$ is isomorphic to the C^*-inductive limit of the W^*-algebras $\mathfrak{U}_V$ with injection maps as defined by the isotony relation. For more details on this see [4] .]

The states of a thermodynamic system are, as a direct generalization of what we saw in the preceding paragraph, positive linear functionals on $\mathfrak{U}$. [Let ω be a state then positivity means $\omega(A^*A) \geq 0, \forall A \in \mathfrak{U}$.]

Let ω_{V_n} be a state for a system contained in a box V_n. Let $\{V_n\}$ be an increasing sequence of volumes that eventually contains every finite volume in R^3. Suppose that for every local observable $A \in \bigcup_{V \subset R^3} \mathfrak{U}_V$

$$\omega(A) = \lim_{n \to \infty} \omega_{V_n}(A) \text{ exists.}$$

Then one shows that ω extends to a positive linear functional on $\mathfrak{U}$.

For a particular self-adjoint A, $\omega(A)$ is interpreted as the thermodynamic expectation value of the observable A. ω *is therefore called a thermodynamic state on* $\mathfrak{U}$.

Since we want ω, when we restrict it to $\mathfrak{U}_V$, to give a state on $\mathcal{B}(\mathcal{H}_V)$ we should have that ω is described by a density operator on $\mathcal{H}_V$, i.e.

$$\omega(A) = (\omega \circ \Phi^{-1})(x) = \mathrm{Tr}\,(\rho_V x) \quad \forall A \in \mathfrak{U}_V,$$

where Φ is the implicit isomorphism that maps $\mathfrak{U}_V$ onto $\mathcal{B}(\mathcal{H}_V)$ and $\Phi^{-1}(x) = A$ with $x \in \mathcal{B}(\mathcal{H}_V)$.

A positive linear functional on $\mathfrak{U}$ that, when restricted to $\mathfrak{U}_V$, is given by a density operator on $\mathcal{H}_V$ (i.e. is of the Gleason type!) is called *locally normal*.
Theorem: *Every thermodynamic limit state is locally normal* [14] .
As we saw above the algebra $\mathfrak{U}$ is perfectly tailored to admit the thermodynamic expectation values, obtained by taking the thermodynamic limit, as positive linear functionals.

A very desirable situation would also be if the dynamics of a thermodynamic system would emerge as a group of automorphisms of $\mathfrak{U}$. This occurs for instance if, while taking the thermodynamic limit not only $\omega_{V_n}(A)$ tends to $\omega(A)$, but also

$$\alpha_t^{V_n}(A) = \exp iH_{V_n} t\, A \exp -iH_{V_n} t$$

tends to $\alpha_t(A)$ (i.e.

$$\| \alpha_t^{V_n}(A) - \alpha_t(A) \| \to 0),$$

where H_{V_n} is the Hamiltonian for a system enclosed in a box V_n. This situation prevails if we are describing a quantum lattice system. Every $\mathfrak{A}_V$ is there an n×n matrix algebra and every positive linear functional on $\mathfrak{A}$ is locally normal.

For simplicity we have assumed that the dynamics for a thermodynamic system is described by a one-parameter abelian group of automorphisms of the C^*-algebra $\mathfrak{A}$ of quasi-local observables.

Theorem: *Let* ω *be a positive linear functional on a* C^**-algebra* $\mathfrak{A}$, *then there exist i) a Hilbert space* $\mathcal{H}_\omega$;

ii) a homomorphism π_ω *of* $\mathfrak{A}$ *into the bounded operators on* $\mathcal{H}_\omega$;

iii) a cyclic vector Ω_ω *in* $\mathcal{H}_\omega$,

such that

$$\omega(A) = (\Omega_\omega, \pi_\omega(A)\Omega_\omega).$$

This is the celebrated Gel'fand-Segal representation-theorem.

[A homomorphism is a map that preserves the algebraic relations, the *-operation included, with $\| \pi_\omega(A) \| \leq \| A \|$.

A cyclic vector is a vector such that if you apply all the images of $\mathfrak{A}$ to it, you get a dense set in $\mathcal{H}_\omega$.]

Remark: The representation in the above theorem is up to unitary equivalence unique.

Theorem: *Let* ω *be a positive linear functional, that is invariant for a group of automorphisms* α_g *of* $\mathfrak{A}$, *i.e.* $\omega(A) = \omega(\alpha_g(A))$, *then we have*

$$\pi_\omega(\alpha_g(A)) = U_g\, \pi_\omega(A) U_g^{-1}$$

$$U_g \Omega_\omega = \Omega_\omega,$$

where U_g is a group of unitary operators on $\mathcal{H}_\omega$.

Corollary: *Let ω be invariant for the group of time-translations represented by the one-parameter group of automorphisms α_t and let $\omega(A\alpha_t B)$ be continuous, then*

$$U_t = \exp iHt.$$

We conclude this paragraph with some definitions and theorems (the proofs of which can be found in [4][15][16]).

Let ω be a positive linear functional on a C^*-algebra $\mathfrak{A}$. Then the image $\pi_\omega(\mathfrak{A})$ of $\mathfrak{A}$ (a subset of $\mathcal{B}(\mathcal{H}_\omega)$) is a C^*-algebra. $\pi_\omega(\mathfrak{A})'$ is the commutant of $\pi_\omega(\mathfrak{A})$, i.e.

$$\pi_\omega(\mathfrak{A})' = \{A \in \mathcal{B}(\mathcal{H}_\omega) : [A,B] = 0, \forall B \in \pi_\omega(\mathfrak{A})\}.$$

$\pi_\omega(\mathfrak{A})''$ is the commutant of $\pi_\omega(\mathfrak{A})'$.

In our case we have also:

$$\pi_\omega(\mathfrak{A})'' = \overline{\pi_\omega(\mathfrak{A})}^W \quad \text{(the weak closure of } \pi_\omega(\mathfrak{A})).$$

A state ω is called *separating* if $A\Omega_\omega = 0$, $A \in \pi_\omega(\mathfrak{A})''$ implies $A = 0$. One can prove: *ω is separating iff Ω_ω is cyclic for $\pi_\omega(\mathfrak{A})'$*. The vector Ω_ω is therefore cyclic for both the algebra $\pi_\omega(\mathfrak{A})''$ and its commutant $\pi_\omega(\mathfrak{A})'$ in this case.

The centre of a representation $\mathfrak{Z} = \pi_\omega(\mathfrak{A})'' \cap \pi_\omega(\mathfrak{A})'$.

3. GIBBS-STATES FOR FINITE SYSTEMS

Let $\omega(A)$ denote the expectation value of the observable A in the canonical ensemble, i.e.

$$\omega(A) = \mathrm{Tr}\,(e^{-\beta H}A)/\mathrm{Tr}\,e^{-\beta H}\ , \qquad \beta = \frac{1}{kT}\ .$$

In order that this expression shall make sense H has to be bounded from below and has to have a completely discrete spectrum with finite multiplicities, such that $\Sigma e^{-\beta\varepsilon_n} < \infty$ where ε_n are the eigenvalues of H, an n-fold degenerate eigenvalue appears n times in this sum. Consider

$$\omega(A\alpha_t B) = \mathrm{Tr}\,(e^{-\beta H}AU_tBU_{-t})/\mathrm{Tr}\,e^{-\beta H}\ ,$$

then one shows [17][18] that $\omega(A\alpha_t B)$ has the following properties:

i) $\omega(A\alpha_t(B))$ is continuous in t, for t real;

ii) $\omega(A\alpha_t(B))$ is analytic for $0 < \mathrm{Im}\, t < \beta$ and for t_0 real:

$$\omega(A\alpha_t(B))/_{t=t_0+i\beta} = \omega(\alpha_{t_0}(B)A).$$

From this follows

ii)' $\int \omega(A\alpha_t B)\, f(t-i\beta)\, dt = \int \omega(\alpha_t(B)A)\, f(t)\, dt$, $\hat{f} \in D$ ($\hat{f}$ is C^∞ has compact support and denotes the Fourier transform of f).

Let α_t be a one-parameter group of automorphisms of $\mathfrak{A}_V$, then a positive linear functional ω satisfies the K.M.S.-condition if

i) $\omega(A\alpha_t B)$ is continuous in t, t real;

ii) $\int \omega(A\alpha_t B)\, f(t-i\beta)\, dt = \int \omega(\alpha_t(B)A)\, f(t)\, dt \ \forall \hat{f} \in D,\ A,B \in \mathfrak{A}_V$.

The representation theorem we discussed in the foregoing paragraph holds for every C^*-algebra and positive linear functional thereupon. From the K.M.S.-condition follows invariance, i.e. $\omega(A) = \omega(\alpha_t(A))$. Thus we can find up to unitary equivalence the representation as we have in §2 for an invariant functional. We shall now describe how this can explicitly be done [17].

Let K_0 be $\rho^{\frac{1}{2}}$ (ρ is positive, therefore $\rho^{\frac{1}{2}}$ exists), then K_0 is a Hilbert-Schmidt operator (A is Hilbert-Schmidt iff $\mathrm{Tr}\,(A^*A) < \infty$).

Let $\mathcal{H}_S$ be the Hilbert space of Hilbert-Schmidt operators. Then

$$K_0 = \Omega_\omega \quad , \qquad \pi_\omega(A)K = AK, \qquad \pi_\omega(\alpha_t(A)) = \hat{U}_t \pi_\omega(A)\hat{U}_t^{-1},$$

where

$$\hat{U}_t = \pi_\omega(U_t) \; \pi'_\omega(U_{-t})$$

with

$$\pi'_\omega(U_{-t})K = K\, U_{-t} \; , \qquad \forall K \in \mathcal{H}_S .$$

It is well known that $\mathcal{H}_S$ can be written as the tensorproduct of $\mathcal{H}$ with its dual $\mathcal{H}'$, i.e.

$$\mathcal{H}_S = \mathcal{H} \otimes \mathcal{H}' .$$

This is not amazing if we look at some typical Hilbert-Schmidt operators, we are familiar with namely $|\phi><\phi|$ or $\sum_{i=1}^{n} |\phi_i><\phi_i|$, etc..

From §2 corollary, we know that we should be able to find the generator $\hat{H}$ of $\hat{U}_t$, it turns out that

$$\hat{H} = \overline{(H \otimes 1 - 1 \otimes H)}$$

where $\overline{(H \otimes 1 - 1 \otimes H)}$ is the closure of $H \otimes 1 - 1 \otimes H$.

$\hat{H}$ is precisely what is commonly called the Liouville operator. Indeed for $P = |\phi><\phi|$ we have

$$\hat{H}|\phi><\phi| \text{ (as vectors on } \mathcal{H}_S) = |H\phi><\phi| - |\phi><H\phi| =$$

$$= \text{(as operators on } \mathcal{H}) \; [P,H] = i\partial_t P .$$

Let H be such that $\mathrm{Tr}\, e^{-H} < \infty$, then one finds at least one positive linear functional that satisfies the K.M.S.-condition with respect to the automorphism group $\alpha_t(A) = U_t A U_{-t}$. It can be shown that for any temperature $T \neq 0$ there is exactly one for this evolution. From now on we normalize our temperatures to 1 for simplicity.

The question may arise whether for an arbitrary Hamiltonian H giving

$$U_t = \exp iHt \qquad \text{and} \qquad \alpha_t(A) = U_t A U_{-t}$$

there exists a positive linear functional that satisfies K.M.S.. The answer is no in general, except when H is such that $\mathrm{Tr}\,(e^{-H}) < \infty$.

Proof: Suppose ω is K.M.S. with respect to α_t, then one shows that

i) ω is separating, i.e. $A\Omega_\omega = 0 \Rightarrow A = 0 \quad (A \in \pi_\omega(\mathfrak{A})'')$;

ii) ω is normal, i.e. $\exists \rho$: $\omega(A) = \mathrm{Tr}\,(\rho A)$ [19].

Suppose $A \in \mathfrak{A}$ is such that $\omega(A^* A) = 0$, this means $(\Omega_\omega, \pi_\omega(A^* A)\Omega_\omega) = 0$, i.e. $\pi_\omega(A)\Omega_\omega = 0$; from i) this implies $\pi_\omega(A) = 0$. $\pi_\omega(A) = 0$ and ii) gives that $A = 0$. Hence $\omega(A^* A) = 0 \to A = 0$. This implies that ρ is invertible and can be written for that matter as e^{-H_0}, where H_0 has a completely discrete spectrum, with finite multiplicities. As we know ω is now K.M.S. with respect to the evolution

$$\alpha_t^0(A) = \exp iH_0 t\, A \exp -iH_0 t,$$

but also with respect to $\alpha_t(A)$. From the fact that π_ω is a faithful representation ($\pi_\omega(A) = 0 \to A = 0$), the fact that a K.M.S.-state is invariant and the unitary group U_t on $\mathcal{H}_\omega$ is uniquely determined it follows that

$$\alpha_t^0(A) = \alpha_t(A).$$

This has as an immediate consequence that

$$\exp iH_0 t\, A \exp -iH_0 t = \exp iHt\, A \exp -iHt.$$

Hence

$$[\exp -iHt \exp iH_0 t, A] = 0 \quad , \qquad \forall A \in \mathfrak{A}_V \quad ,$$

therefore

$$\exp -iHt \exp iH_0 t = \exp i\alpha(t),$$

where $\alpha(t)$ is a real continuous function of t with the properties

$$\alpha(t_1+t_2) = \alpha(t_1) + \alpha(t_2).$$

From this follows that $\alpha(t) = \alpha.t$, where α is a constant. Consequently we arrived at the conclusion that

$$H = H_0 + \alpha,$$

implying that the spectra of H and H_0 are identical up to a shift by α.

What also is clear from this proof is, that for a finite system a Gibbs state is equivalent with a K.M.S. positive linear functional. The fact that there is only one K.M.S.-state for a finite system is sometimes interpreted as the absence of phase transitions for a finite system.

Let us now place ourselves in the context of §2, where we discussed a thermodynamic system and the dynamics is given by a one-parameter group of automorphisms of the algebra of quasi-local observables. For quantum lattice systems it has been shown that equilibrium states are equivalent with K.M.S.-states [20][21], under suitable conditions.

Any self-adjoint operator H on $\mathcal{H}_V$ generates a group of automorphisms of $B(\mathcal{H}_V)$, only those that are bounded from below with completely discrete spectrum and $\mathrm{Tr}\, e^{-\beta H} < \infty$, admit a K.M.S.-, Gibbs- or shall we say equilibrium state.

Let H *be a Hamiltonian that does not admit an equilibrium state, it still generates a continuous unitary group on* $\mathcal{H}_S$ *and a generator*

$$(H \otimes 1 - 1 \otimes H),$$

which deserves the name Liouville operator.

At the beginning of this paragraph we discussed K.M.S.-states (from now on we shall call every positive linear functionals on C^*-algebras states) for the finite system.

For a thermodynamic state ω one generalizes the K.M.S.-condition for a state with respect to an evolution α_t as follows:

i) $\omega(A\alpha_t B)$ is continuous;

ii) $\int \omega(A\alpha_t(B)\ f(t-i\beta)\ dt = \int \omega(\alpha_t(B)A)\ f(t)\ dt, \forall A,B \in \mathfrak{U},\ \hat{f} \in D.$

Among the many properties that follow from this condition we mention a few that we shall need:

i) $\omega(\alpha_t(A)) = \omega(A)$;

From i) follows a unitary group on $\mathcal{H}_\omega$ with

$$U_t\Omega_\omega = \Omega_\omega \quad ,$$

$$\pi_\omega(\alpha_t(A)) = U_t\pi_\omega(A)U_{-t} \quad ,$$

ii) $\mathfrak{Z}_\omega$ is pointwise invariant, i.e. $A \in \mathfrak{Z}_\omega \rightarrow U_tAU_{-t} = A$;

iii) Ω_ω is cyclic and separating for $\pi_\omega(\mathfrak{U})''$;

iv) $\mathfrak{Z}_\omega$ is trivial ($\lambda 1$) is equivalent with $\nexists \omega_1, \omega_2$: $\omega = \lambda\omega_1 + (1-\lambda)\omega_2$, $0 < \lambda < 1$.

we have in addition

v) U_t is unique;

vi) ω is locally normal [19].

The generator on the representation space for the finite system K.M.S.-state was as we saw the Liouville operator. It is clear that the generator of U_t for a thermodynamic K.M.S.-state is the generalisation of what we call the Liouville operator for a finite system. For infinite systems however there is no simple form like we have for the finite system.

Another striking difference between the representations of K.M.S.-states for finite systems and K.M.S.-states for infinite systems is the fact that all representations are unitarily equivalent whereas for infinite systems that is not the case.

[π_1 on $\mathcal{H}_1$ and π_2 on $\mathcal{H}_2$ are unitarily equivalent whenever there exists a map U: $\mathcal{H}_1 \overset{U}{\rightarrow} U\mathcal{H}_1 = \mathcal{H}_2$ such that $\pi_1(A) = U\pi_2(A)U^{-1}$.]

4. PERTURBATION OF THERMODYNAMIC STATES

4.1 *Kinematical perturbations*

An important feature of K.M.S. states is the fact that such states are *separating*. Even if the dynamics of the thermodynamic system is not given by a group of automorphisms and therefore a formulation of K.M.S. is not possible, one can prove that thermodynamic limit states are separating under suitable conditions [13].

Let ω be an invariant state under the action of a one parameter abelian group of automorphisms of the algebra of quasi-local observables. From what we said earlier ω gives rise to $\mathcal{H}_\omega$, Ω_ω, π_ω, U_t. ω is said to be strongly clustering whenever

$$\lim_{|t|\to\infty} \omega(A\alpha_t(B)) \to \omega(A).\omega(B), \qquad \forall A,B \in \mathfrak{U}.$$

[One could drop the invariance and define the notion of strongly clustering as

$$\lim_{|t|\to\infty} \{\omega(A\alpha_t B) - \omega(A)\ \omega(\alpha_t(B))\} \to 0.]$$

Suppose now that we disturb ω in the following way:

$$\omega(A) \to \omega_B(A), \text{ where } \omega_B(A) = \omega(B^* AB) \qquad B \in \mathfrak{U}$$

This means that in the Gel'fand-Segal construction for ω we consider

$$(\Omega_\omega, \pi_\omega(B^*)\pi_\omega(A)\pi_\omega(B)\Omega_\omega) = (\pi_\omega(B)\Omega_\omega, \pi_\omega(A)\pi_\omega(B)\Omega_\omega)$$

instead of

$$(\Omega_\omega, \pi_\omega(A)\Omega_\omega).$$

Theorem: *Let $\{\alpha_t,\ t \in R^1\}$ be a one parameter group of automorphisms (not necessarily representing the dynamics) of $\mathfrak{U}$. For a state ω that is invariant under the action of α_t, i.e. $\omega(\alpha_t(A)) = \omega(A)$, with the additional property that $\omega(A\alpha_t(B))$ is continuous in t and furthermore separating, the following three statements are equivalent:*

i) ω *is strongly clustering;*

ii) $\pi_\omega(\alpha_t(A)) \underset{|t|\to\infty}{\to} \omega(A).1$ *(weak-convergence);*

iii) $\omega_B(\alpha_t(A)) \underset{|t|\to\infty}{\to} \omega_B(1)\omega(A) = \omega(B^*B)\omega(A),\ \forall B \in \mathfrak{A}.$

Proof: Suppose ω is strongly clustering, then

$$\omega(A^*\alpha_t(B)) = (\pi_\omega(A)\Omega_\omega, U_t\pi_\omega(B)\Omega_\omega) \underset{|t|\to\infty}{\to} (\Omega_\omega,\pi_\omega(A^*)\Omega_\omega)(\Omega_\omega,\pi_\omega(B)\Omega_\omega) =$$

$$= (\pi_\omega(A)\Omega_\omega,\Omega_\omega)(\Omega_\omega,\pi_\omega(B)\Omega_\omega) = (\pi_\omega(A)\Omega_\omega, P_{\Omega_\omega}\pi_\omega(B)\Omega_\omega),$$

where P_{Ω_ω} is the projection operator on Ω_ω. Hence we have $U_t \to P_{\Omega_\omega}$ (weakly), i.e.

$$(\phi,U_t\chi) \to (\phi,P_{\Omega_\omega}\chi) \quad \text{for } \phi \text{ and } \chi \in \mathcal{H}_\omega,$$

because $\{\pi_\omega(A)\Omega_\omega,\ A \in \mathfrak{A}\}$ is a dense set in $\mathcal{H}_\omega$.

If iii) holds then we have

$$\omega_B(\alpha_t(A)) = (\pi_\omega(B)\Omega_\omega,\pi_\omega(\alpha_t(A))\pi_\omega(B)\Omega_\omega) \underset{|t|\to\infty}{\to} (\pi_\omega(B)\Omega_\omega,\pi_\omega(B)\Omega_\omega).\omega(A).$$

From this one sees by the same reasoning as above:

$$(\phi,\pi_\omega(\alpha_t(A))\psi) \underset{|t|\to\infty}{\to} \omega(A)(\phi,\psi) \text{ for all } \phi,\psi \in \mathcal{H}_\omega,$$

i.e.

$$\pi_\omega(\alpha_t(A)) \underset{|t|\to\infty}{\to} \omega(A)1 \text{ weakly.}$$

Hence from iii) follows ii).

It follows simply that ii) → i). Indeed

$$\omega(A\alpha_t(B)) = (\pi_\omega(A^*)\Omega_\omega,\pi_\omega(\alpha_t(B))\Omega_\omega) \underset{|t|\to\infty}{\Rightarrow} (\pi_\omega(A^*)\Omega_\omega,\Omega_\omega).\omega(B) = \omega(A).\omega(B).$$

All we still need to prove is i) → iii), because then i) → iii) → ii) → i).

Because we assumed that ω is separating and consequently that Ω_ω is cyclic for the commutant $\pi_\omega(\mathfrak{A})'$ we can for every $B \in \mathfrak{A}$ find $C \in \pi_\omega(\mathfrak{A})'$ such that

$$\|\pi_\omega(B)\Omega_\omega - C\Omega_\omega\| < \varepsilon.$$

Using this we have:

$$|\omega(B^{*}\alpha_t(A)B) - \omega(B^{*}B)\omega(A)| =$$

$$= |(\pi_\omega(B)\Omega_\omega, \pi_\omega(\alpha_t(A))\pi_\omega(B)\Omega_\omega) - (\pi_\omega(B)\Omega_\omega, \pi_\omega(B)\Omega_\omega)(\Omega_\omega, \pi_\omega(A)\Omega_\omega)| \leq$$

$$\leq |(\pi_\omega(B)\Omega_\omega, \pi_\omega(\alpha_t(A))\pi_\omega(B)\Omega_\omega) - (C\Omega_\omega, \pi_\omega(\alpha_t(A))\pi_\omega(B)\Omega_\omega)| +$$

$$+ |(C\Omega_\omega, \pi_\omega(\alpha_t(A))\pi_\omega(B)\Omega_\omega) - (C\Omega_\omega, \pi_\omega(\alpha_t(A))C\Omega_\omega)| +$$

$$+ |(C\Omega_\omega, \pi_\omega(\alpha_t(A))C\Omega_\omega) - (C\Omega_\omega, C\Omega_\omega)(\Omega_\omega, \pi_\omega(A)\Omega_\omega)| +$$

$$+ |(C\Omega_\omega, C\Omega_\omega)\omega(A) - \omega(A)(\pi_\omega(B)\Omega_\omega, C\Omega)| +$$

$$+ |\omega(A)(\pi_\omega(B)\Omega_\omega, C\Omega_\omega) - (\pi_\omega(B)\Omega_\omega, \pi_\omega(B)\Omega_\omega)\omega(A)| \leq$$

$$\leq \|\pi_\omega(B) - C\Omega_\omega\| \|\pi_\omega(\alpha_t(A))\pi_\omega(B)\Omega_\omega\| +$$

$$+ \|C\Omega_\omega\| \|\pi_\omega(\alpha_t(A))\| \|(\pi_\omega(B)-C)\Omega_\omega\| +$$

$$+ |(C^{*}C\Omega_\omega, U_t\pi_\omega(A)\Omega_\omega) - (C^{*}C\Omega_\omega, \Omega_\omega)(\Omega_\omega, \pi_\omega(A)\Omega_\omega)| +$$

$$+ |\omega(A)| \|(\pi_\omega(B)-C)\Omega_\omega\| \|C\Omega_\omega\| +$$

$$+ |\omega(A)| \|(\pi_\omega(B)-C)\Omega_\omega\| \|\pi_\omega(B)\Omega_\omega\| .$$

Using $\|(\pi_\omega(B)-C)\Omega_\omega\| < \varepsilon$,

$\|\pi_\omega(A)\| \leq \|A\|$ (i.e. the homomorphism π_ω is continuous [15]),

$\|\alpha_t(A)\| = \|A\|$ (i.e. every *-automorphism of a C^{*}-algebra is isometric [6]),

and the fact that

$$U_t \underset{|t|\to\infty}{\to} P_{\Omega_\omega} \quad \text{weakly,}$$

we find

$$\omega(B^{*}\alpha_t(A)B) \underset{|t|\to\infty}{\to} \omega(B^{*}B)\omega(A). \qquad \text{q.e.d.}$$

Strongly clustering states have the property that 0 is the only discrete eigenvalue in the spectrum of the generator of U_t, furthermore this eigenvalue has multiplicity one. [Indeed suppose there were χ with $U_t\chi = e^{i\alpha t}\chi$, then

$$(\phi, U_t\chi) \underset{|t|\to\infty}{\to} (\phi, P_{\Omega_\omega}\chi) = 0$$

on the one hand, whereas on the other hand

$$(\phi, U_t\chi) = (\phi,\chi)e^{i\alpha t}.$$

This is a contradiction. By the same argument one shows that the multiplicity of the zero eigenvalue is one.]

Take now a finite volume K.M.S. state, then we know that the state is *separating*, *invariant* and *$\omega(A\alpha_t B)$ is a continuous function in t*. However, we *cannot* proof that *for all* $B \in \mathfrak{A}_V$ we have

$$\omega_B(\alpha_t(A)) \to \omega_B(1)\omega(A).$$

The reason is that $\hat{U}_t$ (see for notation the representation of the finite system K.M.S. state in Chapter 3) has eigenvalues different from 1 and consequently its generator has eigenvalues different from zero. ($|e_n\rangle\langle e_m|$, with $n \neq m$, for instance is an eigenstate of $\hat{U}_t$ with eigenvalue $\exp i(\varepsilon_n - \varepsilon_m)t$.)

The precise situation for the *finite system K.M.S. state* is the following:

$$\omega(B^* \alpha_t(A)B) \qquad \text{tends to a limit as} \qquad |t| \to \infty$$

only for those $B \in \mathfrak{A}_V$ for which

$$\omega(B^*\alpha_t(A)B) = \omega(B^*AB).$$

A proof of this statement goes as follows: one firstly proves that $\omega(B^*\alpha_t(A)B)$ is an almost periodic function (indeed, writing $\omega(B^*\alpha_t(A)B) = \mathrm{Tr}\,(e^{-\beta H}B^*\alpha_t(A)B)$ and inserting the *discrete* spectral decompositions for $e^{-\beta H}$ and U_t one proves that $\omega(B^*\alpha_t(A)B)$ is the sum of a uniformly convergent series of periodic functions and is therefore almost periodic. Secondly one remarks that an almost periodic function tends to a limit only if the function is a constant.

Another point to remark is whether there exist states that satisfy the criterion of the theorem. The answer is yes. The free Bose gas above the critical temperature satisfies the criterion [22][30]. The algebra does not have the quasi-local structure as we discussed, but the quasi-local structure played no role in proving the theorem.

Suppose that ω satisfies the equivalent criteria of the theorem and is K.M.S., while α_t is the K.M.S. automorphism group, then we can conclude that ω is primary, i.e.

$$\mathfrak{Z} = \pi_\omega(\mathfrak{U})'' \cap \pi_\omega(\mathfrak{U})' = \{\lambda 1\},$$

which means that ω is extremal K.M.S. (cf. §3). Indeed, strongly clustering gives that Ω_ω is uniquely invariant and this contradicts a non trivial $\mathfrak{Z}$, since $\mathfrak{Z}$ is pointwise invariant. [One can prove [23][24] that ω is a so-called primary type III state.]

Suppose we would have one of the equivalent conditions of the theorem, then it follows that

$$\omega(B[A,\alpha_t(C)]D) \underset{|t|\to\infty}{\to} 0, \qquad B,D \in \mathfrak{U}.$$

Corollary: *If in addition to conditions of the theorem we would add that* ω *is primary, then we have that the following conditions are equivalent:*

i) ω *is strongly clustering;*

ii) $\omega_B(A) \underset{|t|\to\infty}{\to} \omega_B(1)\omega(A)$;

iii) $\pi_\omega(\alpha_t(A)) \underset{|t|\to\infty}{\to} \omega(A).1$ *(weakly);*

iv) $\omega(B[A,\alpha_t(C)]D) \underset{|t|\to\infty}{\to} 0.$

The conditions of the corollary are satisfied for every extremal K.M.S.-state [25].

4.2 *Dynamical perturbations*

In the preceding section we discussed the response under kinematical disturbances, i.e. the *filtering* operations $\omega \to \omega_B$, $B \in \mathfrak{U}$.

In this section we are going to discuss the dynamical perturbations as treated in [1]. For the complete treatment we refer to [1]. We shall content ourselves with the "pedestrian" way of describing the results obtained in [1] and then try to draw some conclusions related to the theorem and corollary we discussed in 4.1.

Let h be a hermitean element from $\mathfrak{A}$; let furthermore the dynamics be described by a one-parameter group of automorphisms α_t, that is strongly continuous, i.e.

$$\|\alpha_t(A) - A\| \underset{t\to 0}{\to} 0.$$

(This is the situation in quantum lattice systems.) This assumption is of a technical nature in [1], and may perhaps be circumvented.

Starting from α_t one defines a *perturbed* dynamics, i.e. a group of automorphisms τ_t^h defined by:

$$\tau_t^h(A) = \sum_{n=1}^{\infty} i^n \int_{t_1 < \ldots < t_n < t} dt_1 \ldots dt_n \, [\alpha_{t_1}(h), [\alpha_{t_2}(h), \ldots, [\alpha_{t_n}(h), \alpha_t(A)] \ldots]] + \alpha_t(A) ,$$

The existence of the integrals is guaranteed by the strong continuity of the group of automorphisms α_t. The convergence of the sum is in the norm topology on $\mathfrak{A}$ [26] [27].

One way to see that we have, by the expression above, a perturbation of the dynamics becomes clear in a somewhat more familiar sense by the following

Theorem [27]: *Let ω be an α_t invariant state, and let π_ω, U_t, Ω_ω be as before, then*

$$\pi_\omega(\tau_t^h(A)) = \exp i(H+\pi_\omega(h))t \; \pi_\omega(A) \exp -i(H+\pi_\omega(h))t.$$

[In the jargon this means that τ_t^h is implemented by a unitary group which has a generator $H+\pi_\omega(h)$, where U_t is given by $U_t = \exp iHt$.]

Let a state ω satisfy the following criteria:

i) ω is α_t invariant;

ii) the truncated correlation functions up to order 6 vanish for large t as:

$$|\omega^T_{(n)}(\alpha_{t_1}(A_1)\ \ldots\ \alpha_{t_n}(A_n))| \le \frac{C}{1+\sup_{i,j}|t_i-t_j|^{1+\delta}},$$

where $n \le 6$, δ some positive number and A_i, $i=1\ldots n$, belong to a suitably chosen dense subset of $\mathfrak{A}$.

In [1] the following problem is solved:
Find ω^h that is an τ^h_t invariant state on $\mathfrak{A}$, where ω^h is related to ω by the relation:

$$\omega^h(A) = \omega(A) + \omega_1(A) + \ldots$$

(an expansion in h).
The fact that such a functional ω_1 exists (of course defined in a more precise way) as a σ-weak continuous functional on $\pi_\omega(\mathfrak{A})''$ is called *the stability of* ω *for the inner (dynamical) perturbation.*

Due to properties i) and ii) it follows that the spectrum of H is either one-sided or covers the whole real line. Following [1] *we assume that the spectrum of H covers the whole line.* [A situation like this is for instance true in the free Bose gas due to a result of Størmer [29].]

Let us for simplicity *assume* that everything we do can be done inside one representation, namely the one given by ω and furthermore we identify $\pi_\omega(A)$ and A (hence also $\pi_\omega(h) = h$). Then

$$\tau^h_t(A) = \exp i(H+h)t\ A\ \exp -i(H+h)t.$$

(All we obtain can be shown to be rigorously true [1].)
Since we have

$$\omega^h(\tau^h_t(A)) = \omega^h(A) = \omega(\tau^h_t(A)) + \omega_1(\tau^h_t(A)),$$

it follows that

$$0 = \frac{d}{dt}\,\omega^h(\tau^h_t(A)) = i\omega([H+h,A]) + i\omega_1([H+h,A]).$$

Since $\omega([H,A])=0$ due to α_t-invariance of ω, we have to first order in h:

$$i\omega_1([H,A]) = -i\omega([h,A]).$$

Take now

$$i\omega_1([H,\alpha_t(A)]) = -i\omega([h,\alpha_t(A)]).$$

Hence it follows

$$\frac{d}{dt}\omega_1(\alpha_t(A)) = -i\omega([h,\alpha_t(A)])$$

$$\omega_1(\alpha_T(A)) - \omega_1(A) = -i\int_0^T \omega([h,\alpha_t(A)])\,dt.$$

Now it follows from ii) above that

$$\pi_\omega(\alpha_t(A)) \underset{t\to\infty}{\to} \omega(A).1.$$

We therefore have

$$\omega(A)\omega_1(1) - \omega_1(A) = -i\int_0^\infty \omega([h,\alpha_t(A)])\,dt,$$

provided the right-side exists, which is guaranteed. In order that ω^h and ω are both normalized, i.e. $\omega^h(1) = \omega(1) = 1$, we must have that $\omega_1(1) = 0$.

Hence we find

$$\omega_1(A) = i\int_0^\infty \omega([h,\alpha_t(A)])\,dt.$$

By a similar argument one finds

$$\omega_1(A) = -i\int_{-\infty}^0 \omega([h,\alpha_t(A)])\,dt.$$

Hence the scheme only works if we have the following *consistency* requirements:

$$\int_{-\infty}^\infty \omega([h,\alpha_t(A)])\,dt = 0 \quad \text{and} \quad \omega_1(1) = 0.$$

It is shown in [1] that the requirement that this shall be true for *every* $h = h^* \in \mathcal{U}$, implies the K.M.S.-condition.

We therefore have the following:

For an invariant state that has no long-time correlations (truncated correlation functions vanish) and is stable under the action of inner dynamical perturbations, the K.M.S.-condition can be viewed upon as a consistency relation.

We want to conclude with a few remarks in relation to what we said in section 4.1.

Since we assumed invariance of ω and the vanishing of the time-correlation functions the state ω is strongly clustering. Therefore H has only one discrete point in its spectrum. This implies that $\pi_\omega(\mathfrak{A})''$ is primary (of type III). Since in addition the state ω can be shown to be K.M.S., it is separating and therefore we have by the corollary of section 4.1:

$$\omega(A[B,\alpha_t(C)]D) \underset{|t|\to\infty}{\to} 0.$$

In the language of section 4.1 we also have that ω is stable for kinematical perturbations (i.e. $\omega_B(\alpha_t(A)) \to \omega_B(1)\omega(A)$).

As a last remark we notice that the perturbed state ω^h is never a K.M.S.-state with respect to α_t due to a theorem of Takesaki [28]. However ω^h is almost ω, ω^h is *not* α_t-K.M.S. whereas ω is α_t-K.M.S., therefore ω^h is an *almost* equilibrium state (implicit in this last statement is of course the identification of K.M.S.-states with equilibrium states, cf. [20][21], which can be proven under certain circumstances.

REFERENCES

1) R. Haag, D. Kastler, Ewa Trych-Pohlmeyer, Stability and Equilibrium States, Comm.Math.Phys. 38 (1974) 173.

2) G.W. Mackey, Mathematical Foundations of Quantum Mechanics, W.A. Benjamin Inc., New York, Amsterdam.

3) A.M. Gleason, J. Math. and Mech. 6 (1967) 885.

4) S. Sakai, C^*- and W^*-Algebras, Springer Verlag, Berlin (1971).

5) J. Gunson, Physical States on Quantum Logics I, Annales de l'Institut H. Poincaré XVII (1972) 295.

6) R.V. Kadison, Isometries of Operator Algebras, Ann.Math., Princeton 54 (1951) 325-318.

7) R.V. Kadison, Transformations of States in Operator Theory and Dynamics, Topology 3, suppl. 2 (1965) 177-198.

8) V. Bargmann, Ann. Math. 59 (1954) 1.

9) D.W. Robinson, Statistical Mechanics of Quantum Spin Systems. II, Comm. Math. Phys. 7 (1968) 337.

10) F. Rocca, D. Testard and M. Sirugue, On a Class of Equilibrium States under the K.M.S.-Condition I. Fermions, Comm. Math. Phys. 13 (1969) 319.

11) F. Rocca, M. Sirugue and D. Testard, On a Class of Equilibrium States under the K.M.S.-Condition II. Bosons, Comm. Math. Phys. 19 (1970) 119.

12) M. Sirugue and M. Winnink, Translations dans le temps comme groupe d' *-automorphismes, Marseille preprint 71/p.338 (1971).

13) M. Winnink, Thermodynamic States in an Algebraic Approach, In: Statistical Mechanics and Field Theory, edited by R.N. Sen and C. Weil, Keter Publishing House, Jerusalem (1972).

14) S. Sakai, Proc. Jap. Acad. 33 (1957) 439.

15) J. Dixmier, Les C^*-Algèbres et leurs Représentations, Gauthier-Villars, Paris (1964).

16) J. Dixmier, Les Algèbres d'Opérateurs dans l'Espace Hilbertien, Gauthier-Villars, Paris (1969).

17) R. Haag, N.M. Hugenholtz and M. Winnink, On the Equilibrium States in Quantum Statistical Mechanics, Comm. Math. Phys. 5 (1967) 215.

18) M. Winnink, Algebraic Consequences of the K.M.S. Boundary Condition. In: Cargèse Lectures in Physics, Vol. 4, edited by D. Kastler, Gordon and Breach, New York (1970).

19) M. Takesaki and M. Winnink, Local Normality in Quantum Statistical Mechanics, Comm. Math. Phys. 30 (1973) 129.

20) H.J. Brascamp, Equilibrium States for a Classical Lattice Gas, Comm. Math. Phys. 18 (1970) 82.

21) H. Araki, On the Equivalence of the K.M.S.-Condition and the Variational Principle for Quantum Lattice Systems, Comm. Math. Phys. 38 (1974) 1.

22) J.D. Wieringa, Thermodynamic Limit and K.M.S.-States in Quantum Statistical Mechanics. A C^*-Algebraic Approach, Thesis Groningen (1970)

23) N.M. Hugenholtz, On the Factor Type of Equilibrium States in Quantum Statistical Mechanics, Comm. Math. Phys. 6 (1967) 189-193.

24) M. Winnink, An Application of C^*-Algebras to Quantum Statistical Mechanics of Systems in Equilibrium, Thesis Groningen (1968).

25) D.W. Robinson, C^*-Algebras and Quantum Statistical Mechanics. In: Varenna Lectures (1973).

26) R.F. Streater and I.F. Wilde, The Time-Evolution of Quantized Fields with Bounded Quasi-Local Interaction Density, Comm. Math. Phys. 17 (1970) 21-32.

27) D.W. Robinson, Return to Equilibrium, Comm. Math. Phys. 31 (1973) 171.

28) M. Takesaki, Tomita's Theory of Modular Hilbert Algebras and its Applications, Lectures in Math. 128, Springer, Berlin-Heidelberg-New York (1970).

29) E. Størmer, Spectra of States and Asymptotically Abelian C^*-Algebras, Comm. Math. Phys. 28 (1972) 279.

30) H. Araki, On the Algebra of All Local Observables, Progr. Theor. Phys. 32 (1964) 844.

THE STATISTICAL MECHANICS OF CLASSICAL ANALYTIC DYNAMICS

JOSEPH FORD*

School of Physics, Georgia Institute of Technology,

Atlanta, Georgia 30332, U.S.A.

INTRODUCTION

In the following lectures, I shall attempt to describe a contemporary view of how the deterministic equations of classical dynamics can yield solutions exhibiting stochastic or statistical behavior. Strictly speaking, I shall present only the broad outline of this contemporary view by discussing a number of simple systems which illustrate many of its central ideas. This technique allows me to convey much of the essential flavor of the new results without having to introduce numerous sophisticated mathematical concepts unfamiliar to most physicists, including the present author. As is perhaps inevitable in talks prepared for a summerschool audience, much of the following information has been identically presented earlier in the form of published papers and reviews[1)] or published talks[2)] prepared for similar audiences. My conscience permits this republication only because I feel that the ideas are sufficiently significant to bear repetition in several places.

In order to orient the audience to the central problem considered here, let us briefly discuss some historical background. In these lectures, we shall always be considering isolated, conservative, classical mechanical systems. We may thus specify the state of such a system by giving all the position and momentum coordinates (q_i, p_i) of a point in the system phase space (Γ-space), and the time evolution of the system is described by a curve (trajectory) lying on an energy surface in phase space. From equilibrium statistical mechanics, we learn that most (q_i, p_i) points on the system energy surface correspond to thermodynamic equilibrium states (P, V, T, etc.). Thus provided the system curves wander freely over the whole energy surface, statistical mechanics asserts that the system spends most of its journey at thermodynamic equilibrium. On the same grounds, statistical mechanics also asserts that a system, started in a thermodynamic disequilibrium state, will always eventually reach equilibrium.

Thus perhaps the first problem in justifying or establishing a statistical mechanics for classical isolated systems is to demonstrate that isolated physical systems do in fact and in general exhibit phase space trajectories, generated by f = ma, which wander freely over the energy surface. In essence, this is the so-called "ergodic problem" studied by mathematicians since the turn of the century. Here one wishes to validate the equation

$$\lim_{t\to\infty} t^{-1} \int_0^t G[q_i(\tau), p_i(\tau)]\,d\tau = \int G(q_i, p_i)\,dq_i dp_i, \qquad (1)$$

for most physical systems, where $G(q_i, p_i)$ is any interesting physical

Fundamental Problems in Statistical Mechanics, Vol. 3, Editor, E.D.G. Cohen.

observable. On the left in eq. (1) is the experimentally observed time average along a system trajectory of the observable, while on the right is the theoretically calculated phase space average of the same observable, an average to be taken over the energy surface. Using loose, intuitive arguments, one easily grasps that eq. (1) is equivalent to asserting that the system curve wanders freely over the energy surface.

So now what can mathematicians say about the validity of eq. (1)? Until recently, they could only assert that eq. (1) is valid if and only if the system is metrically transitive. This latter term means loosely that the energy surface cannot be decomposed into two finite, non-zero regions such that all system trajectories lie entirely in either one region or the other. In short, the mathematician has essentially only restated the problem. Additionally, the only example of a metrically transitive system the mathematicians could offer was that of geodesic flow on a surface of everywhere negative curvature which is not a very physically interesting system. However, before the physicist begins to giggle too loudly here, one should note that even the most advanced physics tests in classical dynamics completely ignore the ergodic question; indeed they treat only known solvable problems which certainly are not ergodic and do not obey eq. (1). In recent years as we shall discuss later, the mathematicians have done much better, but ergodicity remains one of the central, underlying notions.

Another notion useful in the study of statistical behavior in classical systems is that of mixing. Indeed the concept of mixing is usually considered more intuitively appealing by physicists than is ergodicity. Let us note that observation can never precisely measure the state of a system, so let us represent the imprecise initial state of our system by a small "square" or a small cell on the energy surface. As time goes on, one anticipates that the initial small cell will evolve via Newton's equations into a thin filament uniformly covering the energy surface. Here the mixing in phase space generated by Newton's equations is made analogous to mixing scotch and water where any stirring is presumed eventually to yield a uniform mixture. Since every initial small cell is presumed to spread uniformly over the energy surface as t tends to infinity, mixing implies that states of equal energy are equally likely at equilibrium. This in turn means that the observed values of a physical observable at equilibrium may be calculated using the right side of eq. (1). In short, mixing, if it occurs, may be rigorously shown to imply ergodicity[3)]. However, as with ergodicity, one still must show that mixing actually occurs in classical mechanical systems.

Having elaborated these preliminaries, we can now state our first physically significant result. Sinai[3)] has rigorously proved that the hard sphere gas is ergodic and mixing. Indeed his proof reveals that the deterministic motion of the hard sphere gas yields, in a sense to be discussed later, values for measured observables as random as those generated by a roulette wheel. However, his proof, which is to be published shortly, is quite long and mathematically sophisticated. It will occupy about one hundred journal pages and will involve such concepts as discontinuous transverse foliations, completely positive Kolmogorov entropy, and the like. Thus it is clear that in these brief lectures we shall not be able to present all the mathematical details or, worse, even all the physical consequences of Sinai's theorem. However, by considering extremely simple examples which we may discuss using very simple concepts, we can nonetheless illustrate many of the essential features of Sinai's result and much more.

1. A MODEL FOR ERGODICITY AND MIXING

In phase space, any conservative Hamiltonian system can be considered as an "area" (measure) preserving transformation of the energy surface onto itself. In particular, the hard sphere gas is such a Hamiltonian system. As a consequence, we may illustrate the underlying essentials required for Sinai's proof by considering a judiciously chosen area preserving mapping. In this section, we consider the almost ludicrously simple algebraic mapping of the unit square upon itself given by

$$(x_{n+1}, y_{n+1}) = T(x_n, y_n) = (x_n + y_n, x_n + 2y_n) \quad . \tag{1.1}$$

In eq. (1.1) if a point (x_{n+1}, y_{n+1}) lies outside the unit square, we repeatedly substract unity from each coordiate until the point returns there. A graphical picture of the havoc caused by only two iterations of this mapping is shown in Fig. 1.

In order to understand the source of this behavior, let us differentiate eq. (1.1) and write

$$(dx_{n+1}, dy_{n+1}) = (dx_n + dy_n, dx_n + 2dy_n) \quad . \tag{1.2}$$

By a rotation of axes, we may write eq. (1.2) in the form

$$(d\zeta_{n+1}, d\eta_{n+1}) = (\lambda d\zeta_n, \lambda^{-1} d\eta_n) \quad , \tag{1.3}$$

where $\lambda = 2^{-1}(3 + 5^{\frac{1}{2}}) > 1$. Thus on the first iteration, a small rectangle with sides $(d\zeta_n, d\eta_n)$ is stretched by a factor λ in the ζ-direction and contracted by λ^{-1} in the η-direction while preserving area. After k-iterations, eq. (1.3) becomes

$$(d\zeta_{n+k}, d\eta_{n+k}) = (\lambda^k d\zeta_n, \lambda^{-k} d\eta_n) = (e^{k\ln\lambda} d\zeta_n, e^{-k\ln\lambda} d\eta_n) \quad . \tag{1.4}$$

Hence the mapping exponentially stretches an initially small area element along the ζ-direction while preserving area by exponentially shrinking the initial area

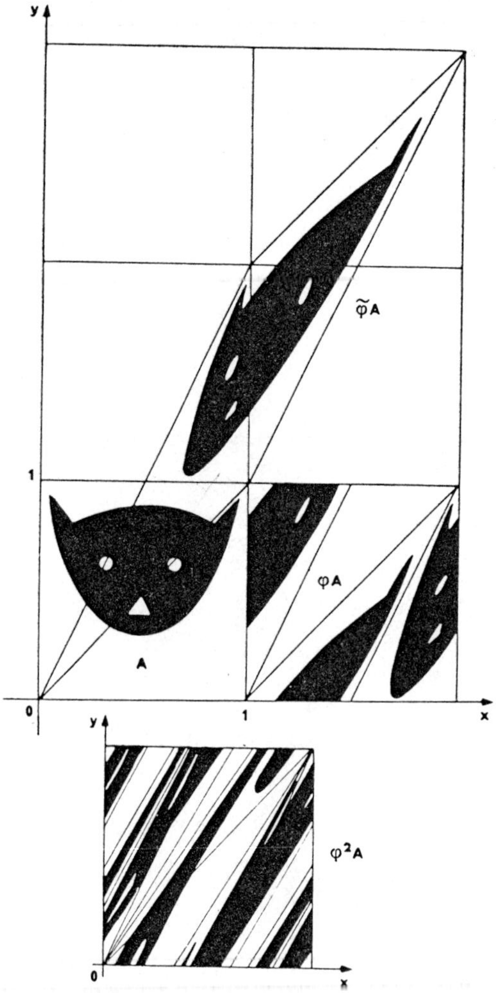

Fig. 1. A drawing of the mapping specified by eq. (1.1). After only two iterations of the mapping, one already has a crazy mixed-up cat.

along the η-direction. This process continues indefinitely causing each (and every) small initial area element (dx_n, dy_n) to evolve into a thin "spiral" filament uniformly covering the unit area. As a consequence, this system is obviously mixing and hence ergodic.

Moreover, it is precisely this type exponential stretching and shrinking of "area" elements on the energy surface which allows Sinai to prove ergodicity and mixing for the hard sphere gas. One can even easily appreciate the physical source of this exponential separation of initially close trajectories. It lies in the fact that the final two velocities for a specified initial velocity, binary, hard sphere collision depends very sensitively on the angle between centers of the spheres. A grazing collision for example leaves the initial velocities almost unchanged while a "direct hit" interchanges the initial velocities. After a host of binary collisions, two trajectories for a hard sphere gas which were initially close together have become widely separated in phase space, leading to ergodic and mixing behavior.

There is a useful alternative view regarding the source of ergodicity and mixing which we illustrate again using the system described by eq. (1.1). Let us first note that the mapping of eq. (1.1) has periodic orbits. For example, the set of points (2/5, 1/5), (3/5, 4/5), (2/5, 1/5) is a periodic orbit as is the set (1/4, 1/4), (1/2, 3/4), (1/4, 0), (1/4, 1/4). Indeed starting with any point (x,y), where x and y are both rational, leads to a periodic orbit. This follows from the fact that eq. (1.1) has integer coefficients and points are returned to the unit square by integer subtraction. Thus a point (x, y) with rational x and y sequentially maps back into itself after passing, at worst, through the whole finite set of points having rational coordinates with the same common denominator as x and y. As a consequence, periodic orbits are dense in the unit square. Moreover all such periodic orbits are unstable in the sense that nearby non-periodic orbits diverge away exponentially due to eq. (1.4). Finally then ergodicity and mixing follow from the fact that the non-periodic orbits are continually "scattered" off the dense set of unstable periodic orbits. In this view each non-periodic orbit is forced to stream via a diffusion process or a "random walk" among the dense set of "scattering" orbits.

We may summarize this section by noting that ergodicity and mixing for the hard sphere gas follow from either of two underlying basic properties. First, almost all initially close trajectories in phase space separate exponentially with time, and second, the system possesses an everywhere dense set of unstable periodic orbits. Mathematicians expect that these results can be relatively easily extended to systems having a general type of purely repulsive interparticle forces. However, the physicist naturally asks what happens to these ideas when attractive interparticle forces are included. It is to this point that we now turn.

2. A MODEL HAVING ATTRACTIVE FORCES

Conservative Hamiltonian systems with attractive forces can exhibit behavior which is astonishing in its variety and its pathology. Since later sections shall dwell on these matters, we here choose to introduce the subject via a simple example which illustrates many of the relevant features of the general problem. Let us consider the most difficult case in which attractive forces have caused the formation of a solid, and let us describe the solid as a set of coupled anharmonic oscillators. Our simplification in this section is to consider a one-dimensional, two-atom "solid" with the Hamiltonian

$$H = (1/2)(p_1^2 + p_2^2 + q_1^2 + q_2^2) + q_1^2 q_2 - (1/3)q_2^3 \qquad (2.1)$$

which has previously been studied by Henon and Heiles[4].

In order to survey the character of the trajectories generated by Hamiltonian (2.1) at a specified energy E, Henon and Heiles reduce the motion to a plane area-preserving mapping in the (q_2, p_2) plane[4]. Starting with a given (q_2, p_2) point, they set $q_1 = 0$ and algebraically solve the equation $H = E$ for $p_1 \geqslant 0$. This provides them with an initial mapping point (q_2, p_2) and with an initial condition (q_1, p_1, q_2, p_2) for numerically integrating to obtain a trajectory for Hamiltonian (2.1). The initial (q_2, p_2) point then maps into the next (q_2, p_2) point on this trajectory at which again $q_1 = 0$ and $p_1 \geqslant 0$. By continuing this process, one easily sees that each trajectory generates a unique set of mapping points in the (q_2, p_2) plane. This mapping may be shown[3] to be area preserving.

Now all the points in the (q_2, p_2) plane generated by a trajectory having energy $E \leqslant 1/6$ must lie in the interior of the oval $(p_2^2 + q_2^2 - (2/3)q_2^3) \leqslant 2E$ as may be verified by setting $q_1 = 0$ in eq. (2.1) with $H = E$ and noting that $p_1 \geqslant 0$. Moreover if Hamiltonian (2.1) is ergodic, then each ergodic trajectory must yield mapping points which uniformly cover this oval since ergodicity requires that such trajectories come arbitrarily close to all the points allowed by the equation $H = E$. On the other hand, if Hamiltonian (2.1) behaves like the known integrable problems in classical mechanics in that it possesses a well-behaved additional constant of the motion $I_0 = I(q_1, p_1, q_2, p_2)$, then we may solve the equation $H = E$ for $p_1 \geqslant 0$ and write $I_0 = I(q_1, E, q_2, p_2)$. In this latter expression for I_0, set $q_1 = 0$ and solve $I_0 = I(0, E, q_2, p_2)$ for p_2. We then obtain $p_2 = p_2(I_0, E, q_2)$. This last equation implies that the trajectories for an integrable system having $H = E$ and $I = I_0$ yield mapping points lying on the curve $p_2 = p_2(I_0, E, q_2)$.

In fig. 2, we display the mapping obtained by Henon and Heiles at energy $E = 1/12$. There one notes that to computer accuracy smooth curves exist everywhere indicating that Hamiltonian (2.1) at this energy behaves like one of the integrable problems of classical mechanics. In addition at this energy, orbits started initially close together separate linearly with time rather than exponentially as shown in fig. 3. The situation depicted in fig. 2 persists up to about energy $E = 1/10$ above which a small region containing a random splatter of mapping points appears. This region grows at the expense of the curve filled regions until at energy $E = 1/8$, one has the mapping shown in fig. 4. Here one observes the so-called divided phase space in which the system appears integrable in certain regions while appearing ergodic in others. In the ergodic region, each trajectory yields mapping points which appear to uniformly cover that region; two initially close points map apart as illustrated in fig. 5 at an exponential rate; and apparently a dense or near dense set of unstable periodic orbits occurs in this region. Finally in fig. 6 at energy $E = 1/6$, Hamiltonian (2.1) appears to have become almost completely ergodic.

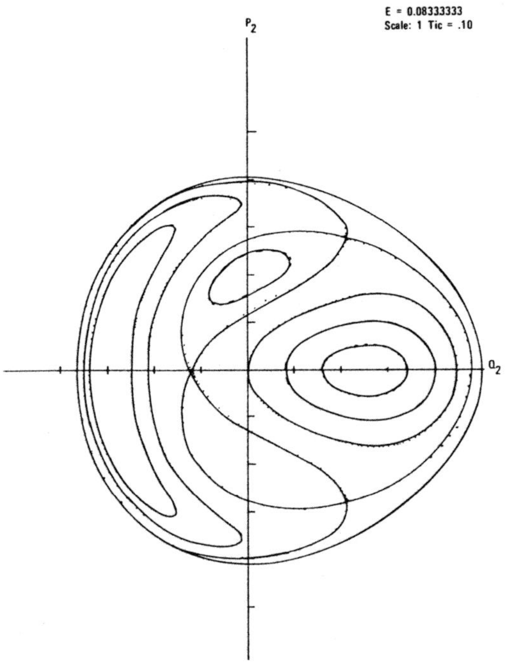

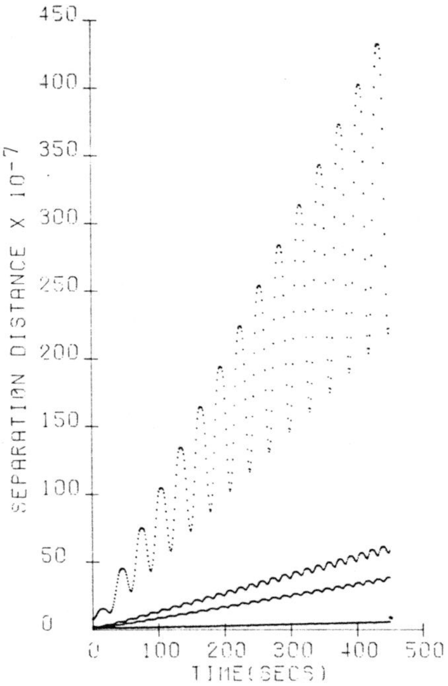

Fig. 2. The mapping plane generated by the Henon-Heiles Hamiltonian (2.1) at energy $E = 1/12$. Here and in the following mapping figures, whenever the mapping points generated by a trajectory appear to lie on a curve, the curve has been drawn in freehand.

Fig. 3. This figure shows the growth of separation distance between two trajectories initially started about 10^{-7} apart in the full phase space for Hamiltonian (2.1) at energy $E = 1/12$. Separation distance versus time is plotted for four distinct trajectory-pairs. Here the separation distance grows linearly with time.

In this section we have examined a Hamiltonian system which exhibits a transition from the integrable system behavior so well known in classical mechanics to the ergodic behavior anticipated by statistical mechanics. In so doing, we have surely raised as many questions as we have answered. What is the physical explanation for the appearance of "ergodic" behavior? How does one predict the transition energy? Does the transition energy tend to zero as the number of system particles tends to infinity and, if so, under what conditions? We shall return to some of these questions as well as others following the next section in which we attempt to indicate how irreversible rate equations and truly stochastic behavior may be obtained for deterministic systems known to be ergodic and mixing.

3. A MODEL FOR IRREVERSIBLE AND STOCHASTIC BEHAVIOR

In the earlier sections, we have demonstrated that Newton's equations can yield trajectories that are as wildly erratic as the founding fathers of

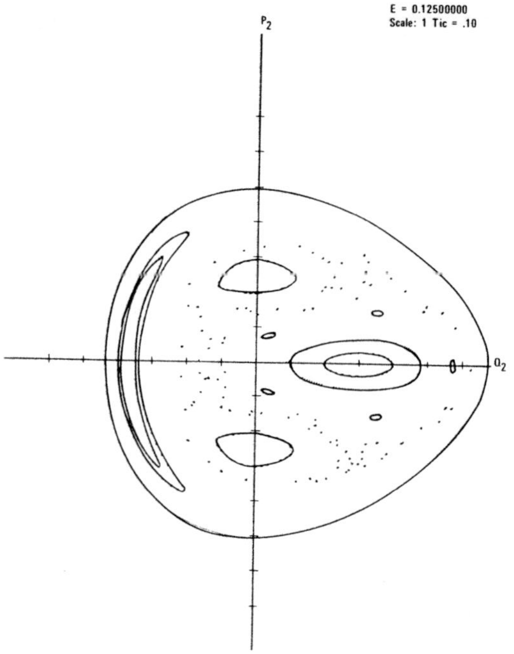

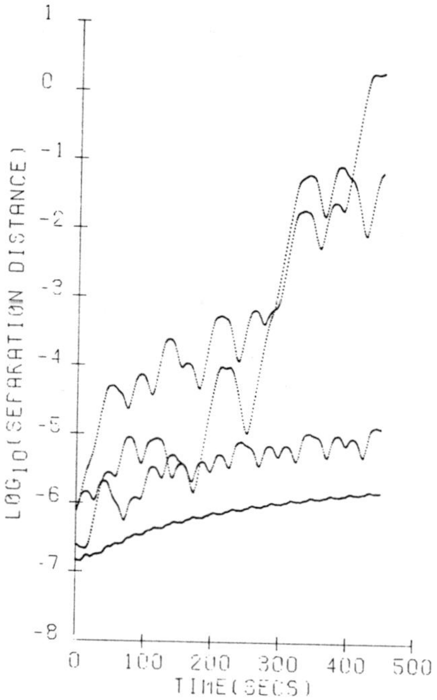

Fig. 4. The mapping plane generated by the Henon-Heiles system at energy $E = 1/8$. The unconnected dots are the mapping points generated by a single trajectory.

Fig. 5. This figure plots $\log_{10}$ of the separation distance versus time for four distinct trajectory pairs of the Henon-Heiles system at energy $E = 1/8$. The generally lower-lying curves are for trajectory-pairs started in the smooth curve region of fig. 4. The generally upper-lying curves are for trajectory-pairs started in the ergodic region of fig. 4. The rapid exponential-order growth of the upper two trajectory-pairs is relatively clear.

statistical mechanics anticipated. In this section we exhibit a simple ergodic and mixing system for which one may derive an irreversible rate equation and for which one may prove that deterministic trajectories can yield a measured quantity with values as random as a coin-toss game.

The transformation we choose to consider is the so-called baker's transformation pictured in fig. 7 and specified algebraically by

$$(x_{n+1}, y_{n+1}) = \begin{cases} [2x_n, y_n/2] , & 0 \leqslant x_n < 1/2 \\ [(2x_n - 1), (y_n + 1)/2] , & 1/2 \leqslant x_n < 1 \end{cases} \quad . \tag{3.1}$$

This area preserving transformation of the unit square upon itself is so intuitively close to the way in which a baker might mix dough that it is fairly obviously ergodic and mixing in the mathematical sense although a rigorous proof is non-

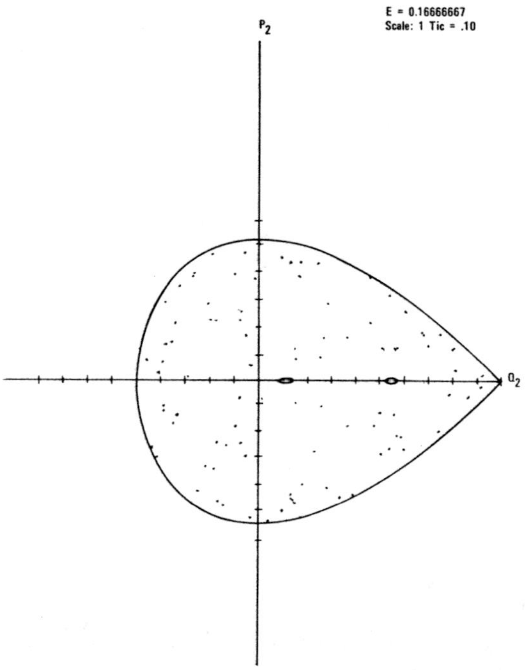

Fig. 6. The mapping plane generated by the Henon-Heiles system at E = 1/6. All the unconnected dots were generated by a single trajectory.

trivial. Let us first note that the mapping (3.1) preserves area, is reversible, and allows one and only one trajectory to pass through each point; and then let us follow Penrose[5] and Lebowitz[6] and define a probability density $f(x_n, y_n, n)$ on each point (x_n, y_n) of the unit square. We require normalization of $f(x_n, y_n, n)$ in the form

$$\iint f(x_0, y_0, 0)\,dx_0 dy_0 = 1 \quad . \tag{3.2}$$

Using standard physical arguments, we may show that Liouville's equation for this system may be written

$$f(x_n, y_n, n) = f(x_0, y_0, 0) \quad , \tag{3.3}$$

where (x_n, y_n) are related to (x_0, y_0) via eq. (3.1), the equations of motion. In particular, we may rewrite eq. (3.3) as

$$f(x, y, n) = \begin{cases} f[\frac{x}{2},\ 2y,\ n-1] & 0 \leqslant y < \frac{1}{2} \\ f[\frac{(x+1)}{2},\ (2y-1),\ n-1] \quad , & \frac{1}{2} \leqslant y < 1 \end{cases} \tag{3.4}$$

where now x and y are the same on both sides of eq. (3.4).

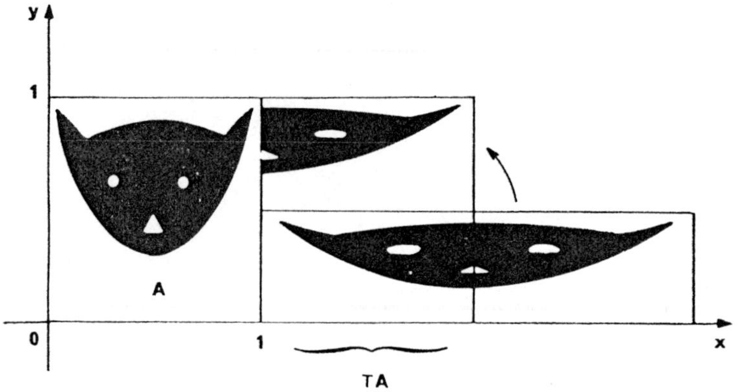

Fig. 7. A drawing of the baker's transformation of the unit square onto itself.

Now even though this system is mixing, $f(x, y, n)$ does not tend to unity as n tends to infinity. Nonetheless because of mixing, there is a "weak approach"[7] of f to unity in the sense that

$$\lim_{n\to\infty} \int g(x, y) f(x, y, n)\,dxdy = \int g(x, y)\,dxdy \tag{3.5}$$

for any well-behaved $g(x, y)$. In physical terms, this means that the equilibrium average value of an observable may be calculated as if f were everywhere equal to unity.

However, we may obtain a true approach to equilibrium by considering the reduced probability distribution $W(x, n)$ defined by

$$W(x, n) = \int dy\, f(x, y, n) \quad . \tag{3.6}$$

Physically speaking, most quantities of physical interest depend not on the full set of phase space variables but on some reduced set. Thus in general, the probability density of interest is analogous to $W(x, n)$ rather than to the full $f(x, y, n)$. It is therefore worthwhile to show that reduced probability densities satisfy irreversible rate equations. By direct integration of eq. (3.4) using the definition of eq. (3.6), we may compute that

$$W(x, n+1) = \tfrac{1}{2}\left[W\left(\frac{x}{2}, n-1\right) + W\left(\frac{x+1}{2}, n-1\right)\right] \quad . \tag{3.7}$$

Equation (3.7) has the obvious solution $W(x) = 1$; moreover one may show[6] that $W(x, n)$ approaches this solution as n tends to infinity. Thus eq. (3.7) is strictly irreversible. It has one other striking feature; it is quite similar to the rate equation for a random walk[8] which latter is a truly stochastic process. This similarity is not accidental.

Suppose we initiate a trajectory of the baker's transformation at an arbitrary point (x_0, y_0) in the unit square. Further suppose that we make a measurement on this trajectory at each iteration determining whether that point on the trajectory has its x-coordinate to the right or left of $x = \frac{1}{2}$. If $x < \frac{1}{2}$, we assert that the quantity measured has value 0; while if $x \geqslant \frac{1}{2}$, we assign it the value 1. If we compute our specified trajectory for all n, $-\infty < n < \infty$, we may write the measured values of our quantity as a doubly infinite sequence of zeros and ones. Although this sequence of measured values is completely determined once (x_0, y_0) is specified, we now prove that it could equally as well have been generated by a completely random coin-toss game.

Let us write each coordinate x_0 and y_0 of the initial arbitrary point as a binary decimal. Then let us form a doubly infinite sequence of zeros and ones by writing x_0 in the usual way to the right of the decimal and by writing y_0 in backward order starting to the left of the decimal. Each iteration of the baker's transformation then corresponds precisely to moving the decimal one place to the right in our doubly infinite sequence since at each step x is thereby doubled and y is halved. Moreover the first digit to the right of the decimal is precisely the instantaneous value of our measured quantity. Finally we note that in general both x_0 and y_0 are irrational and that therefore the doubly infinite sequence of zeros and ones formed by combining their binary representations is a random as a coin-toss game.

For the case of the hard sphere gas started in a definite state, let us measure a quantity G at one second intervals and assume that G has only a finite number N of allowed measured values. We might obtain this situation for a continuous valued G by dividing phase space up into a finite number of small cells and determining only in which cell the value of G lies. Then let us label the possible outcomes with the integers 1 through N. Thus if we measure G on the infinite time interval, $-\infty < t < \infty$, we obtain a doubly infinite sequence of integers completely determined by the equations of motion. However in the same sense as discussed above, although the proof is much more complex, this infinite sequence of measurements might equally as well have been generated by a completely random roulette wheel divided into N equal parts. Much of the contemporary work in mathematical ergodic theory seeks to determine the detailed nature of the equivalence between deterministic and random processes.

In concluding this section, let us call attention to another simple example for which one may derive an irreversible rate equation. Here one considers a ball bouncing between two infinitely heavy walls, one of which oscillates periodically; and one shows that the velocity distribution satisfies a diffusion equation. For details see reference [1)] and the references contained therein.

4. COUPLED NONLINEAR OSCILLATOR SYSTEMS

4.1. Introduction

According to the current folklore in mathematics[9], the proof of ergodicity and mixing for Hamiltonian systems having only repulsive interparticle forces is expected to closely resemble Sinai's proof for the hard sphere gas. However, the inclusion of attractive interparticle forces is expected to all but preclude a general, rigorous proof of ergodicity. With the inclusion of attractive forces, it is expected that phase space divides into ergodic regions pathologically interspersed among the regions of smooth, integrable system type trajectories. Although a rigorous theory perhaps certainly does lie somewhere in the distant future, a combination of analysis and empirical computer experiments is beginning to describe the shape of that future theory. In order to reveal a picture of our present knowledge, in this and the following sections we shall discuss the known results in terms of coupled, Hamiltonian, anharmonic oscillator systems. These systems are of particular interest since they represent the extreme case in which attractive forces have caused the formation of a solid. In particular, the pathology introduced by attractive forces should most clearly reveal its ugly presence for this case. But perhaps even more important, coupled oscillator systems represent an extreme in dense systems, and their study may do much to alleviate the difficulties statistical mechanics is presently facing in treating dense systems.

4.2. Kolmogorov-Arnol'd-Moser theorem

The Hamiltonian which describes oscillatory motion about an equilibrium point may be written

$$H = \sum_{k=1}^{N} (\omega_k/2)(P_k^2 + Q_k^2) + V_3 + V_4 + \ldots \quad , \tag{4.1}$$

where N is the number of oscillators, ω_k are the positive frequencies of the harmonic approximation, and V_3, V_4, etc. are cubic, quartic, etc. polynomials in the (Q_k, P_k) variables. It is convenient to introduce "polar" coordinates (J_k, ϕ_k) via the equations

$$Q_k = (2J_k)^{\frac{1}{2}}\cos\phi_k \quad , \quad P_k = -(2J_k)^{\frac{1}{2}}\sin\phi_k \quad . \tag{4.2}$$

Hamiltonian (4.1) may then be written

$$H = H_0(J_1,\ldots,J_N) + V(J_1,\ldots,\phi_N) \quad , \tag{4.3}$$

where all the pure J-terms resulting from the substitution of eq. (4.2) into eq. (4.1) have been included in the H_0 of eq. (4.3). This inclusion of all pure

J-terms in H_0 is a significant point, as will become apparent later, for in Hamiltonian (4.3) V is a perturbation on the strictly nonlinear oscillator Hamiltonian H_0. In particular, until further notice, we shall regard Hamiltonian (4.3) as the basic oscillator Hamiltonian; only later shall we return to Hamiltonian (4.1) and treat V_3, V_4, etc. as a perturbation on a purely linear oscillator Hamiltonian.

As preparation for stating the Kolmogorov-Arnol's-Moser (KAM) theorem, let us consider the motion generated by H_0, that is, the motion of Hamiltonian (4.3) when V is identically zero. For this case, Hamilton's equations for H_0 read

$$\overset{\circ}{J}_k = 0 \quad , \quad \overset{\circ}{\phi}_k = \partial H_0/\partial J_k \equiv \Omega_k(J_1,\ldots,J_N) \quad . \tag{4.4}$$

These equations may be immediately integrated giving the solutions for H_0 as

$$J_k = \text{constant}, \quad \phi_k = \Omega_k(J_1,\ldots,J_N)\, t + \phi_{k0} \quad . \tag{4.5}$$

In the case of two oscillators (N = 2), the trajectories given by eq. (4.5) may be regarded as lying on a two-dimensional torus of which a cross-sectional view is presented in fig. 8. In this figure we show J_1 and J_2 as "radii" of the torus and ϕ_1 and ϕ_2 as the angular position variables on the torus. In the general case of N oscillators though it is harder to visualize, the solutions given by eq. (4.5) lie on N-dimensional tori. Thus the trajectories for the unperturbed Hamiltonian H_0 lie on smooth, invariant, N-dimensional, integral surfaces (called tori) embedded in the 2N-dimensional phase space. Quite clearly then, the Hamiltonian H_0 is not ergodic; indeed the motion generated by the anharmonic H_0

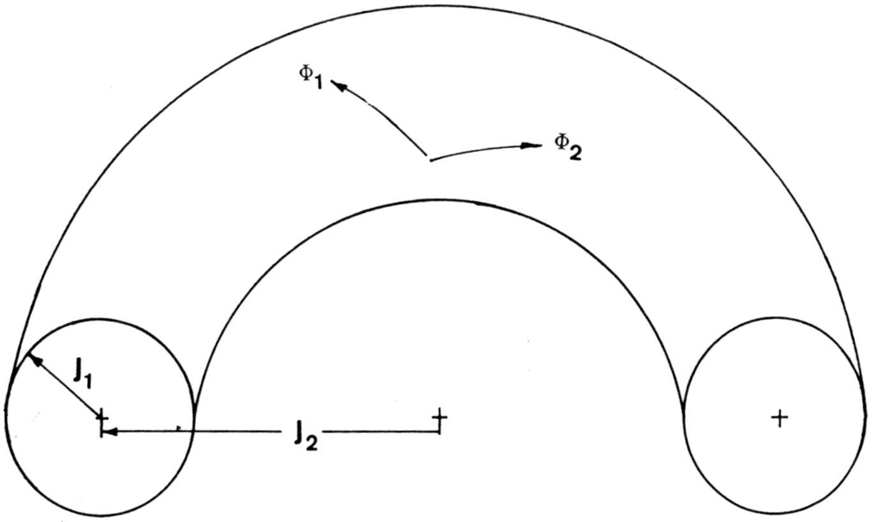

Fig. 8. A cross-sectional view of a two-dimensional torus or doughnut. The variables are those which appear in eq. (4.5) when N = 2.

differs from ordinary coupled harmonic oscillator motion only in that for H_0 the frequencies Ω_k depend on the J_k. Now let us recall that when V is not zero but nonetheless small, statistical mechanics assumes that the trajectories for the full H of eq. (4.3) are in general ergodic. In short, statistical mechanics assumes that a little perturbation goes a long way.

However, in 1954 Kolmogorov stated a theorem[10], later proved by Arnol'd[11] and Moser[12], which states that if, among other things, V is sufficiently small and the Jacobian of the frequencies $\partial(\Omega_1,\ldots,\Omega_N)/\partial(J_1,\ldots,J_N)$ is not identically zero, then most (in the sense of measure theory) system trajectories for Hamiltonian (4.3) continue to lie on smooth, N-dimensional integral surfaces (tori). Indeed the preserved tori of Hamiltonian (4.3) bear strictly quasi-periodic trajectories of the type specified by eq. (4.5) and the preserved tori in phase space are only slightly distorted versions of the H_0-tori. In short, the KAM theorem states that, in general and for the most part, the motion of H differs little from the motion of H_0. Clearly this leaves statistical mechanics (and ergodic theory) with something of a problem.

The first clue indicating that all may not be lost lies in that KAM "most trajectories" loophole. Why only "most trajectories"? Let us here as briefly as possible note that KAM prove their theorem by changing coordinates from the (J_k, ϕ_k) set to a (J'_k, θ_k) set such that Hamiltonian (4.3), written as

$$H = H_0(J_1,\ldots, J_N) + \ldots + f_{\{n_k\}}\cos(\Sigma n_k\phi_k) + \ldots \quad , \tag{4.6}$$

where the V of eq. (4.3) has been expanded in a Fourier series and only one typical term has been explicitly written out in eq. (4.6), becomes

$$H' = H'(J'_1,\ldots, J'_N) \quad , \tag{4.7}$$

where H' is a function of the new momentum coordinates J'_k alone. Clearly if a well-behaved (analytic) canonical transformation could be found which carries eq. (4.6) into eq. (4.7), then all the system trajectories would lie on tori; however, KAM assert only that this transformation exists for most initial conditions. In order to clarify the matter, let us write out the first two terms in one of the transformation equations which would be used to eliminate the specific angle dependent term appearing in eq. (4.6). Though it is certainly not obvious the desired equation reads

$$J'_1 = J_1 - [\, f_{\{n_k\}}\cos(\Sigma n_k\phi_k)/\Sigma n_k\Omega_k + \ldots] \quad . \tag{4.8}$$

Inspection of eq. (4.8) reveals that the KAM condition on the smallness of V is needed to insure that all $f_{\{n_k\}}$ be small, thereby aiding convergence and insuring that the perturbed tori lie close to the unperturbed. The KAM condition on the frequency Jacobian is needed to insure that none of the frequency denominators appearing in eq. (4.8) is identically zero. However, it must be noted that even with this latter KAM condition, as the J_k range over their allowed values, the frequency denominators will still be zero at a countably dense set of Ω_k values. Moreover each member $\{\Omega_k\}$ of this dense set will yield a small denominator over some range of $\{J_k\}$ values since the Ω_k are functions of the J_k and these latter vary. Thus one is led to wonder why the KAM theorem is true for any initial conditions, much less for the majority.

A very intuitive argument which clarifies the matter involves showing that countably dense sets have measure zero. Consider the unit interval (0, 1) on the real axis, and let us delete not only the rationals (h/k), where $k > h$, but also an interval

$$[(h/k) - (\varepsilon/k^3)] \leqslant (h/k) \leqslant [(h/k) + (\varepsilon/k^3)] \tag{4.9}$$

about each rational. The total length of the deleted interval is

$$\sum_{k=1}^{\infty} \sum_{h=1}^{k} (2\varepsilon/k^3) = 2\varepsilon \sum_{k=1}^{\infty} (1/k^2) \quad , \tag{4.10}$$

which may be made as small as we please since the series converges and we may choose ε as small as we please. In analogy, KAM are forced to exclude from their proof not only those initial conditions lying on the tori bearing commensurate frequencies, since such frequencies lead to zero denominators, but also to exclude initial conditions lying in a zone around each of these tori. Nonetheless in analogy with the above argument, the measure of the excluded initial conditions is small provided that V is small. The remaining, non-dense set of tori which are preserved even in the presence of a nonzero V are those tori that bear incommensurate frequencies poorly approximated by the rationals.

From the viewpoint of statistical mechanics, however, we must focus our attention on that small, pathologically distributed set of trajectories which do not lie on preserved tori and inquire about the character of such trajectories. Returning to eq. (4.8), let us note if an angle dependent term $\cos(\Sigma n_k\phi_k)$ yields a zero or near zero denominator $\Sigma n_k\Omega_k$ for some zone of J_k-values then the $\cos(\Sigma n_k\phi_k)$ term which also appears in the Hamiltonian is called by physicists a resonant interaction term and the zone of J_k-values in phase space is called a resonance zone. Now when a given resonant interaction term $\cos(\Sigma n_k\phi_k)$ gives rise to a specified resonance zone of J_k-values, then we must anticipate (in general) that there will be a host of other resonant interaction terms $\cos(n'_k\phi_k)$ whose corresponding resonance zones lie in the same J_k-band. As a consequence, trajectories in such a J_k-region are simultaneously affected by many overlapping resonant interactions. Thus one has here the situation envisioned in the quantum mechanical Golden Rule[13] in which an initial state $(J_1,\ldots, J_N)$ is resonantly coupled to a density of final states $(J_1',\ldots, J_N')$, leading to irreversible behavior. Thus in regions of destroyed tori, one anticipates that the trajectories are very erratic indeed, perhaps ergodically filling the destroyed regions (a result we shall demonstrate in the next section). Thus if we can only increase the size of this relatively small destroyed region, statistical mechanics can proceed as the founding fathers suggested. In the next two sections we demonstrate by example that violation of either KAM assumption is sufficient for widespread breakdown of preserved tori and for erratic and apparently ergodic behavior of most trajectories.

4.3. Ergodicity for large perturbations

In order to illustrate the freely wandering trajectories which can arise in the presence of a large V in Hamiltonian (4.3), we need only consider a two-oscillator system. In a paper on statistical mechanics, it may appear strange indeed to see a detailed discussion of various two-oscillator systems; but we are interested here only in illustrating the sources of irreversibility, and as we shall see, a two-oscillator system exhibits much of the complexity of the many-body problem. Since at the end of the last section we argued that resonance plays a central role in the development of stochastic trajectories, let us begin by considering the effect of an isolated, single resonant interaction. In particular, let us consider

$$H = J_1 + J_2 - J_1^2 - 3J_1J_2 + J_2^2 + \alpha J_1J_2\cos(2\phi_1 - 2\phi_2) \quad , \tag{4.11}$$

where $H_0 = J_1 + J_2 - J_1^2 - 3J_1J_2 + J_2^2$. It is clear from eq. (4.8) that the cos-term represents a resonant interaction in that region of phase space for which $2\Omega_1 \cong 2\Omega_2$. In the language of solid state physics, the cos-term represents the resonant, four-phonon interaction $2\Omega_1 \rightleftarrows 2\Omega_2$. Indeed since

$$\begin{aligned} \Omega_1 &\equiv \partial H_0/\partial J_1 = 1 - 2J_1 - 3J_2 \quad , \\ \Omega_2 &\equiv \partial H_0/\partial J_2 = 1 - 3J_1 + 2J_2 \quad , \end{aligned} \tag{4.12}$$

the cos-term would be expected to strongly distort the unperturbed tori lying in the region for which $J_1 \cong 5J_2$. These assertions could be rigorously proved for Hamiltonian (4.11) since $(J_1 + J_2)$ is a constant of the motion in addition to the Hamiltonian which means that the equations of motion for this system can be solved analytically; however, rather than develop this analytic solution, we here choose to reduce Hamiltonian (4.11) to an area-preserving mapping just as was done in section 2. Indeed the existence of the constant of the motion $(J_1 + J_2)$ means, again as discussed in section 2, that the mapping for Hamiltonian (4.11) can be algebraically computed.

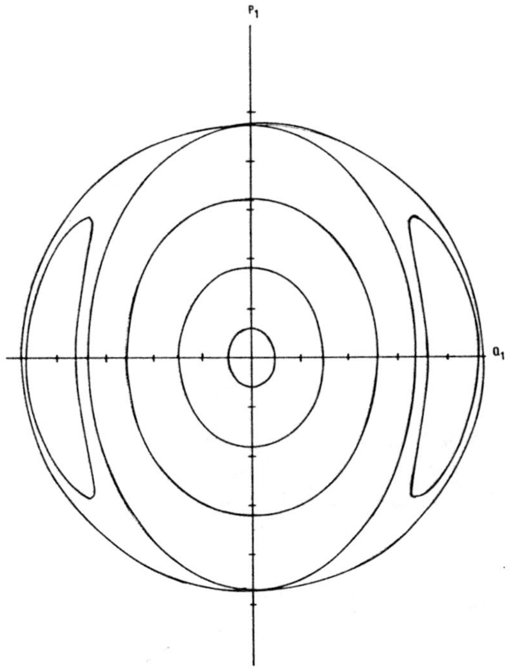

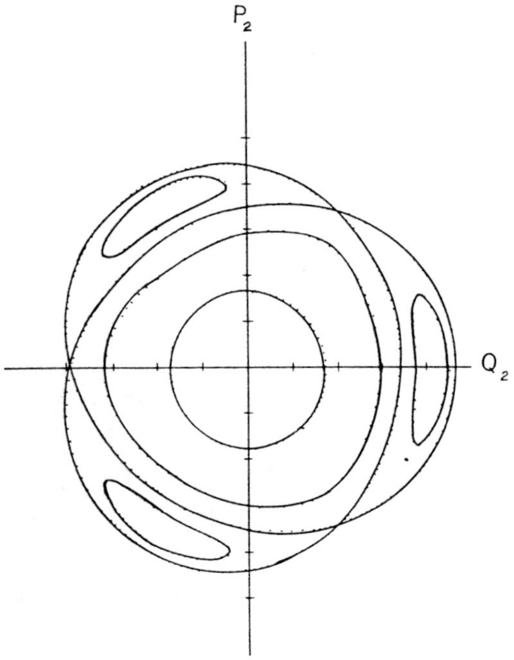

Fig. 9. A typical mapping plane generated by Hamiltonian (4.11). The curves here were computed algebraically. Smooth curves exist everywhere.

Fig. 10. A typical mapping plane for Hamiltonian (4.13). The curves here were rather crudely drawn in freehand. Since this system is integrable, curves exist everywhere.

The mapping for Hamiltonian (4.11) is presented in fig. 9. Were α equal to zero in Hamiltonian (4.11), each curve in fig. 9 would have been a circle centered on the origin since then $J_1 = (1/2)(Q_1^2 + P_1^2)$ would be a constant of the motion. When $\alpha \neq 0$, most of the $\alpha = 0$ circles are merely distorted into ovals as one would expect from the KAM theorem. However, those curves lying in the mapping region corresponding to $J_1 \cong 5J_2$ where $2\Omega_1 \cong 2\Omega_2$ are grossly distorted, because of the resonant $\cos(2\phi_1 - 2\phi_2)$ interaction, into the crescents shown in the resonance zones of fig. 9.

Next let us consider the near-by, isolated, resonant interaction given by

$$H = H_0 + \lambda J_1 J_2^{3/2} \cos(2\phi_1 - 3\phi_2) \tag{4.13}$$

where H_0 is the same as in eq. (4.11). This cos-term represents the resonant five-phonon interaction $2\Omega_1 \rightleftarrows 3\Omega_2$. A typical plot of the mapping generated by Hamiltonian (4.13) appears in fig. 10. For Hamiltonian (4.13), $(3J_1 + 2J_2)$ is a second constant of the motion and the mapping plane must therefore everywhere be covered with smooth curves. Again the $\lambda = 0$ circles are merely distorted into ovals except in the triple-crescent looking resonance zone corresponding to the $2\Omega_1 \cong 3\Omega_2$ resonance. These two examples suffice to give the general picture. Isolated resonant interactions serve to distort the unperturbed mapping plane of circles by introducing resonant, crescent shaped regions. In particular, one may show that as the perturbation parameters such as α and λ increase or equivalently as the total energy $H = E$ increases, the resonant, crescent zones move about and their widths increase. This immediately leads one to speculate on the behavior of unperturbed curves lying in a region simultaneously affected by two overlapping, "isolated" resonant interaction terms. Might they not, as was speculated at the end of the previous section, degenerate into an ergodic splatter of points in the mapping plane?

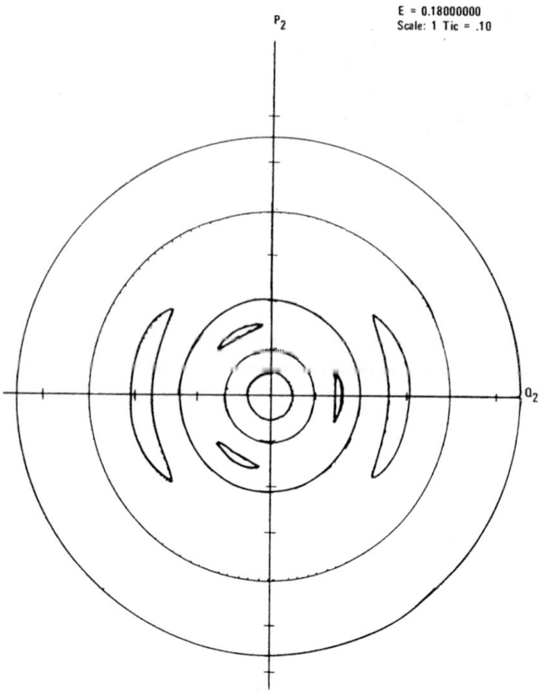

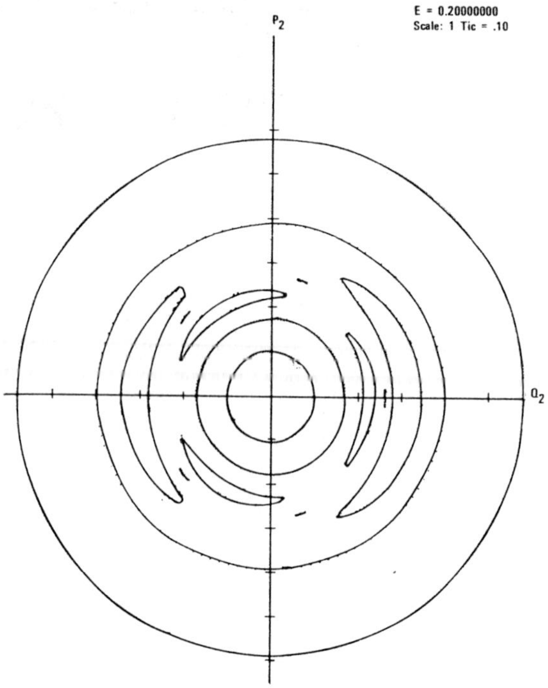

Fig. 11. The numerically integrated mapping plane for Hamiltonian (4.14) at energy $E = 0.18$. The two resonant, crescent regions here do not overlap.

Fig. 12. The numerically integrated mapping plane for Hamiltonian (4.14) at energy $E = 0.20$. Here the two resonant, crescent regions are on the verge of overlap.

With this possibility in mind, we now investigate the Hamiltonian

$$H = H_0 + \alpha J_1 J_2 \cos(2\phi_1 - 2\phi_2) + \lambda J_1 J_2^{3/2} \cos(2\phi_1 - 3\phi_2) \quad , \tag{4.14}$$

where H_0 is the same as in the previous two examples and where the two cos-terms previously studied in isolation now both act simultaneously. Figure 11 plots selected curves in the mapping plane generated by numerically integrating Hamiltonian (4.14) at the energy $H = 0.18$. At this energy it appears that the $2\Omega_1 \cong 2\Omega_2$ and the $2\Omega_1 \cong 3\Omega_2$ resonant zones are widely separated, since at least one smooth oval centered on the origin separates the two resonant, crescent regions. In fig. 12 which shows the mapping plane at energy $E = 0.2$, we note as anticipated that the widths of the two disjoint crescent regions have increased. Indeed here the two resonance regions are very close to overlap, and the computer detects a very narrow higher order resonance zone between the two large, primary resonance zones. These higher order resonances appear due to an interaction between the two explicit resonant interaction terms in Hamiltonian (4.14) as is discussed in another place[14).

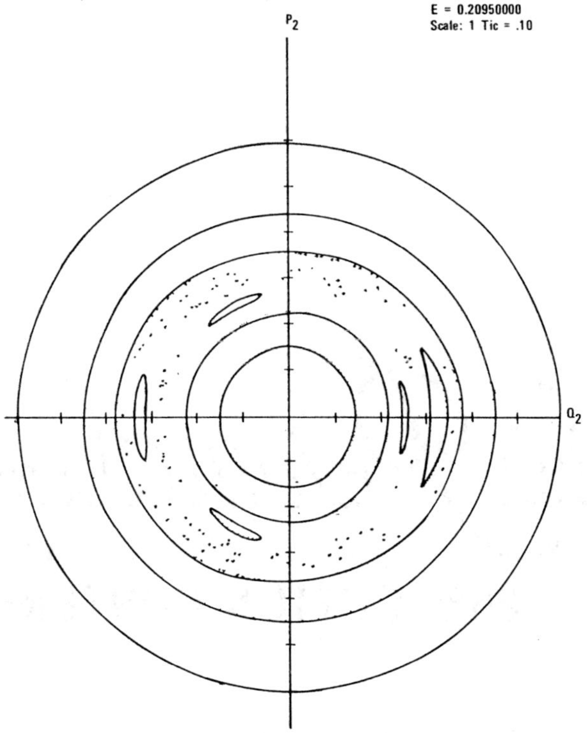

Fig. 13. The numerically integrated mapping plane for Hamiltonian (4.14) at energy E = 0.2095 showing that an erratic splatter of points is generated by a trajectory started in the resonance overlap region.

As the energy is slightly increased to E = 0.2095, one anticipates resonance overlap not only between the primary $2\Omega_1 \cong 2\Omega_2$ and $2\Omega_1 \cong 3\Omega_2$ zones but also among the narrower higher order resonance zones of the type detected by the computer. Trajectories in this region of overlap are thus being affected simultaneously by several resonant interaction terms and hence being simultaneously requested to generate the distinct crescent shaped curves belonging to each resonance zone. As a consequence trajectories in this region develop acute vertigo and wander aimlessly throughout the overlap region as is shown in fig. 13. In particular the random splatter of dots in fig. 13 was generated by a single trajectory. As the energy is further increased, the macroscopic ergodic zone increases in size, eventually filling almost all the available area in the mapping plane. Although we shall not enter into the matter here, one can predict[14)] the energy at which overlap and ergodicity are first observed here using data calculated for the isolated resonant Hamiltonians (4.11,13). In principle, one could also predict the transition for the Henon-Heiles system of section 2 using the principle of resonance overlap, although the calculation is so tedious that it has never been performed. Indeed, Chirikov[15)] has developed an approximate expression for the stochastic transition energy for many-oscillator systems and the reader is referred to his papers for details.

In this section we have demonstrated by example that widespread ergodic-type behavior can occur in nonlinear oscillator systems as the nonlinear perturbation becomes large. In addition we have presented at least an intuitive understanding of the source of this behavior in terms of resonance overlap. Our presentation is deeply rooted in the KAM theory. Even though in its region of validity the KAM theorem precludes wholesale ergodic behavior and therefore might be thought to exclude statistical mechanics, the small set of erratic trajectories moving under the influence of many resonances forms the doorway through which statistical mechanics can be regained as the KAM assumptions are violated. Thus the KAM theorem is very likely to become one of the cornerstones in the foundations of statistical mechanics. Regardless, in this section we have established only that erratic trajectories occur in oscillator systems having a large nonlinear perturbation; we have yet to demonstrate that a very small nonlinear perturbation can under suitable circumstances produce the same effect. This we do in the following section.

4.4 Ergodicity for nearly linear oscillator systems

In order to demonstrate that erratic trajectories are widespread in physically interesting systems even as the nonlinear perturbation tends to zero, we must consider violation of the KAM frequency assumption. In particular, we must return to section 4.2 and regard the nearly linear Hamiltonian (4.1) as the basic oscillator Hamiltonian. However, we again introduce the canonical transformation of eq. (4.2) into Hamiltonian (4.1) to obtain the Hamiltonian

$$H = H_0(J_1,\ldots,J_N) + V_3(J_1,\ldots,J_N) + V_4(J_1,\ldots,J_N) + \ldots \quad , \tag{4.15}$$

where $H_0 = \Sigma\,\omega_k J_k$ with ω_k being the constant, positive frequencies of the harmonic approximation. We now note that the harmonic oscillator Hamiltonian H_0 in eq. (4.15) violates the KAM frequency assumption with a vengeance since here the $\Omega_k \equiv (\partial H_0/\partial J_k) = \omega_k$ do not depend on the J_k. Consequently the Jacobian of the Ω_k with respect to the J_k is identically equal to zero.

Because we choose to consider such a violent abrogation of the KAM frequency condition, it is convenient to discuss Hamiltonian (4.15) in terms of a slightly modified version of the KAM theorem which has been stated by Arnol'd[16). For Hamiltonian (4.15), Arnol'd rigorously proves that most trajectories lie on smooth, N-dimensional integral surfaces (tori) embedded in the 2N-dimensional phase space provided, among other things, that all the V_k or, equivalently, the total energy is sufficiently small and that the harmonic frequencies ω_k do not satisfy low order resonant conditions of the form $\Sigma n_k\omega_k \cong 0$ for integers n_k such that $\Sigma|n_k| \leqslant 4$. Speaking formally, the Arnol'd conditions are sufficient[16) to insure that Hamiltonian (4.15) can be transformed into Hamiltonian (4.3) where H_0 is a strictly nonlinear Hamiltonian and the earlier version of the KAM theorem applies. Speaking less formally, the Arnol'd condition on the V_k is completely equivalent to the earlier condition on the complete V, and nothing new is to be learned from its violation. On the other hand violation of Arnol'd's low order resonance condition is an especially virulent means of violating the earlier KAM condition on the frequency Jacobian. Since it is somewhat difficult to make this latter point clear for the general case, let us illustrate the matter using a specific, physically interesting example.

Consider the simple three-oscillator Hamiltonian

$$H = J_1 + 2J_2 + 3J_3 + \gamma[\,\alpha J_1 J_2^{\frac{1}{2}} \cos(2\phi_1 - \phi_2) + \lambda(J_1J_2J_3)^{\frac{1}{2}}\cos(\phi_1 + \phi_2 - \phi_3)] \,, \tag{4.16}$$

where $\omega_1 = \omega_2/2 = \omega_3/3$ and γ is an overall nonlinearity parameter introduced to "turn off" the nonlinearity as $\gamma \to 0$. These frequencies were chosen to simulate the linear acoustic region of the dispersion curve for solids. The two cos-terms represent the everywhere overlapping, resonant, three-phonon interactions $2\omega_1 \rightleftarrows \omega_2$ and $(\omega_1 + \omega_2) \rightleftarrows \omega_3$. It may be argued[17) that Hamiltonian (4.16) is the simplest model of a solid which can exhibit an ergodic type behavior; whatever the case, Hamiltonian (4.16) certainly violates the Arnol'd low order resonance condition.

If we now introduce the time dependent canonical transformation

$$J_k = J_k' \quad , \quad \phi_k = \Theta_k + kt \;, \qquad k = 1,2,3 \quad , \tag{4.17}$$

then the Hamiltonian (4.16) may be written

$$H' = \gamma[\,\alpha J_1' J_2'^{\frac{1}{2}} \cos(2\theta_1 - \theta_2) + \lambda(J_1' J_2' J_3')^{\frac{1}{2}} \cos(\theta_1 + \theta_2 - \theta_3)] \quad . \tag{4.18}$$

One now observes that γ is merely a multiplicative factor in Hamiltonian (4.18); thus γ affects only the time scale of the motion. Consequently if Hamiltonian (4.18) generated wildly erratic trajectories, they will persist even in the limit as $\gamma \to 0$, excluding $\gamma = 0$ of course. Finally let us note that $(J_1' + 2J_2' + 3J_3')$ is a second constant of the motion for this three-oscillator system which is independent of the Hamiltonian, and hence we may reduce[17)] Hamiltonian (4.18) to a two degrees of freedom Hamiltonian. Then then allows us to generate a mapping for this reduced Hamiltonian just as we have done for the example Hamiltonian systems discussed in the previous sections.

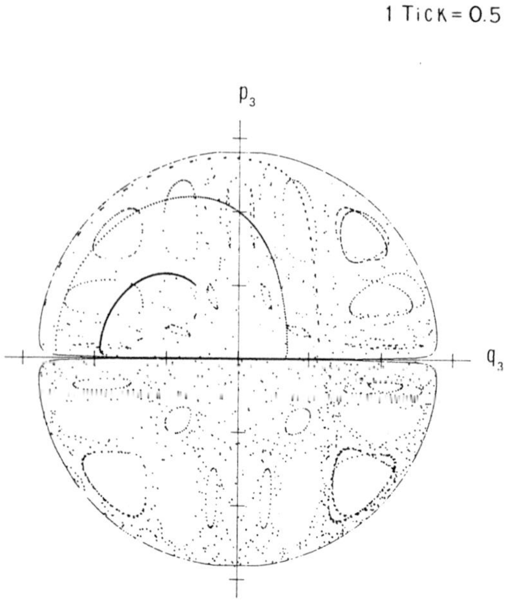

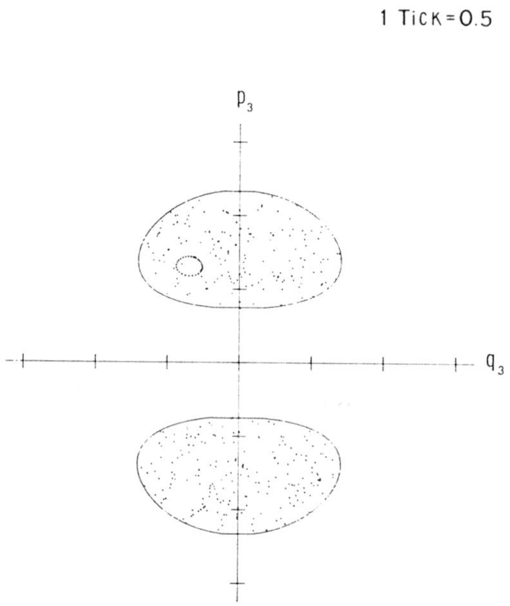

Fig. 14. A typical mapping plane for the reduced two degrees of freedom Hamiltonian equivalent to Hamiltonian (4.16). Here $H' = 3.0$ and $(J_1' + 2J_2' + 3J_3') = 2.999$. This plane contains about 70% smooth curves.

Fig. 15. Another typical mapping plane for the reduced two degrees of freedom Hamiltonian equivalent to Hamiltonian (4.16). Here $H' = 3.0$ and $(J_1' + 2J_2' + 3J_3') = 2.901$. Only about 10% of this plane is covered by curves.

Figures 14 and 15 present typical mappings generated by the reduced Hamiltonian for two distinct values of $(J_1' + 2J_2' + 3J_3')$, all other parameters being the same for both figures. The allowed mapping area in fig. 14 contains about 70% smooth curves, while fig. 15 exhibits only about 10% smooth curves. It is to be emphasized that the erratic regions in these figures are independent of the value of γ. Thus we have at last demonstrated that a small nonlinear perturbation can indeed go a long way toward justifying a basic assumption of statistical mechanics.

The fact that this three-oscillator system is at best stochastic only on a four-dimensional subspace of the five-dimensional energy surface and that it is not completely stochastic even there is in actuality only a minor defect. As the number N of oscillators becomes larger, the number of overlapping, resonant interaction terms goes up as N^2; hence the $N = 3$ system should exhibit the minimum stochasticity to be expected for low order resonant systems. Equally the fact that stochasticity occurs only on a (2N-2)-dimensional surface rather than a (2N-1) dimensional surface becomes less significant as N becomes large. Finally it should be mentioned that Hamiltonian (4.16) is for physical nonlinear oscillator systems the generic, rather than a specific, case, since low order resonances linking all degrees of freedom is assumed to be ubiquitous in physical nonlinear oscillator systems. In particular since the ω_k frequency spectrum becomes dense in the limit as N tends to infinity, one expects the transition energy to statistical behavior to tend to zero in this limit.

5. THE PATHOLOGY OF AREA-PRESERVING MAPPINGS

5.1. Introduction

We have now amply demonstrated that systems having two or at most three degrees of freedom exhibit much of the complexity of the many-body problem and that we may graphically survey this complexity by using the relevant differential equations of motion to generate an area-preserving mapping. In a sense, the foregoing investigations were merely studies of the generic properties of area-preserving mappings. But if we wish to investigate the generic properties of mappings, it would be much easier to directly study algebraic mappings of the form $x_1 = x_1(x_0, y_0)$, $y_1 = y_1(x_0, y_0)$ rather than solve differential equations. This not only eases the problem of numerical computation, it also allows us to use various mapping theorems to further illuminate the pathology of the many-body problem.

Let us introduce the subject by considering the area-preserving mapping T given by the rotation

$$x_1 = x_0\cos\alpha - y_0\sin\alpha \tag{5.1a}$$

$$y_1 = x_0 \sin\alpha + y_0 \sin\alpha \quad . \tag{5.1b}$$

The origin in the (x, y) plane is said to be an elliptic fixed point of T and the invariant curves of T are circles. T maps each point (x, y) through the same angle α ($\alpha/2\pi$ is called the rotation number) on its invariant circle $(x^2 + y^2)^{\frac{1}{2}}$. The Hamiltonian system $H = \alpha J_1 + \lambda J_2$ would generate a mapping in the (Q_1, P_1) plane looking identical to that given by eq. (5.1). Let us now rewrite T using polar coordinates as

$$r_1 = r_0 \tag{5.2a}$$

$$\theta_1 = \theta_0 + \alpha \quad . \tag{5.2b}$$

Then let us generalize slightly and introduce a twist into the rotation via

$$r_1 = r_0 \tag{5.3a}$$

$$\theta_1 = \theta_0 + \alpha(r_0) \quad . \tag{5.3b}$$

Circles are still invariant curves of this twist mapping T_1, but now the angle of rotation α depends on $r = (x^2 + y^2)^{\frac{1}{2}}$. The mapping T_1 is precisely that which would be generated by the H_0 of Hamiltonian (4.11).

The central question now concerns whether or not the invariant curves of T_1 persist under perturbations. Thus let us consider the mapping T_2 given by

$$r_1 = r_0 + f(r_0, \theta_0) \tag{5.4a}$$

$$\theta_1 = \theta_0 + \alpha(r_0) + g(r_0, \theta_0) \quad , \tag{5.4b}$$

where f and g are periodic 2π in θ. For this mapping Moser[18)] has shown that provided (loosely speaking) f and g are sufficiently small then those invariant curves for which

$$\left| \frac{\alpha(r)}{2\pi} - \frac{p}{q} \right| \geqslant \frac{\varepsilon}{q^{5/2}} \quad , \tag{5.5}$$

where p and q are integers, persist under the perturbations f and g, being only slightly distorted. In short, in complete analogy with the KAM theory for the tori of differential equation systems, those unperturbed curves having rational rotation numbers are destroyed by the perturbation; only those curves with rotation numbers poorly approximated by the rationals are preserved. This analogy is not accidental since the preserved tori of the differential equation systems generate the preserved curves of the associated mapping.

But for the mapping equations given in eq. (5.4) we know a little more than

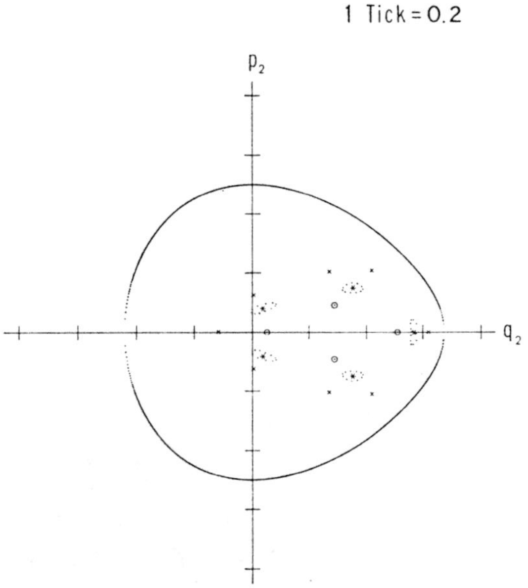

Fig. 16. In the neighborhood of an elliptic fixed point, according to the Moser and Birkhoff theorems, one anticipates the pathology shown in this mapping sketch. Actually the true situation is incredibly more pathological than can be shown in this sketch.

Fig. 17. Selected fixed points of the mapping generated by Hamiltonian (2.1) at energy E = 1/8 illustrating that some of the fixed point structure sketched in fig. 16 can actually be observed. The central elliptic fixed point (not shown) lies at about $Q_2 = 0.3$.

has been stated earlier about the stochastic regions. Let us consider the unperturbed ($f = g = 0$) circles of the eq. (5.4) mapping which bear rational rotation numbers. Such circles are made up entirely of fixed points of $(T_2)^n$, i.e., T_2 applied n times, where $\alpha(r) = 2\pi(m/n)$. Now when f and g are nonzero but small, Birkhoff[19)] has shown that the complete circle of fixed points does not persist. Indeed only 2n of these points persist with half being elliptic and half being hyperbolic fixed points. Thus T_2 will in general yield a mapping of the type pictures in fig. 16. Moreover let us note that both the Moser and Birkhoff theorems will be valid in some neighborhood of each elliptic fixed point in fig. 16. Consequently this whole picture repeats itself about each elliptic fixed point on successive microscopic levels, "boxes within boxes" ad infinitum. In addition, Zehnder[20)] has recently shown that the structure depicted in fig. 16 continues to exist on down arbitrarily close to each elliptic fixed point.

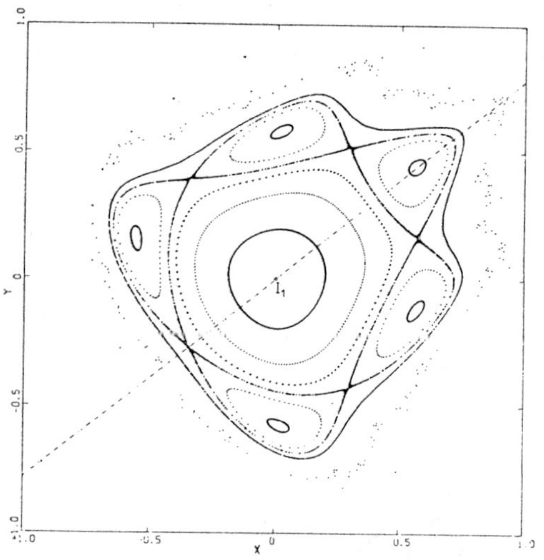

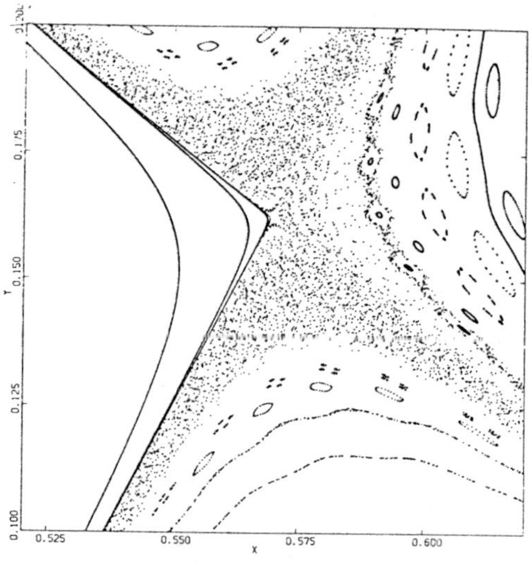

Fig. 18. The Henon algebraic mapping T_3 for cos = 0.24. Here the invariant curves look smooth.

Fig. 19. A magnified view of the region around the rightmost hyperbolic fixed point in fig. 18 showing the fantastic structure which exists on a microscopic scale.

One thus has the incredible result that even simple quadratic, algebraic mappings (see eq. (5.6) below) or the mappings generated by two-oscillator systems such as the Henon-Heiles Hamiltonian (2.1) can yield the wonderous complexity of fig. 16. Indeed in fig. 17, using the highest computer accuracy, we have actually calculated some of the structure indicated in fig. 16 for the Henon-Heiles system. However, an even more striking study has been made by Henon[21)] of the algebraic mapping T_3

$$x_1 = x\cos\alpha - y\sin\alpha + x^2\sin\alpha \tag{5.6a}$$

$$y_1 = x\sin\alpha + y\cos\alpha - x^2\cos\alpha \quad . \tag{5.6b}$$

In fig. 18 we graph T_3 using cos = 0.24 and notice that at this level of computer accuracy the curves around the elliptic fixed points appear smooth. However, in fig. 19, which is a magnified view of the small region near the rightmost hyperbolic fixed point, we see some of the underlying complexity.

5.2. Pathological detail

In order to begin to understand the nature of some of this pathology, let us consider an "integrable" area-preserving mapping T_4 (not explicitly written out here) which yields exact, invariant curves everywhere, of which a few are shown in fig. 20. Let us ignore the elliptic fixed point at the origin and focus our attention on the invariant curves passing through the hyperbolic fixed point. On part 1

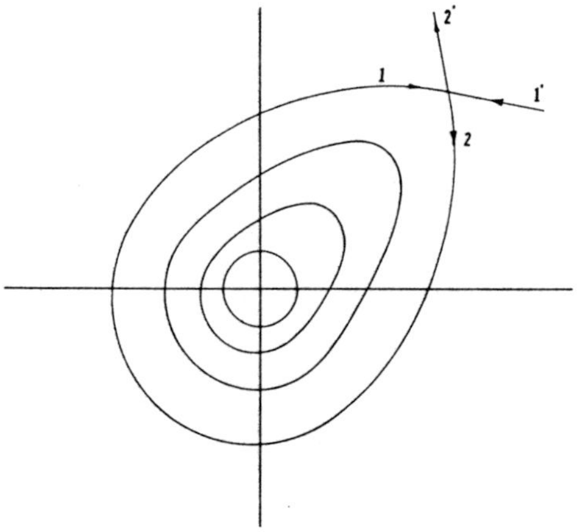

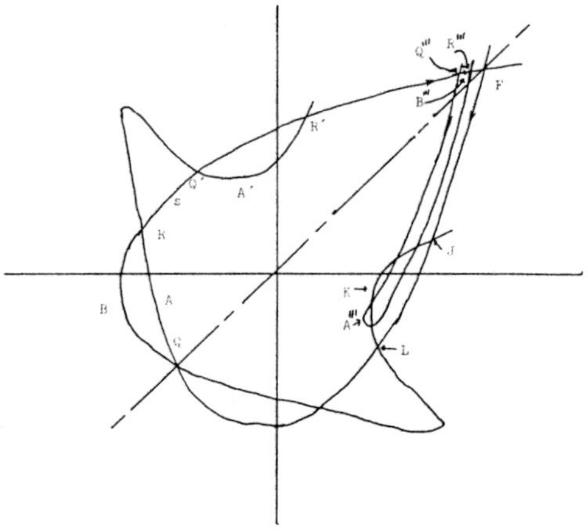

Fig. 20. Invariant curves for an "integrable" mapping T_4 which generates smooth curves everywhere. Attention should be focused on the self-intersecting curve.

Fig. 21. Invariant curves for a small "non-integrable" perturbation on the mapping T_4 shown in fig. 20. Note that the self-intersecting curve. of fig. 20 has "split" into two curves with multiple intersections.

of this curve, successive points generated by the mapping move toward the fixed point, asymptotically approaching it; while on part 2, they move away from the fixed point. Moreover we may generate part 1 by calculating backward iterates $(T_4)^{-n}$ of some point on the curve near the fixed point; while part 2 may be generated by calculating forward iterates $(T_4)^n$ of some point on that curve near the fixed point. In particular, we observe in fig. 20 that the forward and backward curve segments thus generated join smoothly into a single curve. This smooth joining is characteristic of integrable systems; in particular, we note that the integrable Hamiltonians (4.11,13) generate hyperbolic fixed points whose invariant curves join smoothly as may be seen in figs. 9 and 10. If now we add nonintegrable perturbations f and g to the integrable mapping T_4, we find that the forward and backward curves now intersect each other as is shown in fig. 21. Moreover each of these curves begins to oscillate wildly as they asymptotically approach the fixed point. In fig. 21, for example, the segment Q'''A'''R''' lies on the forward iterated curve while the segment JKL lies on the backward iterated curve. The intersection points of these two oscillating invariant curves are called homoclinic points, and it is known[19] that other hyperbolic fixed points lie in every neighborhood of these homoclinic points. Thus the original oscillating invariant curves are intersected by the invariant curves of these neighboring hyperbolic fixed points, which are also oscillating wildly. One thus begins to understand that there is an incredible complexity in such neighborhoods.

The nature of the self-intersecting curves of fig. 16, which were ignored earlier, can perhaps now be made clear. In that figure the backward iterated curve coming from one hyperbolic fixed point intersects the forward iterated curve coming from an adjacent hyperbolic fixed point; and in fig. 16 we have pictured the typical break-up of the integrable system curves that appeared in fig. 10. Returning to fig. 21, there is at least one other feature that is noteworthy. The area QARB eventually maps into thinner and thinner "area filaments" of which Q'''A'''R'''B''' is an early example. Thus points initially close together within these areas quickly map apart. Moreover as the nonlinear parameter increases, these forward and backward invariant curves intersect at an ever increasing angle, "plowing-up" increasing portions of the stable regions surrounding the elliptic fixed points. Finally when there are many overlapping resonances in a region, the oscillating invariant curves belonging to one of the resonances not only intersect each other, they also intersect the invariant curves belonging to other resonances. Thus it is quite understandable that the set of iterates of a given point in such a region appear to occur at random.

Even the elliptic fixed points can turn hyperbolic when the non-linear perturbation is sufficiently strong, either because the perturbation itself is large or because there are overlapping, low order resonances. The hyperbolic fixed point — called hyperbolic with reflection — arising from a converted elliptic fixed point is even more pathological than an ordinary hyperbolic fixed point. In fig. 20 for example on the ingoing invariant curves, iterates of a point on one side of the fixed point asymptotically approach the fixed point from the same side. On the other hand were this a hyperbolic with reflection fixed point, iterates of a point on the ingoing invariant curves would still asymptotically approach the fixed point, but now succeeding iterates lie on alternative sides of the fixed point. As an example consider the two adjacent hyperbolic with reflection fixed points[22] shown in fig. 22. Here the point labeled A_{n+8} is the next iterate of the point labeled A_n, and we note that A_n lies on one ingoing invariant curve while A_{n+8} lies on the other ingoing invariant curve. In addition, one should note that the invariant curves in fig. 22 are much wilder than their cousins in fig. 21.

The two hyperbolic with reflection fixed points shown in fig. 22 are members of a family of sixteen fixed points. Eight are hyperbolic with reflection and eight are ordinary hyperbolic. If the nonlinearity parameter of the mapping were

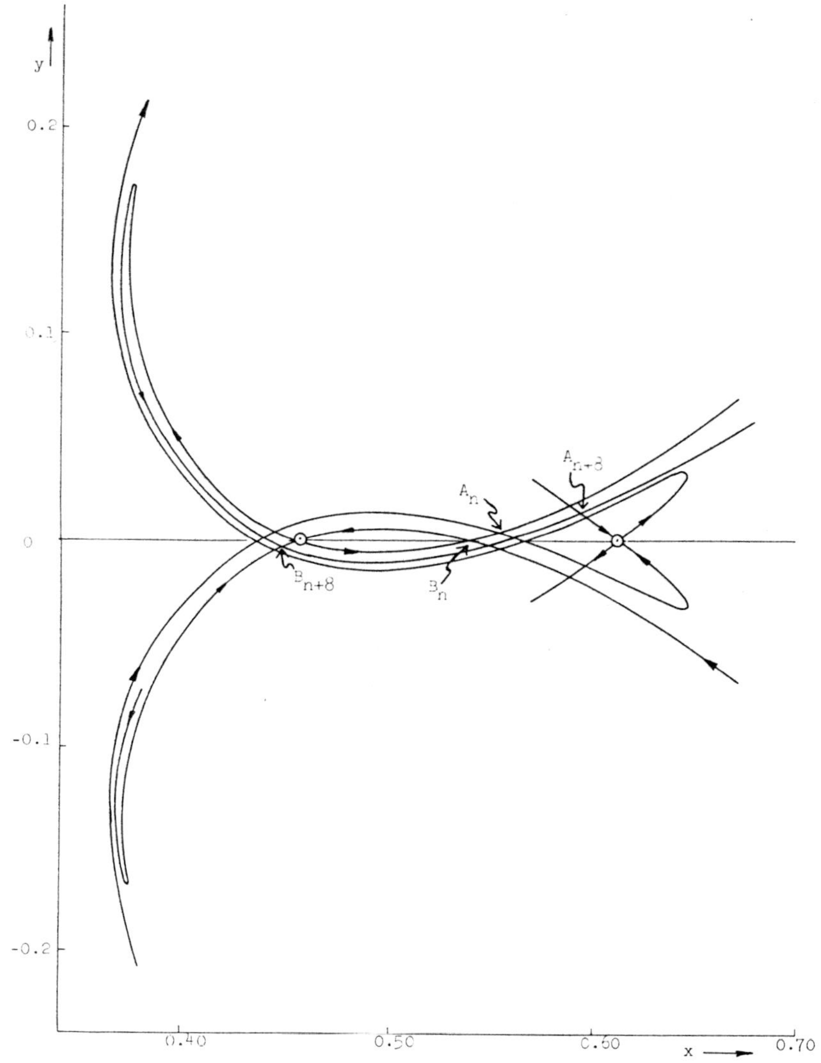

Fig. 22. An example of a hyperbolic with reflection fixed point. Here there are two such fixed points relatively close to each other on the horizontal axis.

lowered then this family would become a family with eight elliptic fixed points separated by eight ordinary hyperbolic fixed points. This possibility allows one to conjecture that in the highly stochastic regions of a mapping, all (or almost all) fixed points are hyperbolic. Indeed in later sections, we shall present strong computer evidence that this is indeed the case. In a region containing only hyperbolic fixed points, the iterates of almost every point would be expected to appear quite random, and two points started close together would be expected to diverge apart at an exponential rate. In short, such regions would be expected to exhibit the ergodic and mixing behavior of the mapping discussed earlier given by eq. (1.1).

Now the ergodic and mixing mapping given by eq. (1.1) was characterized by having real eigenvalues, one larger and one less than unity, which ultimately lead to an exponential expansion in one direction and an exponential contraction in another. Froeschle[23)] has investigated the mapping T_5 given by

$$x_1 = x_0 + \lambda \sin y_0 \tag{5.7a}$$

$$y_1 = x_0 + y_0 + \lambda \sin y_0 \quad , \tag{5.7b}$$

where x and y are periodic of period 2π; and he has attempted to show that the ergodic regions of this mapping have properties similar to that of eq. (1.1). In particular, Froeschle picks some point (x, y) and computes its iterates. He linearizes the mapping about the original point (x, y) and then linearizes about each of its iterates $(T_5)^n(x, y)$. In analogy with the eq. (1.1) mapping if the point (x, y) lies in a exponentiating, stochastic region, then he expects

$$\theta_n = (\ln\lambda_n)/n \quad , \tag{5.8}$$

where λ_n is the largest eigenvalue of the linearized mapping of $(T_5)^n$, to approach a constant value as n tends to infinity. On the other hand if the point (x, y) lies in a smooth curve region of the mapping, he expects θ_n to approach zero as n tends to infinity. In order to minimize fluctuations, Froeschle also calculates the average θ_n given by

$$\mu_n = \frac{1}{n} \sum_{k=1}^{n} [(\ln\lambda_k)/k] \quad . \tag{5.9}$$

In fig. 23 we show a typical plot of the mapping of eq. (5.7). One notes that both regular and irregular regions exist for this mapping. In fig. 24 we plot μ_n, where n = 2,000, for initial points lying along the y-axis, that is, for x = 0 and varying y. The agreement between figs. 23 and 24 is striking. One has that μ_n is zero, as expected, in the regular regions and that it assumes a non-zero value in the irregular regions. It thus appears that the irregular regions are indeed ergodic and mixing.

6. COMPUTER TESTS FOR STATISTICAL BEHAVIOR

6.1. Introduction

We have now fairly well documented that the Hamiltonian systems of classical dynamics will, in general, yield ergodic and mixing behavior; that is to say statistical behavior is a generic property. However many interesting classical systems are certainly not statistical. Indeed most textbooks in classical mechanics constitute a catalog of systems in this latter category. Thus suppose now that we are given a specific, well-defined Hamiltonian; can we decide the category into

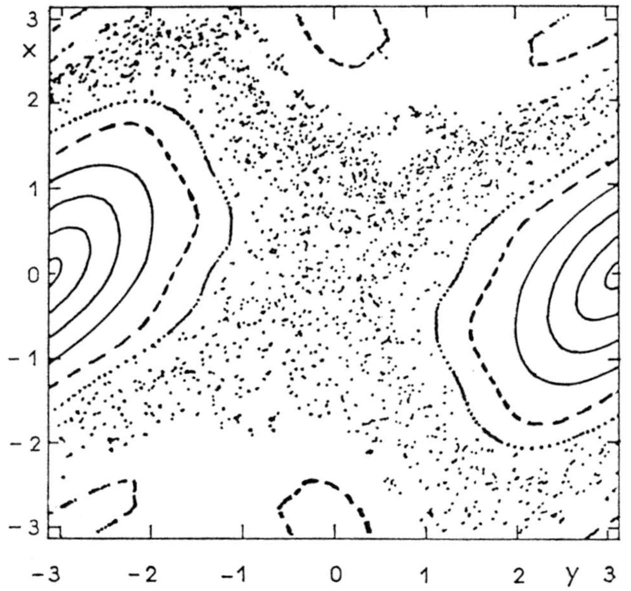

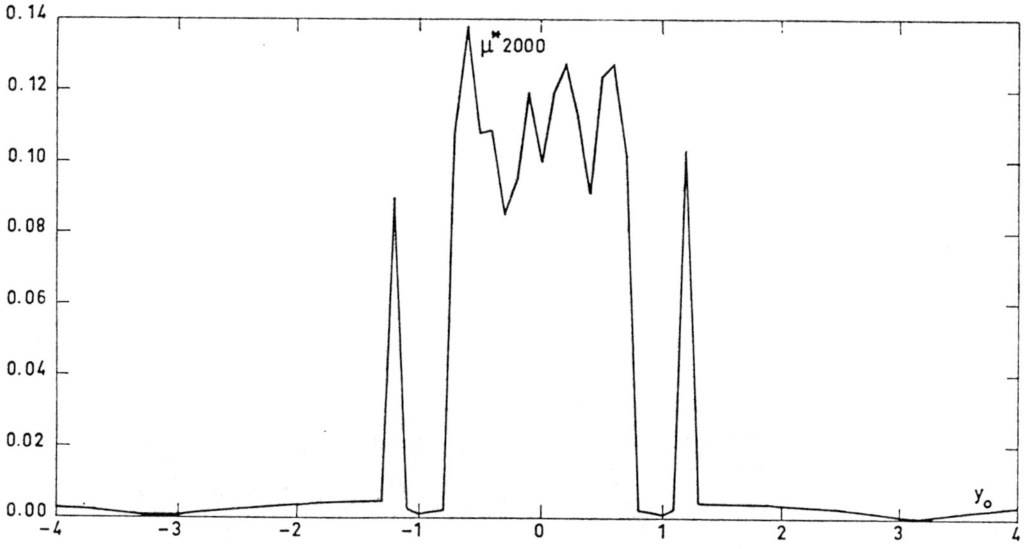

Fig. 23. A typical graph of the mapping given by eq. (5.7) studied by Froeschle.

Fig. 24. A plot of μ_n (called μ_n^* in the figure) given by eq. (5.9) versus y for $n = 2{,}000$ and $x = 0$. Here μ_n is large when y is in the stochastic region of fig. 23.

which it falls? Is it statistical or non-statistical? This is not an easy question for there are no general easily applied analytic tests known. At present, the question must be decided individually for each Hamiltonian. Nonetheless here, as in section 4, a combination of analysis and computer experiments can provide extremely useful information even though it may not establish a rigorous, definitive answer. In the following sections we discuss the current status of this non-rigorous approach.

We shall refer to the above problem as the question of integrability. Now the solvable, non-statistical problems of classical mechanics are integrable in the sense that they have as many well-behaved (analytic) constants of the motion as degrees of freedom. We shall here use this property as the general definition of an integrable system. Integrable systems are certainly not ergodic since all their trajectories lie on N-dimensional integral surfaces embedded in the (2N-1)-dimensional energy surface. All the evidence available indicates that non-integrable systems exhibit statistical behavior of some type due to the breakdown of smooth integral surfaces. A complete catalog of the types of statistical behavior which may occur has not yet been compiled by mathematicians, although they are currently working on the matter.

A number of workers have used a computer to investigate the question of integrability for nonlinear, analytic Hamiltonian oscillator systems having two degrees of freedom. If such a system is integrable, then it has by definition a well-behaved constant of the motion additional to the Hamiltonian itself. Contopoulos[24)] and Birkhoff[19)] have demonstrated that one can always develop a formal power series expression for this additional constant of the motion. Empirical evidence concerning integrability may then be obtained by using numerical integration to establish whether or not this formal series is, to computer accuracy, in fact a constant of the motion.

Several investigators have utilized the fact that the motion for such oscillator systems can be graphically represented as a plane area-preserving mapping. If the system is integrable, then each trajectory must yield a set of mapping points lying on a curve in the mapping plane. Numerical integration may thus be used to provide evidence for or against integrability depending on the presence or absence of smooth curves in the mapping plane. In addition here, further evidence for or against integrability may be obtained by comparing the numerically integrated curves with those analytically calculated using the formal additional constant of the motion.

Using these techniques, as has already been mentioned in section 2, Henon and Heiles numerically established that at energy E = 1/12 the Hamiltonian system

$$H = (1/2)p_1^2 + q_1^2 + p_2^2 + q_2^2) + q_1^2 q_2 - (1/3)q_2^3 \qquad (6.1)$$

yields the smooth curves shown in the mapping plane of fig. 2. Gustavson[25)] subsequently calculated a formal, series constant of the motion for Hamiltonian (6.1) and then demonstrated that the curves calculated using this constant are, to computer accuracy, congruent with the directly integrated curves of fig. 2.

All this evidence indicates that Hamiltonian (6.1) is integrable. However, the mapping calculated by Henon and Heiles at energy E = 1/8, which is shown in fig. 4, reveals a region of non-integrable behavior in which smooth curves no longer appear to exist. In this region, as shown in fig. 5, initially close points map apart at an exponential rate, which of course is another, independent test for non-integrability. Even more significant although we do not show it here, one can numerically locate[26] the hyperbolic fixed points associated with the family of five elliptic fixed points centered about the positive q_2-axis in fig. 4 and then numerically establish that the invariant curves passing through the adjacent hyperbolic fixed points intersect each other forming homoclinic points. The existence of homoclinic points insures[27)] that Hamiltonian (6.1) is, at least locally, non-integrable. Thus the evidence obtained at $E = 1/8$ makes it clear that Hamiltonian (6.1) is non-integrable even though none of the computer tests mentioned thus far are sufficiently sensitive to detect this fact at $E = 1/12$ at least using only standard computer accuracy.

In the following sections, we shall discuss a technique for investigating integrability distinct from and having greater sensitivity than those mentioned above. However, our main reason for devoting so much time to this method is that it provides further insight into the distinction between integrable and non-integrable systems.

6.2. Mathematical preliminaries

Let us now re-examine the area-preserving mapping of fig. 2. The elliptic fixed points on the q_2 or p_2 axis (hereafter referred to as central fixed points) were generated by periodic orbits of Hamiltonian (6.1). If as usual we denote the mapping by the equation

$$(q_2^{(1)}, p_2^{(1)}) = T(q_2^{(0)}, p_2^{(0)}) \quad , \tag{6.2}$$

then these central fixed points satisfy $(q_2, p_2) = T(q_2, p_2)$. Each oval about a central fixed point is — to computer accuracy — an invariant curve generated by a quasi-periodic orbit of Hamiltonian (6.1), and sequential mapping iterates for an initial (q_2, p_2) point lying on an oval rotate about the central fixed point. The average angle of rotation (divided by 2π) is called the rotation number ω, and the ω associated with each invariant curve varies smoothly as one progresses outward from the central fixed point. Now if Hamiltonian (6.1) were integrable, there would be a continuum of ovals about each central fixed point and ω would vary continuously. However, we know from the immediately preceding section that, in fact, Hamiltonian (6.1) is not integrable. Therefore sufficient computer accuracy in fig. 2 should reveal, about each central fixed point, the structure shown in fig. 16 that is predicted by the Moser and the Birkhoff theorems discussed in the paragraphs just following eq. (5.4). In particular the smooth, integrable system ovals having rational $\omega = P/Q$ and consisting entirely of fixed points of T^Q, where Q is the denominator in $\omega = P/Q$, should in general not exist for Hamiltonian (6.1). In their place one should find $2Q$ fixed points, half being elliptic and half hyperbolic. This is yet another distinction between integrable and non-integrable systems which we may seek to investigate on a computer.

In order to fully exploit this difference, we now briefly discuss methods developed by J.M. Greene[28] in connection with algebraic area-preserving mappings. Suppose that we have numerically located a fixed point (q, p) in the mapping plane satisfying

$$(q, p) = T^{Q}(q, p) \quad . \tag{6.3}$$

In order that we may establish the stability character of this fixed point, let us follow Greene and write eq. (6.3) as a linearized mapping, valid in some small neighborhood of this fixed point, in the vector-matrix form

$$\begin{bmatrix} (q^{(1)} - q) \\ \\ (p^{(1)} - p) \end{bmatrix} = \begin{pmatrix} M_{11} & M_{12} \\ \\ M_{21} & M_{22} \end{pmatrix} \begin{bmatrix} (q^{(0)} - q) \\ \\ (p^{(0)} - p) \end{bmatrix} \tag{6.4}$$

where $\{M_{ij}\}$ denote the matrix elements of the linearized eq. (6.3) transformation. We may now use a computer to calculate the matrix elements of M. First, we choose a point $(q^{(0)}, p^{(0)})$ near the fixed point (q, p) such that $(p^{(0)} - p) = 0$ and $(q^{(0)} - q) \neq 0$. We then integrate the differential equations of motion obtaining the next mapping iterate $(q^{(1)}, p^{(1)}) = T^{Q}(q^{(0)}, p^{(0)})$. We may then write

$$M_{11} = (q^{(1)} - q)/(q^{(0)} - q) \tag{6.5a}$$

and

$$M_{21} = (p^{(1)} - p)/(q^{(0)} - q) \quad . \tag{6.5b}$$

Similarly picking a distinct initial point such that now $(q^{(0)} - q) = 0$ and $(p^{(0)} - p) \neq 0$ and calculating the new $(q^{(1)} - q)$ and $(p^{(1)} - p)$ we find

$$M_{12} = (q^{(1)} - q)/(p^{(0)} - p) \tag{6.6a}$$

and

$$M_{22} = (p^{(1)} - p)/(p^{(0)} - p) \quad . \tag{6.6b}$$

Since this is an area-preserving mapping, the condition that the determinant of M must equal unity can be used to insure accuracy in the calculations.

Now introduce the quantity R, called the residue of the fixed point, defined as

$$R \equiv \frac{1}{2} - \frac{1}{4}\,\mathrm{Tr}(M) \quad . \tag{6.7}$$

Greene shows that the fixed point is elliptic when $0<R<1$, ordinary hyperbolic when $R<0$, hyperbolic with reflection when $R>1$, and a fixed point lying on an invariant curve of fixed points when $R = 0$. When $R \neq 0$, as mentioned earlier, the $2Q$ fixed points of T^Q form two families of Q members each. Each member of one family has the same positive residue while each member of the other family has the same negative residue. Empirically it is found that the absolute value of the two residues are approximately equal. Consequently when $0<|R|<1$, T^Q has alternating elliptic-hyperbolic members; and when $|R|>1$, all $2Q$ members are hyperbolic, half being ordinary hyperbolic and half hyperbolic with reflection.

Thus as an initial test for integrability, one may search the mapping plane for fixed points of T^Q, $Q>1$. If all such fixed points have $R = 0$, then one has strong evidence that the system is integrable; if $|R| \neq 0$ for all fixed points and in particular if $|R|>1$ for some, then the system is almost surely non-integrable. A fixed point with $|R|>1$ is especially noteworth since half the members of the associated family are hyperbolic with reflection. All the computer evidence to date indicates that such hyperbolic points always have associated homoclinic points which latter guarantee at least local non-integrability.

But an even stronger test for non-integrable behavior is available. First define the rotation number of a fixed point of T^Q as $\omega = P/Q$, where Q is the integer exponent of T^Q and where P is the integral number of 2π rotations around the central fixed point when following from a fixed point to its self-image through all Q members of the family. Then confine one's attention to fixed points with rotation number $\omega = P/Q$ with P and Q relative prime. Greene then observes that the residue of a fixed point of T^Q is related to Q by the equation

$$|R| = \alpha[\,f(P/Q)]^{Q/2} \tag{6.8}$$

where (P/Q) is the rotation number of the fixed point, where the absolute value sign permits use of negative residue fixed points, and where $f(P/Q)$ is an empirically determined function. If we can determine a smooth $f(P/Q)$ function, then in those mapping plane regions where $f(P/Q)>1$, we have in general that $|R|>1$, which implies that there is a dense or near dense set of hyperbolic fixed points in such regions. Thus $f(P/Q)>1$ is very strong empirical evidence for non-integrable behavior.

6.3. Henon-Heiles system

In this section we use the non-integrable Henon-Heiles Hamiltonian system to illustrate the application of the Greene method just discussed in section 6.2. In seeking data from which to plot f-curves for the Henon-Heiles system at energy

$E = 1/12$, we chose[29] to search the positive q_2-axis for fixed points. Without undue difficulty we located about 200 fixed points on the q_2-axis which were quite evenly distributed over the complete interval from the central fixed point on the q_2-axis to the maximum positive q_2-value allowed by $E = 1/12$. Each fixed point had $|R| \neq 0$, giving a preliminary indication of non-integrability. Inverse rotation numbers began at about $\omega^{-1} = 5.0$ near the central fixed point and monotonically increased to about $\omega^{-1} = 8.5$ near the maximum allowed q_2-value.

For each fixed point we computed R and thence f, using a preliminary value of unity for α. A plot of $f = |R|^{2/Q}$ versus inverse rotation number $\omega^{-1} = (Q/P)$ provided us with a graph looking like a bad case of the measles. This somewhat random splatter of points however had, just as Greene predicts, a lower envelope representing a minimum f-curve. We then found that this minimum f-curve could be determined quite easily by plotting f-values for sequences of fixed points having inverse rotation numbers $\omega^{-1} = k \pm (1/n)$, where $k = 5, 6, 7$ or 8 and $n>1$ is an integer. This minimum f-curve is shown in fig. 25. In this figure, α equals unity. We recomputed this graph using $\alpha = 0.1$ and $\alpha = 10.0$. The net result was a slight upward or downward vertical shift of the fig. 25 curve, which is of no consequence for our purposes. It is to be noted that the minimum f-curve in fig. 25

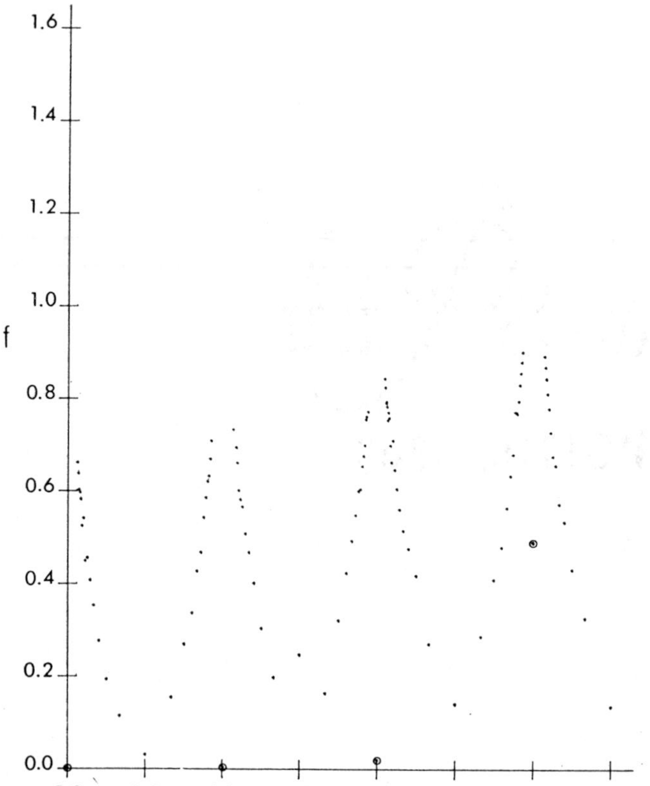

Fig. 25. The minimum f-curve for the Henon-Heiles system at energy $E = 1/12$.

has several narrow spikes which rise above unity, thus showing that there are narrow regions in the fig. 2 (or the equivalent fig. 16) mapping plane which have a dense or near dense set of hyperbolic fixed points. Moreover as Greene points out, there is nothing unique about the ω^{-1} sequences used to obtain fig. 25; thus one anticipates that such spikes exists for every ω^{-1} sequence approaching a rational number or, according to the Moser theorem, approaching even an irrational number well approximated by rationals. In short, these spikes establish that the fantastic complexity indicated in fig. 16 is actually only a crude approximation to the truth; indeed they verify that the regions between the Moser invariant curves are generated by trajectories having an astonishing pathology. In conclusion then, Hamiltonian (5.1) is most assuredly non-integrable.

6.4. The Toda lattice

The Toda lattice[30], which consists of a one-dimensional chain of particles interacting via exponential pair potentials, has received considerable attention in the recent literature. This lattice is of particular significance to physical scientists since it can be shown to propagate certain nonlinear wave forms without change of shape; moreover, certain particular solutions, called solitons[31], have apparently been observed experimentally. However, until recently it was not known whether or not these particular wave form solutions were stable against small perturbations since, prior to the investigation described briefly below, the question of integrability for the Toda lattice was undecided.

In order to investigate integrability using all the techniques previously described, let us consider the three-particle Toda lattice with periodic boundary conditions. The Hamiltonian is

$$H = \frac{1}{2}(P_1^2 + P_2^2 + P_3^2) + e^{-(Q_1-Q_3)} + e^{-(Q_2-Q_1)} + e^{-(Q_3-Q_2)} - 3 \quad . \tag{6.9}$$

Introducing a simple canonical transformation[29] whose explicit form need not concern us here, we may bring Hamiltonian (6.9) to the form

$$H = \frac{1}{2}(p_1^2 + p_2^2 + p_3^2) + (1/24)[e^{(2q_2+2\sqrt{3}\,q_1)} + e^{(2q_2-2\sqrt{3}\,q_1)} + e^{-4q_2}] - (1/8) \quad . \tag{6.10}$$

In Hamiltonian (6.10), q_3 does not appear and therefore p_3 is a constant of the motion corresponding to a uniform translation of the lattice. We may thus drop p_3 from the Hamiltonian and write

$$H = \frac{1}{2}(p_1^2 + p_2^2) + (1/24)[e^{(2q_2+2\sqrt{3}\,q_1)} + e^{(2q_2-2\sqrt{3}\,q_1)} + e^{-4q_2}] - (1/8) \tag{6.11}$$

as the effective Hamiltonian for the three-particle Toda lattice.

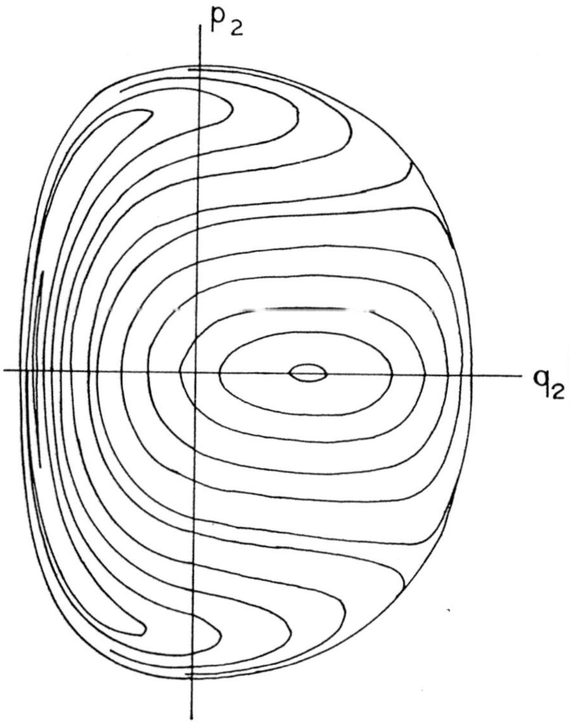

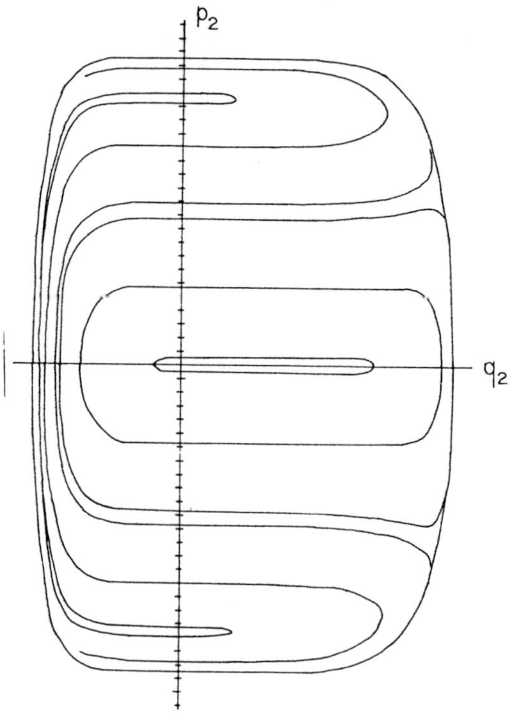

Fig. 26. The mapping plane for the Toda Hamiltonian (6.11) at energy E = 1.

Fig. 27. The mapping plane for the Toda Hamiltonian (6.11) at energy E = 256. Smooth curves appear to exist everywhere both in this figure and in fig. 26 indicating that the Toda lattice is integrable.

However, Hamiltonian (6.11) now possesses only two degrees of freedom, and hence we may graphically inspect the motion for it by generating plane area-preserving mappings. Figures 26 and 27 present such mappings for energies E = 1 and E = 256, respectively. It is to be noted that each mapping resembles that which appears in fig. 2 which is hardly surprising since Hamiltonian (6.11), when expanded into a power series, is through cubic order identical to the Henon-Heiles Hamiltonian. However it is surprising, when comparing Hamiltonian (6.11) with Hamiltonian (6.1) in figs. 26 and 27 that smooth invariant curves appear to everywhere persist at energies so large that the nonlinear terms heavily dominate the motion. The Henon-Heiles system exhibited highly erratic trajectories at energy E = 1/8 whereas the apparently similar Toda system continues to look integrable at energy E = 256.

Next we numerically integrated a host of initially close orbit-pairs for Hamiltonian (6.11) at various energies and observed a linear rather than an exponential growth of separation distance with time. A typical case is presented in fig. 28. We then calculated the formal series constant of the motion for this system up through eighth order in the (q_1, p_1, q_2, p_2) variables. Using this constant

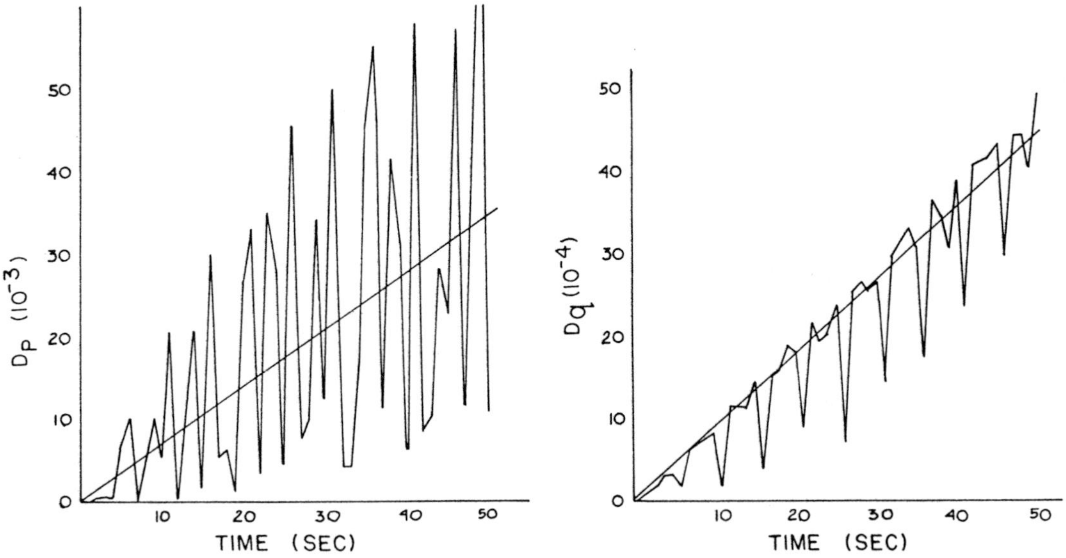

Fig. 28. In this figure D_p and D_q are the separation distances in momentum and position space for two trajectories of the Toda Hamiltonian (6.11) initially started close together. Both separation distances grow linearly with time on the average. System energy here is E = 1024.

we were able to accurately predict the curves in the directly integrated mapping planes. Finally, we located a host of fixed points in each mapping plane, and, even at the largest energy used, all residues were zero to within the computer accuracy available to us. Thus every test indicated that Hamiltonian (6.11) was integrable.

Delightfully enough, upon receipt of a preprint[32)] from me describing the above calculations, M. Henon quickly discovered analytic expressions for the constants of the motion for the Toda lattice, thus, rigorously proving its integrability[33)]. For Hamiltonian (6.11), Henon's additional constant reads

$$I(q_1,p_1,q_2,p_2) = 8p_1(p_1^2 - 3p_2^2) + (p_1 + \sqrt{3}\,p_2)e^{(2q_2 - 2\sqrt{3}\,q_1)}$$

$$- 2p_1 e^{-4q_2} + (p_1 - \sqrt{3}\,p_2)e^{(2q_2 + 2\sqrt{3}\,q_1)} \qquad (6.12)$$

The Toda lattice is thus an excellent example of the interplay between computer experiment and analysis.

This of course does not complete even the known story of computer tests for statistical behavior, but it is perhaps a cheerful note upon which to end these lectures. The reader interested in computer tests for integrability when the number of system particles is greater than two or three may consult references 15, 34, 35 and 36.

REFERENCES

* Research sponsored by the Air Force Office of Scientific Research under Grant No. AFOSR-73-2453.

1) J. Ford, Adv.Chem.Phys. 24(1973)155.

2) J. Ford in Lecture Notes in Physics, Vol. 28: Lectures in Statistical Physics, W.C. Schieve, Ed. (Springer-Verlag, Berlin, 1974).

3) V.I. Arnol'd and A. Avez, Ergodic Problems of Classical Mechanics (Benjamin, New York, 1968).

4) M. Henon and C. Heiles, Astron.J. 69(1964)73.

5) O. Penrose, Foundations of Statistical Mechanics (Pergamon Press, New York, 1974), p. 122.

6) J.L. Lebowitz, "Ergodic Theory and Statistical Mechanics of Non-equilibrium Processes", lecture given at the 10th Annual Eastern Theoretical Physics Conference, Schenectady, New York (preprint).

7) P. Hoyningen-Huene, Helv.Phys.Acta 46(1973)468.

8) M.C. Wang and G.E. Uhlenbeck, Rev.Mod.Phys. 17(1945)323.

9) A.S. Wightman in Statistical Mechanics at the Turn of the Decade, E.G.D. Cohen, Ed. (North-Holland, Amsterdam, 1968), p. 4.

10) A.N. Kolmogorov in Proceedings of the International Congress of Mathematicians, Amsterdam (North-Holland, Amsterdam, 1957), Vol. 1, p. 315.

11) V.I. Arnol'd, Russ.Math.Sur. 18(1963)9.

12) J. Moser, Nachr.Akad.Wiss. Göttingen, II Math.Phys.Kl. 1(1962).

13) E. Merzbacher, Quantum Mechanics (Wiley, New York, 1961).

14) G.H. Walker and J. Ford, Phys.Rev. 188(1969)416.

15) B.V. Chirikov, "Research Concerning the Theory of Non-linear Resonances and Stochasticity", Report No. 267, Institute of Nuclear Physics, Novosibirsk, USSR, 1969 (unpublished). An English translation of this report is available as Translation 71-40, CERN, Genève, 1971.

16) V.I. Arnol'd, Russ.Math.Sur. 18(1963)85.

17) J. Ford and G.H. Lunsford, Phys.Rev. A1(1970)59.

18) J. Moser, Mem.Am.Math.Soc. 81(1968)1.

19) G.D. Birkhoff, Dynamical Systems (American Mathematical Society Publications, New York, 1927).

20) E. Zehnder, Comm. Pure and Appl.Math. 25(1973)131.

21) M. Henon, Quart.Appl.Math. 27(1969) 291.

22) L. Jackson Laslett, AEC Research and Development Report NYO-1480-101, New York University, 1968 (unpublished).

23) C. Froeschle, Astron. and Astrophys. 9(1970)15.

24) G. Contopoulos, Astrophys.J. 138(1963)1297.

25) F.G. Gustavson, Astron.J. 71(1966)670.

26) See, for example, J.H. Bartlett and C.A. Wagner, Celestial Mech. 2(1970)228.

27) J. Moser, Private communication.

28) J.M. Greene, J.Math.Phys. 9(1968)760.

29) For further details on this section, see G.H. Lunsford and J. Ford, J.Math. Phys. 13(1972)700.

30) M. Toda, J.Phys.Soc. Japan 23(1967)501; Prog.Theor.Phys. Suppl. 45(1970)174.

31) N.J. Zabusky, Computer Phys.Comm. 5(1973)1.

32) This preprint has now appeared as J. Ford, S.D. Stoddard and J.S. Turner, Prog.Theor.Phys. 50(1973)1547.

33) M. Henon, Phys.Rev. B9(1974)1921. Also see H. Flaschka, Phys.Rev. B9(1974)1924.

34) L. Galgani and A. Scotti, Rivista Nuovo Cim. 2(1972)189.

35) N. Saito, N. Ooyama, Y. Aizawa, H. Hirooka, Prog.Theor.Phys. Suppl. 45(1970) 209.

36) S.D. Stoddard and J. Ford, Phys.Rev. A8(1973)1504.

STOCHASTIC DIFFERENTIAL EQUATIONS

N.G. van Kampen
Institute for Theoretical Physics
Rijksuniversiteit te Utrecht, The Netherlands.

Note These lectures constitute a short summary of a more complete review, which was prepared during a temporary stay at the University of Texas at Austin, Texas and will appear elsewhere.

1. FIRST LECTURE: THE PROBLEM

Three preliminary questions:

(i) What are stochastic differential equations?

(ii) Where do they occur?

(iii) Why are we interested in them?

Answer to (i). A stochastic quantity or random variable ϖ is defined by its range Ω of possible values and a probability distribution defined on that range. For convenience we shall often use the notation of a continuous range with a probability density $P(\varpi)d\varpi$; the required modification for the discrete case or mixed cases are easily made.

A stochastic or random function $\xi(t)$ of a variable t is actually a function of two variables: $\xi(t;\varpi)$. In physical parlance it is an ensemble of functions of t, the individual sample functions being identified by the label ϖ. Averages are formed by integrating over ϖ

$$\langle\xi(t_1)\xi(t_2)\dots\xi(t_n)\rangle = \int_\Omega \xi(t_1;\varpi)\xi(t_2;\varpi)\dots\xi(t_n;\varpi)\; P(\varpi)d\varpi \;.$$

If all these averages depend on the time differences alone the random function is called "stationary".

A non-stochastic or "sure" ordinary differential equation of order n can always be written as n coupled first order equations

$$\dot u_\nu = F_\nu(t,u_1,u_2,\dots,u_n) \qquad (\nu = 1,2,\dots,n),$$

or more shortly $\dot u = F(t,u)$ when it is understood that u and F are n-component vectors. A stochastic ordinary differential equation has the form

$$\dot u = F(t,u;\varpi) . \tag{1}$$

A stochastic linear ordinary differential equation of order n is

$$\dot u = A(t;\varpi)u + f(t;\varpi) , \tag{2}$$

Fundamental Problems in Statistical Mechanics, Vol. 3, Editor, E.D.G. Cohen.

where A is a stochastic matrix depending on t and f is a vector driving force.

We shall mainly be concerned with homogeneous linear equations of the form

$$\dot{u} = \{A_o + \alpha A_1(t;\varpi)\}u, \tag{3}$$

where A_o is a sure matrix independent of t, and α is a small parameter measuring the size of the fluctuations. Moreover, $A_1(t;\varpi)$ will always be stationary, i.e., all averages like

$$\langle A_{1,\nu\mu}(t_1)A_{1,\kappa\lambda}(t_2)A_{1,\rho\sigma}(t_3)\rangle$$

only depend on the time differences. In particular, $\langle A_1(t)\rangle$ is independent of time and is usually absorbed into A_o. Without loss of generality we may and shall therefore always take $\langle A_1(t)\rangle = 0$.

Note. $A_1(t;\varpi)$ is supposed to be a known stochastic matrix function, that is, all its statistical properties are given beforehand and are not affected by the values of u. Mathematically this remark is obvious but in physical applications it is often hard to know whether this requirement is satisfied.

Answer to (ii). Classic example is Langevin's equation

$$m\dot{u} = -\beta u + \xi(t;\varpi), \tag{5}$$

where the mass m and friction constant β are sure and ξ is a random driving force, with the statistical properties

$$\langle\xi(t)\rangle = 0, \qquad \langle\xi(t_1)\xi(t_2)\rangle = C\,\delta(t_1-t_2)\ .$$

This is of the general type (2), but the coefficient matrix is sure and only the inhomogeneous term is random. Such equations apply to electrical networks with noise sources, to the fluctuations of electro-magnetic fields in media[8), etc. However this type (sometimes called "linear" or "additive"[9)) is wellknown and rather easily solved, and will not be treated here.

Rather we are interested in the type (confusingly called "non-linear"[10) or "multiplicative") in which the coefficients are random. The simplest example is

$$\dot{u} = -i\{\omega_o + \alpha\omega_1(t;\varpi)\}u, \tag{6}$$

where u is a single component complex quantity. This equation has been used to describe the motion of a magnetic spin in a random magnetic field[11) and as a model for a harmonic oscillator with fluctuating frequency[12].

Wave propagation in a medium with random refractive index[13] is governed in the one-dimensional case by

$$\frac{d^2\psi}{dx^2} + \frac{\omega^2}{c^2}\{n_o^2 + \alpha n_1^2(x;\varpi)\}\psi = 0 .$$

This has the form (3) if x is identified with t, and $u_1 = \psi$, $u_2 = d\psi/dx$. In units in which $\omega n_o/c = 1$,

$$\frac{d}{dx}\begin{pmatrix}u_1\\u_2\end{pmatrix} = \{\begin{pmatrix}0 & 1\\-1 & 0\end{pmatrix} + \alpha n_1^2(x;\varpi)\begin{pmatrix}0 & 0\\-1 & 0\end{pmatrix}\}\begin{pmatrix}u_1\\u_2\end{pmatrix} .$$

Alternatively this may be interpreted as a random harmonic oscillator, see however the warning remark in the Third Lecture.

Broadening of spectral lines emitted and absorbed by an atom in an ionized gas requires the study of the Schrödinger equation for the atom

$$-\frac{h}{i}\frac{\partial\psi}{\partial t} = H_o\psi + \vec{E}\cdot\vec{P}\psi. \tag{7}$$

H_o is the Hamiltonian of the unperturbed atom, $\vec{P}$ its dipole moment operator and $\vec{E}(t;\varpi)$ the random electric field caused by passing charged particles[14]. Similar Schrödinger equations are used in magnetic relaxation[15], and in the theory of lasers[16].

Answer to (iii). These examples show that stochastic differential equations occur when a total system is subdivided in a subsystem and an environment. One then tries to establish equations of motion for the subsystem alone, in which the influence of the environment gives rise to random coefficients. Statistical mechanics of irreversible processes is based on a similar subdivision of the total many-body system in macroscopic quantities, which obey their own equations, and the remaining microscopic quantities which give rise to fluctuating terms in the macroscopic equations, as e.g. in the so-called generalized hydrodynamics[17]. The crucial and unsolved problem is how to find the correct subdivision, but once it is found or conjectured, the theory of stochastic differential equations tells the consequences of the fluctuations in the coefficients. We shall see that under proper conditions they give rise to "renormalized" transport coefficients.

What is meant by a "solution" of a given stochastic differential equation? A solution of (1) is a stochastic function $u(t;\varpi)$ which for each individual value of ϖ obeys (1). There are of course many such solutions, because for each ϖ one may select any one of the ∞^n solutions of (1). We shall make the solution unique by imposing an initial condition:

$$u(t;\omega) = a \ , \tag{8}$$

where a is a fixed vector. In scattering problems it is often more suitable to make the solution unique by imposing the radiation condition[13]. The essential point, however, is that some prescription must be given for the solution $u(t;\omega)$ to be well-defined.

Having defined a solution one may then seek to determine its statistical properties, like its average $\langle u(t)\rangle$, the higher moments $\langle u(t)^2\rangle, \ldots,$ or the auto-correlation function. We focus our attention on the average, and show later that this suffices to determine all higher moments as well.

We shall now determine the average of the solution of (6) with initial condition (8), a being a fixed complex number. Clearly

$$u(t;\varpi) = \exp\{-i\omega_o t - i\alpha \int_o^t \omega_1(t';\varpi)dt'\}a. \tag{9}$$

Hence

$$\langle u(t)\rangle = e^{-i\omega_o t} \langle \exp\{-i\alpha \int_o^t \omega_1(t')dt'\}\rangle a. \tag{10}$$

This is still a rather formal expression since in most cases the average of the exponential cannot be computed explicitly.

Alternatively one might expand the exponential so as to obtain a series in powers of α. However, it turns out that the successive terms also contain increasing powers of t (secular terms). Hence the expansion can only be trusted for short times; that is $\alpha t \ll 1$, if ω_1 is taken to be of order unity. This shortcoming can be overcome by summing suitable subseries of the terms. This need not be done explicitly, however, if one utilizes the concept of cumulants.

Cumulants[18,19]. The integral in (9) is itself a stochastic quantity

$$I(\varpi) = \int_o^t \omega_1(t';\varpi)dt'.$$

The cumulants κ_m of a stochastic quantity are defined by setting

$$\langle e^{-i\alpha I}\rangle = \exp\{\sum_{m=1}^{\infty} \frac{(-i\alpha)^m}{m!} \kappa_m\} . \tag{11}$$

They are certain combinations of the moments

$$\kappa_1 = \langle I\rangle$$
$$\kappa_2 = \langle I^2\rangle - \langle I\rangle^2$$
$$\kappa_3 = \langle I^3\rangle - 3\langle I^2\rangle\langle I\rangle + 2\langle I\rangle^3$$

In the present case

$$\kappa_1 = \int_0^t \langle\omega_1(t_1)\rangle dt_1$$

$$\kappa_2 = \int_0^t \int_0^t \{\langle\omega_1(t_1)\omega(t_2)\rangle - \langle\omega(t_1)\rangle\langle\omega(t_2)\rangle\} dt_1 dt_2 .$$

Thus κ_m is an m-fold integral whose integrand we shall again call a "cumulant" and denote

$$\langle\langle\omega_1(t_1)\omega_1(t_2) \ldots . \omega_1(t_m)\rangle\rangle . \tag{12}$$

The precise rule of forming these quantities can be found in ref.[19], but we shall not go beyond α^2.

The essential feature of these cumulants is the following. If $\omega_1(t_1)$ and $\omega_1(t_2)$ were statistically independent then $\langle\langle\omega(t_1)\omega(t_2)\rangle\rangle = 0$. We shall suppose throughout that there exists a "correlation-time" τ_c, such that $\omega(t_1)$ and $\omega(t_2)$ are statistically independent when $|t_1-t_2| \gg \tau_c$. It also follows that (12) vanishes as soon as the m time points contain a gap large compared to τ_c. As a consequence the integral κ_m virtually extends only over a volume of order $\tau_c^{m-1} t$ in the m-dimensional integration space. The successive terms of the expansion (11) are therefore of order $(\alpha\tau_c)^{m-1}(\alpha t)$. Hence the criterion for the validity has now become

$$\alpha\tau_c \ll 1 . \tag{13}$$

This is the basic condition for everything that follows.

No other special statistical properties of $\omega_1(t)$ need be assumed. In these lectures, however, the expansions will always be broken off after the second power of α. That amounts to neglecting all cumulants beyond α_2, that is, to approximating $\omega_1(t)$ by a Gaussian stochastic function. This remark partially justifies the tendency of some physicists to think that every stochastic function must be Gaussian.

2. SECOND LECTURE: SOLUTION

The solution of (6) is obtained by substituting (11) into (10),

$$\langle u(t)\rangle = e^{-i\omega_o t} \exp\{ \sum_{m=1}^{\infty} \frac{(-i\alpha)^m}{m!} \int_0^t \ldots \int_0^t \langle\langle\omega_1(t_1)\ldots\omega_1(t_m)\rangle\rangle dt_1 \ldots dt_m\} a \tag{14}$$

We have already supposed $\langle\omega(t)\rangle = 0$ and consider only the second order in α,

$$\langle u(t)\rangle = e^{-i\omega_o t} \exp\{-\alpha^2 \int_o^t dt_1 \int_o^{t_1} dt_2 \langle\omega_1(t_1)\omega_1(t_2)\rangle\} a.$$

This result can be expressed in an alternative way. On differentiating,

$$\frac{d\langle u(t)\rangle}{dt} = \{-i\omega_o - \alpha^2 \int_o^t \langle\omega_1(t)\omega(t_2)\rangle dt_2\}\langle u(t)\rangle. \tag{15}$$

Thus the average $\langle u(t)\rangle$ obeys itself a differential equation, with time dependent but sure coefficients.

The equation (15) is obeyed regardless of the initial value a, but it still contains the initial time $t = 0$. Hence it is obeyed by all solutions of (6) that were specified by their value at that particular time. Any solutions that would have been specified by assigning a fixed value b at a time $t_o \neq 0$ are not covered. However, this can be remedied as follows. The integrand in (15) differs from zero only when t_2 is within a range τ_c from the upper limit of integration. Hence for $t \gg \tau_c$

$$\int_o^t \langle\omega_1(t)\omega_1(t_2)\rangle dt_2 \approx \int_o^\infty \langle\omega_1(t)\omega_1(t-\tau)\rangle d\tau .$$

The resulting differential equation

$$\frac{d\langle u(t)\rangle}{dt} = \{-i\omega_o - \alpha^2 \int_o^\infty \langle\omega_1(t)\omega_1(t-\tau)\rangle d\tau\}\langle u(t)\rangle\}\langle u(t)\rangle \tag{16}$$

is (approximately) obeyed by all solutions of (6), provided that a transient time of order τ_c has elapsed since the time at which their initial value has been imposed.

Call the integral in (16) c_o (independent of t as ω_1 is supposed stationary). The solution is

$$\langle u(t)\rangle = A \exp(-i\omega_o - \alpha^2 c_o)t .$$

The frequency fluctuations give rise to a damping in the average amplitude, which can be understood as a loss of phase coherence between the individual solutions for different ϖ. Indeed, it is evident from (6) that $\langle|u(t)|^2\rangle = 1$. The constant A is not identical with the initial value a, because this $\langle u(t)\rangle$ is only valid for $t \gg \tau_c$ and differs from the actual $\langle u(t)\rangle$ during the transient time.

The same equation can be used for describing the propagation of a plane monochromatic wave through a medium with randomly varying refractive index, when back scattering is neglected,

$$\frac{\partial u(x)}{\partial x} = -\frac{i\omega}{c}\{n_o + \alpha n_1(x,\varpi)\}u(x) .$$

A time factor $e^{-i\omega t}$ with fixed ω has been extracted and the coordinate x now has the role of independent variable. Again the amplitude decreases exponentially with x owing to the loss of phase coherence, while the intensity remains constant. Propagation of a wave in a random medium including back scattering is considered in the next lecture.

Now consider (3) <u>with more than one component</u>, A_o and A_1 are matrices. As they do not in general commute it is no longer possible to solve the equation explicitly like in (9). Yet it is possible to give a formal expression resembling (9) and use it in a similar way. It is convenient to first transform to the interaction representation:

$$u(t) = e^{A_o t} v(t), \qquad e^{-A_o t} A_1(t;\varpi) e^{A_o t} = V(t;\varpi)$$
$$\dot{v}(t) = \alpha\, V(t;\varpi)v(t), \qquad v(o) = a. \tag{17}$$

<u>Intermezzo</u>. Bourret[11)] has used a method which is not properly justified but yet of great heuristic value. Equivalent to (17) are the integral equations

$$v(t) = a + \alpha \int_o^t V(t_1)v(t_1)dt_1$$

$$v(t) = a + \alpha \int_o^t V(t_1)dt_1 a + \alpha^2 \int_o^t dt_1 \int_o^t dt_2\, V(t_1)V(t_2)v(t_2).$$

From this, as $\langle V(t)\rangle = 0$,

$$\langle v(t)\rangle = a + \alpha^2 \int_o^t dt_1 \int_o^t dt_2 \quad \langle V(t_1)V(t_2)v(t_2)\rangle .$$

This equation is still exact but it merely expresses $\langle v(t)\rangle$ as an integral over a more complicated average. It is now <u>assumed</u> that $\langle V(t_1)V(t_2)v(t_2)\rangle$ may be replaced with $\langle V(t_1)V(t_2)\rangle\langle v(t_2)\rangle$. This is a kind of randomness assumption, inasmuch as it ignores correlations between both factors. It is of the same type as a "Stosszahlansatz" or molecular chaos assumption in statistical mechanics. It cannot be justified except by verifying the result in a different way. It leads to an integral equation for $\langle v(t)\rangle$,

$$\langle v(t)\rangle = a + \alpha^2 \int_0^t dt_1 \int_0^t dt_2 \, \langle V(t_1)V(t_2)\rangle\langle v(t_2)\rangle .$$

Differentiation then yields Bourret's integral equation

$$\frac{d}{dt}\langle v(t)\rangle = \alpha^2 \int_0^t \langle V(t)V(t')\rangle\langle v(t')\rangle dt' \; .$$

It turns out that this is actually correct if terms of order $\alpha^3\tau_c^2$ on the right are neglected. However, to the same order one may replace $\langle v(t')\rangle$ in the integrand with $\langle v(t)\rangle$, so as to obtain a differential equation for $\langle v(t)\rangle$. We now continue with our main argument, which will lead directly to that differential equation.

The formal solution of (17) that resembles (9) is

$$v(t) = \lceil \exp\{\alpha \int_0^t V(t')dt'\} \rceil a, \tag{18}$$

where the symbols $\lceil \dots \rceil$ indicate the "time-ordered product". This is defined by the prescription that one should first expand the exponential

$$v(t) = \lceil 1 + \alpha \int_0^t V(t_1)dt_1 + \frac{\alpha^2}{2} \int_0^t \int_0^t V(t_1)V(t_2)dt_1dt_2 + \dots \rceil a ,$$

and subsequently in each multiple integral reorder the operator V according to decreasing values of their times,

$$v(t) = \{1+\alpha \int_0^t V(t_1)dt_1 + \alpha^2 \int_0^t dt_1 \int_0^{t_1} dt_2 \, V(t_1)V(t_2) + \dots\}a. \tag{19}$$

The proof of (18) consists in observing that (19) is nothing but the familiar perturbation expansion of (17).

Clearly the time ordering operation commutes with averaging:

$$\langle v(t)\rangle = \lceil \langle \exp\{\alpha \int_0^t V(t')dt'\}\rangle \rceil a \; .$$

For the average of the exponent the same expression as in (11) may be utilized. It is true that the matrices V at two different times do not in general commute, but inside $\lceil \dots \rceil$ they may be treated as commuting quantities since ultimately they have to be put in the right order anyway. Again supposing $\langle v(t)\rangle = 0$ one has to order α^2 in the exponent

$$\langle v(t)\rangle = \left\lceil \exp\{\alpha^2 \int_0^t dt_1 \int_0^{t_1} dt_2 \langle V(t_1)V(t_2)\rangle\}\right\rceil a. \tag{20}$$

This result is still rather formal, because the time ordering symbols mean that one cannot just compute the integral first and then put it in the exponent. For this reason it is more convenient to express the same result in another way, namely as a differential equation.

Define the matrix K(t) by

$$K(t_1) = \int_0^{t_1} \langle V(t_1)V(t_2)\rangle dt_2 \ .$$

Comparison with (18) shows that

$$\langle v(t)\rangle = \left\lceil \exp\{\alpha^2 \int_0^t K(t_1)dt_1\}\right\rceil a \tag{21}$$

is nothing but the solution of

$$\frac{d\langle v(t)\rangle}{dt} = \alpha^2 K(t)\langle v(t)\rangle \ . \tag{22}$$

However (21) is not identical with (20), because the time ordering in (21) treats K(t) as one indivisible operator, while in (20) the two factors V are occasionally separated. Fortunately it can be shown that this discrepancy gives correction terms in higher orders[20]. To second order therefore <v(t)> obeys (22). In the original representation

$$\frac{d\langle u(t)\rangle}{dt} = \{A_o + \alpha^2 \int_0^t \langle A_1(t)e^{A_o(t-t')} A_1(t')\rangle e^{-A_o(t-t')} dt'\}\langle u(t)\rangle.$$

After a transient time of order τ_c

$$\frac{d\langle u(t)\rangle}{dt} = \{A_o + \alpha^2 \int_0^\infty \langle A_1(t)e^{A_o\tau} A_1(t-\tau)\rangle e^{-A_o\tau} d\tau\}\langle u(t)\rangle \ . \tag{23}$$

<u>This is our fundamental result</u>. The unperturbed coefficient matrix A_o is "renormalized" by an additional term due to the fluctuations. The addition is of order $\alpha^2\tau_c$, but orders $\alpha^3\tau_c^2$ and higher have also been computed.

3. THIRD LECTURE: APPLICATIONS

There are many applications of (23). The crucial point is the determination of the operator $e^{A_o\tau}$ - which amounts to solving the unperturbed problem. This presents no difficulty in the case of a harmonic oscillator, and indeed random harmonic oscillators have been studied by many authors[10,11,12]. To give this example more physical context I shall formulate it in terms of propagation of a plane monochromatic wave through a medium.

After the time factor $e^{-i\omega t}$ has been extracted Maxwell's equations tell

$$\frac{dE_y}{dx} = \frac{i\omega}{c} H_z, \qquad \frac{dH_z}{dx} = \frac{i\omega}{c} \varepsilon(x) E_y .$$

This has the form (3) with two complex components and, if $\varepsilon(x) = \varepsilon_o + \alpha\varepsilon_1(x;\varpi)$,

$$A_o = \begin{pmatrix} 0 & i\omega/c \\ i\omega\varepsilon_o/c & 0 \end{pmatrix}, \qquad A_1 = \begin{pmatrix} 0 & 0 \\ i\omega\varepsilon_1/c & 0 \end{pmatrix}.$$

The unperturbed solution is, with $k = (\omega/c)\sqrt{\varepsilon_o}$,

$$e^{A_o x} = \begin{pmatrix} \cos kx & i\varepsilon_o^{-1/2}\sin kx \\ i\varepsilon_o^{1/2} \sin kx & \cos kx \end{pmatrix}.$$

Substitution in the integral in (23) yields

$$-\frac{\alpha^2\omega^2}{c^2} \int_0^\infty \langle\varepsilon_1(x)\varepsilon_1(x-\tau)\rangle \begin{pmatrix} 0 & 0 \\ i\varepsilon_o^{-1/2}\sin\tau\cos\tau & \varepsilon_o^{-1}\sin^2\tau \end{pmatrix} d\tau .$$

Thus one has to know concerning $\varepsilon_1(x)$ only the two quantities

$$\frac{1}{2}c_1 = \int_0^\infty \langle\varepsilon_1(x)\varepsilon_1(x-\tau)\rangle \sin\tau\cos\tau\, d\tau, \quad \frac{1}{2}c_2 = \int_0^\infty \langle\varepsilon_1(x)\varepsilon_1(x-\tau)\rangle \sin^2\tau\, d\tau .$$

The final result for the average amplitudes is

$$\frac{d\langle E_y\rangle}{dx} = \frac{i\omega}{c}\langle H_z\rangle$$

$$\frac{d\langle H_z\rangle}{dx} = \frac{i\omega}{c}\varepsilon_o\langle E_y\rangle - \frac{i\alpha^2\omega^2}{2c^2}\varepsilon_o^{-1/2} c_1\langle E_y\rangle - \frac{\alpha^2\omega^2}{2c^2}\varepsilon_o^{-1/2} c_2\langle H_z\rangle .$$

It looks more familiar in the form of a second order equation obeyed by both $\langle E_y\rangle$ and $\langle H_z\rangle$,

$$\frac{d^2\psi}{dx^2} + \frac{\alpha^2\omega^2}{2c^2\varepsilon_o} c_2 \frac{d\psi}{dx} + \left(\frac{\omega^2\varepsilon_o}{c^2} - \frac{\alpha^2\omega^3}{2c^3}\varepsilon_o^{-1/2}c_1\right)\psi = 0.$$

This exhibits the amplitude damping, and also a shift in frequency resulting from the fluctuations.

In the second lecture wave propagation in a random medium did not suffer an energy shift. The difference is that there a first order equation was used, which amounts to neglecting back scattering. That is only justified if $\varepsilon(x)$ varies slowly over a wave length. In fact, in that case the integral for c_1 is practically zero. In this connection the following warning may not be superfluous.

All ordinary (i.e., non-stochastic) harmonic oscillators can be described by one and the same equation, which may be written in several equivalent forms, such as

$$\ddot{x} + \omega^2 x = 0 \qquad \text{or} \qquad \dot{a} = -\, i\omega a.$$

However, when ω is a stochastic function of time these forms are no longer equivalent. It is then necessary to decide which one is appropriate. In the case of plane monochromatic electromagnetic waves in a random medium the first form, namely

$$\frac{d^2E_y}{dx^2} + \frac{\omega^2}{c^2}\,\varepsilon(x)E_y = 0\ ,$$

is correct, while the latter is only an approximation for slowly varying ε_1. Similarly the second one does not describe the level broadening of a two-level atom: owing to the off-diagonal elements of $\vec{P}$ the equation (7) cannot be reduced to a first order linear equation (see Appendix). The correct equation for a pendulum with randomly varying length cannot be obtained by replacing in either one of the equations the constant frequency ω^2 with $g/\ell(t;\varpi)$.

The moral is that one does not arrive at the correct stochastic description of a physical system by merely replacing some of the coefficients in the familiar non-stochastic form of the equations with stochastic ones. One has to start from the fundamental equations and take into account from the beginning that the coefficients depend on time. As an exercise the reader may derive the stochastic differential equation for the pendulum mentioned above.

As a more sophisticated example consider diffusion in a turbulent fluid[21)]

$$\frac{\partial n(\vec{r},t)}{\partial t} = D\,\nabla^2 n - \nabla\cdot\vec{v}n\ . \tag{24}$$

n is the density of test particles diffusing in a fluid with local velocity $\vec{v}(\vec{r},t)$. The word "turbulence" indicates that the function $\vec{v}(\vec{r},t)$ is only statistically known. We suppose $\langle\vec{v}(\vec{r},t)\rangle = 0$ and

$$\langle v_i(\vec{r},t)v_j(\vec{r}\,',t')\rangle = \Gamma_{ij}(\vec{r} - \vec{r}\,',\ t - t')\ . \tag{25}$$

Equation (24) is of type (3) if $\vec{r}$ is regarded as the label ν and

$$A_o = D\nabla^2 , \qquad \alpha A_1 = \nabla \cdot \vec{v} .$$

The symbol ∇ should be read as an operator acting on everything behind it.

Our fundamental result (23) says

$$\frac{\partial}{\partial t} \langle n(\vec{r},t)\rangle = \{D\nabla^2 + \int_0^\infty d\tau \langle \nabla\cdot\vec{v}(\vec{r},t)\, e^{\tau D\nabla^2}\, \nabla\cdot\vec{v}(\vec{r},t-\tau)\rangle e^{-\tau D\nabla^2}\}\langle n(\vec{r},t)\rangle .$$

In order to work out the operator { } we take Fourier transforms in space and obtain in obvious notation

$$\frac{d}{dt}\langle n(\vec{k},t)\rangle = \{-Dk^2 - (2\pi)^{-3} \sum_{i,j} \int_0^\infty d\tau \iint \langle v_i(\vec{q},t)v_j(\vec{q}\,',t-\tau)\rangle \times$$

$$\times (k_i + q_i + q_i')\, e^{-\tau D(\vec{k}+\vec{q}\,')^2} (k_j + q_j')\, e^{\tau D\vec{k}^2}\, d\vec{q}\, d\vec{q}\,'\}\langle n(\vec{k},t)\rangle .$$

One easily finds from (25)

$$\langle v_i(\vec{q},t)v_j(\vec{q}\,',t-\tau)\rangle = \delta(\vec{q}+\vec{q}\,')\,(2\pi)^{3/2}\,\Gamma_{ij}(\vec{q},\tau).$$

Therefore

$$\frac{\partial}{\partial t}\langle n(\vec{k},t)\rangle = \{-Dk^2 - (2\pi)^{-3/2} \sum_{i,j} \int_0^\infty d\tau \int \Gamma_{ij}(\vec{q},\tau)k_i(k_j - q_j)$$

$$e^{-\tau Dq^2 + 2\tau D\,\vec{k}\cdot\vec{q}}\, d\vec{q}\}\langle n(\vec{k},t)\rangle . \qquad (26)$$

In principle this solves the problem: if one knows Γ one performs the integration and obtains a differential equation for the average density $\langle n(\vec{r},t)\rangle$ of the test particles. In the case of isotropic turbulence of an incompressible fluid[22)]

$$\Gamma_{ij}(\vec{q},\tau) = \gamma(q^2,\tau)(q^2\delta_{ij} - q_iq_j) .$$

One easily sees that the integral contains a factor k^2. Hence in this case the result may be written

$$\frac{\partial}{\partial t}\langle n(\vec{k},t)\rangle = -D(k^2)k^2\langle n(\vec{k},t)\rangle$$

where $D(k^2)$ is a renormalized k-dependent diffusion constant.

Unfortunately there is a difficulty. Although the actual Γ is not known, linearized hydrodynamics shows that for small q and large τ

$$\gamma(q^2,\tau) \sim e^{-\nu q^2 \tau} ,$$

where ν is the "kinematic viscosity" of the fluid. As a consequence the integral over τ fails to converge for $|q|<2Dk(D+\nu)^{-1}$. This means that the long wave fluctuations in $\vec{v}$ are too weakly damped by the viscosity to ensure the existence of a finite τ_c. Accordingly the correlations in $n(\vec{r},t)$ survive over infinitely long times and no regime exists in which $\langle n(\vec{r},t)\rangle$ varies autonomously, i.e., independently of the choice of the initial time.

4. FOURTH LECTURE: NONLINEAR EQUATIONS

Stochastic nonlinear differential equations. The general form is (1):

$$\dot{u}_\nu = F_\nu(t,u;\varpi) \quad , \qquad u_\nu(o) = a_\nu \; . \tag{27}$$

This problem can be reduced to the linear case by the following device. For fixed ϖ the equation describes a flow in the n-dimensional phase space of u. When a hypothetical fluid in that space is carried along by the flow its density $\rho(u,t)$ varies according to

$$\frac{\partial\rho(u,t)}{\partial t} = - \sum_{\nu=1}^{n} \frac{\partial}{\partial u_\nu} F_\nu(t,u;\varpi)\rho(u,t) \; . \tag{28}$$

(This resembles the Liouville equation of statistical mechanics, but in this case there is no reason why the fluid should be incompressible; hence $\partial/\partial u_\nu$ has to remain in front of F_ν.)

Equation (28) is a stochastic linear differential equation for ρ, while the u_ν now have the same role as previously the ν. Hence we are able to find $\langle\rho(u,t)\rangle$ from its initial value, provided that the fluctuations in F are small and rapid. The connection with the original equation (27) is given by the following.

Lemma. Let p(u,t) be the probability density of u at time t as determined from (27). On the other hand let $\rho(u,t;\varpi)$ be determined from (28) with initial condition

$$\rho(u,o) = \delta^{(n)}(u - a),$$

where $\delta^{(n)}$ is the n-dimensional delta function. Then

$$p(u,t) = \langle\rho(u,t)\rangle.$$

Proof. Write the solution of (27)

$$u = U(a,t;\varpi).$$

For fixed t and ϖ this maps the vector a into u (Fig. 1). Let the inverse mapping be

$$a = U^{-1}(u,t;\varpi).$$

The solution of (28) follows directly from conservation of density

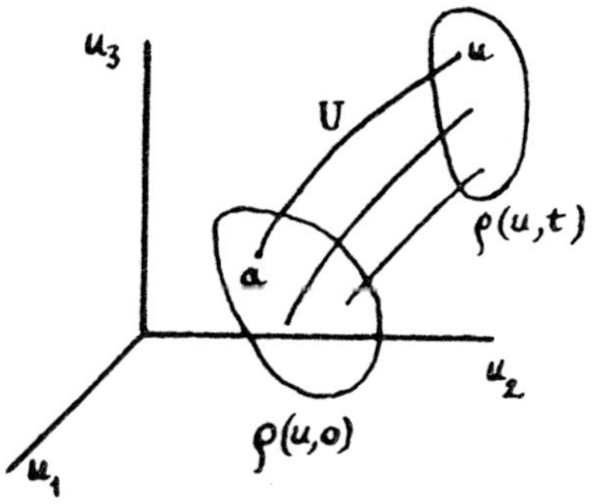

Fig. 1. The flow in u-space.

$$\rho(u,t;\varpi) = \rho[U^{-1}(u,t;\varpi),\ 0;\varpi]\,J(u,t;\varpi)$$

where J is the Jacobian determinant

$$J = \frac{d\{a\}}{d\{u\}} = \frac{d\{U^{-1}(u,t;\varpi)\}}{d\{u\}}.$$

Consequently

$$\langle\rho(u,t)\rangle = \int_\Omega \rho(u,t;\varpi)P(\varpi)d\varpi = \int_\Omega P(\varpi)d\varpi\ \delta[U^{-1}(u,t;\varpi)-a]\,J.$$

However, the familiar formula about transforming variables inside a delta function tells that this may also be written

$$\langle\rho(u,t)\rangle = \int_\Omega P(\varpi)d\varpi\ \delta[u - U(a,t;\varpi)].$$

The right-hand side can be read as the probability that the solution $U(a,t;\varpi)$ takes the value u - which is the definition of $p(u,t)$. Q.E.D.

Note that the same device can be used in the case that F is linear in u, so as to obtain the entire probability distribution of u, rather than just its average. This remark fulfills the promise made in the first lecture.

Now suppose for convenience, in analogy with (3),

$$F(t,u;\varpi) = F_o(u) + \alpha F_1(t,u;\varpi), \quad \langle F_1(t,u)\rangle = 0.$$

Then it is possible to apply the fundamental result (23) to obtain an equation for $\langle\rho(u,t)\rangle$, that is, for $p(u,t)$. Without writing the somewhat lengthly formula in full one sees that it has the form

$$\frac{\partial p(u,t)}{\partial t} = K\, p(u,t) \ , \tag{29}$$

where K is a time-independent operator acting on the u-dependence of p. This equation determines p at later times when it is known at one particular initial time; that is, it describes the random function $u(t,\varpi)$ as a Markov process. Of course, this is an approximation based on the assumption that F_1 has a short correlation time τ_c such that $\alpha\tau_c \ll 1$. Incidentally, an equation of type (29) for a probability density of a Markov process is called a "master equation" (in the original sense[23]).

It is easy to find applications but in most of them no explicit solution of (29) can be obtained. One solvable example is the Malthus-Verhulst equation for the growth of the number of individuals N in a population,

$$\dot{N} = a\,N - b\,N^2 \ .$$

a determines the natural growth and b the death rate through competition. Either one of these constants may be endowed by a fluctuating term, due to environmental influences,

$$a = a_o + \alpha\, a_1(t;\varpi) \qquad \text{or} \qquad b = b_o + \alpha\, b_1(t;\varpi) \, .$$

The result is a master equation for the probability distribution P(N,t) of the size of the population[24]. Note that this calculation refers to fluctuations in N due to <u>external</u> causes, not those due to the finite size of the population[25].

A somewhat unexpected application is the problem of transmission of electromagnetic waves through a slab of a random medium (Fig. 2).

A monochromatic plane polarized wave with amplitude 1 enters at x = L a medium whose refractive index depends on x. Maxwell's equations inside the medium:

$$\frac{dE_y}{dx} = \frac{i\omega}{c} H_z \ , \qquad \frac{dH_z}{dx} = \frac{i\omega}{c}\, \varepsilon(x) E_y \, . \tag{30}$$

As E_y and H_z are continuous at the boundaries:

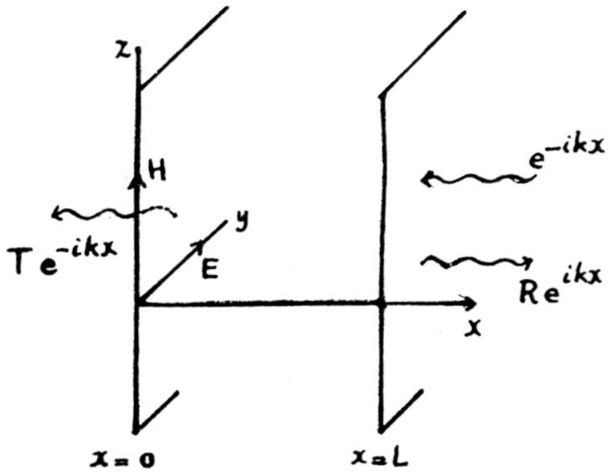

Fig. 2. Reflection by a random medium.

$$E_y(o) = - H_z(o) = T$$

$$E_y(L) = e^{-ikL} + Re^{ikL} \tag{31}$$

$$H_z(L) = - e^{-ikL} + Re^{ikL}.$$

R and T are the complex amplitudes of reflected and transmitted wave and the aim is to compute them.

Suppose ε is a constant plus small fluctuations,

$$\varepsilon = \varepsilon_o + \alpha\, \varepsilon_1(x;\varpi), \qquad \langle\varepsilon_1(x)\rangle = 0.$$

Then (30) is linear and of type (3). Yet the result (23) cannot be utilized because the problem is <u>not</u> to find $\langle E_y\rangle$ and $\langle H_z\rangle$ for given initial values (either at $x = 0$ of $x = L$). Rather one has one relation between E_y and H_z at $x = 0$ and one at $x = L$.

[<u>Note</u>. It would be incorrect to use equation (23) for the averages and solve it with the desired boundary conditions (31). These conditions must be obeyed for each ϖ separately, not just on the average.]

This difficulty is overcome by defining the new complex variable[26)]

$$u = \frac{E_y + H_z}{E_y - H_z} .$$

It obeys the nonlinear first order Riccatti equation

$$\frac{du}{dx} = \frac{1}{2}\, ik\{(\varepsilon-1)(u^2+1) + 2(\varepsilon+1)u\} \equiv F(x,u)$$

with the initial condition $u(o) = 0$. Solution of this equation immediately leads to the reflection because $u(L) = Re^{2ikL}$.

The density ρ is a function of the real and imaginary parts of u, or alternatively, of u and u^*. Equation (28) reads

$$\frac{\partial\rho(u,u^*,x)}{dx} = - \frac{\partial}{\partial u} F\rho - \frac{\partial}{\partial u^*} F^*\rho .$$

From this one can construct the equation (29) for the probability density $p(u,u^*,x)$. Solution of this equation yields for $x = L$ the probability density of R. Unfortunately the equation is rather complicated and so far has not led to definite results.

5. APPENDIX: LINE BROADENING

As an application we compute line broadening due to random perturbations. An atom, of which only the ground level and one excited state with energy $\hbar\Omega$ are relevant, is subjected to a random electric field $E(t)$. The Schrödinger equation for its two-component wave-vector (ψ_1,ψ_o) is

$$\frac{d}{dt}\begin{pmatrix}\psi_1\\ \psi_2\end{pmatrix} = \begin{pmatrix}-i\Omega & 0\\ 0 & 0\end{pmatrix}\begin{pmatrix}\psi_1\\ \psi_o\end{pmatrix} - i\alpha E(t)\begin{pmatrix}0 & 1\\ 1 & 0\end{pmatrix}\begin{pmatrix}\psi_1\\ \psi_o\end{pmatrix}, \tag{32}$$

where $\hbar\alpha$ is the matrix element of the dipole moment between the two states. We suppose $E(t)$ stationary and $\langle E(t)\rangle = 0$, and furthermore that $E(t)$ has a correlation time τ_c such that $\alpha\tau_c \ll 1$ (assuming E of order unity). This equation is of the type (3) and could be solved to give $\langle\psi\rangle$. However, the average wave function has no physical meaning, because in quantum mechanics one is interested in matrix elements, which involve products of ψ and ψ^*. The averages of such products could be found with the aid of the fourth lecture, in which the entire probability distribution of ψ was obtained. A simpler method, however, leads more directly to the desired result.

To find the averages of the four products

$$u_1 = \psi_1^*\psi_1, \quad u_2 = \psi_o^*\psi_o, \quad u_3 = \psi_1^*\psi_o, \quad u_4 = \psi_o^*\psi_1, \tag{33}$$

we write four equations for them, which are consequences of (32),

$$\frac{d}{dt}\begin{pmatrix}u_1\\ u_2\\ u_3\\ u_4\end{pmatrix} = \begin{pmatrix}0 & 0 & -i\alpha E & i\alpha E\\ 0 & 0 & i\alpha E & -i\alpha E\\ -i\alpha E & i\alpha E & i\Omega & 0\\ i\alpha E & -i\alpha E & 0 & -i\Omega\end{pmatrix}\begin{pmatrix}u_1\\ u_2\\ u_3\\ u_4\end{pmatrix}.$$

This is again a linear equation of the form (3), having <u>four</u> components. Hence the result (23) can be used to give the averages of the products (33). This device amounts simply to introducing the density matrix.

As a first step one readily determines

$$e^{A_o\tau} = \begin{pmatrix}1 & 0 & 0 & 0\\ 0 & 1 & 0 & 0\\ 0 & 0 & e^{i\Omega\tau} & 0\\ 0 & 0 & 0 & e^{-i\Omega\tau}\end{pmatrix}.$$

Furthermore

$$A_1(t) = iE(t)\begin{pmatrix}0 & 0 & -1 & 1\\ 0 & 0 & 1 & -1\\ -1 & 1 & 0 & 0\\ 1 & -1 & 0 & 0\end{pmatrix}.$$

The integral in (23) is a matter of algebra. Skipping a few steps and setting

$$\alpha^2 \int_0^\infty \langle E(t)E(t-\tau)\rangle e^{i\Omega\tau} d\tau = \frac{1}{2}(a + ib)$$

we obtain for it

$$\begin{pmatrix} -a & a & 0 & 0 \\ a & -a & 0 & 0 \\ 0 & 0 & -a+ib & a+ib \\ 0 & 0 & a-ib & -a-ib \end{pmatrix}.$$

Add to this A_o to obtain the operator { } in (23). In order to find the evolution of $\langle u\rangle$ we determine the eigenvalues λ from

$$\begin{vmatrix} -a-\lambda & a & 0 & 0 \\ a & -a-\lambda & 0 & 0 \\ 0 & 0 & i\Omega-a+ib-\lambda & a+ib \\ 0 & 0 & a-ib & -i\Omega-a-ib-\lambda \end{vmatrix} = 0. \qquad (34)$$

There is one eigenvalue $\lambda = 0$, with eigenvector (1,1,0,0). This corresponds to an equilibrium state $|\psi_1|^2 = |\psi_2|^2 = \frac{1}{2}$. Thus we find that in equilibrium both states are occupied with the same probability, rather than with the Boltzmann distribution. This is a famous difficulty inherent in the use of (32). The reason is the the perturbing field E(t) causes transitions from ground state to excited state and vice versa with equal probability. It can only be properly overcome by quantizing E so as to include spontaneous emissions. Alternatively one often adds a phenomenological term in the equation for the density matrix to simulate this emission. Such a term is analogous to the friction term in Langevin's equation (5). It is related to the strength of the fluctuations in E by the requirement that the proper temperature should be obtained - which is the fluctuation-dissipation theorem. In this presentation we shall side-step this complication by supposing that the fluctuations in E(t) are so rapid as to correspond to an effective temperature $kT \gg \hbar\Omega$, so that both levels are actually occupied with equal probability. This is realistic for many cases of nuclear magnetic resonance[27].

The second eigenvalue is $\lambda = -2a$ with eigenvector (1,-1,0,0). As the matrix (34) consists of two two-by-two blocks, these two eigenvectors suffice to describe the evolution of $u_1 = |\psi_1|^2$ and $u_2 = |\psi_o|^2$ separately. Thus if the density matrix is diagonal at $t = 0$ it remains diagonal at later times. However we are interested in the dipole moment, which involves the off-diagonal elements.

The quantum mechanical expectation value of P is

$$(\psi, P\psi) = \hbar\alpha(u_3 + u_4).$$

Its average over the random field E is therefore proportional to $\langle u_3\rangle + \langle u_4\rangle$. The evolution of these two components involves the other two eigenvalues

$$\lambda = -a \pm i(\Omega + b) + \mathcal{O}(\alpha^4).$$

Thus <P> is damped by a factor e^{-at} and its frequency is shifted by the amount b. This determines the width and the shift of the line emitted or absorbed by the atom while it is subjected to the random perturbation E(t). The precise formula for the line shape[14)] is based on the auto-correlation function of P, but it is clear that it must involve the same time factors.

Our calculation is essentially based on the assumption $\alpha\tau_c \ll 1$. When τ_c is not small no such simple and general result as (23) exists, as was already mentioned in connection with the diffusion problem. Yet it is possible to compute the line shape even for long τ_c if a special choice for the stochastic function E(t) is made[28)]. That calculation is however outside the scope of these lectures.

In the course of this calculation it appeared that it is possible to find the second moments $\langle u_\nu u_\mu \rangle$ by the same method as originally designed for the averages $\langle u_\nu \rangle$. The detour via the total probability p(u,t) was not necessary thanks to the fact that for linear equations the second moments again obey an enlarged set of linear equations. The same trick also permits to find the evolution of the energy of a random harmonic oscillator, and also higher moments of its amplitude. This is important for stability questions, because the behavior of the average amplitude alone is insufficient to garantuee that the oscillator is stable.

GENERAL REFERENCES

It is impossible to do justice to all of the literature on the subject or related with it. We confine ourselves to representative references, where further literature can be found.

1) R. Kubo, J. Phys. Soc. Japan, 17 (1962) 1100; J. Math. Phys., 4 (1963) 174.
2) S.K. Srinivasan and R. Vasudevan, Introduction to Random Differential Equations and their Applications (American Elsevier Co., New York 1971).
3) T.T. Soong, Random Differential Equations in Science and Engineering (Academic Press, New York 1973).
4) I.I. Gihman and A.V. Skorohod, Stochastic Differential Equations (Springer, Berlin 1972).
5) L. Arnold, Stochastische Differentialgleichungen (Oldenbourg, München 1973).
6) Stochastic Differential Equations. Proceedings of a Symposium in Applied Mathematics of the AMS and the SIAM (J.B. Keller and H.P. McKean eds., American Mathematical Society, Providence, R.I. 1973).
7) R.L. Stratonovich, Topics in the Theory of Random Noise, I and II (Gordon and Breach, New York 1963 and 1967).

REFERENCES CITED IN THE TEXT

8) L.D. Landau and E.M. Lifshitz, Electrodynamics of Continuous Media (Pergamon, Oxford 1960) ch. 13.

9) R.F. Fox, J. Math. Physics 13 (1972) 1196.

10) R.H. Kraichnan, J. Math. Physics 2 (1961) 124.

11) R. Bourret, Can. J. Phys. 43 (1965) 619.

12) e.g. R.J. Glauber, in: Quantum Optics and Electronics (Les Houches Summer School 1964; C. de Witt et al., eds., Gordon and Breach, New York, 1965) p.165.

13) J.B. Keller, Proc. Symp. Appl. Math. 16, 145 (Amer. Math. Soc., Providence 1964); M. Lax, in ref. 6.

14) R.G. Breene, The Shift and Shape of Spectral Lines (Pergamon, Oxford 1962); J. Cooper, in: Atomic Collision Processes (Boulder Lectures in Theoretical Physics, 11C; S. Geltman et al., eds., Gordon and Breach, New York 1969).

15) J.H. Freed, J. Chem. Phys. 49 (1968) 376. Also: Electron Spin Relaxation in Liquids (Lectures NATO Advanced Study Institute, Norway; L.T. Muus and P.W. Atkins, eds., Plenum, New York 1972).

16) W.H. Louisell, Quantum Statistical Properties of Radiation (Wiley, New York 1973) ch. 6; F. Haake, in: Springer Tracts in Modern Physics 66 (Springer, Berlin 1973.

17) R. Zwanzig, in: Statistical Mechanics, New Concepts, New Problems, New Applications (Proceedings of the sixth IUPAP conference on statistical mechanics; S. Rice et al., eds., University of Chicago Press, Chicago 1972).

18) H. Cramer, Mathematical Methods of Statistics (Princeton University Press, Princeton 1946) p. 186.

19) E. Lukacs, Characteristic Functions (Charles Griffin, London 1960); see also: J. Hijmans, in these Proceedings.

20) N.G. van Kampen, Physica, 74 (1974) 215, 239; R.H. Terwiel, ibid. 248.

21) V.A. Lo Dato, in Probalistic Methods in Applied Methematics 3 (A.T. Barucha-Reid, ed., Academic Press, New York 1973); see also: the lectures of P. Mazur and of J. Dorfman in these Proceedings.

22) G.K. Batchelor, The Theory of Homogeneous Turbulence (Cambridge University Press, Cambridge 1953).

23) A. Nordsieck, W.E. Lamb, Jr., and G.E. Uhlenbeck, Physica 7 (1940) 344.

24) An alternative treatment is given by O.J. Heilmann and N.G. van Kampen, Physica, to be published.

25) N.G. van Kampen, in: Irreversibility in the Many-Body Problem (Sitges International School of Physics; J. Biel and J. Rae, eds., Plenum Press, New York 1972).

26) P.L. Sulem and U. Frisch, J. Plasma Phys. 8 (1972) 217.

27) C.P. Schlichter, Principles of Magnetic Resonance (Harper and Row, New York 1963) ch. 5.

28) R. Kubo, in: Stochastic Processes in Chemical Physics (K.E. Shuler, ed., Interscience, New York 1969).

KINETIC AND HYDRODYNAMIC THEORY OF TIME CORRELATION FUNCTIONS

J.R. Dorfman
Institute for Fluid Dynamics and Applied Mathematics
and Department of Physics and Astronomy,
University of Maryland, College Park, Maryland, U.S.A.

1. INTRODUCTION

It is well established experimentally that a wide variety of non-equilibrium phenomena in fluids can be described by the set of Navier-Stokes hydrodynamic equations[1,2]. These equations describe the space and time dependence of the local mass density $\rho(\vec{r},t)$, the local velocity $\vec{u}(\vec{r},t)$ and the local internal energy per unit mass $e(\vec{r},t)$ of the fluid at a point $\vec{r}$, and time t. To obtain these equations, one starts with the conservation laws for mass, momentum, and energy of the fluid,

$$\frac{\partial\rho(\vec{r},t)}{\partial t} + \frac{\partial}{\partial x_\alpha}(\rho(\vec{r},t)u_\alpha(\vec{r},t)) = 0 \tag{1.1}$$

$$\rho(\frac{\partial u_\alpha(\vec{r},t)}{\partial t} + u_\beta\frac{\partial}{\partial x_\beta}u_\alpha(\vec{r},t)) = -\frac{\partial P_{\alpha\beta}}{\partial x_\beta} \tag{1.2}$$

and

$$\rho(\frac{\partial e(\vec{r},t)}{\partial t} + u_\alpha\frac{\partial}{\partial x_\alpha}e(\vec{r},t)) = \frac{-\partial q_\alpha}{\partial x_\alpha} - P_{\alpha\beta}D_{\alpha\beta} \tag{1.3}$$

where we use the summation convention, with $x_\alpha = x, y, z$.
Here $D_{\alpha\beta}$ is the rate of strain tensor

$$D_{\alpha\beta} = \frac{1}{2}(\frac{\partial u_\alpha}{\partial x_\beta} + \frac{\partial u_\beta}{\partial x_\alpha}) \tag{1.4}$$

The tensor $\overleftrightarrow{P}$ is called the pressure tensor, and $\vec{q}$ is the heat flow vector. Although the conservation laws are exact, they only become useful if there is some relation connecting $\overleftrightarrow{P}$ and $\vec{q}$ to ρ, $\vec{u}$, and e.

If the gradients of the hydrodynamic variables are sufficiently small, one assumes that $\overleftrightarrow{P}$ and $\vec{q}$ may be expanded in powers of the gradients, and the form of the expansion is dictated by the macroscopic symmetry properties of the fluid. To zeroth order in the gradients,

$$P_{\alpha\beta} = p(\vec{r},t)\delta_{\alpha\beta} \tag{1.5a}$$

and

$$\vec{q} = 0 \tag{1.5b}$$

Fundamental Problems in Statistical Mechanics, Vol. 3, Editor, E.D.G. Cohen.

where $p(\vec{r},t)$ is the local hydrostatic pressure. The resulting hydrodynamic equations are called the Euler equations. To first order in the gradients

$$P_{\alpha\beta} = p(\vec{r},t)\,\delta_{\alpha\beta} - \sigma_{\alpha\beta} \tag{1.6a}$$

where

$$\sigma_{\alpha\beta} = 2\eta(D_{\alpha\beta} - \frac{1}{3} D_{ii}\delta_{\alpha\beta}) + \zeta D_{ii}\delta_{\alpha\beta} \tag{1.6b}$$

where η and ζ are called the coefficients of shear and bulk viscosity, respectively. Equation (1.6b) is called Newton's law of friction.

Similarly, the heat flow vector $\vec{q}$ is given to first order in the gradients by

$$\vec{q} = - \lambda \vec{\nabla} T(\vec{r},t) \tag{1.7}$$

where $T(\vec{r},t)$ is the local temperature and λ is called the coefficient of thermal conductivity. Equation (1.7) is called Fourier's law of heat conduction. Finally, one must connect $p(\vec{r},t)$ and $T(\vec{r},t)$ to $\rho(\vec{r},t)$ and to $e(\vec{r},t)$. This is done by assuming that ρ, T, p, and e are related by the equilibrium thermodynamic relations of the fluid. The hydrodynamic equations that result when (1.6a), (1.6b) and (1.7) are inserted in the conservation laws (1.1)-(1.3) are the Navier-Stokes hydrodynamic equations.

It should be noted that implicit in the hydrodynamic description, is the assumption that the fluid is close to thermodynamic equilibrium, since the description relies on <u>local</u> thermodynamic properties, $\rho(\vec{r},t)$, $p(\vec{r},t)$, $e(\vec{r},t)$ and $T(\vec{r},t)$ which are related by equilibrium thermodynamic relations.

We will have occasion in the course of these lectures to refer to the linearized Navier-Stokes equations. They are obtained from eq. (1.1)-(1.7) by writing $\rho = \rho_{eq} + \delta q$, $\vec{u} = \vec{u}_{eq} + \delta u$, $e = e_{eq} + \delta e$, $T = T_{eq} + \delta T$, and $p = p_{eq} + \delta p$, where ρ_{eq}, $\vec{u}_{eq}$, e_{eq}, T_{eq} and p_{eq} are the values of ρ, $\vec{u}$, e, T and p in total equilibrium, and retaining terms only of first order in the deviations from equilibrium[2).

In these lectures we will discuss the following questions:

I) Is it possible to derive the hydrodynamic equations, using the microscopic properties of the fluid particles, and the methods of statistical mechanics?

Such a derivation should specify the conditions of the fluid when the hydrodynamic equations provide a good description of its nonequilibrium behavior, and should specify how these equations must be modified to treat a wider class of conditions.

II) How do the transport coefficients associated with the hydrodynamic equations depend on the microscopic, and on the macroscopic properties of the fluid?

The macroscopic derivation of the hydrodynamic equation should provide expressions for the transport coefficients in terms of the properties of the fluid particles and the forces between them. From these expressions we should be able to infer the dependence of the transport coefficients on the density, temperature, and the other macroscopic properties of the fluid.

2. THE BOLTZMANN EQUATION

In the special case that the fluid is a dilute gas, a microscopic derivation of the hydrodynamic equations which answers both questions we have posed is based on the Boltzmann transport equation. Although this equation has been discussed in detail elsewhere[3], we will list here the principal features of the derivation of the hydrodynamic equations based on it, since this approach provides the motivation for the more general theory which we will discuss shortly.

We consider the quantity $f(\vec{r},\vec{v},t)$, the single particle distribution function for the gas, defined so that $f(\vec{r},\vec{v},t)d\vec{r}\,d\vec{v}$ is the number of particles with velocity in a region $d\vec{v}$ about $\vec{v}$ and with position in a region $d\vec{r}$ about the point $\vec{r}$, at time t. The Boltzmann equation describes the change of $f(\vec{r},\vec{v},t)$ with time and is given by

$$\frac{\partial f(\vec{r},\vec{v},t)}{\partial t} = -\vec{v}\cdot\vec{\nabla}_r f + \int d\vec{v}_1 \int bdbd\phi\,|\vec{v}_1-\vec{v}|\,[f(\vec{r},\vec{v}\,',t)f(\vec{r},\vec{v}_1',t) - f(\vec{r},\vec{v},t)f(\vec{r},\vec{v}_1,t)] \tag{2.1}$$

The first term on the right hand side gives the change in f due to the free streaming of molecules with velocity $\vec{v}$.

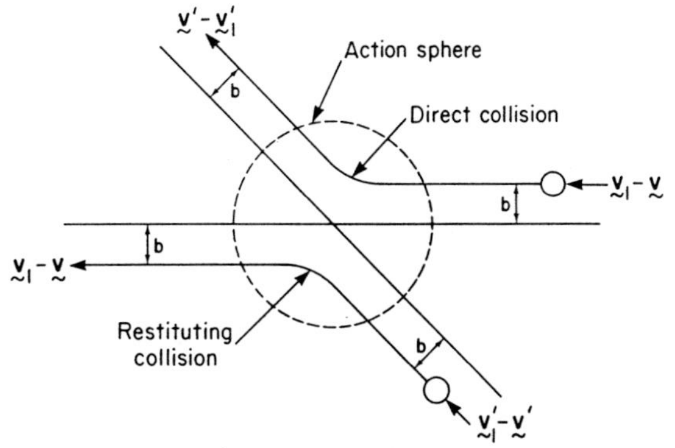

Fig. 1. The collision geometry for the binary collisions which decrease the number of particles with velocity $\vec{v}$ in the system, the <u>direct</u> collisions; and for the collisions which increase this number, the <u>restituting</u> collisions.

The integral expression on the right hand side of eq. (2.1) describes the change in f due to binary collisions. These are of two types:

(a) collisions between molecules with velocity $\vec{v}'$ and others with velocity $\vec{v}_1'$ taking place with impact parameter b, and azimuth ϕ, which <u>increase</u> the number of molecules with velocity $\vec{v}$, in the region $d\vec{r}$ about $\vec{r}$ and

(b) collisions between molecules with velocity $\vec{v}$ and others with velocity $\vec{v}_1$, with impact parameter b, and azimuth ϕ, which <u>decrease</u> the number of molecules with velocity $\vec{v}$ in the region $d\vec{r}$ about $\vec{r}$, (Fig. 1).

The hydrodynamic variables ρ, $\vec{u}$, and e can then be expressed as moments of $f(\vec{r},\vec{v},t)$, viz.

$$\rho(\vec{r},t) = m \int d\vec{v}\; f(\vec{r},\vec{v},t) \tag{2.2a}$$

$$\rho(\vec{r},t)\vec{u}(\vec{r},t) = m \int d\vec{v}\; \vec{v}\; f(\vec{r},\vec{v},t) \tag{2.2b}$$

$$\frac{1}{2}\rho u^2 + \rho e(\vec{r},t) = \frac{m}{2} \int d\vec{v}\; v^2\; f(\vec{r},\vec{v},t) \tag{2.2c}$$

The conservation laws, eqs. (1.1-1.3), together with expressions for $\vec{\vec{P}}$ and $\vec{q}$ in terms of moments of f can be obtained by multiplying eq. (2.1) by m, $m\vec{v}$, and $mv^2/2$ and then integrating over $\vec{v}$.

The Boltzmann equation provides the following picture of nonequilibrium phenomena taking place in dilute gases. Starting from some initial nonequilibrium state, the gas first evolves through a <u>kinetic</u> stage which lasts for a few mean free times between collosions; during this time the state of the gas cannot be described by the first five moments of f alone, but other moments must also be taken into account. After a time $t \gg t_o$, where t_o is the mean free time, the gas evolves to a <u>hydrodynamical</u> stage, where ρ, $\vec{u}$, and e do provide an adequate description of the gas. The contraction of the description of the state of the gas from all moments of f to the first five moments, over a few mean free times is connected to the fact that the first five moments do not vary much over a mean free time since they are conserved in the binary collisions, while the higher moments are not conserved and they rapidly approach their local equilibrium values. In the hydrodynamic stage one assumes that the whole time dependence of $f(\vec{r},\vec{v},t)$ is determined by ρ, $\vec{u}$, and e and that f may be expanded in powers of $\mu = \ell/L$, which is the ratio of the average mean free path of a molecule in the gas, ℓ, to L, the characteristic distance over which there is a change in the hydrodynamic variables, as

$$f(\vec{r},\vec{v},t) = f_o(\vec{r},\vec{v}|\rho,\vec{u},T) + \mu\; f_1(\vec{r},\vec{v}_1|\rho,\vec{u},T) + \ldots \tag{2.3}$$

where

$$f_o(\vec{r},\vec{v}|\rho,\vec{u},T) = n(\vec{r},t)\left(\frac{\beta(r,t)m}{2\pi}\right)^{3/2} e^{-\frac{\beta(\vec{r},t)m}{2}(\vec{v}-\vec{u}(\vec{r},t))^2} \quad (2.4)$$

where

$$n(\vec{r},t) = \rho(\vec{r},t)/m \quad (2.5a)$$

$$\beta(\vec{r},t) = (k_B\, T(\vec{r},t))^{-1} \quad (2.5b)$$

where m is the mass of a molecule and k_B is Boltzmann's constant. For small gradients, i.e. for small μ, equations (2.3) and (2.4) when inserted in the Boltzmann equation (2.1) and its associated conservation laws, lead to explicit expression for f_1, f_2, and so on. The quantity f_1 is obtained as the solution to the linearized Boltzmann equation. When the first two terms of eq. (2.3), $f_o + \mu f_1$, are inserted in the general expressions for the pressure tensor and for the heat flow vector, equations of the form given by (1.6a), (1.6b), and (1.7) are recovered, with $p(\vec{r},t) = k_B\, n(\vec{r},t)T(\vec{r},t)$, $\zeta = 0$ and with explicit expressions for η and λ in terms of the dynamics of two particles. If the method is continued to $O(\mu^2)$ the so-called Burnett level, one finds that the next corrections to the Navier-Stokes equation are of two types. There are linear corrections to (1.6) and (1.7) for the pressure tensor and heat flow vector which involve second order gradients of the hydrodynamic variables, the "linearized Burnett" terms, and nonlinear corrections which involve products of the first order gradients in the variables, the nonlinear Burnett terms. Most of the applications of this method to obtain corrections to the Navier-Stokes equation have been concerned with the linearized Burnett and higher order terms. So far no extensive study of the nonlinear corrections has been carried out.

The Boltzmann equation method for deriving hydrodynamic equations has been generalized in two directions. One generalization is to incorporate in the equations the effects of collisions taking place among three, four, and higher numbers of particles. In this way one can obtain expressions for transport coefficients in terms of density expansions, and this method has been discussed extensively elsewhere[4]. The other generalization is to base a derivation of hydrodynamic equations on the Liouville equation, and to incorporate in this derivation the central assumptions of the Boltzmann equation method, i.e.

a) In the approach of a system to equilibrium from some arbitrary initial non-equilibrium state, one can distinguish two characteristic relaxation times,

a. a microscopic relaxation time, t_{mic} and
b. a macroscopic relaxation time, t_{mac}.

For time $t \sim t_{mic}$, the system can only be described in terms of the molecular processes taking place in it. However for $t_{mic} << t < t_{mac}$, the system is in a hydrodynamical stage, where only the hydrodynamic variables n, $\vec{u}$ and e are needed to describe the system adequately.

This assumption implies that for the description of the behavior of the system over any time interval of order $\sim t_{mic}$, the macroscopic dynamics of the system must be taken into account, but that the hydrodynamic equations can be used for a description of the behavior over any time interval $>> t_{mic}$.

b) In the hydrodynamic stage the distribution function for the system may be expanded about the local equilibrium distribution in powers of the gradients of the hydrodynamic variables, if the gradients are sufficiently small.

The Liouville equation approach to the derivation of hydrodynamic equations has proven to be particularly succesful under the circumstances that the hydrodynamic variables differ only by a small amount from their values in total equilibrium. In this case one can use the Liouville equation to derive the linearized hydrodynamic equations. This approach to the linearized hydrodynamic equations is generally referred to as the time correlation function method, and it has its origin in the work of A. Einstein on Brownian motion[5)]. In its present form the general theory is due to M.S. Green, R. Kubo, H. Mori and R. Zwanzig[6)], and it leads to expressions for transport coefficients which apply to a wide variety of fluid systems[7)].

In order to provide some answers to the questions posed in the Introduction, we will discuss the time correlation method in some detail. We will be especially concerned with the derivation of the general expressions for the transport coefficients and with their evaluation for dilute and moderately dense gases. This evaluation will allow us to make a contact with the Boltzmann and generalized Boltzmann equation methods and we will present some of the remarkable new results in this field. We shall restrict our attention to the theory for linearized hydrodynamic equations since the derivation and properties of nonlinear hydrodynamic equations have not yet been studied very extensively.

3. THE SELF DIFFUSION COEFFICIENT

We shall begin our discussion of the time correlation function method with the analysis of a simple non-equilibrium process, the diffusion of a tagged particle through a gas of particles which are mechanically identical to the tagged one. Although this process cannot be realized in the laboratory, it can be studied on a computer, and Dr. Wood will discuss the computer treatment in considerable detail.

To obtain a macroscopic treatment of the diffusion process we proceed along similar lines to that given above for the Navier-Stokes equations. We define a quantity $P(\vec{r},t)$ which is the probability density for finding the particle at the point $\vec{r}$ at time t. Since the number of tagged particles is conserved, $P(\vec{r},t)$

satisfies a conservation law of the form

$$\frac{\partial P(\vec{r},t)}{\partial t} + \nabla \cdot \vec{J}(\vec{r},t) = 0 \qquad (3.1)$$

where $\vec{J}(\vec{r},t)$ is the probability current. In the hydrodynamic description $\vec{J}(\vec{r},t)$ is related to $P(\vec{r},t)$ by Fick's law of diffusion

$$\vec{J}(\vec{r},t) = - D \vec{\nabla} P(\vec{r},t) \qquad (3.2)$$

where the coefficient D is called the self diffusion coefficient. Combining (3.1) and (3.2) we obtain the diffusion equation

$$\frac{\partial P(\vec{r},t)}{\partial t} = D \nabla^2 P(\vec{r},t) \qquad (3.3)$$

if we assume that D does not depend on $\vec{r}$.

One result that follows from eq. (3.3) that is of interest to us is the following. Suppose the tagged particle is released at time t = 0 from the point $\vec{r} = \vec{r}_o$. The probability of finding the particle at the point $\vec{r}$, at time t later is given by the solution of eq. (3.3) with the initial condition that $P(\vec{r},t=0) = \delta(\vec{r}-\vec{r}_o)$, as

$$P(\vec{r},t) = (4\pi Dt)^{-d/2} \exp\{-(\vec{r}-\vec{r}_o)^2/4Dt\} \qquad (3.4a)$$

where we have considered the general case of diffusion in d-dimensions, for our later convenience. The mean square deviation of $\vec{r}$ from its initial value $\vec{r}_o$, $\langle(\Delta\vec{r})^2\rangle$ is given at time t by

$$\langle(\Delta\vec{r})^2\rangle = \int d\vec{r}(\vec{r}-\vec{r}_o)^2 P(\vec{r},t) = 2\, d\, D\, t \qquad (3.4b)$$

This result, which relates the mean square displacement of the tagged particles to the self diffusion coefficient, will be an ingredient in establishing the connection between the macroscopic and microscopic theories of self diffusion.

To develop a microscopic theory of self diffusion, we begin by considering a collection of N mechanically identical particles, each of mass m, contained in a volume V, and supposing that one of the particles is tagged in some non-mechanical way. We will for simplicity assume that the particles obey classical mechanics. The Hamiltonian of the system, H_N, is

$$H_N(x^N) = \sum_{i=1}^{N} \frac{p_i^2}{2m} + \sum_{i<j} \phi(r_{ij}) \qquad (3.5)$$

where $x^N = (x_1 \ldots x_N)$, $x_i = (\vec{r}_i, \vec{p}_i)$ is the phase of particle i where $\vec{r}_i$ and $\vec{p}_i$ are its position and momentum respectively. The potential energy is taken to be determined by a pairwise additive, central, and short ranged potential $\phi(r_{ij})$ where $r_{ij} = |\vec{r}_i - \vec{r}_j|$. The tagged particle will be taken to be particle 1. Finally, we will impose periodic boundary conditions on the system.

We will consider an ensemble of similar systems distributed on Γ-space according to the distribution function $\rho_N(x^N,t)$, which satisfies Liouville's equation

$$\frac{\partial \rho_N(x^N,t)}{\partial t} = - L_N \rho_N(x^N,t) \tag{3.6}$$

where the Liouville operator L_N is

$$L_N = \sum_{i=1}^{N} \frac{\vec{p}_i}{m} \cdot \frac{\partial}{\partial \vec{r}_i} - \sum_{i<j} \theta_{ij} \tag{3.7a}$$

$$\theta_{ij} = \frac{\partial \phi(r_{ij})}{\partial \vec{r}_i} \cdot \left(\frac{\partial}{\partial \vec{p}_i} - \frac{\partial}{\partial \vec{p}_j}\right) \tag{3.7b}$$

In addition, any dynamical variable $a(x_1,\ldots x_N)$ satisfies the equation of motion

$$\frac{da}{dt} = L_N a \ ,$$

or

$$a(x_1(t),\ldots x_N(t)) = e^{tL_N} a(x_1,\ldots x_N) \tag{3.8}$$

To set up a microscopic theory of self diffusion, we note that if the fluid were in total equilibrium, the probability of finding the tagged particle in a volume $d\vec{r}$ about the point $\vec{r}$ would be $d\vec{r}/V$ for a finite system. We therefore consider an initial situation of the fluid such that the probability distribution of the tagged particle is given by a function $W(\vec{r}_1) \neq 1/V$, and where the remainder of the fluid is in total equilibrium. This latter condition allows us to avoid having to consider any couplings between diffusion and heat flow or viscous flow, so that the only non-equilibrium process is the relaxation of the probability distribution of the tagged particle to its equilibrium value. The normalized N-particle distribution which satisfies the above conditions at t = 0 is given by

$$\rho_N(x^N,t=0) = \frac{V}{Z} e^{-\beta H_N} W(\vec{r}_1) \tag{3.9}$$

where $\beta = (k_B T)^{-1}$, T is the equilibrium temperature of the fluid and Z is given by

$$Z = \int dx_1 \ldots dx_N \, e^{-\beta H_N} \equiv \int d^N x \, e^{-\beta H_N}; \text{ and } \int d\vec{r} \, W(\vec{r}) = 1 \quad (3.10)$$

After a time t, the distribution function is given by eq. (3.6) as

$$\rho_N(x^N,t) = e^{-tL_N} \rho_N(x^N,0) = \frac{V}{Z} e^{-tL_N} e^{-\beta H_N} W(\vec{r}_1) \quad (3.11)$$

The probability of finding particle 1 at the point $\vec{r}$ at time t, averaged over the configuration of all other particles is,

$$P(\vec{r},t) = \int d^N x \, \delta(\vec{r}_1-\vec{r}) \, \rho_N(x^N,t)$$

$$= \frac{V}{Z} \int d^N x \, \delta(\vec{r}_1-\vec{r}) e^{-tL_N} e^{-\beta H_N} W(\vec{r}_1) \quad (3.12)$$

This expression may be transformed, with the aid of Liouville's theorem, to

$$P(\vec{r},t) = \frac{V}{Z} \int d^N x \, e^{-\beta H_N} W(\vec{r}_1) \, \delta(\vec{r}_1(t) - \vec{r}) \quad (3.13)$$

where $\delta(\vec{r}_1(t) - \vec{r}) = e^{tL_N} \delta(\vec{r}_1-\vec{r})$. It will be convenient for the further analysis of $P(\vec{r},t)$ to insert the Fourier development of $\delta(\vec{r}_1(t)-\vec{r})$ into (3.13) and to write $P(\vec{r},t)$ (as in d-dimensions) as

$$P(\vec{r},t) = \frac{1}{V} \sum_{\{\vec{k}\}} e^{-i\vec{k}\cdot\vec{r}} P_{\vec{k}}(t) \quad (3.14)$$

where

$$P_{\vec{k}}(t) = \frac{V}{Z} \int d^N x \, e^{-\beta H_N} W(\vec{r}_1) \, e^{i\vec{k}\cdot\vec{r}_1(t)} \quad (3.15)$$

This expression can be further simplified if we use the fact that $\vec{r}_1(t)-\vec{r}_1$, and H_N depend only on the relative distances $\vec{r}_{ij}$. Then, for a periodic system,

$$P_{\vec{k}}(t) = \frac{V}{Z} \int d^N x \, e^{i\vec{k}\cdot\vec{r}_1} W(\vec{r}_1) \, e^{-\beta H_N} e^{i\vec{k}\cdot(\vec{r}_1(t)-\vec{r}_1)}$$

$$= W_{\vec{k}} \, F(\vec{k},t) \quad (3.16)$$

where $W_{\vec{k}}$ is the Fourier transform of $W(\vec{r}_1)$

$$W_{\vec{k}} = \int d\vec{r}_1 \, e^{i\vec{k}\cdot\vec{r}_1} W(\vec{r}_1) \quad (3.17)$$

$F(\vec{k},t)$ is given by

$$F(\vec{k},t) = \frac{1}{Z} \int d^N x \, e^{-\beta H_N} e^{i\vec{k}\cdot\Delta\vec{r}_1(t)} \equiv \langle e^{i\vec{k}\cdot\Delta\vec{r}_1(t)} \rangle \qquad (3.18)$$

where the angular brackets denote an average over a canonical ensemble, and $\Delta\vec{r}_1(t) = \vec{r}_1(t)-\vec{r}_1(t=0) = \vec{r}_1(t)-\vec{r}_1$. The function $F(\vec{k},t)$ also occurs in the theory of neutron scattering where it is referred to as the intermediate scattering function[8).

The principal advantage of introducing $F(\vec{k},t)$ is that it allows us to introduce the moments of the deviations of the tagged particle from its initial position[9). Of particular interest, of course, is the second moment, since in the macroscopic theory the second moment is related to the self diffusion coefficient. $F(\vec{k},t)$ can be expressed in terms of cumulants of $\Delta\vec{r}_1(t)$ by expanding the exponential in powers of $\vec{k}$, noting that the odd powers of $\vec{k}$ vanish due to the spatial isotropy of the equilibrium average, and re-expressing the final result as an exponential. That is

$$F(\vec{k},t) = 1 - \frac{k^2}{2!} \langle(\hat{\vec{k}}\cdot\Delta\vec{r}_1(t))^2\rangle + \frac{k^4}{4!} \langle(\hat{\vec{k}}\cdot\Delta\vec{r}_1(t))^4\rangle + .. \qquad (3.19)$$

where $\hat{\vec{k}}$ is a unit vector in the direction of $\vec{k}$, and $k = |\vec{k}|$. Then

$$F(\vec{k},t) = \exp \{\frac{-k^2}{2} \langle(\hat{\vec{k}}\cdot\Delta\vec{r}_1(t))^2\rangle +$$

$$+ \frac{k^4}{4!} [\langle(\hat{\vec{k}}\cdot\Delta\vec{r}_1(t))^4\rangle - 3 \langle(\hat{\vec{k}}\cdot\Delta\vec{r}_1(t))^2\rangle^2] + \ldots\} \qquad (3.20)$$

We can combine equations (3.14),(3.15), (3.16) and (3.20) to obtain an equation for $P(\vec{r},t)$

$$\frac{\partial P(r,t)}{\partial t} = \frac{1}{V} \sum_{\{\vec{k}\}} e^{-i\vec{k}\cdot\vec{r}} W_{\vec{k}} \frac{\partial F(\vec{k},t)}{\partial t} =$$

$$= \frac{1}{V} \sum_{\{\vec{k}\}} e^{-i\vec{k}\cdot\vec{r}} W_k \{- k^2 \langle(\hat{\vec{k}}\cdot\vec{v}_1(t)(\hat{\vec{k}}\cdot\Delta\vec{r}_1(t))\rangle$$

$$+ \frac{k^4}{3!} [\langle(\hat{\vec{k}}\cdot\vec{v}_1(t)(\hat{\vec{k}}\cdot\Delta\vec{r}_1(t))^3\rangle - 3\langle(\hat{k}\cdot\Delta r_1(t))^2\rangle\langle(\hat{\vec{k}}\cdot v_1(t))(\hat{\vec{k}}\cdot\Delta\vec{r}_1(t))\rangle]$$

$$+ \ldots\} F(\vec{k},t) \qquad (3.21)$$

The quantities $\langle(\hat{\vec{k}}\cdot\vec{v}_1(t))(\hat{\vec{k}}\cdot\Delta\vec{r}_1(t))\rangle$, and

$$[\langle(\hat{\vec{k}}\cdot\vec{v}_1(t))(\hat{\vec{k}}\cdot\Delta\vec{r}_1(t))^3\rangle - 3\langle(\hat{\vec{k}}\cdot\vec{v}_1(t))(\hat{\vec{k}}\cdot\Delta\vec{r}_1(t))\rangle\langle(\hat{\vec{k}}\cdot r_1(t))^2\rangle]$$

do not depend on the special direction of $\vec{k}$, and we may replace them by the values taken with respect to some fixed direction, the x-direction, say. Then the equation for $P(\vec{r},t)$ becomes

$$\frac{\partial P(\vec{r},t)}{\partial t} = D^{(o)}(t)\nabla^2 P(\vec{r},t) + D^{(2)}(t)\nabla^2\nabla^2 P(\vec{r},t) + \dots \quad (3.22)$$

where

$$D^{(o)}(t) = \langle v_{1x}(t)\Delta r_{1x}(t)\rangle = \int_o^t d\tau \, \langle v_{1x}(t)v_{1x}(\tau)\rangle$$

$$= \int_o^t d\tau \, \langle v_{1x}(\tau)v_{1x}(o)\rangle \quad (3.23a)$$

$$D^{(2)}(t) = \frac{1}{3!}\,[\langle v_{1x}(t)(\Delta r_{1x}(t))^3\rangle - 3\,D_o(t)\langle(\Delta r_{1x}(t))^2\rangle]$$

$$= \int_o^t dt_1 \int_{t_1}^t dt_2 \int_{t_2}^t dt_3 \, [\langle v_{1x}(o)v_{1x}(t_1)v_{1x}(t_2)v_{1x}(t_3)\rangle -$$

$$- \langle v_{1x}(o)v_{1x}(t_1)\rangle\langle v_{1x}(t_2)v_{1x}(t_3)\rangle$$

$$- \langle v_{1x}(o)v_{1x}(t_2)\rangle\langle v_{1x}(t_1)v_{1x}(t_3)\rangle$$

$$- \langle v_{1x}(o)v_{1x}(t_3)\rangle\langle v_{1x}(t_1)v_{1x}(t_2)\rangle] \quad (3.23b)$$

Equilibrium correlation functions of the form $\langle a_1(t_1)a_2(t_2)\dots a_n(t_n)\rangle$ are called <u>time correlation functions</u>, and we have expressed $D^{(o)}(t)$ in terms of the velocity auto correlation function $\langle v_{1x}(o)v_{1x}(\tau)\rangle$ for the tagged particle. In deriving the third equality in (3.23a) and the second in (3.23b), we have used the fact that we may express time correlation function of the form $\langle a_1(t_1)a_2(t_2)\rangle$ as

$$\langle a_1(o)a_2(t_2-t_1)\rangle \quad \text{or as} \quad \langle a_1(t_1-t_2)a_2(o)\rangle \;.$$

Although equation (3.22) looks very much like the macroscopic diffusion equation (3.3), it differs from it in three important respects.

a) The transport coefficients appearing in the macroscopic equation do not depend upon the time, while those appearing in eq. (3.22) have an explicit time dependence, and vanish as $t \to 0$.

b) The microscopic theory leads to an equation of the Navier-Stokes form, plus additional corrections of the form $\nabla^4 P$, $\nabla^6 P$, and so on. Similar higher order corrections also appear in the macroscopic theory if one generalizes Fick's law, eq.

(3.2) to

$$\vec{J} = - D^{(o)} \vec{\nabla}P - D^{(2)} \vec{\nabla}(\nabla^2 P) - \ldots \tag{3.24}$$

but, again the macroscopic theory requires $D^{(2)}$,... as well as $D^{(o)}$ to be independent of time. The quantity $D^{(2)}$ is called the super-Burnett self diffusion coefficient, and we now denote the Navier-Stokes self diffusion coefficient by $D^{(o)}$ instead of D as in (3.3).

c) Equation (3.22) is an exact consequence of the microscopic analysis. We have only used Liouville's theorem, an assumption about the initial state, and the assumption that the manipulations used in deriving expression (3.20) for $F(\vec{k},t)$ are legitimate. However, as we mentioned in the previous section, we should expect to recover the macroscopic hydrodynamic equations from a microscopic theory only after a time long compared to the characteristic microscopic time, t_{mic}, has elapsed after the initial instant. Therefore if we can prove that $D^{(o)}(t)$, $D^{(2)}(t)$, ... reach constant values for $t >> t_{mic}$, we will have derived the Navier-Stokes equation for diffusion of a tagged particle, as well as the higher order linear corrections to it.

As a result of these considerations, we should identify the macroscopic coefficient of self diffusion with the following microscopic expression

$$D^{(o)} = \lim_{t>>t_{mic}} \lim_{\substack{N,V\to\infty \\ N/V=n}} \int_o^t d\tau \, \langle v_{1x}(o) v_{1x}(\tau) \rangle \tag{3.25}$$

Here we have taken the thermodynamic limit $N,V \to \infty$, $N/V = n$ constant since for a large enough system, $D^{(o)}$ should not depend on the boundary conditions imposed on the system. Moreover t is a time which should be long compared to a microscopic relaxation time but short compared to the hydrodynamic relaxation time which characterizes the relaxation of the distribution $P(\vec{r},t)$ to its total equilibrium value. If we can show that $\langle v_{1x}(o) v_{1x}(\tau) \rangle$ approaches zero sufficiently rapidly for $\tau >> t_{mic}$ then $D^{(o)}$ should not depend on what value of t we have chosen and eq. (3.25) may be written as

$$D^{(o)} = \lim_{t\to\infty} \lim_{\substack{N,V\to\infty \\ N/V=n}} \int_o^t d\tau \, \langle v_{1x}(o) v_{1x}(\tau) \rangle \tag{3.26}$$

with similar expressions for the super-Burnett and higher order self diffusion coefficients. This expression for the self diffusion coefficient also provides a macroscopic justification for the relation, eq. (3.4b), between the mean square deviation of the tagged particle and the self diffusion coefficient. If we write the mean square deviation of the tagged particle, in the canonical ensemble, as

$$<(\Delta\vec{r}_1(t))^2> = \int_0^t dt_1 \int_0^t dt_2 <\vec{v}_1(t_1)\cdot\vec{v}_1(t_2)> \qquad (3.27)$$

and we assume that the thermodynamic limit has been taken in eq. (3.27), and differentiate with respect to time, we obtain

$$\frac{d}{dt} <(\Delta\vec{r}_1(t))^2> = 2d \int_0^t dt_1 <v_{1x}(o)v_{1x}(t)> \qquad (3.28)$$

Now for $t >> t_{mic}$ the right hand side should reach the constant value $2d\, D^{(o)}$, and we obtain

$$\frac{d}{dt} <(\Delta r_1(t))^2> = 2d\, D^{(o)} \quad \text{for} \quad t >> t_{mic} \qquad (3.29)$$

Expression (3.26) for the self diffusion coefficient has been derived without having to specify the precise nature of the fluid. Therefore, eq. (3.26) could be used to compute the coefficient of self diffusion for a wide variety of simple monoatomic fluids. In sections 5, et seq. we will consider the evaluation of this expression for $D^{(o)}$ in the case that the fluid is a moderately dense gas. Before turning our attention to that problem, however, we briefly discuss the time correlation function treatment of more general transport processes in fluid systems.

4. VISCOSITY AND THERMAL CONDUCTION

It is possible to develop a microscopic derivation of the linearized Navier-Stokes equations for more general transport processes in fluids along lines similar to those described in the last section[6)]. The essential assumptions of the derivation are similar to those for the theory of self diffusion, viz.

1.) The system starts from an initial state - which for the derivation of the linearized equations is taken to be close to a state of total equilibrium. This assumption incorporates the main idea of the hydrodynamical stage familiar from the theory of the Boltzmann equation. That is, one assumes that if the system starts at some arbitrary non-equilibrium state, it evolves to a stage which is close to local equilibrium. To obtain the linearized equations, one assumes that the system evolves to a state close to total equilibrium, and this state then forms the initial state for the application of the time correlation function method.

With this initial state, the Liouville equation is used to derive equations for ρ, $\vec{u}$, and e, which are similar in structure to the macroscopic hydrodynamic equations, but the transport coefficients are functions of time, and can be expressed as time integrals of time correlation functions. If then we assume that

2.) The time correlation functions approach zero for times greater than a characteristic microscopic relaxation time, but less than a characteristic macroscopic time, then the time integrals of the correlation functions approach constant values and can be identified with the transport coefficients.

In this way one finds expressions for the shear viscosity η, and the thermal conductivity λ

$$\eta = \lim_{t\to\infty} \lim_{\substack{N,V\to\infty \\ N/V=n}} \frac{\beta}{V} \int_o^t d\tau \, \langle J_\eta(o) J_\eta(\tau) \rangle \tag{4.1}$$

$$\lambda = \lim_{t\to\infty} \lim_{\substack{N,V\to\infty \\ N/V=n}} \frac{k_B\beta^2}{V} \int_o^t d\tau \, \langle J_\eta(o) J_\eta(\tau) \rangle \tag{4.2}$$

where the viscosity current, J_η, is

$$J_\eta = \sum_{i=1}^{N} \frac{p_{ix}p_{ij}}{m} - \frac{1}{2} \sum_{i=1}^{N} \sum_{j\neq i}^{N} \frac{\partial \phi(r_{ij})}{\partial r_{ij,x}} r_{ij,y} \tag{4.3}$$

and the thermal conductivity current J_λ is

$$J_\lambda = \sum_{i=1}^{N} \frac{p_{ix}}{m} \left(\frac{p_i^2}{2m} - h\right) + \frac{1}{2} \sum_{i=1}^{N} \sum_{j\neq i}^{N} \left(\frac{p_{ix}}{m} \phi(r_{ij}) - \frac{\vec{p}_i}{m} \cdot \frac{\partial \phi(r_{ij})}{\partial \vec{r}_i} r_{ij,x}\right) \tag{4.4}$$

Here h is the equilibrium enthalpy density, and $J(t) = e^{tL_N}J$. A similar expression can be given for the bulk viscosity, but we will not discuss this transport coefficient in any detail.

This completes our discussion of the formal derivation of the linearized hydrodynamic equations. We shall consider the computation of the time correlation functions appropriate for $D^{(o)}$, η, and λ, for moderately dense gases. The purpose of such calculations is to learn if these correlation functions decay sufficiently rapidly in time for the derivations to be valid, and if so, to study the dependence of the transport coefficients on the macroscopic properties of the gas.

5. THE TIME CORRELATION FUNCTIONS, GENERAL REMARKS

One of the main features of the time correlation function method is that it provides a general framework which enables us to make detailed comparisons between theoretical results, the results of computer simulated molecular dynamics, and experimental results. Although Dr. Wood will discuss the results of computer studies of the time correlation functions in detail, I will describe here the main features of these results in order to provide a background for the theory.

Of all the time correlation functions, the velocity auto-correlation function has been studied most extensively. Of particular interest to us, is the work of Alder, Wainwright, and co-workers[10)], and of Wood and Erpenbeck[11)] on the velocity auto-correlation function for systems of hard spheres or hard disks. These results have the most direct bearing on the long time behavior of this function, which is of crucial interest for the theory.

Figure 2 shows a rough sketch of the computer results for the dimensionless velocity autocorrelation function $\rho_D(t)$,

$$\rho_D(t) = \frac{\langle v_{1x}(o)v_{1x}(t)\rangle}{\langle v_{1x}^2(o)\rangle} = \beta m \langle v_{1x}(o)v_{1x}(t)\rangle \tag{5.1}$$

for hard disks or hard spheres.

For time t less than a few t_o, where t_o is the mean free time between collisions, $\rho_D(t)$ decays exponentially. After several t_o, the decay of $\rho_D(t)$ is no longer exponential. If the density is not too high ($V/V_o \geq 1.8$ where V_o is the volume at close packing) $\rho_D(t)$ remains positive over the time intervals studied on the computer, $0 \leq t \leq 50\ t_o$, and appears to decay to zero as an inverse power of t. In two dimensions $\rho_D(t)$ decays as t^{-1} for $t > 10\ t_o$, and in three dimensions, the data is consistent with a decay $\rho_D(t) \sim t^{-3/2}$ for $t > 25\ t_o$. For very high densities $\rho_D(t)$ becomes negative for $t > 5\ t_o$ and there is some evidence that for longer times, $t > 30\ t_o$, $\rho_D(t)$ may become positive again and decay to zero through positive values. In any event, the $t^{-d/2}$ decay observed in the computer calculations, first by Alder and Wainwright and later by Wood and Erpenbeck, has serious implications for the derivation of hydrodynamic equations, which we will discuss in some detail later.

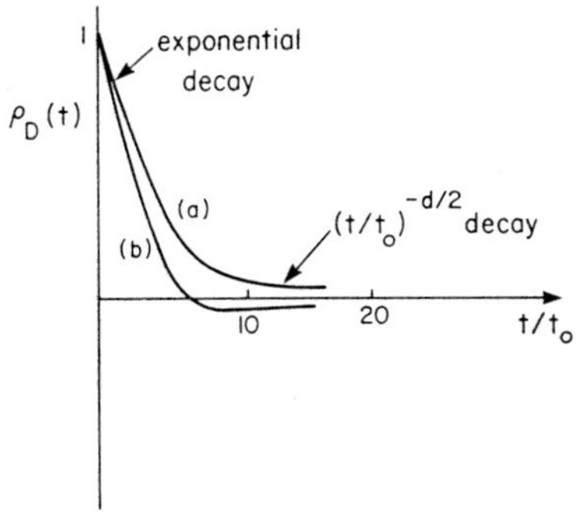

Fig. 2. A rough sketch of the main features of the computer results for the normalized velocity autocorrelation function $\rho_D^{(d)}(t)$ as a function of time for hard disk or hard sphere systems. Curve (a) shows the main features for systems at low densities; curve (b), at high densities. Here t_o is the mean free time between collisions.

Two types of theories have been employed to explain the observed behavior of $\rho_D(t)$ in time; (a) kinetic theory - which determines the properties of time correlation functions from a study of the motion of the particle in the fluid; and (b) hydrodynamic and "semi"-hydrodynamic theories where at some point, hydrodynamic arguments are used to effect the calculations of the time correlation functions.

The kinetic theory is, in principle, capable of determining the time dependence of the correlation functions over all time intervals, and for all densities of the gas. So far, however, only the short and the long time behavior have been studied in detail[12,13,14,15,16]. The intermediate region in time, say for $5\, t_o \leq t \leq 25\text{-}30\, t_o$, has not been studied very thoroughly, and the dynamical events which are responsible for the negative part of $\rho_D(t)$ at high densities have not yet been identified.

As we shall show presently, the application of kinetic theory to the calculation of $\rho_D(t)$ for hard spheres or disks, leads to the conclusions that (a) this function should decay exponentially (or more correctly, as a sum of exponentials) over a few mean free times, and that (b) $\rho_D(t) \sim (t/t_o)^{d/2}$ for the long times appropriate for comparison with the computer experiments. We will also show here that similar results hold for hard sphere or hard disk systems for the time correlation functions for the kinetic parts of the viscosity and thermal conductivity correlation functions - which will be defined in the next section.

The hydrodynamic theories which have been employed to compute $\rho_D^{(d)}(t)$ and the other time correlation functions are of two types:

(i) A pure hydrodynamic theory, due to Zwanzig and Bixon[17], where a molecule moving through a fluid of similar molecules in three dimensions is treated as though it were a sphere moving through a continuous fluid and the hydrodynamic equations are used to describe its motions. Zwanzig and Bixon computed $\rho_D(t)$ over the entire range of times. Of particular interest is the fact that by assuming the fluid has viscoelastic properties, Zwanzig and Bixon obtained a negative region for $\rho_D(t)$. In addition, those authors also obtained the result that $\rho_D(t) \sim \alpha t^{-3/2}$ for long times, with a positive coefficient α.

(ii) A semi-hydrodynamic theory, where molecular theory is followed to a certain point and then hydrodynamic concepts are applied[18,19,20]. This method can only treat the long time behavior of the time correlation functions and also leads to the $t^{-d/2}$ behavior. We will discuss the method of Ernst, Hauge, and Van Leeuwen[18] as it applies to $\rho_D(t)$, in detail in section 9.

The calculations of the time correlation functions based on the mode coupling theory[19,21,22] or on the methods of bilinear hydrodynamics[23,24] may also be classified as semi-hydrodynamic theories. We will not have an opportunity to discuss these methods in these lectures, but instead refer the reader to the literature for the details.

There is, in the hydrodynamic treatments of the time correlation functions, a problem of consistency. That is, can hydrodynamic equations be employed to compute the transport coefficients which themselves appear in the hydrodynamic equations? In section 10, we shall discuss this question as it applies to the semi-hydrodynamic theory discussed in section 9.

6. KINETIC THEORY AND THE TIME CORRELATION FUNCTIONS, THE SHORT TIME BEHAVIOR

We consider now the calculation of time correlation functions appropriate to the coefficients of self diffusion, shear viscosity and thermal conductivity for a system of hard spheres or hard disks. This specialization is made in order to compare the theoretical results with the computer results of Alder and Wainwright and of Wood and Erpenbeck for such systems. For simplicity we will restrict our attention to the kinetic parts of the shear viscosity and thermal conductivity time correlation functions, obtained by neglecting the potential energy contribution to the currents J_η and J_λ, and to the enthalpy density h. Therefore we shall consider the dimensionless quantities $\rho_\eta^{(d)}$ and $\rho_\lambda^{(d)}$ defined in d- dimensions by

$$\rho_\eta^{(d)}(t) = \frac{\langle J_\eta^k(o) J_\eta^k(t)\rangle}{\langle (J_\eta^k(o))^2\rangle} = \frac{\langle J_\eta^k(o) J_\eta^k(-t)\rangle}{\langle (J_\eta^k(o))^2\rangle} \tag{6.1}$$

and

$$\rho_\lambda^{(d)}(t) = \frac{\langle J_\lambda^k(o) J_\lambda^k(t)\rangle}{\langle (J_\lambda^k(o))^2\rangle} = \frac{\langle J_\lambda^k(o) J_\lambda^k(-t)\rangle}{\langle (J_\lambda^k(o))^2\rangle} \tag{6.2}$$

where, from eq. (4.3) and (4.4), the kinetic parts of the currents are given by

$$J_\eta^k = \sum_{i=1}^{N} \frac{p_{ix} p_{iy}}{m} \tag{6.3a}$$

and

$$J_\lambda^k = \sum_{i=1}^{N} \frac{p_{ix}}{m} \left(\frac{p_i^2}{2m} - \frac{d+2}{2\beta}\right) \tag{6.3b}$$

In addition we consider $\rho_D^{(d)}$ given by

$$\rho_D^{(d)}(t) = \beta m \langle v_{1x}(o) v_{1x}(t)\rangle = \beta m \langle v_{1x}(o) v_{1x}(-t)\rangle \tag{6.4}$$

In the second equality in (6.1), (6.2), and (6.4) we have used the fact that the equilibrium averages obey $\langle a(o)b(t)\rangle = \langle a(-t)b(o)\rangle$, since the origin of the time is immaterial for the equilibrium averages.

For hard core potentials, a difficulty arises if one tries to compute $J^k(\pm t)$ as $e^{\pm tL_N} J^k$ from eq. (3.7) and (3.8), since the operator θ_{ij} does not exist for such potentials. Ernst et al.[25)] showed that this difficulty can be overcome, provided one considers the operator $e^{\pm tL_N}$ in combination with the potential energy part of the canonical distribution function $W(\vec{r}_1,\ldots\vec{r}_N) = \exp-\beta \sum_{i<j} \phi(r_{ij})$.
For hard disks or spheres

$$\phi(r_{ij}) = \begin{cases} \infty & r_{ij} < \sigma \\ 0 & r_{ij} > \sigma \end{cases} \tag{6.5}$$

where σ is the diameter of the disks or spheres. Consequently, $W(\vec{r}_1,..\vec{r}_N)$ vanishes whenever $r_{i,j} < \sigma$ for at least one pair of particles (i,j) and is unity otherwise. Here we will consistently use the operator e^{-tL_N} in the combination $e^{-tL_N} W(r_1..r_N)$ and a representation of the operator L_N in this combination is denoted by $\overline{L}_N$ where

$$\overline{L}_N = L_N^o - \sum_{i<j} \overline{T}(i,j) \tag{6.6}$$

where

$$L_N^o = \sum_{i=1}^{N} \frac{\vec{p}_i}{m} \cdot \frac{\partial}{\partial \vec{r}_i} \tag{6.7}$$

The operator $\overline{T}(i,j)$ is called a binary collision operator and is given by

$$\overline{T}(i,j) = \sigma^{d-1} \int_{\vec{v}_{ij}\cdot\hat{\vec{\sigma}}>o} d\hat{\vec{\sigma}} |\vec{v}_{ij}\cdot\hat{\vec{\sigma}}| [\delta(\vec{r}_{ij}-\vec{\sigma}) b_\sigma - \delta(\vec{r}_{ij}+\vec{\sigma})] \tag{6.8}$$

Here $\vec{\sigma} = \sigma\hat{\vec{\sigma}}$, $\vec{v}_{ij} = \vec{v}_i - \vec{v}_j$, and the operator b_σ changes the velocities $\vec{v}_i$ and $\vec{v}_j$ to those before the (i,j) collision, $\vec{v}_i'$, $\vec{v}_j'$ according to the formula

$$b_\sigma f(\vec{v}_1,..,\vec{v}_i,..\vec{v}_j,..\vec{v}_N,\vec{r}_1,..\vec{r}_N) =$$

$$= f(\vec{v}_1,..\vec{v}_i',..\vec{v}_j',..\vec{v}_N,\vec{r}_1,..\vec{r}_N) \tag{6.9}$$

where

$$\vec{v}_i' = \vec{v}_i - (\vec{v}_{ij}\cdot\hat{\vec{\sigma}})\hat{\vec{\sigma}} \tag{6.10a}$$

$$\vec{v}_j' = \vec{v}_j + (\vec{v}_{ij}\cdot\hat{\vec{\sigma}})\hat{\vec{\sigma}} \tag{6.10b}$$

as illustrated in Figure 3. The δ-functions in eq. (6.8) are to be evaluated at $\vec{r}_{ij} = \pm\vec{\sigma}^{(+)}$ with $|\vec{\sigma}^{(+)}| = \lim_{\varepsilon\to o} (\sigma+\varepsilon)$.

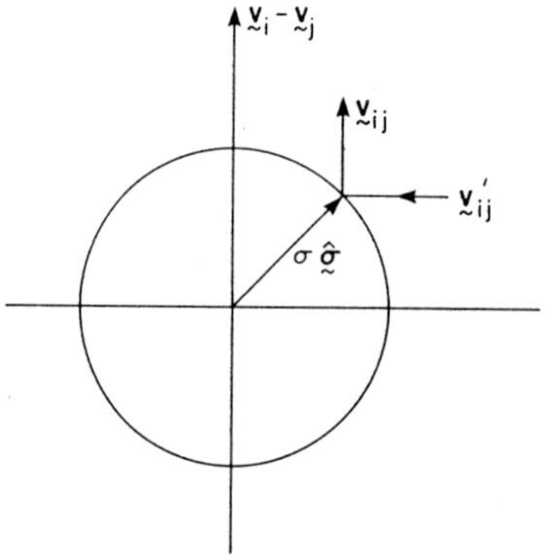

Fig. 3. A collision between two hard disks or spheres, as seen in the relative coordinate system, fixed on particle j. The relative velocity before collision is $\vec{v}_{ij}'$, and after collision, $\vec{v}_{ij}$. The location of the center of particle i at the instant of the collision is given by the vector $\vec{\sigma} = \sigma\hat{\vec{\sigma}}$, where σ is the particle's diameter.

Using the definition of the angular brackets as an average over a canonical distribution, and eqs. (6.1), (6.2), (6.4), and (6.7), we can write the time correlation functions $\rho_\eta^{(d)}(t)$ and $\rho_\lambda^{(d)}(t)$ in the canonical ensemble as

$$\rho_\mu^{(d)}(t) = \lim_{\substack{N,V\to\infty \\ N/V=n}} \langle j_\mu^2(\vec{v}_1)\rangle^{-1} Z^{-1} \int d^N x\, j_\mu(\vec{v}_1) e^{-t\bar{L}_N} e^{-\beta H_N} \sum_{i=1}^{N} j_\mu(\vec{v}_i) \tag{6.11}$$

where for $\mu = \eta$, $j_\eta(\vec{v}_1) = v_{ix}v_{iy}$, and for $\mu = \lambda$,

$$j_\lambda(\vec{v}_i) = v_{ix}\left(\frac{\beta m v_i^2}{2} - \frac{d+2}{2}\right).$$

$\rho_D^{(d)}(t)$ is

$$\rho_D^{(d)}(t) = \lim_{\substack{N,V\to\infty \\ N/V=n}} \beta m\, Z^{-1} \int d^N x\, v_{1x}\, e^{-t\bar{L}_N} e^{-\beta H_N} v_{1x} \tag{6.12}$$

An immediate consequence of eq. (6.11) and (6.12) which is useful for comparing with the computer results is the initial slope of the correlation functions $\dot{\rho}^{(d)}(o)$, defined as

$$\dot{\rho}^{(d)}(o) = \lim_{t\to 0} \frac{\partial \rho^{(d)}(t)}{\partial t} \tag{6.13}$$

For a non-hard core potential, one can use the expression for L_N given by eq. (3.7) to show that the initial slope is zero. However, for hard core potentials $\dot{\rho}^{(d)}(o)$ is not zero, a result of the fact that the particles suffer instanteneous collisions. If we carry out the differentiation with respect to t, and use the facts that there are periodic boundary conditions, that

$$\int d\vec{v}_i\, j_\mu(\vec{v}_i)\, \varphi_o(\vec{v}_i) = 0 \tag{6.14}$$

where $j_\mu(\vec{v}_i)$ is defined below eq. (6.11) and φ_o is the Maxwell-Boltzmann velocity distribution function

$$\varphi_o(\vec{v}_i) = \left(\frac{\beta m}{2\pi}\right)^{d/2} e^{-\beta\frac{m}{2} v_i^2} \tag{6.15}$$

and that

$$\int d\vec{v}_i \int d\vec{v}_j\, \bar{T}(i,j)\, f(x_i x_j) = 0 \tag{6.16}$$

which follows from eq. (6.8), we obtain

$$\dot{\rho}_\mu^{(d)}(o) = \langle j_\mu^2(\vec{v}_1)\rangle^{-1} \, n\int d\vec{v}_1 \int d\vec{v}_2 \int d\vec{r}_2 \; j_\mu(\vec{v}_1)\overline{T}(1,2)$$
$$\cdot\, g(\vec{r}_1,\vec{r}_2)\varphi_o(\vec{v}_1)\varphi_o(\vec{v}_2)(j_\mu(\vec{v}_1) + j_\mu(\vec{v}_2)), \text{ for } \mu = \eta,\lambda \tag{6.17}$$

and

$$\dot{\rho}_D^{(d)}(o) = \beta mn \int d\vec{v}_1 \int d\vec{v}_2 \int d\vec{r}_2 \; v_{1x}\overline{T}(1,2) g(\vec{r}_1,\vec{r}_2)\varphi_o(\vec{v}_1)\varphi_o(\vec{v}_2) v_{1x} \tag{6.18}$$

where $g(r_1,r_2)$ is the equilibrium pair distribution function[26)]

$$g(\vec{r}_1,\vec{r}_2) = \lim_{\substack{N,V\to\infty \\ N/V=n}} \frac{V^2}{Q} \int d\vec{r}_3 \ldots \; d\vec{r}_N \; W(r_1,\ldots r_N) \; ,$$
$$Q = \int d\vec{r}_1 \ldots \; d\vec{r}_N \; W(r_1,\ldots r_N) \; . \tag{6.19}$$

Expressions (6.17) and (6.18) can be expressed in terms of more familiar objects if we notice that the δ functions in $\overline{T}(1,2)$ require that $g(\vec{r}_1,\vec{r}_2)$ be evaluated at $r_{ij} = \sigma^{(+)}$ and $g(\sigma^{(+)}) = \chi(\sigma)$ is the pair distribution function at the point of contact. Moreover, the $\vec{v}_2$ integration in (6.17) and (6.18) can be carried out and this leads to

$$\dot{\rho}_\mu^{(d)}(o) = \langle j_\mu^2\rangle^{-1} \; n\,\chi(\sigma) \int d\vec{v}_1 \; j_\mu(\vec{v}_1)\lambda(\vec{v}_1) j_\mu(\vec{v}_1)\varphi_o(\vec{v}_1) \tag{6.20}$$

for $\mu = \eta,\lambda$ and

$$\dot{\rho}_D^{(d)}(o) = \beta mn \; \chi(\sigma) \int d\vec{v}_1 \; v_{1x} \; \lambda_D(\vec{v}_1) \; v_{1x} \; \varphi_o(\vec{v}_1) \tag{6.21}$$

Here $\lambda(v_1)$ is the linearized Boltzmann collision operator for hard disks or hard spheres[3)], defined by

$$\lambda(\vec{v}_1)\varphi_o(\vec{v}_1) f(\vec{v}_1) = \sigma^{d-1} \int d\vec{v}_2 \int_{\vec{v}_{12}\cdot\hat{\sigma}>0} d\hat{\sigma} \; |\vec{v}_{12}\cdot\hat{\sigma}| \, (b\sigma - 1)(1 + P_{12})$$
$$\varphi_o(\vec{v}_1)\varphi_o(\vec{v}_2) f(\vec{v}_1) \tag{6.22}$$

where P_{12} is the permutation operator which interchanges particle indices 1 and 2, and $f(\vec{v}_1)$ is an arbitrary function of $\vec{v}_1$. Also $\lambda_D(\vec{v}_1)$ is the Lorentz-Boltzman collision operator[3)]

$$\lambda_D(\vec{v}_1) = \sigma^{d-1} \int d\vec{v}_2 \int_{\vec{v}_{12}\cdot\hat{\sigma}>0} d\hat{\sigma}\ |\vec{v}_{12}\cdot\hat{\sigma}|\,(b\sigma-1)\varphi_o(\vec{v}_2) \tag{6.23}$$

Expressions (6.20) and (6.21) for the initial slope of the time correlation functions are exact for hard sphere of hard disk systems and they can be evaluated readily, cf. eq. (7.16). Computer data is available on this slope for $\rho_D^{(d)}(t)$, and eq. (6.21) is in good agreement with the data[9,10].

7. THE HIERARCHY EQUATIONS

We will develop the kinetic theory calculation of $\rho^{(d)}(t)$ by defining a set of non-equilibrium correlation functions, which will be shown to obey the B.B.G.K.Y. hierarchy equations, and then we will use a cluster expansion method to solve these equations to various degrees of approximation. This procedure has been used for the time correlation functions by Pomeau[13], by Ernst, Hauge, and Van Leeuwen[27], and by Ernst and Dorfman[28].

We begin by noting that $\rho_\eta^{(d)}(t)$, $\rho_\lambda^{(d)}(t)$ and $\rho_D^{(d)}(t)$ can be expressed in terms of the single particle correlation functions $\Phi_\eta^{(d)}(\vec{v}_1,t)$, $\Phi_\lambda^{(d)}(\vec{v}_1,t)$ and $\Phi_D^{(d)}(\vec{v}_1,t)$, respectively, as

$$\rho_\mu^{(d)}(t) = \int d\vec{v}_1\ j_\mu(\vec{v}_1)\Phi_\mu^{(d)}(\vec{v}_1,t) \tag{7.1}$$

with

$$\Phi_\mu^{(d)}(\vec{v}_1,t) = \lim_{\substack{N,V\to\infty \\ N/V=n}} \frac{m^d V}{Z} \langle j_\mu^2(\vec{v}_1)\rangle^{-1} \int dx_2 \ldots \int dx_N e^{-t\bar{L}_N} e^{-\beta H_N} (1+\delta_\mu \sum_{i=2}^{N} P_{1i}) j_\mu(\vec{v}_1) \tag{7.2}$$

where $\mu = \eta$, λ, or D and $\delta_\mu = 1$ for $\mu = \eta, \lambda$ and $\delta_\mu = 0$ for $\mu = D$. Expression (7.2) is obtained from (6.11) and (6.12) by separating the $\vec{v}_1$ integration from the integrals over $\vec{r}_1, x_2, \ldots x_N$ and by noting that one of the $\vec{r}_i$ integrals produces a factor of V, since only relative coordinates appear in the integrand on the right hand side of eq. (7.2).

The hierarchy equations are derived by computing $\frac{\partial\Phi_\mu^{(d)}(\vec{v}_1,t)}{\partial t}$ which leads to

$$\frac{\partial\Phi_\mu^{(d)}(\vec{v}_1,t)}{\partial t} = n\int d2\ \bar{T}(12)\ \Phi_\mu^{(d)}(x_1,x_2,t) \tag{7.3}$$

where $d2 = d\vec{v}_2\, d\vec{r}_2$ and the two particle correlation function $\Phi_\mu^{(d)}(x_1,x_2,t)$ is given by

$$\Phi_\mu^{(d)}(x_1,x_2,t) = \tag{7.4}$$
$$= \lim_{\substack{N,V\to\infty \\ N/V=n}} \langle j_\mu^2(\vec{v}_1)\rangle^{-1} \frac{m^{2d}V^2}{Z} \int dx_3 \ldots \int dx_N e^{-t\bar{L}_N} e^{-\beta H_N} (1+\delta_\mu \sum_{i=2}^{N} P_{1i}) j_\mu(\vec{v}_1)$$

To obtain an equation for $\Phi_\mu^{(d)}(x_1,x_2,t)$, we take the time derivative of eq. (7.4), which leads to

$$\frac{\partial}{\partial t}\Phi_\mu^{(d)}(x_1,x_2,t) + \bar{L}_2(12)\Phi_\mu^{(d)}(x_1,x_2,t) = \tag{7.5}$$
$$= n\int d3(\bar{T}(13) + \bar{T}(23))\Phi_\mu^{(d)}(x_1,x_2,x_3,t)$$

where

$$\bar{L}_2(12) = L_2^o(1,2) - \bar{T}(12)$$

$$L_2^o(12) = \vec{v}_1 \cdot \frac{\partial}{\partial \vec{r}_1} + \vec{v}_2 \cdot \frac{\partial}{\partial \vec{r}_2}$$

and

$$\Phi_\mu^{(d)}(x_1,x_2,x_3,t) = \tag{7.6}$$
$$= \lim_{\substack{N,V\to\infty \\ N/V=n}} \frac{\langle j_\mu^2(\vec{v}_1)\rangle^{-1} m^{3d}V^3}{Z} \int dx_4 \ldots \int dx_N e^{-t\bar{L}_N} e^{-\beta H_N} (1+\delta_\mu \sum_{i=2}^{N} P_{1i}) j_\mu(\vec{v}_1)$$

Equation (7.3) and (7.5) are called the first and second hierarchy equations, respectively. As they stand they are not useful since to determine $\Phi_\mu^{(d)}(\vec{v}_1,t)$, we need to know $\Phi_\mu^{(d)}(x_1,x_2,t)$, and to determine this function, we need to know $\Phi_\mu^{(d)}(x_1,x_2,x_3,t)$, etc. Therefore, to obtain a useful expression for $\Phi_\mu^{(d)}(\vec{v}_1,t)$ from the hierarchy equations, some way must be found to express $\Phi_\mu^{(d)}(x_1,\ldots x_j,t)$ for $j > 1$ in terms of lower order functions.

In the 1967 Summerschool on Fundamental Problems in Statistical Mechanics, Cohen[3] discussed a method by means of which $\Phi_\mu(x_1,x_2,t)$ can be expressed in terms of $\Phi_\mu^{(d)}(\vec{v}_1,t)$ as a power series in the density. If one then inserts this density expansion for $\Phi_\mu^{(d)}(x_1,x_2,t)$ into the first hierarchy equation, eq. (7.3), a closed equation for $\Phi_\mu^{(d)}(\vec{v}_1,t)$ is obtained in the form

$$\frac{\partial\Phi_\mu^{(d)}(\vec{v}_1,t)}{\partial t} = \sum_{\ell=1}^{\infty} n^\ell K_{\ell+1}(\vec{v}_1,t)\Phi_\mu^{(d)}(\vec{v}_1,t)$$

where the collision operator $K_2(\vec{v}_1,t)$ is determined by the dynamical events taking place in a system containing only two particles; the collision operator $K_3(\vec{v}_1,t)$ is determined by the dynamical events taking place in a system of three particles, and so on. This procedure is completely systematic and is designed to be used to obtain expansions for the transport coefficients in a power series in the density. However, it can be shown that all but the first few collision operators $K_{\ell+1}(\vec{v}_1,t)$ diverge[29] as $t \to \infty$, since certain dynamical events among the $\ell+1$ particles give contributions to this operator which become infinite as $t \to \infty$. This divergence has as a consequence the result that all but the first few terms in the expansion of the transport coefficients as a power series in the density are infinite. Therefore to obtain a better equation for $\Phi_\mu^{(d)}(\vec{v}_1,t)$, and an improved expansion for the transport coefficients in terms of the density, it is necessary either to resum the diverging parts of the density expansion of the collision operator given above, or to find another procedure for computing $\Phi_\mu^{(d)}(\vec{v}_1,t)$ which avoids having to make power series expansions in the density. The resummation procedure was discussed by Cohen[3,4], and here we will follow the second alternative, which leads to exactly the same "renormalized" equation for $\Phi_\mu^{(d)}(\vec{v}_1,t)$. In the method to be used here, we express $\Phi_\mu^{(d)}(x_1,\ldots x_j,t)$ in terms of appropriately defined cluster functions $\chi_\mu(x_1,x_2,t)$, $\chi_\mu(x_1,x_2,x_3,t)$, ... $\chi_\mu(x_1,x_2,\ldots x_j,t)$, which will be determined by solving the hierarchy to various degrees of approximation. This method will be seen to lead to expressions for $\Phi_\mu^{(d)}(x_1,x_2,t)$ in terms of $\Phi_\mu^{(d)}(\vec{v}_1,t)$ where the most divergent terms in the density expansion are summed to a "renormalized" expression.

We begin by defining the set of cluster functions $\chi_\mu(x_1,\ldots x_j,t)$ by

$$\Phi_\mu^{(d)}(x_1,x_2,t) = \Phi_\mu^{(d)}(\vec{v}_1,t)\varphi_o(\vec{v}_2) + \delta_\mu\Phi_\mu^{(d)}(v_2,t)\varphi_o(\vec{v}_1) + \chi_\mu^{(d)}(x_1,x_2,t) \qquad (7.7a)$$

$$\begin{aligned}\Phi_\mu^{(d)}(x_1,x_2,x_3,t) = {} & \Phi_\mu^{(d)}(v_1,t)\varphi_o(\vec{v}_2)\varphi_o(\vec{v}_3) + \delta_\mu(\Phi_\mu^{(d)}(v_2,t)\varphi_o(\vec{v}_1)\varphi_o(\vec{v}_3) + \\ & + \Phi_\mu^{(d)}(v_3,t)\varphi_o(\vec{v}_1)\varphi_o(\vec{v}_2)) + \chi_\mu^{(d)}(x_1,x_2,t)\varphi_o(\vec{v}_3) + \\ & + \chi_\mu^{(d)}(x_1,x_3,t)\varphi_o(\vec{v}_2) + \delta_\mu\,\chi_\mu^{(d)}(x_2,x_3,t)\varphi_o(\vec{v}_1) + \\ & + \chi_\mu^{(d)}(x_1,x_2,x_3,t). \qquad (7.7b)\end{aligned}$$

The form of the cluster expansion (7.7) is suggested by the fact that $\Phi_\mu^{(d)}(x_1,x_2,\ldots x_j,t)$ as well as $\Phi_\mu^{(d)}(v_1,t)$ depend linearly on $(1+\delta_\mu \sum_{i=2}^N P_{1i})j_\mu(\vec{v}_1)$. Therefore, if $(1+\delta_\mu \sum_{i=2}^N P_{1i})j_\mu(\vec{v}_1)$ is eliminated from $\Phi_\mu^{(d)}(x_1,\ldots x_j,t)$ in favor of $\Phi_\mu^{(d)}(v_1,t)$, the resulting expression for $\Phi_\mu^{(d)}(x_1,\ldots x_j,t)$ must be a <u>linear</u>

functional of $\Phi_\mu^{(d)}(\vec{v}_1,t)$. The first terms on the righthand side of (7.7a,b) represent the functional in terms of products of single particle functions, and the corrections to this are contained in the still undetermined functions $\chi_\mu^{(d)}(x_1,x_2,\ldots x_j,t)$. For the case of self diffusion the tagged particle plays a special role, and the cluster functions in (7.7b) are so defined as to take this into account.

The cluster functions also satisfy a set of hierarchy equations, which for $\Phi_\mu^{(d)}(\vec{v}_1,t)$, $\chi_\mu^{(d)}(x_1,x_2,t)$, ... are

$$\frac{\partial\Phi_\mu^{(d)}(\vec{v}_1,t)}{\partial t} = n\int d2\ \overline{T}(12)\,[(1+\delta_\mu P_{12})\Phi_\mu^{(d)}(\vec{v}_1,t) + \chi_\mu^{(d)}(x_1,x_2,t)] \tag{7.8}$$

$$\begin{aligned}\frac{\partial\chi_\mu^{(d)}(x_1,x_2,t)}{\partial t} &+ (L_2^{(o)}-\overline{T}(12))\chi_\mu(x_1,x_2t) = \overline{T}(12)(1+\delta_\mu P_{12})\Phi_\mu(\vec{v}_1,t)\varphi_o(\vec{v}_2)\\ &+ n\int d3\{\overline{T}(13)(1+\delta_\mu P_{13})\varphi_o(\vec{v}_3)\chi_\mu(x_1,x_2,t)\\ &+ \overline{T}(23)(1+P_{23})\varphi_o(\vec{v}_3)\chi_\mu(x_1,x_2,t)\\ &+ (\overline{T}(13)+\overline{T}(23))\chi_\mu(x_1,x_2,x_3,t)\}\end{aligned} \tag{7.9}$$

where we have used the fact that

$$\int d\vec{r}_3\int d\vec{v}_3\ \overline{T}(13)\varphi_o(\vec{v}_1)\varphi_o(\vec{v}_3) = 0 \tag{7.10}$$

These equations will be solved in the following way. First, $\chi_\mu^{(d)}(x_1,x_2,t)$ on the right hand side of eq (7.8) will be neglected. This will lead to a closed equation for $\Phi_\mu^{(d)}(\vec{v}_1,t)$, which gives the first approximation to $\Phi_\mu^{(d)}(\vec{v}_1,t)$. To find the next approximation to this function, we neglect $\chi_\mu^{(d)}(x_1,x_2,x_3,t)$ in eq. (7.9) and obtain a closed expression for $\chi_\mu(x_1,x_2,t)$. The solution of this equation is then inserted on the right hand side of eq. (7.8) to give an equation which leads to the second approximation to $\Phi_\mu^{(d)}(\vec{v}_1,t)$. To get the next approximation, we would neglect $\chi_\mu(x_1,x_2,x_3,x_4,t)$ in the equation for $\chi_\mu(x_1,x_2,x_3,t)$, and repeat the procedure. Although the method is straightforward, it has the disadvantage that it is not immediately clear which dynamical events contribute to $\Phi_\mu^{(d)}(\vec{v}_1,t)$ in each order of approximation. As we mentioned earlier, we are interested in obtaining an equation for $\Phi_\mu^{(d)}(\vec{v}_1,t)$ in which the contributions from those dynamical events that lead to the divergences in the density expansion of the collision operator have been re-summed. Therefore it will be necessary to analyze each successive approximation to $\Phi_\mu^{(d)}(\vec{v}_1,t)$, in order to determine which dynamical processes taking place in the system contribute to $\Phi_\mu^{(d)}(\vec{v}_1,t)$ to that order of approximation. From this analysis, we can determine which dynamical events should give the dominant contribution to $\Phi_{\mu}^{(d)}(\vec{v}_1,t)$ over the times of interest here, and we will then compute their contribution.

Applying the method outlined above, we obtain the equations for the first approximation to $\Phi_{\mu}^{(d)}(\vec{v}_1,t)$ as

$$\begin{aligned}\frac{\partial\Phi_{\mu,1}^{(d)}(\vec{v}_1,t)}{\partial t} &= n\int d2\,\overline{T}(12)(1+\delta_{\mu}P_{12})\varphi_o(\vec{v}_2)\Phi_{\mu}^{(d)}(\vec{v}_1,t) \\ &= n\,\lambda_{\mu}(\vec{v}_1)\Phi_{\mu}^{(d)}(\vec{v}_1,t)\end{aligned} \tag{7.11}$$

where

$$\lambda_{\mu}(\vec{v}_1) = \begin{cases}\lambda(\vec{v}_1) & \text{for } \mu=\eta,\lambda \\ \lambda_D(\vec{v}_1) & \text{for } \mu = D\end{cases} \tag{7.12}$$

and $\lambda(\vec{v}_1)$ and $\lambda_D(\vec{v}_1)$ are defined by eqs. (6.22) and (6.23). Equation (7.11) is the linearized Boltmann equation for $\mu = \eta$ or λ, and it is the Lorentz-Boltzmann equation for $\mu = D$. The solution of this equation is

$$\begin{aligned}\Phi_{\mu,1}^{(d)}(\vec{v}_1,t) &= e^{nt\lambda_{\mu}(v_1)}\,\Phi_{\mu}^{(d)}(\vec{v}_1,t=0) = \\ &= \langle j_{\mu}^2(\vec{v}_1)\rangle^{-1}\,e^{n\lambda_{\mu}(v_1)t}\,\varphi_o(\vec{v}_1)j_{\mu}(\vec{v}_1)\end{aligned} \tag{7.13}$$

The corresponding first approximation for $\rho_{\mu}^{(d)}(t)$ is then

$$\rho_{\mu,1}^{(d)}(t) = \langle j_{\mu}^2(v)\rangle^{-1}\int d\vec{v}_1\, j_{\mu}(\vec{v}_1)\,e^{n\lambda_{\mu}(v_1)t}\,j_{\mu}(\vec{v}_1)\varphi_o(\vec{v}_1) \tag{7.14}$$

The corresponding first approximation to the initial slope of $\rho_{\mu}^{(d)}(t)$ is

$$\dot{\rho}_{\mu,1}^{(d)}(o) = \langle j_{\mu}^2(v)\rangle^{-1}\, n\int d\vec{v}_1\, j_{\mu}(\vec{v}_1)\lambda_{\mu}(\vec{v}_1)j_{\mu}(\vec{v}_1)\varphi_o(\vec{v}_1) \tag{7.15}$$

This is the low density limit of the exact value given in eqs. (6.20) and (6.21), since for low densities $\chi(\sigma) \approx 1$.

Although expression (7.14) may be expressed in terms of the eigenfunctions and eigenvalues of the operator $n\lambda_{\mu}(v_1)$ as a sum of exponentials, a good approximation is obtained by regarding $\langle j_{\mu}^2\rangle^{-1}\int d\vec{v}\, j_{\mu}\lambda_{\mu}j_{\mu}\varphi_o$ as an approximate eigenvalue of λ_{μ}. This leads to

$$\rho_{\eta,1}^{(d)}(t) = e^{-nt(\beta\eta_{oo})^{-1}} \tag{7.16a}$$

$$\rho_{\lambda,1}^{(d)}(t) = e^{-nt(\lambda_{oo}\beta m/C_{p,o})^{-1}} \tag{7.16b}$$

$$\rho_{D,1}^{(d)}(t) = e^{-nt(\beta m\, D_{oo})^{-1}} \tag{7.16c}$$

where η_{oo}, λ_{oo}, D_{oo} are the Boltzmann equation values of the coefficients of shear viscosity, thermal conductivity, and self diffusion in the first Enskog approximation, and $C_{p,o}$ is the ideal gas specific heat at constant pressure. Consequently $\rho_{\mu,1}^{(d)}(t)$ decays exponentially over a few mean free times, where t_o, the mean free time is given at low densities by

$$t_o^{(d)} = \left(\frac{\beta m}{\pi}\right)^{1/2} [n(2\sigma)^{d-1}]^{-1} \tag{7.17}$$

By neglecting the cluster function $\chi_\mu^{(d)}(x_1,x_2,t)$ in eq. (7.10a) we have obtained an approximation to $\rho_\mu^{(d)}(t)$ which takes into account, via the Boltmann equation, binary collisions between the particles, and which gives the initial slope correctly at low densities. In order to extend the results to higher densities and to incorporate into the theory the effects of those dynamical events which are responsible for the divergences mentioned above, we will consider the next step in the approximate solution of the hierarchy equations. To obtain an approximation to $\chi_\mu(x_1,x_2,t)$, we consider equation (7.9) and we neglect the term on the right hand side containing the three particle cluster function $\chi_\mu(x_1,x_2,x_3,t)$. This leads to the equation

$$\frac{\partial\chi_\mu^{(d)}(x_1,x_2,t)}{\partial t} + (L_2^{(o)} - \overline{T}(12) - n\Lambda_\mu(12))\chi_\mu^{(d)}(x_1,x_2,t) = = \overline{T}(12)(1+\delta_\mu P_{12})\Phi_\mu^{(d)}(\vec{v}_1,t)\varphi_o(\vec{v}_2) \tag{7.18}$$

where the operator $\Lambda_\mu(1,2)$ is

$$\Lambda_\mu(12) = \int d3\, [\overline{T}(13)(1+\delta_\mu P_{13})+\overline{T}(23)(1+P_{23})]\varphi_o(\vec{v}_3) \tag{7.19}$$

In order to obtain the solution of eq. (7.18), in the most convenient form, we take the Laplace transform of eq. (7.18) and write

$$\varepsilon\, \tilde{\chi}_\mu^{(d)}(x_1,x_2,\varepsilon) + (L_2^{(o)} - \overline{T}(12) - n\Lambda_\mu(12)\tilde{\chi}_\mu^{(d)}(x_1,x_2,\varepsilon) = = \overline{T}(12)(1+\delta_\mu P_{12})\varphi_o(\vec{v}_2)\tilde{\Phi}_\mu^{(d)}(\vec{v}_1,\varepsilon) + \chi_\mu(x_1,x_2,t=0) \tag{7.20}$$

with solution

$$\tilde{\chi}_{\mu}^{(d)}(x_1,x_2,\varepsilon) = \{\varepsilon+L_2^{(o)}-\bar{T}(12)-n\Lambda_{\mu}(12)\}^{-1}[\bar{T}(12)(1+\delta_{\mu}P_{12})\varphi_o(\vec{v}_2)\tilde{\Phi}_o^{(d)}(\vec{v}_1,\varepsilon)$$

$$+ \chi_{\mu}^{(d)}(x_1,x_2,t=0)] \qquad (7.21)$$

where $\tilde{\Phi}(\vec{v}_1,\varepsilon)$, $\tilde{\chi}_{\mu}^{(d)}(x_1,x_2,\varepsilon)$ are the Laplace transforms of $\Phi_o^{(d)}(\vec{v}_1,t)$, $\chi_{\mu}^{(d)}(x_1,x_2,t)$ respectively. If we now take the Laplace transform of eq. (7.8) and insert expression (7.21) for $\tilde{\chi}_{\mu}^{(d)}(x_1,x_2,\varepsilon)$, we obtain an equation for $\tilde{\Phi}_{\mu}^{(d)}(\vec{v}_1,\varepsilon)$ which is

$$[\varepsilon-n\lambda_{\mu}(\vec{v}_1)-nR_{\mu}(\vec{v}_1,\varepsilon)]\tilde{\Phi}_{\mu}^{(d)}(\vec{v}_1,\varepsilon) = \Phi_{\mu}^{(d)}(\vec{v}_1,t=0)+nI_{\mu}(\vec{v}_1,\varepsilon) \qquad (7.22)$$

where

$$R_{\mu}(\vec{v}_1,\varepsilon) = \int d2\ \bar{T}(12)[\varepsilon+L_2^{(o)}-\bar{T}(12)-n\Lambda_{\mu}(12)]^{-1}\bar{T}(12)(1+\delta_{\mu}P_{12})\varphi_o(\vec{v}_2) \qquad (7.23a)$$

and

$$I_{\mu}(\vec{v}_1,\varepsilon) = \int d2\ \bar{T}(12)[\varepsilon+L_2^{(o)}-\bar{T}(12)-n\Lambda_{\mu}(12)]^{-1}\chi_{\mu}^{(d)}(x_1,x_2,t=0) \qquad (7.23b)$$

The operator appearing on the left hand side of eq. (7.22) contains the linearized Boltzmann collision operator plus the operator $nR_{\mu}(\vec{v}_1,\varepsilon)$.

In order to determine the properties of $\Phi_{\mu}^{(d)}(\vec{v}_1,\varepsilon)$ in this approximation, we first analyze the dynamical events which contribute to $R_{\mu}(\vec{v}_1,\varepsilon)$ and to $I_{\mu}(\vec{v}_1,\varepsilon)$. We first consider $R_{\mu}(\vec{v}_1,\varepsilon)$. An examination of expression (7.23a) for the operator reveals that it is obtained by summing up contributions from certain sequences of binary collision events involving 2, 3, 4, ... particles. It is possible to determine which sequences of collisions contribute to $R_{\mu}(\vec{v}_1,\varepsilon)$ by expanding this operator as a power series in the density and examing each term, since each term in the density expansion will be determined by the dynamical events taking place among a fixed number of particles. We therefore write

$$R_{\mu}(\vec{v}_1,\varepsilon) = R_{\mu}^{(o)}(\vec{v}_1,\varepsilon) + nR_{\mu}^{(1)}(\vec{v}_1,\varepsilon) + n^2R_{\mu}^{(2)}(\vec{v}_1,\varepsilon) + \ldots \qquad (7.24a)$$

where

$$R_{\mu}^{(o)}(\vec{v}_1,\varepsilon) = \int d2\ \bar{T}(12)(\varepsilon+L_2^{(o)}-\bar{T}(12))^{-1}\bar{T}(12)(1+\delta_{\mu}P_{12})\varphi_o(\vec{v}_2) \qquad (7.24b)$$

$$R_{\mu}^{(1)}(\vec{v}_1,\varepsilon) = \int d2\int d3\ \bar{T}(12)(\varepsilon+L_2^{(o)}-\bar{T}(12))^{-1}[\bar{T}(13)(1+\delta_{\mu}P_{13}) +$$

$$+ \bar{T}(23)(1+P_{23})](\varepsilon+L_2^{(o)}-\bar{T}(12))^{-1}\bar{T}(12)(1+\delta_{\mu}P_{12})\varphi_o(\vec{v}_2)\varphi_o(\vec{v}_3) \qquad (7.24c)$$

$$R_\mu^{(2)}(\vec{v}_1,\varepsilon) = \int d2 \int d3 \int d4\ \bar{T}(12)(\varepsilon+L_2^{(o)}-\bar{T}(12))^{-1}[\bar{T}(13)(1+\delta_\mu P_{13}) + \\ + \bar{T}(23)(1+P_{23})](\varepsilon+L_2^{(o)}-\bar{T}(12))^{-1}[\bar{T}(14)(1+\delta_\mu P_{14}) + \\ + \bar{T}(24)(1+P_{24})](\varepsilon+L_2^{(o)}-\bar{T}(12))^{-1}\bar{T}(12)(1+\delta_\mu P_{12}) \cdot \\ \cdot \varphi_o(\vec{v}_2)\varphi_o(\vec{v}_3)\varphi_o(\vec{v}_4) \tag{7.24d}$$

The dynamical events which contribute to $R_\mu^{(i)}(\vec{v}_1,\varepsilon)$, and in particular, their contribution for small ε have already been studied in detail[29], because:

i) The kinetic parts of the transport coefficients η and λ, as well as the coefficient of self diffusion D, can be computed in terms of $\lim_{\varepsilon\to o} \tilde{\Phi}_\mu^{(d)}(\vec{v}_1,\varepsilon)$, through the relations

$$\lim_{T\to\infty} \int_o^T dt\ \rho_\mu^{(d)}(t) = \lim_{\varepsilon\to o} \int_o^\infty dt e^{-\varepsilon t} \rho_\mu^{(d)}(t) = \lim_{\varepsilon\to o} \int d\vec{v}_1 j_\mu(\vec{v}_1)\tilde{\Phi}_\mu^{(d)}(\vec{v}_1,\varepsilon) \tag{7.25}$$

so that the limit $\varepsilon\to o$ is important for determining the transport coefficients, and

ii) If one attempts to derive expressions for the transport coefficients as a power series in the density, either by following the systematic procedure outlined by Cohen, or by solving eq. (7.22) for $\tilde{\Phi}_\mu^{(d)}(\vec{v}_1,\varepsilon)$ as a power series in n, one finds that the coefficients of all but the first few powers of n diverge in the limit as $\varepsilon\to o$. The <u>most divergent</u> contributions to each order in the density are the same for both the systematic theory and the hierarchy method using eq. (7.22). Therefore the results of the analysis of the divergences in the systematic density expansion can be directly applied to a discussion of the most divergent parts of the operators $R_\mu^{(i)}(\vec{v}_1,\varepsilon)$.

It should be pointed out that the systematic theory for $\tilde{\Phi}_\mu(\vec{v}_1,\varepsilon)$ and equation (7.22) for $\Phi_\mu(\vec{v}_1,\varepsilon)$ differ only by the fact that the contributions from certain less divergent events in each order of the density are not included in eq. (7.22). However, we shall eventually restrict our attention to the most divergent terms in each order of the density, and for these terms the two methods are identical.

Here we will summarize what is known about the operators $R_\mu^{(i)}(\vec{v}_1,\varepsilon)$. In order to analyze the dynamical events which contribute to them we first note that the operators $\bar{T}(i,j)$ describe a binary collision taking place between particles i, and j, while the operators $(\varepsilon + L_n^{(o)})^{-1}$ describe the motion of a group of n particles <u>backwards</u> in time, along the trajectories that the particles would follow if they did not interact with each other.

We now consider each order in the density in turn.

a) $R_\mu^{(o)}(\vec{v}_1,\varepsilon)$: The operator $\overline{T}(12)(\varepsilon + L_2^{(o)} - \overline{T}(12))^{-1}\,\overline{T}(12)$, appearing in eq. (7.24b) is determined by the dynamics of two particles. This operator vanishes since the two $\overline{T}(12)$ operators in the numerator require that two binary collisions take place between the two particles. However, it is impossible for two hard spheres to collide more than once without the intervention of a third particle. Thus

$$\overline{T}(12)(\varepsilon + L_2^{(o)} - \overline{T}(12))^{-1}\,\overline{T}(12) = 0 \tag{7.26a}$$

so that

$$R_\mu^{(o)}(\vec{v}_1,\varepsilon) = 0 \tag{7.26b}$$

The arguments given above also imply that[25)]

$$\overline{T}(12)(\varepsilon + L_2^{(o)}))^{-1}\,\overline{T}(12) = 0 \tag{7.26c}$$

which we will use below

b) $R_\mu^{(1)}(\vec{v}_1,\varepsilon)$: Using the result (7.26b), we may write $R_\mu^{(1)}(\vec{v}_1,\varepsilon)$, given by eq. (7.24c), as

$$R_\mu^{(1)}(\vec{v}_1,\varepsilon) = \int d2 \int d3\; \overline{T}(12)(\varepsilon+L_2^{(o)})^{-1}\,[\overline{T}(13)(1+\delta_\mu P_{13}) + \\ + \overline{T}(23)(1+P_{23})]\,(\varepsilon+L_2^{(o)})^{-1}\overline{T}(12)(1+\delta_\mu P_{12})\varphi_o(\vec{v}_2)\varphi_o(\vec{v}_3) \tag{7.27}$$

The dynamical events that contribute to this operator consist of sequences of three binary collisions among the three particles (1,2,3). In order to see how these sequences develop in time, we consider the inverse Laplace transform of $R_\mu^{(1)}(\vec{v}_1,\varepsilon)$, given by

$$\int d2 \int d3 \int_0^t dt_1\; \overline{T}(12)\; e^{-(t-t_1)L_2^{(o)}}\,[\overline{T}(13)(1+\delta_\mu P_{13})+\overline{T}(23)(1+P_{23})]\,\cdot \\ \cdot\; e^{-t_1 L_2^{(o)}}\;\overline{T}(12)(1+\delta_\mu P_{12})\varphi_o(\vec{v}_2)\varphi_o(\vec{v}_3)$$

Here there is a binary collision between particles 1 and 2 at time t, say. Then we follow the trajectories of the particles <u>backward</u> in time to time t_1, ($t_1 < t$), where either particle 1 or particle 2 is colliding with particle 3. If we then follow the motion of the particles backwards in time again to time $t = 0$, there is either a (1,2), a (1,3), or a (2,3) collision. The (1,3) or (2,3) collision appears at time $t = 0$ because the permutation operators P_{23} and P_{13} in the integrand convert $\overline{T}(12)$ on the extreme right to $\overline{T}(13)$ and $\overline{T}(23)$ respectively.

Some of the collision sequences which are described by

$$\overline{T}(12)(\varepsilon + L_2^{(o)})^{-1}\ \overline{T}(23)(1 + P_{23})(\varepsilon + L_2^{(o)})^{-1}\ \overline{T}(12)$$

are illustrated in Figure 4.

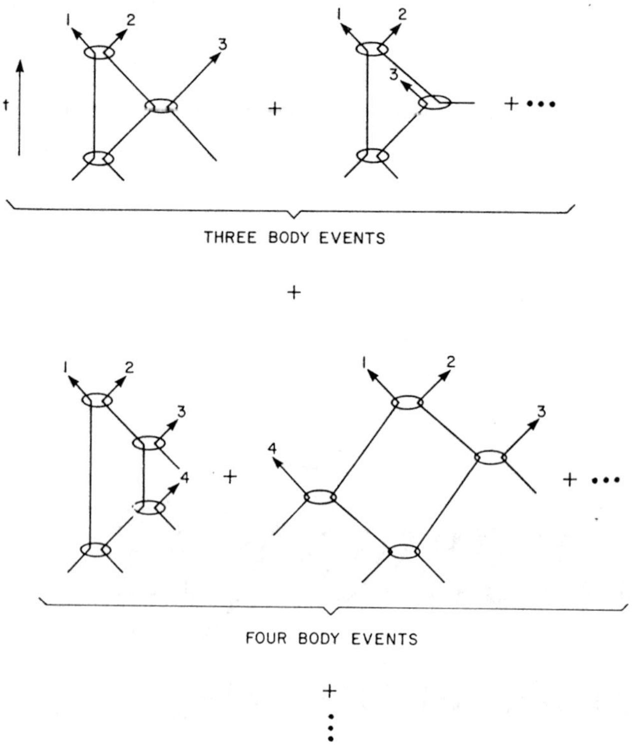

Fig. 4. Examples of simple ring events. Only representative three- and four-body events are shown.

A more complete discussion of all the three body events is given by Sengers, et al.[25]. In the three body events illustrated in Fig. 4, the (1,2) collision at time t is the collision at the top of each of the diagrams, the (2,3) collision at time t_1 is the middle collision in each diagram and the (1,2) or (1,3) collision at t = 0 is at the bottom of the diagram. Due to the graphical representation of these events given by Kawasaki and Oppenheim[30], the dynamical events which contribute to $R_{\mu}^{(1)}(\vec{v}_1,\varepsilon)$ are generally referred to as three body "ring-events". These dynamical events are correlated sequences of binary collisions. That is, the particles (1,2) which collide at time t, have either previously collided with each other, or they have both collided with the same third particle before they collide with each other. As we shall see below, the dynamical events which contribute to $R_{\mu}^{(\ell)}(\vec{v}_1,\varepsilon)$ are correlated binary collision sequences taking place among $\ell+2$ particles. In contrast, the dynamical events which contribute to the Boltzmann equation, for $\Phi_{\mu}^{(d)}(\vec{v}_1,t)$, eq. (7.11), are uncorrelated binary collision sequences[3,4]. Moreover, $R_{\mu}^{(\ell)}(\vec{v}_1,\varepsilon)$ contains contributions from correlated binary collision sequences such that the time interval between the first and last collision in the sequences can take on any value. Those dynamical events which take place over a bounded time interval lead to well behaved contributions to $R_{\mu}^{(\ell)}(\vec{v}_1,\varepsilon)$ as $\varepsilon \to 0$. Although any particular sequence can take place over an arbitrarily large time interval, the divergences in $R_{\mu}^{(\ell)}(\vec{v}_1,\varepsilon)$ as $\varepsilon \to 0$ result from the fact that the phase space volumes for certain correlated sequences of binary collisions diverge when the time interval between the first and last collision becomes arbitrarily large[4,29].

For the case of hard disks[29], the three body ring events produce a log ε divergence of $R_{\mu}^{(1)}(\vec{v}_1,\varepsilon)$ as $\varepsilon \to 0$. For the case of hard spheres $R_{\mu}^{(1)}(\vec{v}_1,\varepsilon)$ is finite as $\varepsilon \to 0$.

c) Higher orders in n: A dynamical analysis of the operator $R_{\mu}^{(\ell)}(\vec{v}_1,\varepsilon)$ along the lines sketched above for $R_{\mu}^{(1)}(\vec{v}_1,\varepsilon)$ can readily be given. We find that sequences of binary collisions among $\ell+2$ particles contribute to these terms, and those sequences can be further classified into two types.

i) Simple ring events, and

ii) Repeated ring events.

The contribution from simple ring events among $\ell+2$ particles are contained in the operator $R_{\mu,s}^{(\ell)}(\vec{v}_1,\varepsilon)$ given by

$$R_{\mu,s}^{(\ell)}(\vec{v}_1,\varepsilon) = \int d2\ \overline{T}(12)(\varepsilon+L_2^{(c)})^{-1}[\Lambda_{\mu}(12)(\varepsilon+L_2^{(o)})^{-1}]^{\ell}\ \cdot \\ \cdot\ \overline{T}(12)(1+\delta_{\mu}P_{12})\varphi_o(v_2) \tag{7.28}$$

and consist of sequences of $\ell+2$ collisions among the $\ell+2$ particles. Some typical examples of simple ring events among four particles are illustrated in Fig. 4. For a gas of hard disks there are dynamical arguments which indicate that $R_{\mu,s}^{(\ell)}(\vec{v}_1,\varepsilon) \sim \varepsilon^{-(\ell-1)}$ for small ε and $\ell \geq 2$. Similar arguments indicate that for a gas of hard spheres $R_{\mu,s}^{(2)} \sim \log \varepsilon$ and $R_{\mu,s}^{(\ell)} \sim \varepsilon^{-(\ell-2)}$ for $\ell \geq 3$, for small ε.

The repeated ring events consist of at least $\ell+3$ successive binary collisions among the $\ell+2$ particles and are composed of successive simple ring events, each of which involves fewer than $\ell+2$ particles. Examples of 4 and 5 particle repeated ring events are illustrated in Figure 5. We will not give here the explicit form of the repeated ring operator, but note that as $\varepsilon \to 0$ the simple ring events among $\ell+2$ particles give a more divergent contribution to $R_{\mu}^{(\ell)}(\vec{v}_1,\varepsilon)$ than do the repeated ring events involving the same number of particles. For example, the four body repeated ring events illustrated in Figure 5 give a contribution to $R_{\mu}^{(2)}(\vec{v}_1,\varepsilon)$ which is proportional to $(\log \varepsilon)^2$ in two dimensions and is finite in three dimensions, while the four body simple ring events are, as mentioned above, proportional to ε^{-1} and log ε for two and three dimensional systems, respectively. In general, the simple ring events give the most divergent contribution to each of the

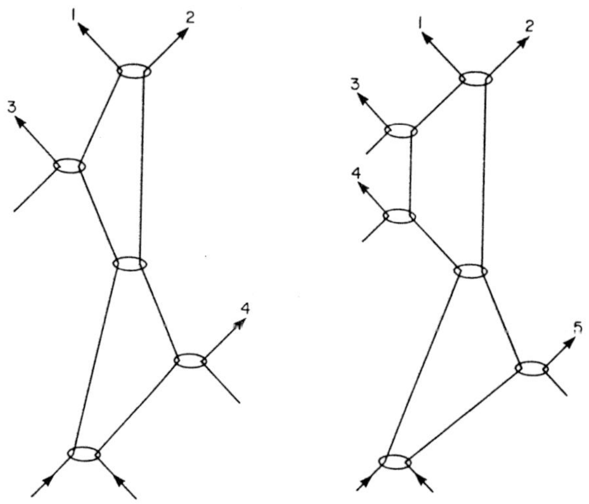

Fig. 5. Representative repeated-ring events among four or five particles.

operators $R_\mu^{(\ell)}(\vec{v}_1,\varepsilon)$. Finally, we note that the unexpanded expression for $R_\mu(\vec{v}_1,\varepsilon)$ eq. (7.23a) is, in effect, a "resummation" of the contributions from all the simple ring and all repeated ring events in each order of the density.

A similar dynamical analysis can be made for $I_\mu(\vec{v}_1,\varepsilon)$, where the dynamics is now contained in the expression $\overline{T}(12)[\varepsilon+L_2^{(o)}-\overline{T}(12)-n\Lambda_\mu(12)]^{-1}\chi_\mu(x_1,x_2,t=0)$. Since $\chi_\mu(x_1,x_2,t=0) = (g(\vec{r}_1,\vec{r}_2)-1)(1+\delta_\mu P_{12})\varphi_o(\vec{v}_2)\Phi(\vec{v}_1,t=0)$, the (g-1) has the effect of replacing the collision at time t=0 in the binary collision sequences, by an equilibrium correlation between the two particles, since (g-1) restricts the particles to be within a few molecular distances of each other.

In order to proceed with the analysis, we will make the following simplifications[31]:

i) We will take into account the contributions to $R_\mu(\vec{v}_1,\varepsilon)$ from the simple ring events, and neglect the contributions from repeated ring events.

Although it is not yet possible to give a rigorous justification for restricting our attention to the contributions from the most divergent events, it does seem plausible that for times greater than several mean free times, and for sufficiently low densities, the most divergent terms will give the dominant contribution to $\rho_\mu^{(d)}(t)$. This can be argued on the basis of the following facts.

a) After a few mean free times t_o, the contributions to $\rho_\mu^{(d)}(t)$ from uncorrelated binary collisions, will have decayed to zero, according to eqs. (7.16a-c).

b) If we now consider the contributions to $\rho_\mu^{(d)}(t)$ from correlated sequences of binary collisions, we first note that the divergences in $R_\mu^{(\ell)}(\vec{v}_1,\varepsilon)$ come from the contributions of those dynamical events which take place over a time scale large compared to a mean free path. If we now consider a large but finite time t, or equivalently, a small but non zero value of ε, then for sufficiently small density, the simple ring events will give the dominant contributions to the sum $\sum_\ell R_\mu^{(\ell)}(\vec{v}_1,\varepsilon)$. To see this explicitly, we consider the series

$\sum_{\ell=1}^{\infty} n^{\ell} R_{\mu}^{(\ell)}(\vec{v}_1,\varepsilon)\tilde{\Phi}_{\mu}^{(d)}(\vec{v}_1,\varepsilon)$ which appears in the density expansion of eq. (7.22), for a gas of hard disks, and for small but non zero ε. As discussed above, this series has the form

$$n\sigma^2 a_1 \log(t_c\varepsilon)^{-1} + (n\sigma^2)^2[a_2(t_c\varepsilon)^{-1} + b_2(\log(t_c\varepsilon)^{-1})^2 + \ldots]$$

$$+ (n\sigma^2)^3[a_3(t_c\varepsilon)^{-2} + \ldots] + \ldots$$

where $t_c = \sigma(m/kT)^{1/2}$ is a time inserted to make the quantity εt_c dimensionless. The contributions from the simple ring events are the most divergent in each order of the density and have coefficients a_1, a_2, ..., while the contributions from the repeated ring events are less divergent, and have coefficients b_2, b_3,.... Only the coefficient a_1 is known at present[29)], but the other coefficients are assumed here to be finite. It is helpful now to consider the inverse Laplace transform of this series, which is given for large t, by

$$(n\sigma^2)a_1\frac{1}{t} + (n\sigma^2)^2[\frac{a_2}{t_c}+\frac{2b_2}{t}\log\frac{t}{t_c} + \ldots] + (n\sigma^2)^3[\frac{a_3 t}{t_c^2} + \ldots] + \ldots$$

For t on the order of several mean free times, the contributions to this series from the simple ring events are all of the same order of magnitude, but the repeated ring corrections are smaller by factors of order n or nlogn. Therefore for sufficiently small densities, it is reasonable to suppose that for times greater than several mean free times there is a time interval over which the simple ring events give the dominant contributions to the above sum, or equivalently, that for sufficiently small ε there is a range of values of ε where the simple rings give the dominant contributions to the Laplace transform of this series.

ii) In addition, we will neglect the contributions in eq. (7.22) from the initial condition term $I_{\mu}(\vec{v}_1,\varepsilon)$, as this term too can be shown to give contributions to $\rho_{\mu}^{(d)}(t)$ of higher order in the density than those of interest to us here coming from the simple ring events in $R_{\mu}(\vec{v}_1,\varepsilon)$.[27)]

Therefore we consider $\Phi_{\mu}^{(d)}(\vec{v}_1,\varepsilon)$ to be determined by the equations

$$\tilde{\Phi}_{\mu}^{(d)}(\vec{v}_1,\varepsilon) = [\varepsilon - n\lambda_{\mu}(\vec{v}_1) - nR_{\mu,s}(\vec{v}_1,\varepsilon)]^{-1}\varphi_o(\vec{v}_1)j(\vec{v}_1)<j_{\mu}^2(\vec{v})>^{-1} \quad (7.29)$$

where

$$R_{\mu,s}(\vec{v}_1,\varepsilon) = \int d2\,\overline{T}(12)[\varepsilon + L_2^o - n\Lambda_{\mu}(12)]^{-1} \cdot \overline{T}(12)(1+\delta_{\mu}P_{12})\varphi_o(\vec{v}_2) \quad (7.30)$$

is the contribution to $R_\mu(\vec{v}_1,\varepsilon)$ from the simple ring events, as can be seen from an inspection of eq. (7.28).

The determination of the long time behavior of $\rho_\mu^{(d)}(t)$ to be carried out later will be greatly facilitated if we go over to a Fourier representation of $R_{\mu,s}(\vec{v}_1,\varepsilon)$. To do this, we use the fact that $R_{\mu,s}(\vec{v}_1,\varepsilon)$ does not depend on $\vec{r}_1$ and write

$$R_{\mu,s}(v_1,\varepsilon) = \int d\vec{v}_2 \int d\vec{r}_1 \int d\vec{r}_2\ \delta(\vec{r}_1)\ \overline{T}(12)\,[\varepsilon+\vec{v}_1\cdot\vec{\nabla}_{r_1}+\vec{v}_2\cdot\vec{\nabla}_{r_2}-n\Lambda_\mu(12)]^{-1}$$

$$\cdot\ \overline{T}(12)(1+\delta_\mu P_{12})\varphi_o(\vec{v}_2) \tag{7.30a}$$

Then by inserting δ-functions and using their Fourier representations, we obtain

$$R_{\mu,s}(\vec{v}_1,\varepsilon) = \int d\vec{v}_2 \int \frac{d\vec{k}}{(2\pi)^d}\ \overline{T}_{-k}(12)\,[\varepsilon+i\vec{k}\cdot\vec{v}_{12}-n\lambda_{\mu,k}(\vec{v}_1)-n\lambda_{-k}(\vec{v}_2)]^{-1}\ \cdot$$

$$\cdot\ \overline{T}_k(12)(1+\delta_\mu P_{12})\varphi_o(\vec{v}_2) \tag{7.31}$$

where

$$\overline{T}_k = \sigma^{d-1} \int_{\vec{v}_{12}\cdot\hat{\sigma}>0} d\hat{\sigma}(\vec{v}_{12}\cdot\hat{\sigma})(e^{-i\vec{k}\cdot\vec{\sigma}}\,b_\sigma - e^{+i\vec{k}\cdot\vec{\sigma}}) \tag{7.32a}$$

$$\lambda_{\mu,k}(\vec{v}_1) = \lambda_D(\vec{v}_1) \qquad \text{for } \mu = D \tag{7.32b}$$

$$= \lambda_k(\vec{v}_1) \qquad \text{for } \mu = \eta,\ \lambda \tag{7.32c}$$

and

$$\lambda_k(\vec{v}_1) = \int d\vec{v}_3\ (\overline{T}_o(13) + \overline{T}_k(13)P_{13})\varphi_o(\vec{v}_3) \tag{7.32d}$$

with

$$T_o(13) = \lim_{k\to o} \overline{T}_k(13) \tag{7.32e}$$

We have used the property that

$$\int d\vec{r}_1 \int d\vec{r}_2\ e^{-i\vec{k}_1\cdot\vec{r}_1-i\vec{k}_2\cdot\vec{r}_2}\ \overline{T}(12)\ e^{i\vec{k}_1'\cdot\vec{r}_1+i\vec{k}_2'\cdot\vec{r}_2}$$

$$= (2\pi)^d\ \delta(\vec{k}_1+\vec{k}_2-\vec{k}_1'-\vec{k}_2')\ \overline{T}_{k_1-k_1'}(12) \tag{7.33}$$

8. THE LONG TIME BEHAVIOR OF $\rho_{\mu}^{(d)}(t)$

In this section we shall compute the behavior of $\rho_{\mu}^{(d)}(t)$ in time for hard spheres and hard disks by iterating the operator on the right hand side of eq. (7.26) about $(\varepsilon - n\lambda_{\mu}(\vec{v}_1))^{-1}$. In this way we obtain the initial exponential decay, eq. (7.14), as well as the long time behavior $\rho_{\mu}^{(d)}(t) \sim t^{-d/2}$.

Using eq. (7.29), and iterating, we obtain

$$\tilde{\Phi}_{\mu}^{(d)}(\vec{v}_1,\varepsilon) = \tilde{\Phi}_{\mu,1}^{(d)}(\vec{v}_1,\varepsilon) + \tilde{\Phi}_{\mu,2}^{(d)}(\vec{v}_1,\varepsilon) + \ldots \tag{8.1}$$

where

$$\tilde{\Phi}_{\mu,1}^{(d)}(\vec{v}_1,\varepsilon) = (\varepsilon - n\lambda_{\mu}(\vec{v}_1))^{-1} j_{\mu}(\vec{v}_1)\varphi_o(\vec{v}_1)\langle j_{\mu}^2(\vec{v}_1)\rangle^{-1} \tag{8.2a}$$

$$\tilde{\Phi}_{\mu,2}^{(d)}(\vec{v}_1,\varepsilon) = (\varepsilon - n\lambda_{\mu}(\vec{v}_1))^{-1} nR_{\mu,s}(\vec{v}_1,\varepsilon)(\varepsilon - n\lambda_{\mu}(\vec{v}_1))^{-1} \cdot j_{\mu}(\vec{v}_1)\varphi_o(\vec{v}_1)\langle j_{\mu}^2(\vec{v}_1)\rangle^{-1} \tag{8.2b}$$

Here we will only compute the first two iterates. It can be seen that the higher iterates give similar contributions to the repeated ring contributions which we have neglected. Therefore we must, for consistency, neglect the third and higher order iterates in eq. (8.1).

The Laplace inversion of $\tilde{\Phi}_{\mu,1}^{(d)}(\vec{v}_1,\varepsilon)$ leads to eq. (7.13) and the result eq. (7.14) for $\rho_{\mu,1}^{(d)}(t)$ is thereby recovered. We now consider $\tilde{\Phi}_{\mu,2}^{(d)}(\vec{v}_1,\varepsilon)$. Since the long time behavior of $\Phi_{\mu,2}^{(d)}(\vec{v}_1,t)$ is directly related to the small ε behavior of its Laplace transform $\tilde{\Phi}_{\mu,2}^{(d)}(\vec{v}_1,\varepsilon)$, we consider this function for small values of ε. We begin by noting that the $\vec{k}$-integral in $R_{\mu,s}(\vec{v}_1,\varepsilon)$ in eq. (7.31), can be divided into two pieces, for which $0 \leq k \leq k_o$ and $k_o \leq k \leq \infty$, respectively, where k_o^{-1} is on the order of a mean free path. The contribution coming from $k > k_o$ will be neglected, for we assume that this part of the $\vec{k}$-integration incorporates the effects of collisions that take place on a time scale on the order of, or less than, a mean free time, in which we are not interested here.

We consider now the region $k < k_o$ and examine the operator $[\varepsilon + i\vec{k}\cdot\vec{v}_{12} - n\lambda_{\mu,\vec{k}}(\vec{v}_1) - n\lambda_{-\vec{k}}(\vec{v}_2)]^{-1}$ which appears on the right hand side of equation (7.31). The action of this operator on a function can be computed in terms of the eigenvalues and eigenfunctions of the operator $i\vec{k}\cdot\vec{v}_1 - n\lambda_{\mu,\vec{k}}(\vec{v}_1)$ and $-i\vec{k}\cdot\vec{v}_2 - n\lambda_{-\vec{k}}(\vec{v}_2)$.

In the small k region we can use perturbation theory to discuss the eigenvalues and eigenfunctions of the operators $i\vec{k}\cdot\vec{v}_1 - n\lambda_{\mu,\vec{k}}(\vec{v}_1)$ and $-i\vec{k}\cdot\vec{v}_2 - n\lambda_{-\vec{k}}(\vec{v}_2)$ in terms of the eigenfunctions and eigenvalues of the linearized Boltzmann collision operators $\lambda_{\mu,o}(\vec{v}_1) = \lambda_{\mu}(\vec{v}_1)$ and $\lambda_o(\vec{v}_2) = \lambda(\vec{v}_2)$, respectively. This follows because $\lambda_{\vec{k}}$ and $\lambda_{-\vec{k}}$ can be expanded about their values for $k = 0$, and the k-dependent terms in this expansion as well as the operators $i\vec{k}\cdot\vec{v}_1$, and $i\vec{k}\cdot\vec{v}_2$ can be regarded as perturbations on the operators $\lambda_\mu(\vec{v}_1)$ and $\lambda_o(\vec{v}_2)$. Moreover, the perturbing terms coming from the k-expansion of the $\lambda_{\pm\vec{k}}$ operators can be shown to give contributions to $\rho_\mu^{(d)}(t)$ which are of higher order in the density than we will consider here[32]. Consequently we replace the operator $i\vec{k}\cdot\vec{v}_1 - n\lambda_{\mu,\vec{k}}(\vec{v}_1)$ by $i\vec{k}\cdot\vec{v}_1 - n\lambda_\mu(\vec{v}_1)$, and the operator $-i\vec{k}\cdot\vec{v}_2 - n\lambda_{-\vec{k}}(\vec{v}_2)$ by $-i\vec{k}\cdot\vec{v}_2 - \lambda(\vec{v}_2)$.

We therefore consider the ring operator $nR_{\mu,s}(\vec{v}_1,\varepsilon)$ in eq. (8.2b) to be replaced by $nR^o_{\mu,s}$ where

$$nR^o_{\mu,s}(\vec{v}_1,\varepsilon) = n\int d\vec{v}_2 \int_{k<k_o} \frac{d\vec{k}}{(2\pi)^d} T_{-k}(12) \cdot [\varepsilon+i\vec{k}\cdot\vec{v}_{12}-n\lambda_\mu(\vec{v}_1)-n\lambda(\vec{v}_2)]^{-1} \cdot \overline{T}_k(12)(1+\delta_\mu P_{12})\varphi_o(\vec{v}_2) \tag{8.4}$$

Following Pomeau[13], we notice that among the eigenvalues of the operators $i\vec{k}\cdot\vec{v}_1 - n\lambda_\mu(\vec{v}_1)$ and $-i\vec{k}\cdot\vec{v}_2 - n\lambda(\vec{v}_2)$, there are those which go to zero as $k \to 0$. These eigenvalues and the corresponding eigenfunctions give the leading contributions to $\tilde{\Phi}_\mu^{(d)}(\vec{v}_1,\varepsilon)$ for small ε, or to $\Phi_\mu^{(d)}(\vec{v}_1,t)$ for long times. The eigenfunctions of $i\vec{k}\cdot\vec{v}_1-n\lambda_D(\vec{v}_1)$ and $i\vec{k}\cdot\vec{v}_1-n\lambda(\vec{v}_2)$ with eigenvalues going to zero as $k \to 0$ are called hydrodynamic modes, and they arise from the eigenfunctions of $\lambda_D(\vec{v}_1)$ and $\lambda(\vec{v}_1)$ belonging to the eigenvalue zero, under the perturbation $i\vec{k}\cdot\vec{v}_1$ for small k.

The eigenfunctions and eigenvalues of the operators $i\vec{k}\cdot\vec{v}_1-n\lambda_D(\vec{v}_1)$ and $i\vec{k}\cdot\vec{v}-n\lambda(\vec{v}_1)$ are given by the solutions of the equations

$$(i\vec{k}\cdot\vec{v}_1-n\lambda_D(\vec{v}_1)\psi^{(\omega)}(\vec{k},\vec{v})\varphi_o(\vec{v}_1) = \omega(k)\psi^{(\omega)}(\vec{k},\vec{v}_1)\varphi_o(\vec{v}_1)$$

$$(i\vec{k}\cdot\vec{v}_1-n\lambda(\vec{v}_1))\Theta^{(\Omega)}(\vec{k},\vec{v}_1)\varphi_o(\vec{v}_1) = \Omega(k)\Theta^{(\Omega)}(\vec{k},\vec{v}_1)\varphi_o(\vec{v}_1)$$

One can impose the condition that $\psi^{(\omega)}(\vec{k},\vec{v}_1)$ and $\Theta^{(\Omega)}(\vec{k},\vec{v}_1)$ be normalized according to

$$\int d\vec{v}_1 \, (\psi^{(\omega)}(\vec{k},\vec{v}_1))^2 \varphi_o(\vec{v}_1) = 1 \tag{8.5a}$$

and

$$\int d\vec{v}_1 \, (\Theta^{(\Omega)}(\vec{k},\vec{v}_1))^2 \varphi_o(\vec{v}_1) = 1 \tag{8.5b}$$

and we can require that different eigenfunctions be orthogonal,

$$\int d\vec{v}_1 \, \psi^{(\omega')}(\vec{k},\vec{v}_1)\psi^{(\omega)}(\vec{k},\vec{v}_1)\varphi_o(\vec{v}_1) = 0 \tag{8.5c}$$

and

$$\int d\vec{v}_1\ \theta^{(\Omega')}(\vec{k},\vec{v}_1)\theta^{(\Omega)}(\vec{k},\vec{v}_1)\varphi_o(\vec{v}_1) = 0 \tag{8.5d}$$

Finally, we suppose that $\psi^{(\omega)}(\vec{k},\vec{v})$, $\theta^{(\Omega)}(\vec{k},\vec{v})$, $\omega(k)$, and $\Omega(k)$ can be expanded in powers of k as

$$\psi^{(\omega)}(\vec{k},\vec{v}) = \psi_o^{(\omega)}(\vec{v}) + k\psi_1^{(\omega)}(\vec{v}) + \ldots \tag{8.6a}$$

$$\theta^{(\Omega)}(\vec{k},\vec{v}) = \theta_o^{(\Omega)}(\vec{v}) + k\ \theta_1^{(\Omega)}(\vec{v}) + \ldots \tag{8.6b}$$

$$\omega(k) = \omega_o + k\omega_1 + k^2\omega_2 + \ldots \tag{8.6c}$$

and

$$\Omega(k) = \Omega_o + k\Omega_1 + k^2\Omega_2 + \ldots \tag{8.6d}$$

There is only one hydrodynamic mode for the operator $i\vec{k}\cdot\vec{v}_1 - n\lambda_D(v_1)$ with eigenvalue

$$\omega_D(k) = D_o k^2 + \mathcal{O}(k^4) \tag{8.7a}$$

and eigenfunction

$$\psi_D(\vec{k},\vec{v}_1) = 1 + \mathcal{O}(k) \tag{8.7b}$$

where D_o is the coefficient of self diffusion as determined by the Lorentz-Boltzmann equation. There are d+2 hydrodynamic modes of the operator $i\vec{k}\cdot\vec{v} - n\lambda(\vec{v})$:

a) Two sound modes

with

$$\Omega^{(\pm)}(k) = \pm ikc_o + \frac{1}{2}\Gamma_{so}\ k^2 + \mathcal{O}(k^3) \tag{8.8a}$$

and

$$\theta^{(\pm)}(\vec{k},\vec{v}) = \left(\frac{d}{2(d+2)}\right)^{1/2}\left(\frac{\beta m v^2}{d} \pm (\beta m c_o)\hat{k}\cdot\vec{v}\right) + \mathcal{O}(k) \tag{8.8b}$$

where $c_o = \left(\frac{d+2}{d\beta m}\right)^{1/2}$ is the ideal gas sound velocity, $\Gamma_{so} = \frac{2(d-1)}{d}\nu_o + (\gamma_o - 1)D_{T,o}$, where $\gamma_o = C_{p_o}/C_{v_o} = \frac{d+2}{d}$, C_{p_o} and C_{v_o} being the ideal gas specific heats at constant pressure and volume, respectively; $\nu = \eta_o/nm$, $D_{T,o} = \lambda_o/nC_{p_o}$, where η_o and λ_o are the coefficients of viscosity and thermal conductivity, respectively, as obtained from the Boltzmann equation.

b) One heat mode

$$\Omega^{(T)}(k) = k^2 D_{T,o} + \mathcal{O}(k^4) \tag{8.9a}$$

and

$$\Theta^{(T)}(\vec{k},\vec{v}) = \left(\frac{2}{d+2}\right)^{1/2}\left(\frac{\beta m v^2}{2} - \frac{d+2}{2}\right) + \mathcal{O}(k) \tag{8.9b}$$

and

c) d-1 shear modes

$$\Omega^{(v_i)}(k) = \nu_o k^2 + \mathcal{O}(k^4) \qquad (i = 1,\ldots,d-1) \tag{8.10a}$$

and

$$\Theta^{(v_i)}(\vec{k},\vec{v}) = (\beta m)^{1/2}\,\hat{\vec{k}}^{(i)}\cdot\vec{v} + \mathcal{O}(k) \tag{8.10b}$$

where $\hat{\vec{k}}$, $\hat{\vec{k}}^{(1)},\ldots\hat{\vec{k}}^{(d-1)}$ form a Cartesian set of mutually orthogonal unit vectors.

For the determination of the long time behavior of $\rho_\mu^{(d)}(t)$ we neglect the contribution of the non hydrodynamic modes to $\Phi_{\mu,2}^{(d)}(\vec{v}_1,\varepsilon)$, since these modes lead to a rapid exponential decay. We will also neglect the $\vec{k}$ dependence of the $\overline{T}_{-\vec{k}}$ and $\overline{T}_{\vec{k}}$ operators appearing in the numerator of eq. (8.4), since it can easily be shown that the terms involving higher powers of $\vec{k}$ lead to a more rapid decay of $\rho_\mu^{(d)}(t)$ than the terms retained. For similar reasons, we need only to use the eigenfunctions $\psi(\vec{k},\vec{v})$ and $\Theta(\vec{k},\vec{v})$ to order k^o and the eigenvalues $\omega(k)$ and $\Omega(k)$ to order k^2. Consequently we write for small ε

$$\begin{aligned}\Phi_{\mu,2}^{(d)}(\vec{v},\varepsilon) \sim \sum_{\Omega,\Omega'}{}' \; n\int d\vec{v}_2\int \frac{d\vec{k}}{(2\pi)^d}\,(\varepsilon-n\lambda(\vec{v}_1))^{-1}\,T_o(12)\,\cdot \\ \cdot\,\Theta^{(\Omega)}(\vec{k},\vec{v}_1)\Theta^{(\Omega')}(-\vec{k},\vec{v}_2)\varphi_o(\vec{v}_1)\varphi_o(\vec{v}_2)\,\cdot \\ \cdot\,(\varepsilon+\Omega(k)+\Omega'(k))^{-1}\int d\vec{v}_1\int d\vec{v}_2\;\Theta^{(\Omega)}(\vec{k},\vec{v}_1)\Theta^{(\Omega')}(-\vec{k},\vec{v}_2)\,\cdot \\ \cdot\,T_o(12)(1+P_{12})(\varepsilon-n\lambda(\vec{v}_1))^{-1}\varphi_o(\vec{v}_1)\varphi_o(\vec{v}_2)\,j_\mu(\vec{v}_1)\langle j_\mu^2(\vec{v}_1)\rangle^{-1}\end{aligned} \tag{8.11a}$$

for $\mu = \eta,\ \lambda$

and

$$\Theta^{(\Omega)}(\vec{k},\vec{v}_1)\Theta^{(\Omega')}(-\vec{k},\vec{v}_2)$$

$$\Phi^{(d)}_{D,2}(\vec{v}_1,\varepsilon) \sim \sum_{\Omega}{}'\beta mn \int d\vec{v}_2 \int \frac{d\vec{k}}{(2\pi)^d}(\varepsilon - n\lambda_D(\vec{v}_1))^{-1} T_o(12)\psi_D(\vec{k},\vec{v}_1)\Theta^{(\Omega)}(-\vec{k},\vec{v}_2)$$

$$\cdot\ (\varepsilon+\omega_D(k)+\Omega(k))^{-1} \int d\vec{v}_1 \int d\vec{v}_2\ \psi_D(\vec{k},\vec{v}_1)\Theta^{(\Omega)}(-\vec{k},\vec{v}_2) \tag{8.11b}$$

$$\cdot\ T_o(12)(\varepsilon - n\lambda_D(\vec{v}_1))^{-1}\varphi_o(\vec{v}_1)\varphi_o(\vec{v}_2)v_{1x}$$

where the prime on the summation indicates that only hydrodynamic modes are to be taken into account. For small ε, we can neglect ε in the denominators $(\varepsilon - n\lambda_\mu(\vec{v}_1))^{-1}$ appearing in (8.11a) and (8.11b). We can also use the fact that to lowest order in k, the eigenfunctions $\psi_D(\vec{k},\vec{v}_1)$ and $\Theta^{(\Omega)}(\vec{k},\vec{v}_1)$ are composed of collision invariants, so that

$$T_o(12)(\Theta_o^{(\Omega)}(\vec{k},\vec{v}_1) + \Theta_o^{(\Omega)}(\vec{k},\vec{v}_2))\varphi_o(\vec{v}_1)\varphi_o(\vec{v}_2) = 0 \tag{8.12a}$$

and

$$T_o(12)(\Theta_o^{(\Omega)}(\vec{k},\vec{v}_1) + \Theta_o^{(\Omega)}(\vec{k},\vec{v}_2)(\Theta_o^{(\Omega')}(-\vec{k},\vec{v}_1) +$$

$$+ \Theta_o^{(\Omega')}(-\vec{k},\vec{v}_2))\varphi_o(\vec{v}_1)\varphi_o(\vec{v}_2) = 0 \tag{8.12b}$$

Then if we calculate $\rho^{(d)}_{\mu,2}(t)$, by

$$\rho^{(d)}_{\mu,2}(t) = \int d\vec{v}_1\ j_\mu(\vec{v}_1)\Phi^{(d)}_{\mu,2}(\vec{v}_1,t) \tag{8.13}$$

we obtain

$$\rho^{(d)}_{\mu,2}(t) \sim \frac{1}{2n\langle j_\mu^2(\vec{v}_1)\rangle} \sum_{\Omega,\Omega'}{}' \int \frac{d\vec{k}}{(2\pi)^d} e^{-t(\Omega(k)+\Omega'(k))}\ \cdot$$

$$[\int d\vec{v}_1\ j_\mu(\vec{v}_1)\Theta_o^{(\Omega)}(\vec{k},\vec{v}_1)\Theta_o^{(\Omega')}(-\vec{k},\vec{v}_1)\varphi_o(\vec{v}_1)]^2 \tag{8.14a}$$

for $\mu = \eta, \lambda$

and

$$\rho^{(d)}_{D,2}(t) \sim \frac{\beta m}{n}\sum_{\Omega}{}' \int \frac{d\vec{k}}{(2\pi)^d} e^{-t(\omega_D(k)+\Omega(k))} [\int d\vec{v}_1 v_{1x}\Theta_o(-\vec{k},\vec{v}_1)\varphi_o(\vec{v}_1)]^2 \tag{8.14b}$$

The dominant contributions for $\rho^{(d)}_{\eta,2}(t)$ and $\rho^{(d)}_{\lambda,2}(t)$ for large times come from those combinations of Ω and Ω' such that the sum $\Omega(k)+\Omega'(k) \sim k^2$.

These combinations are easily seen to arise from (a) two shear modes (b) two heat modes, (c) a heat and a shear mode and (d) two sound modes such that one has the eigenvalue $ikc_o + \frac{1}{2}\Gamma_{so}\cdot k^2$ and the other $-ikc_o + \frac{1}{2}\Gamma_{so}\cdot k^2$. Similarly, the dominant contribution to $\rho^{(d)}_{D,2}(t)$ comes from Ω such that $\omega_D + \Omega \sim k^2$. By considering the tensorial character of these modes, and by direct calculation of (8.14a) and (8.14b) one finds that

$$\rho^{(2)}_{\eta,2}(t) \sim (32\pi n t_o)^{-1}[\nu_o^{-1} + (\nu_o+\lambda_o/(2nk_B))^{-1}](t_o/t) \qquad (8.15a)$$

$$\rho^{(2)}_{\lambda,2}(t) \sim (4\pi n t_o)^{-1}[\nu_o+\lambda_o/(2nk_B)]^{-1}(t_o/t) \qquad (8.15b)$$

$$\rho^{(2)}_{D,2}(t) \sim (8\pi n t_o)^{-1}(\nu_o + D_o)^{-1}(t_o/t) \qquad (8.15c)$$

$$\rho^{(3)}_{\eta,2}(t) \sim (120 n\pi^{3/2} t_o^{3/2})^{-1}[7(2\nu_o)^{-3/2} + \left(\frac{4\lambda_o}{15nk_B} + \frac{4\nu_o}{3}\right)^{-3/2}](t_o/t)^{3/2} \qquad (8.15d)$$

$$\rho^{(3)}_{\lambda,2}(t) \sim (12 n\pi^{3/2} t_o^{3/2})^{-1}[(\nu_o + \frac{2\lambda_o}{5nk_B})^{-3/2} + \frac{1}{3}\left(\frac{4\lambda_o}{15nk_B} + \frac{4\nu_o}{3}\right)^{-3/2}](t_o/t)^{3/2} \qquad (8.15e)$$

$$\rho^{(3)}_{D,2}(t) \sim (12 n\pi^{3/2} t_o^{3/2})^{-1}(\nu_o + D_o)^{-3/2}(t_o/t)^{3/2} \qquad (8.15f)$$

Equations (8.15a-f) exhibit the $t^{-d/2}$ behavior of the time correlation functions, and are consistent with the computer results extrapolated to low density.

It is possible to extend these results to higher density by incorporating into the calculation the k-dependence of the $\lambda_{\vec{k}}$ operators as well as a class of less divergent terms which were neglected in deriving eq. (8.15)[32]. These less divergent terms are associated with excluded volume corrections to the ring events and are similar to the excluded volume corrections incorporated in Enskog's extension of the Boltzmann equation to higher densities. Although these excluded volume corrections to the ring events do not exhaust the set of less divergent events that can contribute to or modify the $t^{-d/2}$ behavior, it is reasonable that they should give the dominant corrections to eq. (8.15) for the range of times of interest for the computer experiments. This is because for a number of other cases, the Enskog corrections are dominant among the contributions of all dynamical events. By including these Enskog-like corrections to the ring events, one computes expressions which should be a good approximation to $\rho^{(d)}_{\mu}(t)$ for higher densities over the time intervals of interest[33]. For example, for $\rho^{(d)}_{D}(t)$ we obtain

$$\rho^{(d)}_{D}(t) \tilde{\sim} \alpha^{(d)}_{D,E}(n)(t_{o,E}/t)^{d/2} \qquad (8.16)$$

where

$$t_{o,E} = t_o/\chi(\sigma) = (\frac{\beta m}{\pi})^{1/2}(n\chi(\sigma)(2\sigma)^{d-1})^{-1} \tag{8.17}$$

is the mean free time between collisions in the Enskog theory, and

$$\alpha^{(2)}_{D,E}(n) = (8\pi n t_{o,E})^{-1}(\nu_E+D_E)^{-1} \tag{8.18a}$$

and

$$\alpha^{(3)}_{D,E}(n) = (12n\pi^{3/2}t^{3/2}_{o,E})^{-1}(\nu_E+D_E)^{-3/2} \tag{8.18b}$$

where ν_E and D_E in (8.18a) and (8.18b) are the values of the coefficients of kinematic viscosity and of self diffusion for hard disks or hard spheres respectively as determined by the Enskog theory.

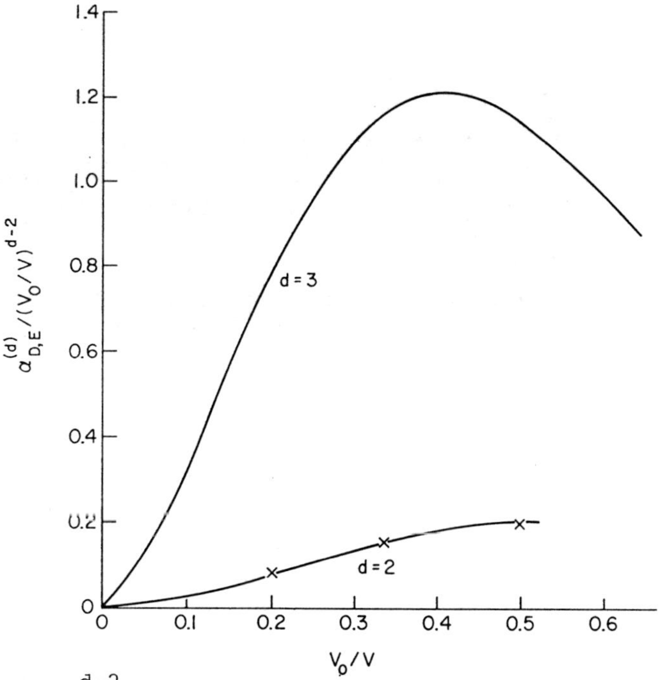

Fig. 6. $\alpha^{(d)}_{D,E}/(V_o/V)^{d-2}$ plotted as a function of the reduced volume (V_o/V), where V_o is the volume at close packing, for d=2 and d=3. The crosses indicate the computer results of Alder and Wainwright for d=2.

In Figure 6, we plot $\alpha^{(d)}_{D,E}$ as a function of density, and compare it with the available computer data. The agreement with the computer data is quite good.

In section 10 we will discuss the general implications of the $t^{-d/2}$ decay of $\rho^{(d)}_\mu(t)$ for the derivation of hydrodynamic equations. We conclude this section with a number of remarks about the kinetic theory treatment of $\rho^{(d)}_\mu(t)$.

1. It should be possible to extend the theory to include a wider class of intermolecular potentials than those for hard spheres or disks. This has not yet been done, but there is little doubt that the $t^{-d/2}$ decay would be valid for a large class of systems with short ranged repulsive potentials.

2. It is interesting to note that if the resummation of the most divergent events is not carried out, the log ε divergence in the density expansion of $\Phi_\mu^{(d)}(\vec{v}_1,\varepsilon)$ leads to a term proportional to t^{-1} in $\rho_\mu^{(d)}(t)$ in both two and three dimensions; this comes from simple ring events among three and four bodies respectively. However, for two dimensional systems the coefficient of the unresummed t^{-1} term is not consistent with the computer results for $\rho_\mu^{(2)}(t)$. Thus, the quantitative agreement of expression (8.18a) with the computer results can be taken as a vindication of the resummation in two dimensions. In three dimensions, the coefficient of the unresummed t^{-1} term is not yet available, but the agreement of expression (8.18b) with the computer results is an indication that the resummation is necessary in three dimensions also.

3. Although the inclusion of the simple ring events is very successful in the calculation of $\rho_\mu^{(d)}(t)$ for the times considered here, in order to extend the kinetic theory calculation of $\rho_\mu^{(d)}(t)$ to longer times, the less divergent dynamical events, which we have neglected here, should be taken into account. Work in this direction has been done by Pomeau and Resibois[13], and by Ernst, van Beijeren and de Schepper[34]. These authors found that for d=3 the $t^{-3/2}$ behavior persists for longer times, even if one includes the contributions from a large class of less divergent events. However, for two dimensional systems, Ernst and co-workers find corrections to the t^{-1} behavior of $\rho_\mu^{(2)}(t)$ for longer times than are considered here. For details we refer the reader elsewhere[13,34].

4. Equations (8.14a) and (8.14b) are the low density limits of the formulas that would be used to compute $\rho_\mu^{(d)}(t)$ from the mode-coupling formula of Kadanoff and Swift[35], Kawasaki[36], and Ferrell[37]. However, the mode-coupling formula is the result of a phenomenological theory for the time correlation functions, and the kinetic theory provides a microscopic justification of it, at least for low densities.

5. If one computes the long time behavior of $\rho_\mu^{(d)}(t)$ by using the operator $R_\mu(\vec{v}_1,\varepsilon)$, eq. (7.23a), instead of the simple ring operator $R_{\mu,s}(\vec{v}_1,\varepsilon)$, and by including all the iterates in the appropriate version of eq. (8.1), then the results, eqs. (8.15a-f), are still obtained. This procedure is not consistent, however, with the fact that we have neglected a large class of dynamical events whose contributions to $\tilde{\Phi}_\mu^{(d)}(\vec{v}_1,\varepsilon)$ are just as divergent as those from the repeated ring events. In the method used in this section, we have consistently neglected all but the most divergent events.

9. THE HYDRODYNAMIC CALCULATION OF $\rho_\mu^{(d)}(t)$ FOR LONG TIMES

In section 5 we discussed the various hydrodynamic approaches to the time correlation functions. Here we shall treat in some detail a semi-hydrodynamic method, due to Hauge, Ernst en van Leeuwen[18], which also leads to the $d^{-d/2}$ decay of the time correlation functions.

It is not obvious at first sight how one can apply hydrodynamic methods to the calculation of $\rho_\mu^{(d)}(t)$. The reason is that hydrodynamics deal with the relaxation of spatial inhomogeneities in the density, velocity, and temperature of a fluid system, while as $\rho_\mu^{(d)}(t)$ is a spatially homogeneous quantity. Therefore the central idea of the semi-hydrodynamic method is to artificially introduce a spatial inhomogeneity into the calculation and then use hydrodynamics to describe the final stages of the relaxation of the system to equilibrium. Consequently the method can only give the asymptotically long behavior of $\rho_\mu^{(d)}(t)$, and not its behavior for all times. Here we will discuss only $\rho_D^{(d)}(t)$ in detail, and we refer to the literature for a more complete discussion[18].

We begin by writing $\rho_D^{(d)}(t)$ in the form

$$\rho_D^{(d)}(t) = \lim_{\substack{N,V\to\infty \\ N/V=n}} \frac{\beta m}{V} \int d\vec{r}_o \int d\vec{v}_o \int d\vec{v} \int d\vec{r}\; v_{ox} v_x\, V\langle \delta(\vec{v}_1-\vec{v}_o) W(\vec{r}_1-\vec{r}_o)$$

$$\cdot\, \delta(\vec{v}_1(t)-\vec{v})\,\delta(\vec{r}_1(t)-\vec{r})\rangle \tag{9.1}$$

where we have inserted into the equilibrium average a distribution of the initial positions of the tagged particle described by $W(\vec{r}_1-\vec{r}_o)$, which must satisfy

$$\int d\vec{r}_1\, W(\vec{r}_1-\vec{r}_o) = \int d\vec{r}_o\, W(\vec{r}_1-\vec{r}_o) = 1 \tag{9.2}$$

This function is introduced solely for the purpose of setting up the initial spatial inhomogeneity in the fluid, the presence of which will ultimately allow us to introduce hydrodynamic methods into the calculation of $\rho_D^{(d)}(t)$. The factors of V are inserted for later convenience.

We now define a single particle nonequilibrium distribution function $f_D(\vec{r},\vec{v},t)$ by means of the conditional probability

$$\varphi_o(\vec{v}_o) f_D(\vec{r},\vec{v},t) = V \langle \delta(\vec{v}_1-\vec{v}_o) W(\vec{r}_1-\vec{r}_o)\,\delta(\vec{v}_1(t)-\vec{v})\,\delta(\vec{r}_1(t)-\vec{r})\rangle \tag{9.3a}$$

or

$$f_D(\vec{r},\vec{v},t) = \frac{\langle \delta(\vec{v}_1-\vec{v}_o) W(\vec{r}_1-\vec{r}_o)\,\delta(\vec{v}_1(t)-\vec{v})\,\delta(\vec{r}_1(t)-\vec{r})\rangle}{\langle \delta(\vec{v}_1-\vec{v}_o) W(\vec{r}_1-\vec{r}_o)\rangle} \tag{9.3b}$$

$f_D(\vec{r},\vec{v},t)$ can be thought of as the nonequilibrium distribution for the tagged particle at point $\vec{r}$ with velocity $\vec{v}$ at time t in the fluid, that results from the initial velocity and density disturbance such that at t=0 the particle has velocity $\vec{v}_o$ and is distributed about the point $\vec{r}_o$ with distribution $W(\vec{r}_1-\vec{r}_o)$.

Although it is impossible to compute $f_D(\vec{r},\vec{v},t)$ exactly for all times for a general fluid one now makes some crucial assumptions:

1. After a time which is short compared to the asymptotic decay of the correlation functions, $f_D(\vec{r},\vec{v},t)$ approaches the local equilibrium distribution function

$$f_D(\vec{r},\vec{v},t) \to P(\vec{r},t)\left(\frac{\beta(\vec{r},t)m}{2\pi}\right)^{d/2} e^{-\frac{\beta(\vec{r},t)m}{2}(\vec{v}-\vec{U}(\vec{r},t))^2} \tag{9.4}$$

where $P(\vec{r},t)$, $\vec{U}(\vec{r},t)$ and $T(\vec{r},t) = (k_B\beta(\vec{r},t))^{-1}$ are the probability of finding the tagged particle, the local velocity, and the local temperature respectively at the point $\vec{r}$ in the fluid at time t. The first of these quantities is defined by the conditional probability,

$$P(\vec{r},t) = \frac{\langle\delta(\vec{v}_1-\vec{v}_o)W(\vec{r}_1-\vec{r}_o)\delta(\vec{r}_1(t)-\vec{r})\rangle}{\langle\delta(\vec{v}_1-\vec{v}_o)W(\vec{r}_1-\vec{r}_o)\rangle} = \int d\vec{v}\; f_D(\vec{r},\vec{v},t) \tag{9.5a}$$

and $\vec{U}(\vec{r},t)$ and $T(\vec{r},t)$ can be defined in terms of similar conditional probabilities. To do this we first define the local density $n(\vec{r},t)$, by

$$n(\vec{r},t) = \frac{\langle\delta(\vec{v}_1-\vec{v}_o)W(\vec{r}_1-\vec{r}_o)\sum_{i=1}^{N}\delta(\vec{r}_i(t)-\vec{r})\rangle}{\langle\delta(\vec{v}_1-\vec{v}_o)W(\vec{r}_1-\vec{r}_o)\rangle} \tag{9.5b}$$

and the local velocity, $\vec{U}(\vec{r},t)$, as

$$n(\vec{r},t)\vec{U}(\vec{r},t) = \frac{\langle\delta(\vec{v}_1-\vec{v}_o)W(\vec{r}_1-\vec{r}_o)\sum_{i=1}^{N}\vec{v}_i(t)\delta(\vec{r}_i(t)-\vec{r})\rangle}{\langle\delta(\vec{v}_1-\vec{v}_o)W(\vec{r}_1-\vec{r}_o)\rangle} \tag{9.5c}$$

A similar definition can be given for $T(\vec{r},t)$, but we will not use it here.

2. For sufficiently long times, the long wavelength components of the quantities $P(\vec{r},t)$, $\vec{U}(\vec{r},t)$ and $T(\vec{r},t)$ satisfy hydrodynamic equations. That is, for sufficiently small gradients, $P(\vec{r},t)$ is assumed to satisfy

$$\frac{\partial P(\vec{r},t)}{\partial t} = D\,\nabla^2\,P(\vec{r},t) \tag{9.6}$$

where D is the coefficient of self diffusion, and $\vec{U}$ is assumed to satisfy

$$\frac{\partial\vec{U}(\vec{r},t)}{\partial t} = \frac{-c^2}{\gamma n}\nabla n(\vec{r},t)+\nu\nabla^2\vec{U}+(D_\ell-\nu)\nabla(\nabla\cdot U)-(c^2\alpha)/\gamma)\nabla T \tag{9.7}$$

where $n(\vec{r},t)$ is the local density of the fluid, n is its value at total equilibrium, c is the adiabatic sound velocity, $\gamma = C_p/C_v$, $\alpha = -n^{-1}(\partial n/\partial T)_P$ is the coefficient of thermal expansion at equilibrium, and $D_\ell = \frac{1}{nm}[\frac{2(d-1)}{d}\eta + \zeta]$, where ζ is the coefficient of the bulk viscosity and $\nu = \eta/nm$ is the kinematic viscosity.

3. $W(\vec{r}_1-\vec{r}_o)$ is slowly varying over distances of the order of the equilibrium correlation length ξ in the fluid and vanishes for $|\vec{r}_1-\vec{r}_o| \geq \ell$ where $\xi << \ell << V^{1/d}$, V being the volume of the container. This assumption is made in order to set up an initial density disturbance with gradients that are small over some characteristic microscopic length and which extends only over a region that is small compared to the macroscopic size of the system.

Underlying the first two assumptions is the picture that the initial density and velocity disturbance $\delta(\vec{v}_1-\vec{v}_o)W(\vec{r}_1-\vec{r}_o)$ sets up a nonequilibrium process in the fluid. The fluid, through the molecular interactions, rapidly reaches a local equilibrium state, which then decays to total equilibrium via hydrodynamic processes. Thus we see clearly that the method of calculating $\rho_D^{(d)}(t)$ by relying on the hydrodynamic equations, at best can only be used to compute the asymptotically long time behavior of this function.

To proceed further, we insert (9.3a) and (9.4) into (9.1), to obtain

$$\rho_D^{(d)}(t) \sim \beta m \int d\vec{v}_o \int d\vec{r}\, v_{ox}\, P(\vec{r},t)U_x(\vec{r},t)\varphi_o(\vec{v}_o) \qquad (9.8a)$$

or

$$\rho_D^{(d)}(t) \sim \beta m \int d\vec{v}_o \int \frac{d\vec{k}}{(2\pi)^d}\, v_{ox}\, U_x(\vec{k},t)P(-\vec{k},t)\varphi_o(\vec{v}_o) \qquad (9.8b)$$

where we have inserted the Fourier transforms of the functions $P(\vec{r},t)$ and $\vec{U}(\vec{r},t)$,

$$P(\vec{k},t) = \int d\vec{r}\, P(\vec{r},t)\, e^{i\vec{k}\cdot\vec{r}} \qquad (9.9a)$$

and

$$\vec{U}(\vec{k},t) = \int d\vec{r}\, \vec{U}(\vec{r},t)\, e^{i\vec{k}\cdot\vec{r}} \qquad (9.9b)$$

into the right hand side of eq. (9.8a), to obtain (9.8b).

As in the kinetic theory calculation, it is assumed that the dominant long time contribution to $\rho_D^{(d)}(t)$ comes from the region of the $\vec{k}$-integral where $k < k_o$ and k_o is the inverse of some microscopic length, which would be the mean free path in a gas or the range of the intermolecular potential in a dense fluid. For small values of $\vec{k}$, one can compute $P(\vec{k},t)$ and $\vec{U}(\vec{k},t)$ as the solutions of the Fourier transforms of the linearized Navier-Stokes hydrodynamic equations. This follows since small $\vec{k}$ corresponds to small gradients, and for small gradients these equations are supposed to be valid. Therefore, by taking the Fourier transforms of equations (9.6) and (9.7), and by performing the time integrals, we find

$$P(\vec{k},t) = P(\vec{k},t=0)\, e^{-Dk^2t} \qquad (9.10)$$

$$\vec{U}(k,t) = \hat{k}(\hat{k}\cdot\vec{U}(k,t)) + [\vec{U}(k,t) - \hat{k}(\vec{U}(k,t)\cdot\hat{k})]$$

$$= \hat{\vec{k}}(A_k^+(o)e^{-\omega_+ t} - A_k^-(o)e^{-\omega_- t}) + [\vec{U}(k,o) - \hat{k}(\vec{U}(k,o)\cdot\hat{k})]\, e^{-\nu k^2 t} \qquad (9.11)$$

where $\vec{U}(\vec{k},o) = \vec{U}(\vec{k},t{=}0)$, and where $\omega_\pm$ are the sound mode frequencies from hydrodynamics

$$\omega_\pm = \pm\, ikc + \frac{1}{2}\Gamma_s k^2 \qquad (9.12a)$$

and the sound damping constant Γ_s, is

$$\Gamma_s = D_\ell + (\gamma-1)\lambda/nC_p \qquad (9.12b)$$

The quantities $A_k^\pm(o)$ are associated with the sound modes, and as they will not be used further here, we refer to the literature for their definition[18]. If we now insert these values into the small k part of expression (9.8b), we find that the dominant long time behavior of $\rho_D^{(d)}(t)$ is given by

$$\rho_D^{(d)}(t) \sim \beta m \int d\vec{v}_o \int_{k<k_o} \frac{d\vec{k}}{(2\pi)^d}\, e^{-(D+\nu)k^2 t}\, P(-\vec{k},o)\, \cdot$$

$$[U_x(\vec{k},o) - \hat{k}_x(\hat{\vec{k}}\cdot U(\vec{k},o))]\, v_{ox}\varphi_o(\vec{v}_o) \qquad (9.13)$$

The initial values $P(\vec{k},t{=}0)$ and $\vec{U}(\vec{k},o)$ can be obtained by taking the Fourier transforms of $P(\vec{r},o)$ and $\vec{U}(\vec{r},t{=}0)$. It follows from eq. (9.5) that

$$P(\vec{r},o) = W(\vec{r}-\vec{r}_o) \qquad (9.14)$$

so that

$$P(\vec{k},o) = e^{i\vec{k}\cdot\vec{r}_o}\, W(\vec{k}) \qquad (9.15)$$

where $W(\vec{k})$ is the Fourier transform of $W(\vec{r})$. Similarly $U(\vec{k},o)$ can be obtained from (9.5b) and (9.5c). We first compute $n(\vec{r},o)$ by using eq. (9.5b) for t=0, to obtain

$$n(\vec{r},o) = W(\vec{r}-\vec{r}_o) + n\int d\vec{r}_1\, W(\vec{r}_1-\vec{r}_o)g(\vec{r}_1,\vec{r})$$

$$= W(\vec{r}-\vec{r}_o) + n + \int d\vec{r}_1\, W(\vec{r}_1-\vec{r}_o)(g(\vec{r}_1,\vec{r})-1) \qquad (9.16a)$$

where $g(\vec{r}_1,\vec{r})$ is the pair distribution function in the canonical ensemble, and we have used eq. (9.2). We now make use of assumption 3 which asserts that $W(\vec{r}_1-\vec{r}_o)$

is slowly varying over the region where $g(\vec{r}_1,\vec{r})-1$ differs from zero, and that $W(\vec{r}_1-\vec{r}_o)$ vanishes for $|\vec{r}_1-\vec{r}_o| \geq \ell$. Then $n(\vec{r},o)$ is given by

$$n(\vec{r},o) = W(\vec{r}-\vec{r}_o) + n + W(\vec{r}-\vec{r}_o) \int_{|\vec{r}_1-\vec{r}_o|\leq\ell} d\vec{r}_1 \, (g(\vec{r}_1,\vec{r})-1) \qquad (9.16b)$$

where the $\vec{r}_1$ integration extends over a region of linear dimension ℓ, which is small compared to $V^{1/d}$ but large compared to a correlation length. Since the integration extends only over a small region of the container, we can assume that the integral $\int d\vec{r}_1 (g(r_1,r)-1)$ is given by its value in the grand canonical ensemble[26], viz.

$$n \int_{|\vec{r}_1-\vec{r}_o|\leq\ell} d\vec{r}_1 \, (g(\vec{r}_1,\vec{r})-1) = k_B T \left(\frac{\partial n}{\partial P}\right)_T -1 \qquad (9.16c)$$

and hence

$$n(\vec{r},o) = n + k_B T \, W(\vec{r}-\vec{r}_o) \left(\frac{\partial n}{\partial P}\right)_T \qquad (9.16d)$$

Similarly

$$n(\vec{r},o)\vec{U}(\vec{r},o) = \vec{v}_o \, W(\vec{r}-\vec{r}_o) \qquad (9.17)$$

Since we are considering only small departures from equilibrium in using the linearized hydrodynamic equations, we can replace $n(\vec{r},o)$ in (9.17) by n and write

$$\vec{U}(r,o) = \frac{1}{n} \vec{v}_o \, W(\vec{r}-\vec{r}_o) \qquad (9.18)$$

Then

$$\vec{U}(\vec{k},o) = \frac{1}{n} \vec{v}_o \, e^{i\vec{k}\cdot\vec{r}_o} \, W(\vec{k}) \qquad (9.19)$$

If we now insert (9.15) and (9.19) into (9.13) we obtain

$$\rho_D^{(d)}(t) \sim \frac{1}{n} \int_{k<k_o} \frac{d\vec{k}}{(2\pi)^d} \, W(\vec{k})W(-\vec{k})e^{-(\nu+D)k^2 t}(1-\hat{k}_x^2) \qquad (9.20)$$

Moreover, for small k, we can replace $W(-\vec{k})W(\vec{k})$ by 1. Then for large times

$$\rho_D^{(2)}(t) \sim [8\pi n(\nu+D)t]^{-1} \qquad (9.21a)$$

and

$$\rho_D^{(3)}(t) \sim [12n(\pi(\nu+D)t)^{3/2}]^{-1} \quad (9.21b)$$

These results are identical with (8.16), and (8.18) as derived from kinetic theory except that in (9.21a,b) the full Navier-Stokes transport coefficients appear instead of their Enskog theory value.

There are a number of remarks that must be made concerning the derivation.

1. The smoothness condition, together with the replacement of eq. (9.16a) by (9.16d), restrict the validity of eq. (9.21) to regions away from the gas liquid critical point, since in this region the microscopic correlation length is large.

2. Without further specifying the form of $W(\vec{r}-\vec{r}_o)$, it is difficult to estimate the time scale on which eq. (9.21a) and (9.21b) are valid. The best one can do is to notice that they are valid for $[(\nu+D)t]^{1/2} > L$ where L is a charateristic distance over which $W(\vec{r}-\vec{r}_o)$ varies.

3. In spite of the similarities between the kinetic theory results and those obtained in this section, there are some important differences between the methods and between the results.

a.) The method given here is independent of the nature of the molecular potential, and of the density of the fluid.

b.) The method given here relies on the validity of the linearized hydrodynamic equations, and it is the validity of these equations we are trying to establish. Therefore, one should at least require that the theory be self consistent. That is, if we assume that the transport coefficients in the hydrodynamic equations are finite, then the time integral of $\rho_D^{(d)}(t)$ must be finite. In two dimensions, the calculation is not self consistent. We will return to this point in the next section.

10. DISCUSSION

We conclude with a number of remarks.

1. Although we have confined our attention here to the kinetic parts of the time correlation functions, it can be shown that the $t^{-d/2}$ decay still holds if the potential energy contribution to the currents J_η and J_λ are included[39,40].

2. The molecular dynamics calculation[10] of the velocity autocorrelation function for a gas of hard disks exhibited a vortex-type of velocity correlation between a chosen molecule and the surrounding molecules which is very similar to the hydrodynamic flow field surrounding a moving volume element in a fluid which is initially at rest. This vortex pattern, which is illustrated in Figure 7, suggests that a fraction of the momentum transferred to the moving particle to the particle in front of it is eventually returned to it from behind. This process causes the velocity autocorrelation function to be larger than it would be if

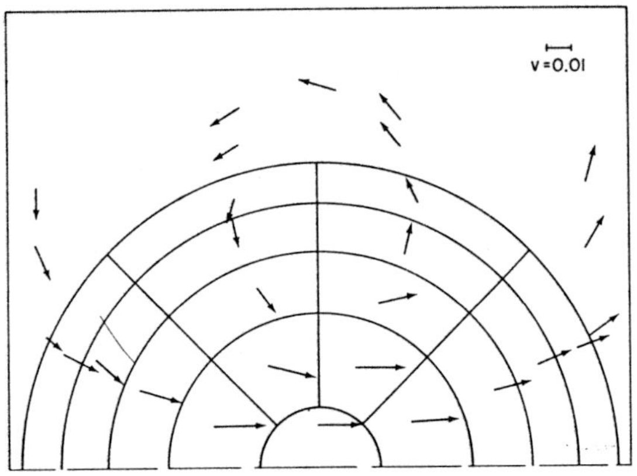

Fig. 7. The velocity correlation between a central particle and its neighborhood at a density corresponding to 1/2 of close packing for 224 hard disks. Because of symmetry only the upper half of the neighbors are shown. The size of the central particle is shown by the smallest half circle, and the sizes of the other four concentric circles are chosen so as to include about six neighboring particles. These circles have been partitioned into four parts. So as to have a measure of the direction relative to the velocity vector of the central particle at zero time. The arrows give the direction and magnitude of the average velocity in each section after about 10 collision times. The scale of the velocity is indicated as 0.01 of the initial velocity. A number of additional arrows are included in the figure to show the extension of the vortex pattern outside the areas covered by the molecular dynamics calculations. These arrows are obtained by a hydrodynamic simulation of the molecular flow. [Alder and Wainwright, Ref. 10.]

these vortices did not occur, and is intimately connected with the slow $t^{-d/2}$ decay of the correlation functions. Consequently, the ring events discussed in section 7 may provide the molecular basis for the vortex pattern.

3. The main point of the calculation of the time correlation functions is to determine whether or not the limit

$$\lim_{T\to\infty} \int_0^T dt\, \rho_\mu^{(d)}(t)$$

exists, or more generally, that the transport coefficients as defined by eqs. (3.26), (4.1) and (4.2) exist. The result that the time correlation functions for three dimensional systems decay in time as $t^{-3/2}$ is consistent with the existence of the transport coefficients in three dimensions. For two dimensional systems an asymptotic decay of $\rho_\mu^{(2)}(t) \approx t^{-1}$ would lead to the result that the transport coefficients diverge in two dimensions, and thus that the linearized Navier-Stokes equations do not provide a correct description of hydrodynamic processes in two dimensional fluids. It must be pointed out, however, that an asymptotic decay of $\rho_\mu^{(d)}(t) \approx t^{-1}$ has not been established for two dimensional systems. The kinetic theory calculation of $\rho_\mu^{(d)}(t)$ given here is restricted to times on the order of several mean free times, and cannot be extended further unless dynamical events which have been neglected here are taken into account. Moreover, in two dimensions, the semi-hydrodynamic theory is not self consistent, since the assumption that the transport coefficients are finite, leads to the conclusion that the transport coefficients diverge. An heuristic attempt to formulate a self consistent theory which may be qualitatively correct proceeds along the following lines[10]. Instead of using the complete transport coefficients (as defined by the infinite time integrals) in the semi-hydrodynamic calculation of $\rho_\mu^{(d)}(t)$, one uses the transport coefficients $D(t)$, $\nu(t)$, etc., as defined by eq. (3.23a) for D and similarly for ν, η, and λ, that have developed in the fluid up to time t. An argument in support of this idea comes from the kinetic theory calculation of $\rho_\mu^{(d)}(t)$ for higher densities, where the Enskog theory expressions for the transport coefficients are used in the calculation of $\rho_\mu^{(d)}(t)$. These values are good approximations for $D(t)$, $\nu(t)$, ... over the time interval studied on the computer, and their use leads to an expression for $\alpha_{D,E}^{(d)}(n)$ which is in good agreement with the computer results. To obtain a self consistent theory for the time dependent transport coefficients one regards the expressions for $\rho_\mu^{(d)}(t)$ as defining a set of coupled differential equations. For example, if one uses the fact that

$$\rho_D^{(d)}(t) = \beta m \frac{d\,D(t)}{dt}$$

equation (9.21a) becomes,

$$\beta m \frac{d\,D(t)}{dt} = [8\pi n(D(t) + \nu(t))t]^{-1} \tag{10.1}$$

and similar equations can be given for $\nu(t)$, $\lambda(t)$. These equations lead to the self consistent value for $\rho_D^{(2)}(t) \approx [t(\log t)^{1/2}]^{-1}$ and $D(t)$ still diverges as $(\log t)^{1/2}$ as $t \to \infty$. However, the asymptotic behavior of $\rho_\mu^{(d)}(t)$ can only be theoretically established by careful kinetic theory calculations, where one can control all the approximations that are made, and there is some progress in this direction[34].

4. In view of the very slow time decay of the time correlation functions, it is not clear to what extent the Navier-Stokes transport coefficients can be used even in three dimensions to describe phenomena that vary on a time scale of 50-100 t_o; for on this time scale there is not yet a clear separation of microscopic and macroscopic effects. However, the usual application of the Navier-Stokes equations are made to phenomena that vary on a much longer time scale, and then the slow time decay of the correlation function does not interfere with the hydro-

dynamic processes.

5. If one attempts to compute the Burnett, super-Burnett, transport coefficients, such as $D^{(2)}(t)$ as given by eq. (3.23b), one finds that these coefficients appear to diverge as $t \to \infty$, for both two and three dimensional systems. For example, for a three dimensional fluid

$$D^{(2)}(t) \sim \frac{-D^2}{10\pi^{3/2}\beta m(D+\nu)^{5/2}} \; t^{1/2}$$

This result has been derived from the kinetic theory for a gas of hard spheres by Ernst, de Schepper, and van Beijeren[4], and by Dufty and McLennan[42], and from a more hydrodynamic approach by Keyes and Oppenheim[43]. This result implies that the generalization of Fick's law as described by eq. (3.24) is not correct for three dimensional systems, or equivalently that the k expansion appearing in the integrand of eq. (3.21) is not a good representation of $\frac{\partial F(k,t)}{\partial t}$ for long times. Ernst and the author[44] have recently made a thorough examination of all the transport coefficients associated with the Burnett and super-Burnett equations and have shown that all such transport coefficients diverge as $t \to \infty$.

Recent work on the higher gradient corrections to the Navier-Stokes equations seems to indicate that for three dimensional systems, the corrections to (1.6b) for the pressure tensor and to (1.7) for the heat vectors are non-analytic functions of the gradients. For example, if we consider the Fourier transform of the heat flow vector $\vec{q}_k$, then for small $\vec{k}$, $\vec{q}_k$ is given by

$$\vec{q}_k = i\vec{k}\, T_k + \mathcal{O}(k^{3/2})$$

instead of the value

$$\vec{q}_k = 2i\vec{k}\, T_k + \mathcal{O}(k^2)$$

which would be required by the Burnett hydrodynamic equations. Here T_k is the Fourier transform of the deviation of the temperature from its equilibrium value. For further details we refer the reader to the literature[19,22,44].

DEDICATION

These lectures are dedicated to the memory of Theodore H. Berlin.

ACKNOWLEDGEMENTS

The author would like to thank Drs. E.G.D. Cohen, M.H. Ernst, H. van Beijeren, and W.W. Wood for their help in preparation of these lectures. He would like to thank the Department of Chemical Physics, Weizmann Institute for Science, Rehovot, Israel, for its warm hospitality during July 1974 when part of these lectures were prepared. Finally, financial support from the National Science Foundation, under grant NSF GP 38965X is gratefully aknowledged.

REFERENCES

1) c.f. L. Landau & L. Lifshitz, Fluid Mechanics, (Addison Wesley, Reading, Mass., 1958).

2) c.f. G.W. Ford and J. Foch, in Studies in Statistical Mechanics, V, J. de Boer and G.E. Uhlenbeck, eds., (North Holland, Amsterdam, 1970).

3) c.f. S. Chapman and T.G. Cowling, Mathematical Theory of Non-Uniform Gases, 3rd Ed., (Cambridge Univ. Press, 1970). See also E.G.D. Cohen in Fundamental Problems in Statistical Mechanics, Vol. I, E.G.D. Cohen, ed., (North Holland, Amsterdam, 1962), p. 110.

4) c.f. E.G.D. Cohen, in The Boltzmann Equation, E.G.D. Cohen and W. Thirring, eds., (Springer Verlag, Vienna, 1973), and references contained therein.

5) A. Einstein, Ann. Phys. 17 (1905) 549.

6) For a review and references, see R. Zwanzig, Ann.Rev.Phys.Chem. 16 (1965) 67, and W.A. Steele, in Transport Phenomena in Fluids, H.J.M. Hanley, ed., (Marcel Dekker, New York, 1970), Chapter 8.

7) Although we consider only the relations between the time correlation functions and the transport coefficients, time correlation functions also appear in the theory of neutron scattering, of light scattering, and of spectral line shapes.

8) c.f. A. Sjölander, in Thermal Neutron Scattering, P.A. Egelstaff, ed., (Academic Press, New York, 1965), p. 291.

9) We here follow the presentation of J.A. McLennan, Phys.Rev., A8 (1973) 1479.

10) B.J. Alder and T.E. Wainwright, Phys. Rev. Letters 18 (1967) 988; J. Phys. Soc. Jap., Suppl. 26 (1968) 267; Phys. Rev. A1 (1970) 18; B.J. Alder, D.M. Gass and T.E. Wainwright, J. Chem. Phys. 53 (1970) 3813 ; Phys. Rev. A4 (1971) 233.

11) W.W. Wood, in this volume, and W.W. Wood in The Boltzmann Equation, E.G.D. Cohen and W. Thirring, eds., op. cit., p. 451.

12) J.R. Dorfman and E.G.D. Cohen, Phys. Rev. Letters, 25 (1970) 1257; Phys. Rev., A6 (1972) 776; and W.W. Wood, J.J. Erpenbeck, J.R. Dorfman and E.G.D. Cohen (to be published).

13) Y. Pomeau, Phys. Rev., A3 (1971) 1174; and Y. Pomeau and P. Resibois, Phys. Letters, A44 (1973) 97; P. Resibois, Physics, 70 (1973) 413.

14) J. Dufty, Phys. Rev., A5 (1972) 2247.

15) See also E. Hauge, Phys. Rev. Letters, 28 (1972) 1501; E.H. Hauge and J.T. Ubbink, Physica, 70 (1973) 297; G.F. Mazenko, Phys. Rev., A7 (1973) 209, 222; and Phys. Rev. A9 (1974) 360; R. Kapral and M. Weinberg, Phys. Rev., A8 (1973) 1008.

16) There is a large literature on the short time behavior. For references c.f. H.H.U. Konijnendijk and J.M.J. van Leeuwen, Physica, 64 (1973) 342.

17) R. Zwanzig and M. Bixon, Phys. Rev. A2 (1970) 2005.
18) M.H. Ernst, E.H. Hauge, and J.M.J. van Leeuwen, Phys. Rev. Letters, 25 (1970) 1254; Phys. Rev., A4 (1971) 2055.
19) Y. Pomeau, Phys. Rev., A5 (1972) 2569; A7 (1973) 1134.
20) R. Zwanzig, in Proceedings of the Sixth IUPAC Conference on Statistical Mechanics, S.A. Rice, K.F. Freed and J.C. Light, eds., (University of Chicago Press, Chicago, 1972).
21) K. Kawasaki, Prog. Theoret. Phys. (Kyoto), 45 (1971) 1961; Phys. Letters 34A (1971) 12.
22) M.H. Ernst and J.R. Dorfman (to be published).
23) T. Keyes and I. Oppenheim, Phys. Rev., A7 (1973) 1384; see also J. Deutch in A.I.P. Proceedings, No. 11, Transport Phenomena, J. Kestin, ed., (American Institute of Physics, New York, 1973) p. 71.
24) D. Bedeaux and P. Mazur, Physica, 73 (1974).
25) M.H. Ernst, J.R. Dorfman, W.R. Hoegy, and J.M.J. van Leeuwen, Physica, 45 (1969) 127. See also J.V. Sengers, M.H. Ernst, and D.T. Gillespie, J. Chem. Phys., 56 (1972) 5583.
26) T. Hill, Statistical Mechanics, (McGraw-Hill, New York, 1956), p. 184.
27) E.H. Hauge, M.H. Ernst, and J.M.J. van Leeuwen, Private communication.
28) M.H. Ernst and J.R. Dorfman, Physica, 61 (1972) 157.
29) The literature on this divergence is extensive. For references prior to 1969, see M.H. Ernst, L.K. Haines, and J.R. Dorfman, Rev. Mod. Phys., 41 (1969) 296. For explicit calculations for hard disk systems see J.V. Sengers, Phys. Fluids, 9 (1966) 1685; and L.K. Haines, J.R. Dorfman and M.H. Ernst, Phys. Rev., 144 (1966) 207. For more recent work on hard sphere systems see Y. Pomeau and A. Gervois, Phys. Rev., A9 (1974) 2196.
30) K. Kawasaki and I. Oppenheim, Phys. Rev., 139A (1965) 1763.
31) We now follow the presentation of J.R. Dorfman and E.G.D. Cohen, ref. 12.
32) J.R. Dorfman and E.G.D. Cohen (to be published).
33) G.F. Mazenko, ref. 15, has arrived at a somewhat different result for the high density value of the coefficient of the $t^{-3/2}$ tail in three dimensions. Although there seem to be some inconsistenciesin this work, c.f. G.F. Mazenko, Phys. Rev., A9 (1974) 360; and C. Boley, Ann. Phys. (to appear), the reason for the disagreement between Mazenko's results and those given here has not yet been clarified.
34) M.H. Ernst, H. van Beijeren, and I. de Schepper, private communication; and M.H. Ernst and H. van Beijeren (to be published).
35) L.P. Kadanoff and J. Swift, Phys. Rev., 166 (1968) 89.
36) K. Kawasaki, Ann. Phys., 61 (1970) 1; see also Critical Phenomena, M.S. Green, ed., (Academic Press, New York, 1971), p. 342.

37) R.A. Ferrell, Phys. Rev. Letters 24 (1970) 1169; see also Dynamical Aspects of Critical Phenomena, J.I. Budnick, and M.P. Kawatra, Eds., (Gordon and Breach, New York, 1972), p. 1.

38) Strictly speaking one should add terms proportional to the gradients of the hydrodynamic variables to the right hand side of eq. (9.4), since as discussed in Section 2, the local equilibrium function is simply the first term in an expansion of the single particle distribution function in powers of the gradients. However, the terms neglected in (9.4) can be shown to lead to a more rapid decay of $\rho_D^{(d)}(t)$ than $t^{-d/2}$.

39) M.H. Ernst, E.H. Hauge, and J.M.J. van Leeuwen (to be published).

40) M.H. Ernst and H. van Beijeren (to be published).

41) I.M. de Schepper, H. van Beijeren, and M.H. Ernst (to appear in Physica).

42) J. Dufty and J.A. McLennan, Phys. Rev. A9 (1974) 1266.

43) T. Keyes and I. Oppenheim, Physica 70 (1973) 100.

44) M.H. Ernst and J.R. Dorfman (to be published).

COMPUTER STUDIES ON FLUID SYSTEMS OF HARD-CORE PARTICLES

W. W. Wood *)

Los Alamos Scientific Laboratory

of the University of California.

1. INTRODUCTION

During the last two decades computational studies of the equilibrium and transport properties of simple models of molecular systems have exerted a profound influence on the progress of statistical mechanical research. In these lectures we will review the two principal techniques which are used in such studies, i.e., the "Monte Carlo" and the "molecular dynamics" methods, with an emphasis upon conveying an understanding of the principles upon which they are based and an appreciation of their limitations, rather than dwelling on details of implementation. We will then summarize a few of the principal results which have been obtained to date, and describe some current studies of the self-diffusion process discussed by Prof. Dorfman in his lectures, which should be consulted for a thorough discussion of the theoretical foundations in this area.

Although more complicated molecular models have been considered practically from the beginning, in these lectures we will limit our discussion almost exclusively to hard-core systems, partly because such expertise as your lecturer possesses regarding the molecular dynamics method is limited to these systems, and partly because it is for these systems that one can make the most detailed comparisons with the predictions of the more fundamental theories.

In Section 2. Monte Carlo methods for the computation of equilibrium thermodynamic properties are discussed, followed in Section 3. by a discussion of the computation of both equilibrium and transport properties by molecular dynamics techniques. Section 4. contains a discussion of a few previous results for various hard-core systems, with Section 5. being devoted to some current studies of self-diffusion in hard disks and spheres. The short concluding section attempts to sketch a few direction in which future work might be profitable.

No effort has been made to present an exhaustive review and compilation of references, as that would be beyond the scope of these lectures. A few references giving more extensive and detailed treatments, especially work on systems of particles with other than hard-core interactions, are Alder[1)], Berne[2)], Berne and Forster[3)], Ree[4)], McDonald and Singer[5)], and Verlet[6)].

2. MONTE CARLO

2.2. Monte Carlo methods in general.

In numerical computation a Monte Carlo method is one in which explicitly stochastic or probabilistic techniques are used in solving some problem, which may be strictly deterministic (e.g., the evaluation of a definite integral), or may itself involve probabilistic elements (e.g., the absorption of neutrons by matter

Fundamental Problems in Statistical Mechanics, Vol. 3, Editor, E.D.G. Cohen.

described in bulk terms). The monograph by Hammersley and Handscomb[7] is a standard reference, with discussions of a wide range of applications. The name "Monte Carlo" and its first large scale applications originated at Los Alamos during World War II, in the hands of Fermi, Ulam, and von Neumann, although Hammersley and Handscomb mention some earlier isolated instances of the use of such methods (e.g., in the discovery of the well-known "Student's t-distribution").

Evidently, then, in order to discuss such methods we will need some of the notions and definitions of probability theory, chief of which are the notions of a statistical population and of sampling from such a population. The various statistical mechanical ensembles are examples of statistical populations which are familiar to all of us. And everyone will recall in this connection the frequent assumption that the possible outcomes of a physical experiment are normally distributed about a mean which is the "true value" which the experiment is intended to measure, and the further assumption that the performing of the experiment corresponds to sampling from this distribution. The observations or events or states which make up the statistical population may in some cases take on only a discrete set of values (e.g., the outcome of rolling a die), and in other cases they may have a continuum of values (e.g., the energy in the canonical ensemble). In the abstract, a Monte Carlo calculation is nothing more than a carrying out on a calculator of a sequence of such sampling operations from appropriate distributions, then combining these results in such a way as to give a final quantity (the "answer") which can be shown to have an expectation value equal to the "true" value, i.e., the value of a definite integral, or the expectation value of the physical stochastic process (e.g., the probability of a neutron penetrating some specified thickness of shielding).

Thus, the fundamental Monte Carlo procedure is that of sampling from a statistical population with a given probability density, or as we will uasually say, sampling from a given probability density.

2.1.1. Pseudo-random number generators

How does one cause a digital calculator, in many ways the epitome of a mindless deterministic automaton, to perform such a stochastic procedure? The basic tool is provided by the pseudo-random number generators, which are merely various methods of generating a sequence of numbers $x_1, x_2, x_3, \ldots$ which appear to be independent samples from the rectangular probability density,

$$p(x) = 1 \quad \text{for } 0 < x < 1 \qquad\qquad (2.1)$$
$$= 0 \quad \text{otherwise}$$

By independent we mean in the sense of independent trials in probability theory (e.g., successive rolls of a die), i.e., the outcome of the $n + 1^{th}$ trial (the value of x_{n+1}) is independent of the outcomes of any of the preceding or following trials. The emphasis on the work "appear" in the above definition is very important, and correlates with the prefix "pseudo" in the title of this class of procedures, inasmuch as all the commonly used procedures are in fact completely deterministic: x_n is a completely determined function of one or more of its predecessors x_{n-1}, ... The art lies of course in selecting a function which is complicated enough to approximate the desired properties, and simple enough to compute with reasonable efficiency. The most frequently used generators in fact belong to the very simple multiplicative congruential family in which positive integers z_1, z_2, ... are generated by

$$z_n = \lambda\, z_{n-1} \quad \text{modulo } M$$

with (2.2)

$$x_n = z_n/M$$

On binary machines the modulus M is usually taken to be of the form 2^B, where B is an integer, and the parameters λ and z_1 usually satisfy the congruences

$$\lambda \equiv 5 \text{ modulo } 8$$

(2.3)

$$z_1 \equiv 1 \text{ or } 5 \text{ modulo } 8 \ .$$

Quite a bit is known about the statistical properties (i.e., how well they approximate independent samples from the rectangular probability density) of this class of generators from number theory considerations[†].
We mention here only a few of the known properties of such a generator:

1. It has period 2^{B-2}, producing once per period all the numbers z_n congruent to 1 and 5 modulo 8 between 0 and 2^B, in an order which depends on the specific multiplier λ.

2. There exist rather simple procedures[10] for computing directly z_n given n and n given z_n, for specified λ and z_1.

3. Successive pairs of points (x_1,x_2), (x_3,x_4), ... form a lattice[11,12] in the unit square, with similar properties in spaces of higher dimensionality. The shape of the fundamental unit cell of the lattice depends on the multiplier, with

---

[†] See, e.g., the monograph by Jansson[8] and a forthcoming one by Dieter and Ahrens[9].

some values of λ producing very elongated unit cells. Nevertheless, with appropriate multipliers such generators have been found to produce reliable results[†)].

2.1.2. Non-uniform random number generators

Given a procedure for generating uniformly distributed random numbers, there exist various techniques for sampling from more general distributions. If the cumulative distribution $P(x)$ corresponding to the desired probability density $p(x)$ is easily invertible, then one can compute numbers distributed according to $p(x)$ by means of the relation $x = P^{-1}(\xi)$ from uniformly distributed random numbers ξ. For example, the numbers $x = -\ln \xi$ are exponentially distributed over the positive x axis.

The "rejection technique" of von Neumann is applicable to the general class of probability densities $p(x)$ which are zero outside some interval $[a,b]$ and bounded, $p(x) < c$, inside the interval. The procedure is

1. $0 \to n$
2. Generate uniformly distributed random numbers ξ_{2n}, ξ_{2n+1}
3. $a + (b-a)\xi_{2n+1} \to x$
4. If $c\xi_{2n} \le p(x)$, accept x and exit; otherwise $n + 2 \to n$, go to 2.

More efficient procedures are known for many special cases, and we will mention only the Box-Muller (sine-cosine) method for generating normally distributed numbers. If ξ_1 and ξ_2 are two independent uniform random numbers, then the numbers

$$
\begin{aligned}
u_1 &= (-2 \ln \xi_1)^{1/2} \cos 2\pi\xi_2 \\
u_2 &= (-2 \ln \xi_1)^{1/2} \sin 2\pi\xi_2
\end{aligned}
\tag{2.4}
$$

are independently normally distributed with zero mean and unit variance. Still more efficient procedures are known; see Hammersley and Handscomb[7)], Jannson[8)], and Dieter and Ahrens[9)].

2.1.3. Evaluation of definite integrals.

Consider now the problem of evaluating a multidimensional integral

---

†) See, e.g., Wood[11)] in the case of statistical mechanical calculations of the type described in these lectures. This reference also gives an example using the very poor multiplier $\lambda = 5$, in which the results were nevertheless quite reasonable. This suggests that at least in some cases such calculations are quite insensitive to gross abnormalities in the generator.

$$F = \int d\vec{x}\ f(\vec{x}) \tag{2.5}$$

over the n-dimensional hypercube, $f(\vec{x})$ being a given bounded function. The simplest Monte Carlo procedure (sometimes referred to as the "crude Monte Carlo" procedure) is to generate a sequence of independent, uniformly distributed points $\vec{x}_i$, $i = 1, 2, \ldots M$, in the hypercube, and calculate the average value

$$F_M = M^{-1} \Sigma f(\vec{x}_i) \tag{2.6}$$

over this set of points. It is easy to show that this estimate has an expectation value equal to the desired integral,

$$\langle F_M \rangle = F \tag{2.7}$$

and the variance

$$\text{var } F_M = \langle F_M^2 \rangle - \langle F_M \rangle^2 = M^{-1} \int d\vec{x}\,[f(\vec{x})-F]^2 = M^{-1} [\int d\vec{x}\ f(\vec{x})^2 - F^2] \tag{2.8}$$

Thus, by increasing M the expected error can be made as small as one likes, in principle. However, if the significant contribution to the integral comes from only a very small portion of the hypercube, then quite large values of M may be necessary. For example, suppose that $f(\vec{x})$ vanishes everywhere, except over a small region of volume ε in which it is identically equal to unity. (This situation arises in the statistical mechanics of hard-core systems.) Then $F = \varepsilon$, $\text{var } F_M = \varepsilon(1-\varepsilon)/M$, and the relative error $(\text{var } F_M)^{1/2}/F$ is $[(1-\varepsilon)/\varepsilon M]^{1/2} \sim (\varepsilon M)^{-1/2}$. An estimate good to 1%, say, would then require $M \gtrsim 10^4 \varepsilon^{-1}$.

Suppose that $f(\vec{x})$ is roughly proportional to a known function $g(\vec{x})$, so that the regions which make important contributions to the integral of $f(\vec{x})$ are also important regions for the integral

$$G = \int d\vec{x}\ g(\vec{x}) \tag{2.9}$$

We further assume that $g(\vec{x})$ is everywhere positive, and that its integral G is known. We can then write

$$\begin{aligned} F &= GH \\ H &= \int d\vec{x}\ h(\vec{x}) p(\vec{x}) \\ h(\vec{x}) &= f(\vec{x})/g(\vec{x}) \\ p(\vec{x}) &= g(\vec{x})/G \end{aligned} \tag{2.10}$$

with $p(\vec{x})$ being interpreted as a probability density. Finally, we suppose that we know how to sample points from $p(\vec{x})$. Repeating the "crude Monte Carlo" procedure, but with the sequence of points $\vec{x}_1, \vec{x}_2, \ldots, \vec{x}_M$ now being samples from $p(\vec{x})$, we form the estimates

$$H_M = M^{-1} \Sigma\, h(\vec{x}_i)$$
$$F_M = G\, H_M \qquad (2.11)$$

with $\langle F_M \rangle = F$ and

$$\text{var } H_M = M^{-1} \int d\vec{x}\, [h(\vec{x}) - H]^2 \qquad (2.12)$$

and standard relative error in F_M equal to

$$(\text{var } F_M)^{1/2}/F_M = [(MH)^{-1} \int d\vec{x}\, [h(\vec{x}) - H]^2]^{1/2} \qquad (2.13)$$

It may happen, with a suitable choice of $g(\vec{x})$, that this relative error can be made smaller than that of the crude Monte Carlo estimate. But with an unfortunate choice of $g(\vec{x})$ the opposite can also be the case. This procedure is called "importance sampling", because in sampling with probability proportional to the known function $g(\vec{x})$ we are attempting to weight more heavily the regions making the important contributions to the desired integral.

2.2. Statistical Mechanical Preliminaries

2.2.1. Canonical Ensemble Relations

We will limit our discussion here to one-component systems of classical structureless particles interacting through central forces, and to the canonical ensemble[†)]. Then the Helmholtz free energy $A(N,V,T)$ of a system of N particles confined to a volume V in equilibrium with a heat bath at temperature T is given by

$$\exp[-\beta A(N,V,T)] = \lambda^{-dN} N!^{-1} Q(N,V,T) \qquad (2.14)$$

where $\lambda = (\beta h^2/2\pi m)^{1/2}$ is the thermal wavelength, d is the dimensionality, and

---

†) For a recent application of very sophisticated Monte Carlo techniques to a quantum mechanical system see Kalos, Levesque, and Verlet[13)]. For calculations in the isothermal-isobaric ensemble, see Wood[14)] for systems of single-component hard disks, and McDonald[15)] for binary mixtures of Lennard-Jones 12-6 particles.

$$Q(N,V,T) = \int d\vec{r}^N \exp[-\beta U(\vec{r}^N)] \tag{2.15}$$

is the configuration integral. The symbols have their usual meanings, $\beta = 1/k_B T$, k_B = Boltzmann's constant, h = Planck's constant, m = particle mass. The potential energy is assumed to be given by a sum of pair-wise interactions

$$U(\vec{r}^N) = \frac{1}{2} \sum_i \sum_j{}' u(r_{ij}) \tag{2.16}$$

where u(r) is the inter-particle pair potential, and $r_{ij} = |\vec{r}_j - \vec{r}_i|$ is the distance between the centers of particles i and j. The symbol $\vec{r}^N$ stands for the collection $\vec{r}_1, \vec{r}_2, \ldots \vec{r}_N$, and in the multiple integration in eq. (2.15) each $\vec{r}_i$ runs over the entire volume V. In eq. (2.16) the summations run over both i and j from 1 to N, with the prime indicating that terms j = i are omitted.

From the Helmholtz free energy as given by eq. (2.14) all the other thermodynamic quantities can be obtained by standard thermodynamic relations. For example, the internal energy E is given by

$$E = \frac{1}{2} d\, N\, k_B\, T + \langle U(\vec{r}^N)\rangle \tag{2.17}$$

and the pressure p of the system is given by the virial equation

$$pV/N\, k_B\, T = 1 - d^{-1} \beta\, \langle W(\vec{r}^N)\rangle / N \tag{2.18}$$

where

$$W(\vec{r}^N) = \frac{1}{2} \sum_i \sum_j{}' r_{ij}\, d\, u(r_{ij})/d\, r_{ij} \tag{2.19}$$

The angular brackets symbolize the usual canonical ensemble configurational average

$$\langle f(\vec{r}^N)\rangle = Q(N,V,T)^{-1} \int d\vec{r}^N f(\vec{r}^N) \exp[-\beta U(r^N)] \tag{2.20}$$

2.2.2. Finite Periodic Systems

Before discussing Monte Carlo techniques for the evaluation of expressions of the form (2.20), we note that it would be out of question to consider the arithmetical computation of functions such as $U(\vec{r}^N)$ if N were to have a value appropriate to macroscopic thermodynamic systems, i.e. of the order of Avogrado's number. Even with the largest calculating machinery currently available, we can deal with systems of at the most a few thousand particles. To make such small systems have properties approximating those of systems of macroscopic size we impose "periodic boundary conditions". It is then, first of all, necessary that the volume V of the system have a shape that is d-dimensional space-filling under appropriate translations. For notational convenience we will formally suppose it to be a "cube"†) of edge $L = V^{1/d}$ (i.e., a square for d = 2). We can thus imagine space to be filled by indefinite replication of the volume V and its N constituent particles; see Fig. 2.1. for a two-dimensional representation.

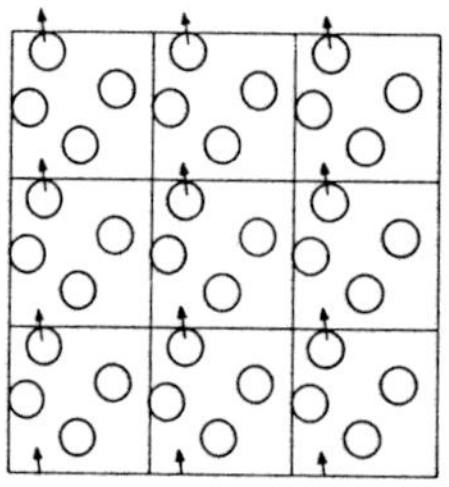

Fig. 2.1. A periodic system of four hard disks.

If particle i in the original volume V was located at position $\vec{r}_i$ (relative to a fixed origin) then "image" particles are located at positions $\vec{r}_i + L\vec{\nu}$ where $\vec{\nu} = (\nu_1, \nu_2, \ldots, \nu_d)$ and each ν_i takes on all integer values from $-\infty$ to $+\infty$. Each particle i in a given cell interacts in principle with all the other particles j in all cells, including its own. Thus, eqs. (2.16) and (2.19) giving the potential energy and virial assigned to the N particles in one cell of volume V are replaced by

$$U(\vec{r}^N) = \frac{1}{2} \sum_{\vec{\nu}} \sum_i \sum_j{}' u(|L\vec{\nu} + \vec{r}_{ij}|)$$
$$W(\vec{r}^N) = \frac{1}{2} \sum_{\vec{\nu}} \sum_i \sum_j{}' |L\vec{\nu} + \vec{r}_{ij}| du(|L\vec{\nu} + \vec{r}_{ij}|)/d|L\vec{\nu} + \vec{r}_{ij}| \qquad (2.21)$$

the sum over $\vec{\nu}$ ranging over all integer component vectors as previously described. The remaining equations of the previous section, i.e., eqs. (2.14), (2.15), (2.17), (2.18), and (2.20) are unchanged, the integrations being carried out over any one of the cells of volume V. According to eq. (2.21), $U(\vec{r}^N)$ is periodic with period L in any and all of its arguments, e.g., $U(\vec{r}_1+L\vec{\nu}_1, \vec{r}_2+L\vec{\nu}_2, \ldots, \vec{r}_N+L\vec{\nu}_N) = U(\vec{r}_1, \vec{r}_2, \ldots, \vec{r}_N)$ for any set of N integer vectors $\vec{\nu}_i$, i = 1, 2, ..., N.

Finally, in the case of long-ranged interactions, such as the Lennard-Jones potential, the pair potential u(r) is set equal to zero beyond some cutoff distance r_c in order that the summation over $\vec{\nu}$ can be restricted to a finite set

†) Actually, as will be mentioned shortly, in two-dimensions the appropriate shapes are rectangles. It is not difficult to modify the arguments to apply to these cases, but for notational simplicity, we omit doing so.

of integer vectors. The most common choice of cutoff is $r_c = L/2$, which results in at most one vector $\vec{\nu}$ contributing to the sums in eq. (2.21) for each pair of particles, the so-called minimum image-distance convention. Corrections for the missing interactions at distances greater than r_c can be made in approximate fashion.

The properties of such periodic systems are discussed in some detail elsewhere[16] and we will here only state some of the results.

1.) The system has d ideal-gas degrees of freedom corresponding to free translation of the center of mass.

2.) As a consequence of 1.), the single particle density $\rho_1(\vec{s}_1) = \langle \sum_i \delta(\vec{r}_i - \vec{s}_1) \rangle$ is uniform, $\rho_1(\vec{s}_1) = n = N/V$ irrespective of whether the system is in a fluid or crystalline phase.

3.) The radial distribution function

$$g(\vec{s}_1, \vec{s}_2) = n^{-2} \langle \sum_{\vec{\nu}_1} \sum_{\vec{\nu}_2} \sum_i \sum_j{}' \delta(L\vec{\nu}_1 + \vec{r}_i - \vec{s}_1) \delta(L\vec{\nu}_2 + \vec{r}_j - \vec{s}_2) \rangle \tag{2.22}$$

depends only on the relative vector $\vec{s}_{12} = \vec{s}_2 - \vec{s}_1$. Even in fluid systems some residual dependence on the orientation of $\vec{s}_{12}$ is to be expected, the dependence vanishing and g becoming a function of just the magnitude s_{12} in the thermodynamic limit. The radial distribution function as actually calculated for finite N is the spherical average of the slightly orientationally dependent $g(\vec{s}_{12})$.

4.) Except perhaps at very low densities, the volume V should be chosen to be a unit cell for the crystallographic lattice appropriate to the high-density behavior of the system. For three dimensional systems this will be either the face-centered or hexagonal close-packed lattice, with the former being the usual choice. For hard disks it is the planar triangular lattice for which the convenient possible values of N are of the form $2\nu_1\nu_2$ where ν_1 and ν_2 are integers, and V is a rectangle with sides in the ratio $\nu_2\sqrt{3}/\nu_1$. In three dimensions V is usually taken to be a cube, with the possible values of N being of the form $4\nu^3$, with ν an integer.

2.3. Feasibility of Using "Crude Monte Carlo" to Calculate Thermodynamic Properties

If we introduce the normalized canonical ensemble probability density

$$\rho_N(\vec{r}^N) = Q(N,V,T)^{-1} \exp[-\beta U(\vec{r}^N)] \tag{2.23}$$

then eq. (2.20) takes on the same form as the function H, eq. (2.10), in our discussion of importance sampling, e.g.,

$$\langle U(\vec{r}^N) \rangle = \int d\vec{r}^N \, U(\vec{r}^N) \rho_N(\vec{r}^N) \tag{2.24}$$

There is, however, a crucial difference. We don't know how to numerically evaluate $\rho_N(\vec{r}^N)$. We can, of course, calculate $U(\vec{r}^N)$ for small periodic systems of the type discussed in the previous section, but we don't know how to evaluate $Q(N,V,T)$ analytically. In fact, if we could do so, the entire problem would be solved.

Let us first consider the possibility of using "crude Monte Carlo" to evaluate $Q(N,V,T)$ from its definition eq. (2.15)

$$Q(N,V,T) = \int d\vec{r}^N \exp[-\beta U(\vec{r}^N)]$$

and let us consider the case of hard spheres of diameter σ. For this system $U(\vec{r}^N)$ takes on only the values 0 (for the allowed states in which no particles overlap) and ∞ (one or more overlaps). Thus, the integrand takes on only the values 0 and 1, i.e., it is just the same type which we considered as an example of the difficulties which the "crude Monte Carlo" method can encounter. In order to get an idea of the order of magnitude of $Q(N,V,T)/V^N$, which is equal to the quantity ε of the previous discussion (the probability of finding a nonvanishing integrand at a randomly selected point $\vec{r}^N$), we note that for hard spheres

$$Q(N,V,T)/V^N = \exp[N(S_{ex}/Nk_B)] \tag{2.25}$$

where S_{ex}/N is the excess entropy per particle with respect to the ideal gas value at the same density and temperature. At low densities we can use the virial expansion, which is known from the work of Ree and Hoover[17] through the seventh virial coefficient for both hard disks and spheres, and at higher densities their P(3,3) Padé approximant can be used up to the vicinity of the freezing transition. At very low densities, for hard spheres,

$$-S_{ex}/Nk_B = 2.96192\ \tau^{-1} + 2.74155\ \tau^{-2} + \mathcal{O}(\tau^{-3})$$

where

$$\tau = V/V_o \tag{2.26}$$

and

$$V_o = \frac{1}{2}\sqrt{2}\ N\ \sigma^3$$

is the close packed volume. From Hoover and Ree's[18] tabulation of S_{ex}/Nk_B calculated from the Padé approximant, we have the values given in Table 2.1.

TABLE 2.1.

Excess Entropy S_{ex}/Nk_B for hard spheres[18)]

V_o/V	$-S_{ex}/Nk_B$
0	0
0.05	0.155
0.10	0.326
0.20	0.726
0.30	1.225
0.40	1.864
0.50	2.702
0.60	3.843
0.70	5.463

From these values and Eq. (2.25) it is clear that "crude Monte Carlo" can be useful only for small N and low density. It should also be noted that this procedure requires the use on each trial configuration $\vec{r}^N$ of new randomly-selected positions of all particles. As Widom[19)] has discussed in detail, the process of sequential addition of particles, in which $\vec{r}_n$ is rejected if it overlaps with any of the particles $\vec{r}_1, \vec{r}_2, \ldots, \vec{r}_{n-1}$, and a new randomly selected value of $\vec{r}_n$ being then tested with the same $\vec{r}_1, \ldots, \vec{r}_{n-1}$, does not sample from the canonical ensemble. In the only actual attempt, as far as we are aware, at using the "crude Monte Carlo" method on hard sphere or similar systems, the sequential addition process was in fact used[20)].

Considering next the "importance sampling" method which was described in § 2.1.3., it is difficult to see how to construct a suitable $g(\vec{r}^N)$. At sufficiently high densities, near close-packing, one might be able to use a product of gaussian functions sharply peaked around the lattice sites. As far as we are aware, nothing along these lines has been tried. At medium densities, particularly those of interest in the theory of liquids, the construction of a useful $g(\vec{r}^N)$ would appear to be a difficult task. The admissible points in configuration space for hard spheres [i.e., the points with $U(\vec{r}^N) = 0$], or for more general interactions, the regions of space in which $U(\vec{r}^N)$ is of the order of Nk_BT, then constitute an exceedingly small, convoluted, and filamentary portion of the total configuration space. A more sophisticated Monte Carlo method is evidently required.

2.4. The Metropolis, Rosenbluth, Teller Method

Such a method was developed by Metropolis, Rosenbluth, Rosenbluth, Teller, and Teller[21)]; see also Rosenbluth and Rosenbluth[22)]. Its development was based in part on the realization that for most purposes it would suffice to be able to evaluate averages such as eq. (2.20), which give the usual thermodynamic internal energy and equation of state, rather than trying to evaluate Q(N,V,T) itself. If these quantities are available in sufficient precision and detail, the other functions such as Q(N,V,T) and the related variables entropy and free energy can be obtained by integration of the equation of state. So what was needed was a method of moving a state point $\vec{r}^N$ about in such a way that its average history would give averages of the type desired, i.e., it should weight more heavily the region of low energy, and avoid entirely regions of infinite potential energy in the case of hard-core particles. In other words, one needed to construct the right kind of random walk process, a subject which has long formed a part of probability theory. The appropriate procedure in fact turned out to be the quite well-known Markov chain, which we discuss in the next section.

2.4.1. Markov Chains

Markov processes, and in particular the special case of Markov chains, are discussed in detail in many textbooks in probability theory [e.g., Feller[23], Doob[24], Kemeny and Snell[25]]. We summarize here only the more important features for our application. The previous discussed "crude Monte Carlo" and "importance sampling" procedures are "independent trials" processes in which the probability of occurrence of each state at the tth trial is independent of the outcome of the preceding trials. Markov processes are generalized stochastic processes in which the probabilities depend on the outcomes of the previous trials. We consider only the case in which the set of possible states is finite. We also follow the usual terminology[†] in which a succession of states is considered to develop in "time", so that we speak of the occurrence of some state at time t, and we consider here the discrete case in which t takes on the values 0,1,2, ... The state at t = 0 is called the initial state. We denote the possible states of the system by $\vec{r}^N_1$, $\vec{r}^N_2$, ..., $\vec{r}^N_M$, where M is the number of states. The particular one of these states which actually occurs at time t in some actual development of the process is denoted by $\vec{r}^N(t) \equiv \vec{r}^N_{i(t)}$, and the equivalent sequences $\vec{r}^N(o)$, $\vec{r}^N(1)$,... and i(o), i(1), ... are called a realization of the process. If $f(\vec{r}^N)$ is any function of the state variables, then

$$\bar{f}(t) = t^{-1} \sum_{t'=0}^{t-1} f[\vec{r}^N(t')] \tag{2.27}$$

is called the realization average of $f(\vec{r}^N)$ after t steps. We further assume that the probability of occurrence of each state at any time t > 0 depends only on the state at time t - 1. In particular, it is independent of the state at any earlier

[†] It is important to note that this "time" variable measuring the number of steps in the random walk has in general no relation to physical molecular times. The molecular velocities have of course been "integrated out" of the probability density, and we are concerned only with configurational averages.

times t - 2, t - 3, etc., and of t itself. Such a process is called a finite, stationary Markov chain. It is completely described by giving 1.) the probabilities of occurrence of the various states at t = 0, and 2.) the "one-step" probability matrix p_{ij} giving the probability that state i will be immediately succeeded by state j. The subscripts i and j each run over the complete set of states, so that under the previous assumptions it follows that the matrix is square and of finite size, and that

$$p_{ij} \geq 0 \qquad\qquad \sum_j p_{ij} = 1 \tag{2.28}$$

The "n-step" transition probability $p_{ij}^{(n)}$, i.e., the probability of reaching state j in n steps from state i, is just the (i,j)-element of the n-th power of the one-step probability matrix. A chain is <u>ergodic</u> if for every pair of states i and j there exists some finite n such that $p_{ij}^{(n)} > 0$. If then the recurrence probabilities $p_{ii}^{(n)}$ are non-zero only for n equal to a multiple of some integer q > 1, the chain is called periodic with period q; otherwise it is <u>aperiodic</u>. We will limit our discussions to chains which are <u>ergodic</u> and <u>aperiodic</u>. It can be shown that for such chains the limits

$$\lim_{n\to\infty} p_{ij}^{(n)} = u_j \tag{2.29}$$

exist, are independent of i, and are uniquely given as the solution of the system of "steady-state" equations

$$\sum_i u_i p_{ij} = u_j \qquad j = 1, 2, \ldots, M \tag{2.30}$$

subject to the conditions

$$u_i \geq 0 \qquad\qquad \sum u_i = 1 \tag{2.31}$$

Also, under suitable restrictions on the function $f(\vec{r}^N)$, the realization average $\overline{f}(t)$ given by eq. (2.27) converges <u>in probability</u> as $t \to \infty$ to the corresponding "ensemble average" $\langle f(\vec{r}^N)\rangle$,

$$\lim_{t\to\infty} \overline{f}(t) \sim \langle f(\vec{r}^N)\rangle \tag{2.32}$$

with

$$\langle f(\vec{r}^N)\rangle = \sum_i u_i f_i$$
$$f_i = f[\vec{r}_i^N] \qquad (2.33)$$

For large t the deviation $\bar{f}(t) - \langle f(\vec{r}^N)\rangle$ is asymptotically normally distributed with a variance proportional to t^{-1} (central limit theorem for Markov chains).

2.4.2. Construction of a Probability Matrix.

From the discussion of the previous section, it is immediately clear that a random walk of Markov chain type should provide a suitable Monte Carlo technique for estimating averages such as the average potential energy, as given by eq. (2.24). We will assume that we can replace the continuous configuration space $\vec{r}^N$ by a suitable discretization $\vec{r}_1^N, \vec{r}_2^N, \ldots, \vec{r}_M^N$ with a finite (albeit a very large) number M of states. This must be possible if any sort of arithmetic numerical calculation is to be useful. We assume that it is done in such a way that each state $\vec{r}_i^N$ corresponds to the same volume Δr^N of configuration space. The finite sum approximation to eq. (2.24), for example, is then

$$\langle U(\vec{r}^N)\rangle = \sum_i U(\vec{r}_i^N) u_i$$
$$u_i = \Delta r^N \rho_N(\vec{r}_i^N) \qquad (2.34)$$

which is of the same form as eq. (2.33). The corresponding realization average, eq. (2.27) with $f(\vec{r}^N) = U(\vec{r}^N)$, which we can calculate by actually developing on the calculating machine a realization of the Markov chain, will then converge (in probability) to the desired value given by eq. (2.34), provided we can find a probability matrix satisfying eq. (2.30) and the other conditions mentioned in the previous section. And, most importantly, we see from eq. (2.30) that we do not need to know the ensemble probabilities u_i themselves, rather it is sufficient to know the quantities $\exp[-\beta U(\vec{r}_i^N)]$, to which the u_i are proportional. We need only to construct the matrix p_{ij} so that it satisfies the equations

$$\sum_i p_{ij} \exp[-\beta U(\vec{r}_i^N)] = \exp[-\beta U(\vec{r}_j^N)], \quad j = 1, 2, \ldots M \qquad (2.35)$$

the normalization of the u_i being allowed to take care of itself. Next we note that it is sufficient, for eq. (2.35) to be satisfied, that the "microscopic reversibility" conditions

$$p_{ij} \exp[-\beta U(\vec{r}_i^N)] = p_{ji} \exp[-\beta U(\vec{r}_j^N)] \qquad (2.36)$$

be satisfied for all pairs (i,j) of states, along with the normalization and sign conditions given in eq. (2.28). It is a rather simple matter to construct probability matrices satisfying these conditions.

The most frequently used procedures are of the following type. Let A_{ij} be any symmetric stochastic matrix, i.e., any symmetric matrix with non-negative elements and normalized rows ($\sum_j A_{ij} = 1$). Then the matrix

$$p_{ij} = \begin{cases} A_{ij} & \text{for } U(\vec{r}^N_j) \le U(\vec{r}^N_i) \\ A_{ij}\exp\{-\beta[U(\vec{r}^N_j)-U(\vec{r}^N_i)]\} & \text{for } U(\vec{r}^N_j) > U(\vec{r}^N_i) \end{cases} \quad j\neq i \qquad (2.37)$$

$$p_{ii} = 1 - \sum_{j\neq i} p_{ij}$$

clearly satisfies eqs. (2.35), as well as the normalization and sign conditions. There is considerable latitude in the choice of the matrix A_{ij}. The usual procedure is to define for each state i, a set S_i of ΔM "neighboring"states. These neighbor sets are subject to the symmetry condition that if state j is contained in S_i, then i is contained in S_j. We then take

$$\begin{aligned} A_{ij} &= (\Delta M)^{-1} && \text{for } j \in S_i,\ j \neq i, \\ &= 0 && \text{otherwise} \end{aligned} \qquad (2.38)$$

The simplest choice of the neighbor set S_i of the state $\vec{r}^N_i = \{\vec{r}_1^{(i)}, \vec{r}_2^{(i)}, \ldots \vec{r}_N^{(i)}\}$ is the union of all the sets $C_k(\delta)$, k = 1,2,...N, where $C_k(\delta)$ consists of all the $\hat{\vec{r}}^N = \{\hat{\vec{r}}_1, \hat{\vec{r}}_2, \ldots \vec{r}_N\}$ having $\hat{\vec{r}}_\ell = \vec{r}_\ell^{(i)}$ for $\ell \neq k$ and $\hat{\vec{r}}_k$ contained in the d-dimensional "cube" of half-edge δ centered at $\vec{r}_k^{(i)}$. Here δ is a disposable parameter which, at least in principle, can be chosen to optimize the convergence of the Monte Carlo procedure. The number of states ΔM in the neighbor sets S_i of course depends on δ.

All of the foregoing description of the construction of the matrix p_{ij} will probably be much clearer from a simple description of the program for developing a realization on a calculator. Suppose that we have previously generated states up through $\vec{r}^N(t)$, and that $U[\vec{r}^N(t)]$ has been calculated. The next state $\vec{r}^N(t + 1)$ is generated as follows.

1.) Choose randomly and uniformly (i.e., with probability N^{-1}) one of the N particles, say particle k.

2.) Give particle k a trial position $\hat{\vec{r}}_k$ chosen randomly and uniformly in the d-dimensional cube of half-edge δ, centered at $\vec{r}_k(t)$. That is, if $\{x_{k1}(t), x_{k2}(t), \ldots x_{kd}(t)\}$ are the components of $\vec{r}_k(t)$, then the components of $\hat{\vec{r}}_k$ are $x_{k\alpha}(t) + (2\xi_\alpha - 1)\delta$, $\alpha = 1,2,\ldots,d$, where the numbers ξ_α are independent, uniformly distributed random numbers.

3.) Letting $\hat{\vec{r}}_\ell = \vec{r}_\ell(t)$ for $\ell = 1,2,\ldots, k-1, k+1, k+2, \ldots N$, we then have the trial state $\hat{\vec{r}}^N = \{\hat{\vec{r}}_1, \hat{\vec{r}}_2, \ldots, \hat{\vec{r}}_N\}$ with $\hat{\vec{r}}_k$ determined as in 2.

4.) Calculate $U(\hat{\vec{r}}^N)$ and $\Delta U = U(\hat{\vec{r}}^N) - U[\vec{r}^N(t)]$.

a. If $\Delta U \le 0$, take $\hat{\vec{r}}^N$ as the next state $\vec{r}^N(t+1)$.

b. If $\Delta U > 0$, generate a uniformly distributed random number ξ.

i. If $\exp[-\beta\Delta U] < \xi$, take $\hat{\vec{r}}^N$ as the next state $\vec{r}^N(t+1)$.

ii. Otherwise, take $\vec{r}^N(t+1)$ to be the same as the current state $\vec{r}^N(t)$.

It remains to show that the Markov chain defined by a probability matrix constructed according to the above procedure is ergodic and aperiodic. It is not difficult to show that it is aperiodic. If at least one of the neighbor states of some state i has higher potential energy than state i, then $p_{ii} > 0$, so that state i is aperiodic. And it then follows, although we omit the proof, that all states are aperiodic, i.e., the Markov chain is aperiodic, if it is ergodic. Thus, the latter property is the crucial one. In discussing the ergodic problem, we begin by omitting[†)] from the set of possible states all those with $U(\vec{r}^N) = \infty$. This is clearly legitimate, since according to the above procedure such states will never occur (assuming that they are not allowed to be chosen as the initial state) in the realization, and they of course do not contribute to the desired ensemble average. Having eliminated such "forbidden" states, we have to enquire whether the remaining "allowed" states form an ergodic set under the prescribed transition probabilities. On physical grounds it is clear that this will be the case when the particle density N/V is sufficiently low, even in the case of hard-core particles. On the same grounds it is equally clear that such will not be the case, for a fixed number of hard-core particles sufficiently near the close-packed density. A detailed discussion of the significance of Monte Carlo calculations under these last-mentioned conditions would take us too far afield here[16)]. For nonsingular interaction laws, the chain can be seen to be formally ergodic. But if the interactions are strongly repulsive, the situation is likely to be the same as for hard-core particles, from a practical point of view. From a physical point of view it seems likely, but certainly has not been proved, that the chain will be ergodic when the values of N, V, and T are such that the stable equilibrium phase is a fluid.

Many legitimate variants of the above procedure are possible[16)], including that in which particle k in Step 1 of the above procedure is chosen sequentially

---

†) The omission is solely for discussion of the ergodic properties of the remaining states. There exists no simple valid procedure for omitting the "forbidden states" (i.e., those with $U(\vec{r}^N) = \infty$) from among the sets S_i of neighbor states. See the subsequent discussion of attempts to avoid the repetition of state $\vec{r}^N(t)$ at time t + 1.

in the order 1, 2, ..., N, rather than randomly. It should perhaps be mentioned that there have been several attempts at avoiding the "undesirable" repetition at time t + 1 of the state at time t, by repeatedly starting over again at Step 1 or 2 until the trial state $\hat{\vec{r}}^N$ is finally accepted. This leads to convergence of the procedure to an ensemble average with other than the desired probability distribution, similar to the behavior of the sequential addition process for hard-core particle discussed in connection with the "crude Monte Carlo" method.

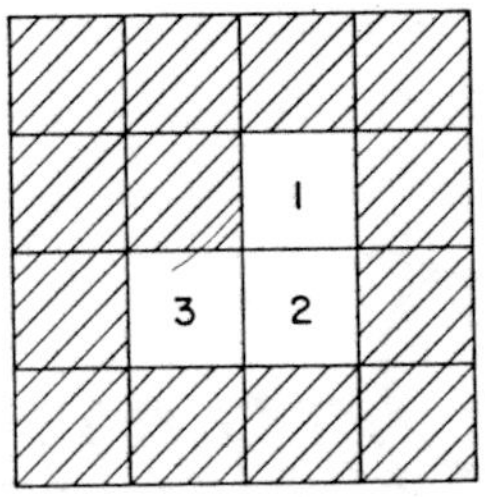

Fig. 2.2. A simple three-state system.

A simple example is shown in Fig. 2.2., where the squares (states) labeled 1, 2, and 3 are supposed to all have $U(\vec{r}^N) = 0$, and the shaded squares have $U(\vec{r}^N) = \infty$. The neighbor sets S_i of each square is assumed to be the four adjacent squares in the horizontal and vertical directions. The correct procedure corresponds to the probability matrix and correct steady state vector

$$(p_{ij}) = \begin{pmatrix} 3/4 & 1/4 & 0 \\ 1/4 & 1/2 & 1/4 \\ 0 & 1/4 & 3/4 \end{pmatrix}$$

$$u_i = (1/3,\ 1/3,\ 1/3)$$

while the incorrect "try and try again" procedure gives

$$(p_{ij}) = \begin{pmatrix} 0 & 1 & 0 \\ 1/2 & 0 & 1/2 \\ 0 & 1 & 0 \end{pmatrix}$$

$$(u_i) = (1/4,\ 1/2,\ 1/4)$$

Little precise information is known concerning the optimum value of δ in the procedure described. Values which lead to acceptance of the trial state $\hat{\vec{r}}^N$ on about one-half the trials have been found to give useful results in all the cases of which we are aware.

The central limit theorem mentioned at the end of Section 2.4.1. can be used to develop procedures for estimating the statistical reliability of the computed thermodynamic properties. From the foregoing discussion, it will be clear that for fluid phases the principal systemmatic error will usually arise from the use of a relatively small number of particles. For the most part one attempts to control and estimate these errors by comparing calculations using several different values of N.

3. MOLECULAR DYNAMICS

3.1. Generalities

In statistical mechanics and kinetic theory, the term "molecular dynamics" has come to refer to the investigation of the properties of classical N-particle systems by numerically integrating the Newtonian equations of motion

$$m\, d^2 \vec{r}_i/dt^2 = m\, d\vec{v}_i/dt = \vec{F}_i \qquad i = 1,2,\ldots,N$$
$$\vec{F}_i = -\vec{\nabla}_i\, U(\vec{r}^N) = -\partial U(\vec{r}^N)/\partial r_i = -\sum_j{}' \partial u(r_{ij})/\partial \vec{r}_i \qquad (3.1)$$

where $\vec{F}_i$ is the total force exerted on particle i by all the other particles of the system, m is the particle mass, $\vec{v}_i$ the velocity of particle i, and all other symbols have the same significance as in the preceding section. The pioneering work was done by Alder and Wainwright for hard-core systems, with the first results beginning to appear[26] about 1956, and by Rahman[27] for the Lennard-Jones 12-6 interaction. In addition to the equations of motion one needs, of course, to specify some initial phase $\vec{x}^N(o) = [\vec{r}^N(o), \vec{v}^N(o)]$, which is chosen quite arbitrarily in many cases (see below). The numerical integration procedure gives to some approximation (depending upon the accuracy of the algorithm used and upon the number of significant figures carried in the computation) the phase $\vec{x}^N(t)$ of the system at time t, from which one evaluates at time t any desired function $f(\vec{x}^N)$ of the phase. There are fundamentally three types of problems which have been studied in this way:

1. The approach to equilibrium.
2. Equilibrium thermodynamic functions.
3. Equilibrium time correlation functions.

We will discuss each of these applications in subsequent sections, limiting our consideration for the most part to systems of hard disks and spheres. For these systems, the force law in eq. (3.1) is singular, and calculation of the trajectory of the system in phase space is greatly simplified, since the particles move in straight lines between collisions. Essentially, then, the procedure is to calculate the sequence of phases $\vec{x}^N(t_1)$, $\vec{x}^N(t_2)$, ..., $\vec{x}^N(t_i)$,... where t_i is the time of the ith collision, starting from the specified initial phase $\vec{x}^N(o)$, with

$t_{i-1} < t_i$, and $\vec{x}^N(t_i)$ denotes the phase preceding the ith collision†). If one wishes to calculate a phase function $f[x^N(t)]$ at a time such that $t_{i-1} < t \le t_i$, one takes $\vec{r}^N(t) = \vec{r}^N(t_i) + (t-t_i)\vec{v}^N(t_i)$ and $\vec{v}^N(t) = \vec{v}^N(t_i)$. Thus, the only integration errors are the round-off or truncation errors in calculating the resultant velocities of the elastic collisions corresponding to the finite number of significant figures carried by the calculating machinery. As far as both calculation speed and accuracy of the trajectory are concerned, it is accordingly clear that hard-core systems have a considerable advantage over more complicated interaction laws. Nevertheless, as we will subsequently discuss in more detail, the accuracy of the trajectory calculation is severely limited even in hard-core systems.

Just as in the case of the Monte Carlo method, we are of course limited to values of N which are very small compared to macroscopic systems, so that the same periodic boundary conditions are customarily used. As a result of the absence of external forces, the total energy assigned to the N-particle system,

$$E(t) = \frac{1}{2} m \sum_i v_i^2(t) + U[\vec{r}^N(t)] \tag{3.2}$$

with $U(\vec{r}^N)$ given by eq. (2.21), and the total linear momentum

$$\vec{M}(t) = m \sum_i \vec{v}_i(t) \tag{3.3}$$

are constants of the motion††)

3.2. Approach to equilibrium

The equilibrium statistical mechanical ensemble corresponding to the dynamical system described in the previous section is a special case of the micro-canonical ensemble in which the total momentum

$$\vec{M} = \sum m\vec{v}_i \tag{3.4}$$

is fixed, as well as the usual micro-canonical variables E, V, and N. Let us call

††) Because of the collisions between particles in adjacent replicas of V, I know of no useful definition of a conserved total angular momentum assignable to the N particle system.

†) In hard core systems truly simultaneous collisions of more than two particles occur with probability zero, and can be ignored. The pre-collision phase $\vec{x}^N(t_i)$ is the phase in which the colliding pair is in contact, and the velocities are the pre-collision velocities.

this ensemble, for lack of any established name, the "molecular dynamics ensemble". In this ensemble all states $\vec{x}^N = (\vec{r}^N, \vec{v}^N)$ consistent with the specified values of $\vec{M}$, E, V, and N are equi-probable. According to the quasi-ergodic hypothesis the dynamical trajectory $\vec{x}^N(t)$ starting from any $\vec{x}^N(o)$ should, except possibly for a set of initial phases $\vec{x}^N(o)$ of zero measure, spend equal amounts of time in any arbitrarily chosen sets of equal (non-zero) measure in the allowed phase space. Nevertheless, we recognize the existence of "exceptional states" $\vec{x}^N(o)$ whose trajectories $\vec{x}^N(t)$ have short-time behaviors which are in some recognizable sense unusual compared to that of the great preponderance of states. Typically, these are states in which some state function $f(\vec{x}^N)$ corresponding to a macroscopic variable has a value $f[\vec{x}^N(o)]$ which departs considerably from its ensemble average $\langle f(\vec{x}^N)\rangle$. The function $f[\vec{x}^N(t)]$ will then exhibit initially large values of $\Delta f(t) = |f[\vec{x}^N(t)] - \langle f(\vec{x}^N)\rangle|$, but these will tend to decrease with time until the fluctuation becomes of order N^{-1}, where it will tend to remain over very long times with only rare fluctuations of larger magnitude (Fig. 3.1.).

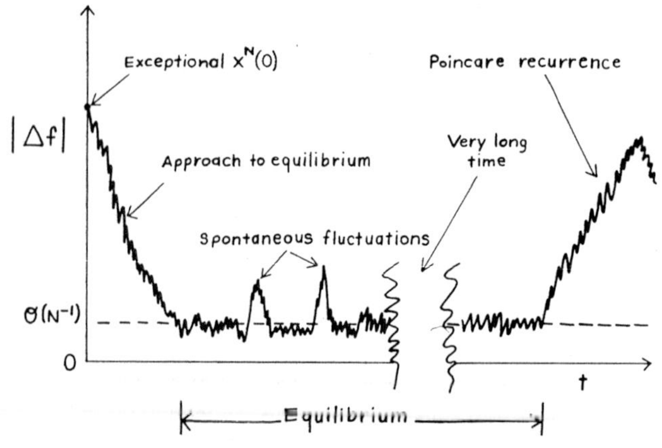

Fig. 3.1. Temporal evolution of a dynamical system.

An example, if N is reasonably large, is the initial state in which all N particles are given positions lying in, say, the left-half of the volume V. Somewhat loosely, we speak of such exceptional initial states as being "non-equilibrium" initial states, and of the system as "approaching equilibrium" over the time interval in which the fluctuation $\Delta f(t)$ is large compared to N^{-1}, and finally as being "in equilibrium" at subsequent times when the fluctuation is of order N^{-1}. We know from the Poincaré recurrence theorem that after some (typically very long) time t the state $\vec{x}^N(t)$ will come back very close to the exceptional initial state $\vec{x}^N(o)$, so that large fluctuations must ultimately appear. However, such times are believed to be very long, at least for fluid systems of a reasonably large number of particles[†)].

Relatively few studies of the approach to equilibrium in hard-core systems have been carried out, compared to calculations in the equilibrium region. In tho-

†) The famous Fermi, Pasta, Ulam[28)] calculation on an anharmonic linear chain is an example of a quite different behavior.

se which have been done, the function studied has usually been the Boltzmann H-function

$$H(t) = \int d\vec{r} \int d\vec{v}\; f(\vec{r},\vec{v},t) \ln f(\vec{r},\vec{v},t) \tag{3.5}$$

which is related to the entropy for sufficiently low-density systems. Here $f(\vec{r},\vec{v},t)d\vec{r}\,d\vec{v}$ is the number of particles which at time t have positions lying in the region $d\vec{r}$ around $\vec{r}$ and velocities in the region $d\vec{v}$ around $\vec{v}$. For a large system at low density the time evolution of $f(\vec{r},\vec{v},t)$ is governed by the Boltzmann equation, with its equilibrium form corresponding to a uniform density distribution and a Maxwellian velocity distribution. In a finite system one has of course to "discretize" $f(\vec{r},\vec{v},t)$ in configuration and velocity space by use of finite regions $\Delta\vec{r}$ and $\Delta\vec{v}$ in place of $d\vec{r}$ and $d\vec{v}$. Replacing the integrals in eq. (3.5) by sums over the discrete values of $\vec{r}$ and $\vec{v}$, one obtains a finite system version of the Boltzmann H-function. By calculating on the computer the "observed" discrete distribution function $f(\vec{r},\vec{v},t)$ at a series of values of t during the development of the phase space trajectory $\vec{x}^N(t)$ from some specified initial phase $\vec{x}^N(o)$, one obtains after carrying out the summations the "observed" values of H(t). Alder and Wainwright[26] carried out a calculation of this kind, the initial state being one with the particles located on lattice sites and having randomly oriented velocities of equal magnitude. They observed the expected overall decrease in H(t) from its initially large values, with the "equilibrium state" in which H(t) fluctuates near its equilibrium value being reached after a very few collisions per particle. They also attempted a rough comparison of the "observed" $f(\vec{r},\vec{v},t)$ with a solution of the Boltzmann equation, using for $f(\vec{r},\vec{v},o)$ a uniform spatial distribution and a velocity distribution more peaked than the Maxwellian distribution. A more precise comparison of molecular dynamics results with the solution of the Boltzmann equation could be made by specifying the desired initial distribution $f(\vec{r},\vec{v},o)$ and sampling from this distribution by Monte Carlo techniques a number of initial phases $x^N(o)$. The distribution function $f(\vec{r},\vec{v},t)$ obtained by averaging over the resulting set of trajectories would be appropriate for comparison with the Boltzmann equation or its modification by Enskog for dense gases. In this way, one could investigate, for instance, the effects of finite density (e.g., the adequacy of the Enskog dense gas approximation) on the approach to equilibrium of the one-particle distribution function.

An interesting example of a molecular dynamics calculation of the H-function along a single trajectory is given by Orban and Bellemans[29]. The system studied consisted of 100 hard disks at quite low density, $V/V_o = 25$, where V_o is the close-packed volume, with the initial phase having regular lattice positions and randomly oriented velocities of equal magnitude. In addition to calculating H(t) as described above, they also investigated its behavior upon reversing the velocities at $t/t_o \cong 1$ and 2, where t_o is the mean free time, a procedure which sheds some light on the effects of accumulated error in the calculation of the trajectory. Their results are shown in Fig. 3.2., where we first note the expected decrease of H(t), with equilibrium values being reached after about 2 collisions per particle.

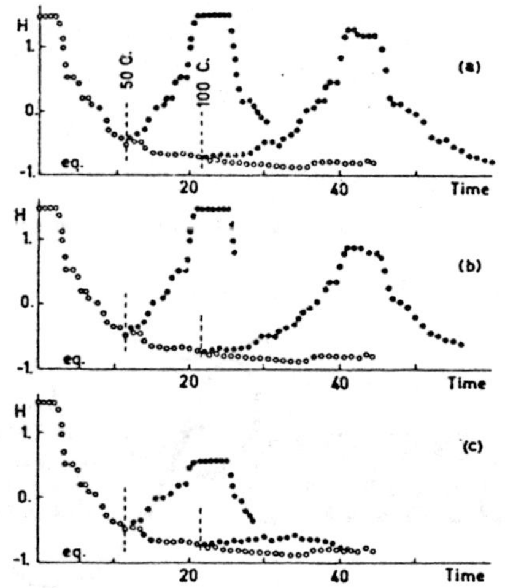

Fig. 3.2. The Boltzmann H-function versus time (arbitrary units) for a system of 100 hard disks at $V/V_o = 25$, as calculated by Orban and Bellemans[29] under normal time development (open) circles), and with velocity reversal (closed circles) after one and 2 collisions per particle (on the average; i.e., after a total of 50 and 100 collisions). In (a) the velocities were exactly reversed, while in (b) a small, and in (c) a larger, random perturbation was added to the reversed velocities.

If the trajectory calculations were exact, reversing the velocities at time t would cause the system to retrace its steps, with the initial state being exactly regained at time 2t. Within the accuracy of Fig. 3.2. we see that this is indeed the case for reversal at $t/t_o \cong 1$ (with no random perturbation of the reversed velocities), but not quite so at $t/t_o \cong 2$. From this we can conclude that this trajectory calculation probably becomes rapidly inaccurate beyond $t/t_o \cong 4$, and perhaps somewhat earlier (since some cancellation of error is possible in reversing an inaccurate algorithm). We will return to this question in Section 5.1.

3.3. Equilibrium thermodynamic properties

From the discussion in the previous section it is clear that, to the extent we are successful in approximating the properties of macroscopic systems by use of rather small periodic systems, the thermodynamic properties of macroscopic systems with the assumed interaction law should in principle be well approximated by time averages calculated by molecular dynamics. We take here the viewpoint that macroscopic experimental measurements correspond to time averages of microscopic variables over times long compared to the microscopic time scale. And according to the quasi-ergodic hypothesis, they should be identical to the corresponding statistical mechanical averages evaluated in the molecular dynamics ensemble.

The above remarks have to be qualified, however, by noting that the molecular dynamics calculation of equilibrium properties actually contains a dominant component of statistical averaging, rather than exact time averaging, due to the propagation of the above-mentioned round-off errors in the case of hard-core systems, and the presumably larger errors associated with finite-difference integration techniques in the case of continuous interaction laws. In the work of Orban and Bellemans discussed in the previous section, we saw that the trajectory is probably quite inaccurate beyond about 4 collisions per particle. As we will see in a later section, at higher densities and by use of calculators which carry more significant figures, the hard-core trajectories can be calculated accurately to several tens of collisions per particle. But both of these numbers are very small compared to the lengths of the trajectories used in practice. For example, in Alder and Wainwright's study[30)] of the phase transition in hard disks, to be discussed in more detail later, typical trajectories were about 23 000 collisions per particle in length. In some current work on the (super) Burnett self-diffusion coefficient, also to be discussed in a later section, trajectories more than ten times as long have been used. Trajectories of such length can evidently have little resemblance to the true trajectory, except in some statistical sense which is difficult to precisely define. It is thus perhaps reassuring that where detailed comparisons have been made, the thermodynamic properties computed by molecular dynamics methods have been found to be in good agreement with those obtained by the Monte Carlo method.

As an example of an equilibrium molecular dynamics calculation, we will consider in some detail the calculation of the equation of state of d-dimensional hard-core systems as carried out by Alder and Wainwright. The definition of the finite-system pressure is based on the classical mechanical virial equation of state [see, e.g., Hirschfelder, Curtiss, and Bird[31)]]

$$dpV = 2\,\overline{K(\vec{v}^N)} - 2\,\overline{W(\vec{r}^N)} \tag{3.6}$$

in which $K(\vec{v}^N) = \frac{1}{2} m \Sigma v_i^2$ is the kinetic energy and the bars denote time-averages, e.g.,

$$\overline{W(\vec{r}^N)} = t^{-1} \int_0^t dt'\, W[\vec{r}^N(t)] \tag{3.7}$$

Strictly speaking, we should take the limit $t \to \infty$ in eq. (3.7), since the left-hand side is supposed not to be dependent on t. In actual practice in molecular dynamics calculations, one must of course be satisfied with large but finite values of t. Care is needed in calculating time and ensemble averages of $W(\vec{r}^N)$ for hard-core systems because of the singular character of $\vec{\nabla}_i U(\vec{r}^N)$ for hard-core systems. Letting $\vec{F}_i(t)$ denote the force exerted on particle i at time t by the other particles of the system, we have

$$\overline{W} = -\frac{1}{2t}\int_o^t dt' \sum_i \vec{r}_i(t')\cdot\vec{F}_i(t') \tag{3.8}$$

For hard cores the force is impulsive, being zero except at the instants of collision. Let us denote the collision times by t_i, $0 < t_1 < t_2 < \ldots < t_\nu < t$, $\nu = \nu(t)$ denoting the number of collisions occurring in the time interval t. Denote the colliding pair of particles at time t_γ by (i_γ, j_γ). With use of the usual relation for impulsive forces we then have

$$\overline{W} = -\frac{m}{2t}\sum_{\gamma=1}^{\nu}[\vec{r}_i(t_\gamma)\cdot\Delta\vec{v}_i(t_\gamma) + \vec{r}_j(t_\gamma)\cdot\Delta\vec{v}_j(t_\gamma)] \tag{3.9}$$

where for simplicity of notation we omit the γ subscripts on i and j. The symbol $\Delta\vec{v}_i(t_\gamma)$ denotes the change in the velocity of the particle on the collision at t_γ,

$$\Delta\vec{v}_i(t_\gamma) = \vec{v}_i'(t_\gamma) - \vec{v}_i(t_\gamma) \tag{3.10}$$

if $\vec{v}_i'(t_\gamma)$ denotes the velocity just after the collision and $\vec{v}_i(t_\gamma)$ that just before. The elastic collision law is

$$\Delta\vec{v}_i(t_\gamma) = -\Delta\vec{v}_j(t_\gamma) = -\vec{r}_{ij}(t_\gamma)[\vec{r}_{ij}(t_\gamma)\cdot\vec{v}_{ij}(t_\gamma)]/\sigma^2 \tag{3.11}$$

where

$$\begin{aligned}\vec{r}_{ij} &= \vec{r}_i - \vec{r}_j\\ \vec{v}_{ij} &= \vec{v}_i - \vec{v}_j\end{aligned} \tag{3.12}$$

The time averaged virial then becomes

$$\overline{W} = \frac{m}{2t}\sum_\gamma \vec{r}_{ij}(t_\gamma)\cdot\vec{v}_{ij}(t_\gamma)\ , \tag{3.13}$$

in which form it can be directly evaluated in a molecular dynamics calculation. From this result we see that for given values of N and V and fixed initial positions $\vec{r}^N(o)$, $\overline{W}$ depends only on the <u>relative</u> initial velocities $\vec{v}_{ij}(o)$, or equivalently on the initial velocities relative to the center of mass

$$\begin{aligned} \hat{\vec{v}} &= \vec{v}_i - \vec{v}_o \\ \vec{v}_o &= N^{-1} \Sigma \vec{v}_i = \vec{M}/Nm \end{aligned} \tag{3.14}$$

In particular, $\overline{W}$ is independent of $\vec{M}$ for fixed values of N, V, $\vec{r}^N(o)$, and $\hat{\vec{v}}^N(o)$. In addition, we note from eq. (3.13) that if a given set of initial relative velocities $\hat{\vec{v}}^N(o)$ are multiplied by a factor α, then $\overline{W}$ is multiplied by α^2, one factor α coming from the factor $\vec{v}_{ij}(t_\gamma)$ and the other from the occurrence of α times as many collisions in a fixed time t. (Here we are of course using the fact that for hard-core systems the relative coordinates $\vec{r}_{ij}(t)$ are transformed to $\vec{r}_{ij}(t/\alpha)$ by this scaling of the initial relative velocities.)

If we now assume, however, the validity of a quasi-ergodic hypothesis, the time average $\overline{W}$ should in fact not depend upon the particular choice of $\vec{r}^N(o)$ and $\vec{v}^N(o)$, but rather only on the system parameters N, V, E, and $\vec{M}$. It will be convenient to replace E by the kinetic energy relative to the center-of-mass,

$$\hat{E} = \frac{1}{2} m \Sigma \hat{v}_i^2 = E - \frac{1}{2} M^2/Nm , \tag{3.15}$$

which is of course also a conserved quantity since E and M are. Because of the above mentioned independence of $\overline{W}$ with respect to M for fixed values of the relative velocities $\hat{\vec{v}}_i(o)$, we see that $\overline{W}$ will depend only on N, V, and $\hat{E}$. And finally, from the above-described scaling with the initial velocities it follows that $\overline{W}$ must be proportional to $\hat{E}$, the proportionality factor being a function only of N and V, or more conveniently of N and the number density N/V with the dependence on N being expected to vanish in the thermodynamic limit. Thus, we write

$$\begin{aligned} \overline{W} &= \hat{E}\, h(N/V,N) \\ h(N/V,N) &= (m/2\hat{E}t) \sum_\gamma \vec{r}_{ij}(t_\gamma)\cdot\vec{v}_{ij}(t_\gamma). \end{aligned} \tag{3.16}$$

Returning now to the virial equation of state, eq. (3.6), we see that it reduces to

$$dpV = 2E - 2\overline{W} = 2E - 2\hat{E}\, h(N/V,N)$$

which is an obviously unsatisfactory result, since it gives a pressure depending upon the total momentum M, which corresponds to a bulk flow velocity of the fluid through the periodic mesh. The obvious remedy, and one which is consistent with the assumptions made in the derivation of the virial equation of state, is to replace E in the previous equation by $\hat{E}$. Thus, the <u>defining equation</u> for the molecular dynamics pressure p_{MD} is taken to be

$$dp_{MD}V = 2\hat{E} - 2\overline{W} = 2\hat{E} - 2\hat{E}\ h(N/V,N) \tag{3.17}$$

The molecular dynamics temperature is defined as

$$T_{MD} = 2\hat{E}/dNk_B \tag{3.18}$$

Combining the last two equations, we obtain the molecular dynamics equation of state

$$(pV/Nk_BT)_{MD} = 1 - h(N/V,N) \tag{3.19}$$

with the right-hand side depending as expected only on the density in the thermodynamic limit.

Let us next see how this equation of state is related to the canonical ensemble equation of state, eq. (2.18), which is the one calculated by the Monte Carlo method. First of all let us recall the well-known reduction of eq. (2.18) to the form

$$(pV/Nk_BT)_{NVT} = 1 + (d-1)d^{-1}\pi n \sigma^d\ g(\sigma;n,N) \tag{3.20}$$

in which $g(\sigma;n,N)$ is the radial distribution function at contact for hard-cores of diameter σ at density $n = N/V$, and possibly exhibiting a finite system dependence on N; see Wood[16)] for a derivation appropriate to finite periodic systems. To relate this expression to the molecular dynamics result, we first express the canonical ensemble $\langle W\rangle_{NVT}$ in terms of the average $\langle W\rangle_{NVEM}$ in the "molecular dynamics ensemble",

$$\langle W\rangle_{NVEM} = Z_{NVEM}^{-1}\int d\vec{r}^N \int d\vec{v}^N\ \delta(E - \tfrac{1}{2}m\,\Sigma v_i^2)\,\delta(\vec{M}-m\Sigma\vec{v}_i)\,A(\vec{r}^N)\,W$$

$$A(\vec{r}^N) = \begin{cases} 1 & \text{if } U(\vec{r}^N) = 0 \\ 0 & \text{if } U(\vec{r}^N) = \infty \end{cases} \tag{3.21}$$

$$Z_{NVEM} = \int d\vec{r}^N \int d\vec{v}^N\ \delta(E - \tfrac{1}{2}m\,\Sigma v_i^2)\,\delta(M-m\Sigma\vec{v}_i)\,A(\vec{r}^N)\ .$$

By a standard application of δ-functions, we have

$$\langle W\rangle_{NVT} = Z_{NVT}^{-1} \int d\vec{r}^{N} \int d\vec{v}^{N} \; W \exp\{-\beta[\tfrac{1}{2} m \Sigma v_i^2 + U(\vec{r}^{N})]$$

$$= Z_{NVT}^{-1} \int dE \exp(-\beta E) \int d\vec{M} \; Z_{NVEM} \langle W\rangle_{NVEM} \qquad (3.22)$$

$$Z_{NVT} = \int d\vec{r}^{N} \int d\vec{v}^{N} \exp\{-\beta [\tfrac{1}{2} m \Sigma v_i^2 + U(\vec{r}^{N})]\}$$

We now make the quasi-ergodic assumption that $\langle W\rangle_{NVEM}$ is equal to the corresponding time average calculated in eq. (3.16), whereupon we find

$$\langle W\rangle_{NVT} = Z_{NVT}^{-1} h(N/V,N) \int dE \exp(-\beta E) \int d\vec{M} \; Z_{NVEM} \hat{E} \qquad (3.23)$$

Substituting for Z_{NVEM} from eq. (3.21) and integrating over the δ-functions, we obtain directly

$$\langle W\rangle_{NVT} = h(N/V,N) \langle \hat{E}\rangle_{NVT} \qquad (3.24)$$

The canonical ensemble average of the kinetic energy relative to the center of mass is easily found, using eqs. (3.15) and (3.4), to be given by

$$\langle \hat{E}\rangle_{NVT} = (1 - 1/N) \langle E\rangle_{NVT} = \frac{1}{2} dNk_BT(1 - 1/N) \qquad (3.25)$$

Using eqs. (3.24) and (3.25) in eq. (2.18) we obtain the canonical ensemble equation of state in the form

$$(pV/Nk_BT)_{NVT} = 1 - h(N/V,N)(1 - 1/N) \qquad (3.26)$$

Comparing this result with the molecular dynamics equation of state given in eq. (3.19), we see that the two are related by

$$(pV/Nk_BT - 1)_{MD} = (1 - 1/N)^{-1}(pV/Nk_BT - 1)_{NVT} \qquad (3.27)$$

When this correction factor $N/(N-1)$ was taken into account, Hoover and Alder[32] found the Monte Carlo and molecular dynamics results for the equation of state of systems of 12 hard disks to be in agreement within the statistical errors.
By comparing eqs. (3.26) and (3.20) we can relate the proportionality factor $h(N/V,N)$ to the radial distribution function,

$$h(N/V,N) = -(1 - 1/d)n\,\sigma^{d} g(\sigma;n,N)N/(N - 1) \qquad (3.28)$$

The procedures used for estimating the statistical error and the systematic error (which again is expected to be mainly due to the use of finite values of N) in the calculated equilibrium properties are very similar to the ones used in the Monte Carlo method.

3.4. Equilibrium Time Correlation Functions

As an example of the calculation of linear transport coefficients and their related time correlation functions, we will consider the self-diffusion process discussed in Professor Dorfman's lectures. There it was shown that the self-diffusion current is given by

$$\vec{J}(\vec{r},t) = -D^{(o)}(t)\, \vec{\nabla} n_1(\vec{r},t) - D^{(2)}(t)\vec{\nabla}\nabla^2\, n_1(\vec{r},t) - \ldots \tag{3.29}$$

where $n_1(\vec{r},t)$ is the number density of tagged particles at position $\vec{r}$ at time t, and $\vec{\nabla}$ is the usual gradient operator. The time correlation function expression for the Fick's law coefficient $D^{(o)}(t)$ is

$$D^{(o)}(t) = (\beta m)^{-1} \int_o^t dt'\, \rho_D(t') \tag{3.30}$$

where

$$\rho_D(t) = (\beta m) \langle v_{1x}(o) v_{1x}(t) \rangle \tag{3.31}$$

is the normalized velocity autocorrelation function, $v_{1x}(t)$ being the x-component of the velocity of a typical particle at time t. Alternatively, one can write eq. (3.30) in the form

$$D^{(o)}(t) = \langle v_{1x}(o)\ \Delta x_1(t) \rangle \tag{3.32}$$

where

$$\Delta x_1(t) = x_1(t) - x_1(o) \tag{3.33}$$

is the x-component of the displacement at time t of a typical particle relative to its position at time zero. Finally, the mean square x-component of the displacement is related to $D^{(o)}(t)$ by

$$\begin{aligned} D^{(o)}(t) &= d[t\Delta^{(o)}(t)]/dt \\ \Delta^{(o)}(t) &= \langle \Delta x_1(t)^2 \rangle / 2t \end{aligned} \tag{3.34}$$

In these equations the angular brackets denote an equilibrium statistical mechanical ensemble average over the <u>initial</u> positions $\vec{r}^N(o)$ and $\vec{v}^N(o)$.

The corresponding relations for the (super) Burnett coefficient $D^{(2)}(t)$ are, for computational purposes, most conveniently written down in reverse order, beginning with the "Einstein" relation analogous to eq. (3.34),

$$
\begin{aligned}
D^{(2)}(t) &= d[t\Delta^{(2)}(t)]/dt \\
\Delta^{(2)}(t) &= [\langle \Delta x_1(t)^4 \rangle - 3\langle \Delta x_1(t)^2 \rangle^2]/24t
\end{aligned}
\tag{3.35}
$$

By carrying out the differentiation and using Liouville's theorem we obtain

$$
D^{(2)}(t) = \frac{1}{6}\langle v_{1x}(o)\Delta x_1(t)^3\rangle - \frac{1}{2}\langle \Delta x_1(t)^2\rangle\langle v_{1x}(o)\Delta x_1(t)\rangle \tag{3.36}
$$

By a second differentiation we can write $D^{(2)}(t)$ as the integral of a rather complicated "two-point" correlation function

$$
\begin{aligned}
D^{(2)}(t) &= \int_o^t dt'\, c^{(2)}(t') \\
c^{(2)}(t) &= \frac{1}{2}\langle v_{1x}(o)v_{1x}(t)\Delta x_1(t)^2\rangle - \langle v_{1x}(o)\Delta x_1(t)\rangle^2 - \\
&\quad - \frac{1}{2}\langle \Delta x_1(t)^2\rangle\langle v_{1x}(o)v_{1x}(t)\rangle
\end{aligned}
\tag{3.37}
$$

By two further differentiations and some reduction one obtains the aesthetically more pleasing expression

$$
D^{(2)}(t) = \int_o^t dt_1 \int_{t_1}^t dt_2 \int_{t_2}^t dt_3\, c^{(2)}(t_1,t_2,t_3) \tag{3.38}
$$

involving the symmetrical "four-point" correlation function

$$
\begin{aligned}
c^{(2)}(t_1,t_2,t_3) = {} & \langle v_{1x}(o)v_{1x}(t_1)v_{1x}(t_2)v_{1x}(t_3)\rangle - \\
& -\langle v_{1x}(o)v_{1x}(t_1)\rangle\langle v_{1x}(t_2)v_{1x}(t_3)\rangle - \\
& -\langle v_{1x}(o)v_{1x}(t_2)\rangle\langle v_{1x}(t_1)v_{1x}(t_3)\rangle - \\
& -\langle v_{1x}(o)v_{1x}(t_3)\rangle\langle v_{1x}(t_1)v_{1x}(t_2)\rangle
\end{aligned}
$$

The less-symmetrical "two-point" function given in eq. (3.37) is, however, more easily computed on the machines, since it is a function of a single time variable.

The quantities $\rho_D(t)$ as given by eq. (3.31), $D^{(o)}(t)$ by eq. (3.32), $\Delta^{(o)}(t)$ by eq. (3.34), $c^{(2)}(t)$ by eq. (3.37), $D^{(2)}(t)$ by eq. (3.36), and $\Delta^{(2)}(t)$ by eq.

(3.35) are all expressed as averages of straightforwardly computable functions of the phases of particle 1 at time 0 and time t along the trajectory. We describe their evaluation by means of molecular dynamics using $\rho_D(t)$ as an example. By a well-known argument based on Liouville's theorem eq. (3.31) can be rewritten in the form

$$\rho_D(t) = \beta m \langle v_{1x}(t')v_{1x}(t' + t)\rangle \tag{3.40}$$

in which the right-hand side is actually independent of t', the angular brackets still referring to an ensemble average over $\vec{r}^N(o)$ and $\vec{v}^N(o)$. In the molecular dynamics technique employed by Alder and Wainwright this ensemble average is replaced by the molecular dynamics time average over t', just as discussed in the previous section. Instead of "observing" one velocity component of a single particle 1 as indicated in eq. (3.40) an average is taken over all N particles and all d components. In addition, the velocities $\hat{\vec{v}}^N$ relative to the center of mass [previously defined in eq. (3.14)] are used in place of $\vec{v}^N$, inasmuch as a non-zero conserved total momentum $\vec{M}$ would obviously lead to a nonvanishing velocity autocorrelation at long times†). Finally, of course, the "molecular dynamics temperature" T_{MD} defined in eq. (3.18) is used in β, so that eq. (3.40) becomes††)

$$\hat{\rho}_D(t) = \beta m(dN\nu\Delta t)^{-1} \sum_{\gamma=1}^{\nu} \sum_{i=1}^{N} \sum_{k=1}^{d} \hat{v}_{ik}(t_\gamma)\hat{v}_{ik}(t_\gamma + t)$$
$$t_\gamma = (\gamma - 1)\Delta t \tag{3.41}$$

The spacing Δt of the "time origins" t_γ is in practice adjusted to roughly optimize the statistical quality of the results obtained for a given amount of machine time, too small a value of Δt resulting in successive values of the summand being highly correlated so that the increased computing time does not produce a proportionate increase in the precision of the results.

As Prof. Dorfman has discussed in his lectures, recent theoretical interest has centered on the long-time behavior of the correlation function $\rho_D(t)$ and

---

†) Correspondingly, $\Delta x_i(t)$ is calculated in the coordinate frame in which the center of mass is at rest.

††) We use here the symbol $\hat{\rho}_D(t)$ to denote the use of velocities relative to the center of mass, reserving the unadorned symbol $\rho_D(t)$ to designate the autocorrelation function defined in terms of the velocity variables of some ensemble in which the velocity of the center of mass fluctuates (e.g., the canonical or micro-canonical ensembles). The distinction will be of use subsequently, in Section 5.

$c^{(2)}(t)$, this interest having been aroused by the slow decay of $\hat{\rho}_D(t)$ observed in the molecular dynamics investigations of Alder and Wainwright[33,34]. We will discuss these results in more detail in a subsequent section. Because of their great theoretical significance it seemed important that these results be independently confirmed and, if possible, extended. Accordingly, Dr. J.J. Erpenbeck and I at Los Alamos have recently undertaken such an investigation, a few results from which will be given in a subsequent section. Here it is appropriate to summarize the differences between our molecular dynamics technique and that just outlined. We have already mentioned that the "time-averaging" carried out in the usual molecular dynamics method contains a large component of statistical averaging due to the necessarily increasing inaccuracy of the trajectory integrations with increasing time. Although we had no serious doubts concerning the validity of the equilibrium thermodynamic properties computed in this way (as mentioned in the previous section, they were known to agree well with Monte Carlo results), the question of the trajectory accuracy seemed to be of greater import in the calculation of time correlation functions such as the velocity autocorrelation function. As discussed by Prof. Dorfman, the "observed" $\hat{\rho}_D(t)$ does not begin to approach the leading asymptotic terms of the theoretical predictions until $t/t_o > 10$ or 20 (t_o being, as before, the mean free time). Accordingly, from a conservative point of view, it seemed desirable to be able to compute the trajectory accurately over several tens of collisions <u>per particle</u>. We therefore included in the machine program the option of computing the trajectory in either "single-precision" arithmetic as used by Alder and Wainwright (about 14 decimal places on CDC6600 and 7600 machinery) or in "double-precision" (twice as many decimal places).

Finally, in order to be able to investigate the effects of combining the time-averaging of the usual molecular dynamics procedure with a precisely defined statistical mechanical ensemble average, we used a Monte Carlo procedure to carry out the ensemble average over initial phases symbolized by the angular brackets in eq. (3.40). We use the micro-canonical ensemble, sampling (i.e., averaging over) the configuration space $\vec{r}^N(o)$ by means of the Metropolis-Rosenbluth-Teller procedure described in section 2.4.; note that for hard-core systems the micro-canonical and canonical configurational probability densities are identical. To sample from the micro-canonical velocity distribution in $\vec{v}^N(o)$, we first used gaussian random numbers generated by the Box-Muller method (Section 2.1.2.) to sample from the canonical (Maxwell) distribution in $\vec{v}^N$, followed by a radial projection of these points onto a hypersphere of constant energy. The resulting values of $\vec{r}^N(o)$ and $\vec{v}^N(o)$ are then used as the initial phase of a trajectory, along which a time-averaged velocity autocorrelation function is generated as indicated in eq. (3.41) in which we again use the velocities relative to the center of mass. Averaging over a number H of such trajectories, we obtain

$$\hat{\rho}_D(t) = \beta m(nd\nu\, H\, \Delta t)^{-1} \sum_{q=1}^{H} \sum_{i=1}^{N} \sum_{\gamma=1}^{\nu} \sum_{k=1}^{d} \hat{v}_{ikq}(t_\gamma)\hat{v}_{ikq}(t_\gamma+t) \qquad (3.42)$$

with $\hat{v}_{ikq}(t)$ denoting the k-th component of the relative velocity of particle i at time t on the q-th trajectory.

It is intuitively apparent that the behavior of time correlation functions such as $\hat{\rho}_D(t)$ at large values of t must be influenced by the finite periodic character of the systems which are studied. The success of the hydrodynamic theories discussed by Prof. Dorfman in accounting for the behavior of the velocity autocorrelation function in infinite systems at times greater than $10t_o$ or so, has recently led us to investigate their utility in accounting quantitatively for finite system effects at similar times, and we will later mention some of the results. For qualitative purposes, it is frequently convenient to have a rough estimate of the time at which the time correlation function may be suspect due to gross finite system effects. For this purpose, one frequently uses the time t_a required for a macroscopic sound wave to traverse the period of the system. Table 3.1. gives a few values of t_a/t_o for several fluid densities and values of N, calculated using the usual adiabatic sound speed and the Ree and Hoover[17] Padé-approximants P(3,3) for the equations of state[†].

TABLE 3.1.

Acoustic Traversal Times t_a/t_o

(a) Hard disks

V/V_o \ N	168	504	870	1512	5822
2	20.4	35.3	46.4	61.2	120.0
3	17.7	30.7	40.3	53.1	104.2
5	14.4	25.0	32.8	43.3	85.0
10	10.6	18.4	24.2	31.8	62.5
20	7.7	13.3	17.4	23.0	45.1
30	6.3	10.9	14.3	18.9	37.0

(b) Hard Spheres

V/V_o \ N	108	500	1372	4000
2	13.7	22.9	32.0	45.7
3	11.7	19.5	27.3	39.0
5	9.3	15.4	21.6	30.9
10	6.4	10.7	14.9	21.3
18	4.5	7.5	10.5	15.1

†) Note that the acoustic traversal time t_a is just a measure of the "hydrodynamic time" t_{hyd} mentioned in Prof. Dorfman's lectures. From Table 3.1. one can get some feeling for the system sizes required in order to achieve some specified ratio of the hydrodynamic and microscopic time scales.

4. SOME RESULTS FROM COMPUTER STUDIES ON VARIOUS SYSTEMS

In this section we will briefly discuss a small, highly eclectic, selection of computer investigations which seem to me to be of special interest or importance to the theoretical understanding of the behavior of simple fluids.

4.1. The Phase Transition in Hard Disks and Spheres

As a result of indications of the presence of a phase transition observed for both the hard disk and hard sphere systems in earlier work at Los Alamos and Livermore, Alder and Wainwright[30] carried out extensive molecular dynamics calculations of the equation of state of hard disks near the apparent transition density, obtaining the results shown in Fig. 4.1.a.

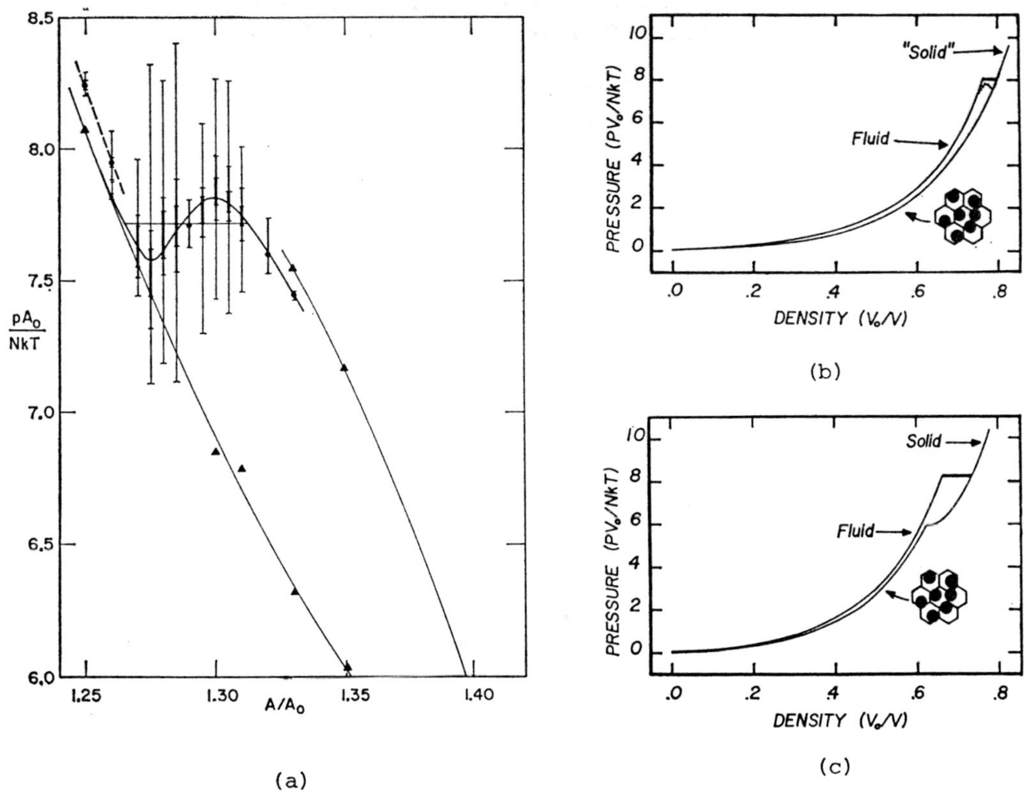

Fig. 4.1. (a) The hard disk equation of state obtained by Alder and Wainwright[30] In this figure A and A_o denote the area ("volume", in the terminology of the text) and close-packed area, respectively, of the system. (b) and (c) The hard disk (b) and sphere (c) equations of state, Hoover and Ree[18]. The curve labeled solid is the equation of state of the constrained system at all densities, and of the unconstrained system in the solid phase. The Alder and Wainwright "Van der Waals loop" of Fig. (a) is shown just below the Hoover and Ree tie line in (b).

The triangles with the light curves drawn through them are for systems of 72 particles, and are typical of the earlier results obtained on slower machinery for small systems. In the density region near the apparent phase transition such small systems had been observed in both canonical ensemble Monte Carlo calculations and molecular dynamics calculations to make infrequent excursions (at constant density, of course) between the upper and lower curves. The states on the lower curve displayed an ordered structure resembling the triangular lattice configuration from which the computer experiment is usually started, and the inhibited diffusion characteristic of a solid phase. The states on the upper curve showed the more random structure and freer diffusion characteristic of a fluid phase. At densities slightly smaller than that corresponding to the right-most triangles in the figure, the states on the lower curve rapidly became too transient for an average value to be estimated. At densities slightly greater than the left-hand terminus of the upper light curve, transitions from the lower to the upper curve were no longer observed. At the intermediate densities at which transitions between the two curves (i.e., between the two sets of states) were observed, they were too infrequent to permit any estimate of the overall average, or true equilibrium pressure. Thus, while the results were very suggestive, convincing evidence for a true first-order transition was lacking.

The new results in 1962 were the points shown as the circles with complicated error bars in Fig. 4.1.a. These points are for systems of 870 hard disks. Three error bars are shown for most points, the largest one at each point being the overall range of the pressures observed over intervals of about 115 collisions per particle, the next larger ones extend between the 25-th and 75-th percentiles of the same observations. The shortest set of error bars are Alder and Wainwright's error estimates based on the reproducibility of independent runs from different initial phases, each typically about 23 000 collisions per particle in length. The "Van der Waals loop" shown as the heavy curve in the figure was drawn through these points, and the horizontal tie line obtained by the familiar equal areas construction. The resulting transition densities, pressure, and entropy change are given in Table 4.1.

TABLE 4.1.

Hard-Core Phase Transition Parameters

	Disks		Spheres
	N = 870 (ref.30)	$N = \infty$ (ref.18)	$N = \infty$ (ref.18)
V/V_o (fluid)	1.312	1.314	1.499 ± .007
V/V_o (solid)	1.266	1.253	1.359 ± .006
pV_o/Nk_BT	7.72	8.08	8.28 ± 0.13
$\Delta S/Nk_B$	0.36	0.49	1.16 ± 0.08

These results provided rather convincing evidence for the existence of the first-order transition in hard disks. The two points connected by the short dashed curve in Fig. 4.1.a. at densities just above the melting transition correspond to presumably meta-stable "glassy" phases into which the system could be forced by procedures which we will not describe here. The existence of such meta-stable phases shows that the time-averaging at these densities does not cover all of phase space, but it seems reasonable to believe that the true overall average pressure at these densities is close to the lower curve shown in the figure.

No similar investigation to that just discussed has ever been carried out for hard-sphere systems. It would probably require the use of at least 10 000 particles and much computer time. Instead Hoover and Ree[18)] made very plausible the existence of a similar phase transition in hard spheres, and confirmed the Alder and Wainwright results for hard disks, by a clever indirect procedure based on the following assumptions.

1. Above some unknown reduced density V_o/V_s the lower or "solid" branch of the equation of state is in fact the true equation of state of a stable solid phase.

2. Below some other reduced density $V_o/V_f < V_o/V_s$ the upper or "fluid" branch of the equation of state is in fact the true equation of state of a stable fluid phase.

3. Between these two densities there occurs a first-order phase transition, the transition densities V_o/V_s and V_o/V_f and the transition pressure being determined by the conditions that the two phases have the same pressure and the same specific Gibbs free energy (chemical potential).

The problem then is to assign values of the free energy, or equivalently the entropy, along the two branches of the equation of state, in the absence of a connecting "Van der Waals loop".

The procedure makes use of an auxiliary hard-core system in which the center of each particle is constrained to remain within a Wigner-Seitz cell, in the style of the familiar Lennard-Jones-Devonshire cell theory of condensed phases; see Fig. 4.1.b. and c. At low densities the equation of state of the constrained system, and its Gibbs free energy relative to the unconstrained system at the same pressure, can be calculated theoretically. At sufficiently high densities in the presumed solid phase, it can be argued theoretically, and from Monte Carlo (or molecular dynamics) calculations carried out on both systems, that they have identical properties; i.e., at such densities the constrained and unconstrained systems have the same equation of state and Gibbs free energy. By carrying out Monte Carlo calculations of the equation of state of the constrained system at intermediate and solid densities, Hoover and Ree were then able (by integration of the equation of state) to calculate the Gibbs free energy of the unconstrained system along the solid branch of the equation of state[†)]. The Gibbs free energy of the liquid phase of the unconstrained system was of course already known from a similar integration of the equation of state obtained from earlier Monte Carlo and molecular dynamics work. The intersection of the two free energy curves when plotted against their corresponding pressures gives the transition pressure and free energy. They included in their procedures an approximate extrapolation to the thermodynamic limit, obtaining the results shown in table 4.1.

For hard disks the agreement with the Alder and Wainwright estimates of the transition parameters is seen to be fairly good; though the differences are not small on the scale of Fig. 4.1.a., they are at least in part attributable to the finite size of the system considered by Alder and Wainwright.

More recently Torrie, Valleau, and Bain[35)] have made a direct Monte Carlo estimate of the entropy difference between the unconstrained and single-occupancy hard sphere system at $V_o/V = 0.6$. The object is to avoid the necessity in the Hoover-Ree procedure of calculating the single-occupancy equation of state over an extended range of densities. In describing their procedure we begin by defining for fixed values of N,V, and T the restricted configurational integrals

$$\underset{\sim}{Q}_k = \int d\vec{r}^N A_k(\vec{r}^N) \exp[-\beta U(\vec{r}^N)] , \quad k = 0,1,\ldots,N \qquad (4.1)$$

with

$$A_k(\vec{r}^N) = 1 \quad \text{for } K(\vec{r}^N) \geq k,$$
$$= 0 \quad \text{otherwise,}$$

and where for any configuration $\vec{r}^N$ the variable $K(\vec{r}^N)$ is the number of singly occupied cells in the same Wigner-Seitz subdivision of the volume V into N cells as in the Hoover-Ree procedure. We see that $\underset{\sim}{Q}_o$ is just the unconstrained configurational $Q(N,V,T)$, since $A_o(\vec{r}^N) = 1$ for all $\vec{r}^N$, while $\underset{\sim}{Q}_N$ is the single-occupancy integral. Thus the desired entropy difference $\delta S = S_o - S_N$, which is just the so-called communal entropy of the cell theories of the condensed phase, is given by

---

†) In principle it is not necessary that the solid phase and the single occupancy equations of state should coincide over the entire range of stability of the solid phase. The entropy of the stable solid phase can be calculated by integration along the single occupancy equation of state from low density up to a density at which the two equations of state agree, then back down along the equation of state of the stable solid into the vicinity of the phase transition. In actuality, Hoover and Ree appear to have used the single occupancy equation of state for the entire solid phase, presumably on the basis of comparisons with unconstrained Monte Carlo calculations.

$$\exp(-\delta S/k_B) = Q_N/Q_o = \langle A_N \rangle = \int d\vec{r}^N \, A_N(\vec{r}^N)\rho_N(\vec{r}^N). \tag{4.2}$$

From this equation we see that the desired entropy difference could in principle be calculated by a Monte Carlo estimate of the average $\langle A_N \rangle$ using the Metropolis, Rosenbluth, Teller procedure. We note, of course, that this average is just the fraction of single occupancy states, and also that the Monte Carlo calculation must be carried out at a low enough density for the configurational averaging to be complete, i.e., at a density at which the stable phase is the fluid phase and at which the unstable solid phase readily melts. On the other hand, if we are indeed to minimize the density range over which we must calculate the single-occupancy equation of state, the calculation should be done reasonably close to the transition region - hence the choice by Torrie, et al., of $V_o/V = 0.6$.

However, from the work of Hoover and Ree it is known that at this density $\delta S/Nk_B \approx 0.3$. It then follows from eq. (4.2) that the desired ratio $\langle A_N \rangle$ is a very small number for N of the order of 100 or so. Thus such a procedure would suffer from the same sort of inefficiency as the "crude Monte Carlo" estimation of Q(N,V,T) which we discussed in Section 2.3. Torrie, et al., circumvented this difficulty, in the first instance by introducing "importance sampling" into the Metropolis-Rosenbluth-Teller procedure. Suppose that we artificially increase the "observed" frequency of occurrence of singly occupied states by devising a Markov chain which corresponds to the modified probability density

$$\begin{aligned} \rho'_N(\vec{r}^N) &= W_{K(\vec{r}^N)} \exp[-\beta U(\vec{r}^N)]/Q'_o \\ Q'_o &= \int d\vec{r}^N \, W_{K(\vec{r}^N)} \exp[-\beta U(\vec{r}^N)] \end{aligned} \tag{4.3}$$

Here the weights W_k, $k = 0, 1, \ldots, N$ are selected in advance to appropriately favor the larger values of k. The required Markov chain procedure is an obvious generalization of the usual one, and as before it does not require knowledge of Q'_o. Denoting by primes averages computed with the modified probability density $\rho'_N(\vec{r}^N)$, we can now estimate by the Metropolis-Rosenbluth-Teller technique the enhanced single occupancy fraction $\langle A_N \rangle'$. And using eq. (4.3) we can relate $\langle A_N \rangle'$ to the desired, unmodified average $\langle A_N \rangle$, since

$$\begin{aligned} \langle A_N \rangle' &= Q'^{-1}_o \int d\vec{r}^N \, W_{K(\vec{r}^N)} \, A_N(\vec{r}^N) \exp[-\beta U(\vec{r}^N)] \\ &= (W_N/Q'_o) \int d\vec{r}^N \, A_N(\vec{r}^N) \exp[-\beta U(\vec{r}^N)] \\ &= W_N \langle A_N \rangle \, Q_o/Q'_o. \end{aligned} \tag{4.4}$$

A separate expression relating Q_o and Q'_o through "observable" quantities is obtained by writing

$$Q_o = \int d\vec{r}^N \exp[-\beta U(\vec{r}^N)] = \sum_{k=0}^{N} \int d\vec{r}^N a_k(\vec{r}^N) \exp[-\beta U(\vec{r}^N)] \quad (4.5)$$

with

$$a_k(\vec{r}^N) = 1 \quad \text{if } K(\vec{r}^N) = k$$
$$= 0 \quad \text{otherwise} \quad (4.6)$$

Note that $a_k(\vec{r}^N) = A_k(\vec{r}^N) - A_{k+1}(\vec{r}^N)$ for $k = 0, 1, ..,N-1$, and $a_N(\vec{r}^N) = A_N(\vec{r}^N)$. Rewriting eq. (4.5) as

$$Q_o = \sum_{k=0}^{N} W_k^{-1} \int d\vec{r}^N a_k(\vec{r}^N) W_{K(\vec{r}^N)} \exp[-\beta U(\vec{r}^N)]$$

we see that

$$Q_o = Q'_o \sum_{k=0}^{N} W_k^{-1} \langle a_k\rangle' . \quad (4.7)$$

Using this relation together with eqs. (4.2) and (4.4) we obtain finally

$$\exp(-\delta S/k_B) = Q_N/Q_o = \langle A_N\rangle = W_N^{-1}\langle A_N\rangle'/ \sum_{k=0}^{N} W_k^{-1}\langle a_k\rangle' , \quad (4.8)$$

from which we can estimate the desired entropy difference from the observed weighted averages $\langle a_k\rangle'$.

Torrie, et al., in this way successfully calculated $\delta S/Nk_B$ for 32 hard spheres at $V_o/V = 0.6$. For 108 particles it was necessary to use a "multi-stage" procedure of the form

$$\exp(-\delta S/k_B) = Q_N/Q_o = \frac{Q_{N_1}}{Q_o} \frac{Q_{N_2}}{Q_{N_1}} \frac{Q_{N_3}}{Q_{N_2}} \cdots \frac{Q_N}{Q_{N_\nu}} \quad (4.9)$$

for suitably chosen values $0 < N_1 < N_2 < \ldots < N_\nu < N$, with each ratio $Q_{N_1}/Q_o,\ldots,$ Q_N/Q_{N_ν} being estimated by a procedure similar to that just described. Extrapolating approximately to the limit of an infinite system, they obtained $\delta S/Nk_B$ = $0.295 \pm .008$, compared to Hoover and Ree's value $0.312 \pm .015$. The maximum corresponding increases in the reduced transition parameters (cf. Table 4.1) as estimated by them are 0.11 in pV_o/Nk_BT and 0.003 in V_o/V_s and V_o/V_f. Little if any economy of machine time compared to the Ree-Hoover procedure was found, but the procedure may be advantageous for systems where another, lower-density phase transition (e.g., the liquid-vapor transition) interferes with a straightforward application of the Hoover-Ree method.

It seems appropriate to close this summary of the present state of knowledge of the hard disk and sphere phase transition by remarking that, insofar as known to me, there still exist no adequate theoretical demonstration of the existence of the transition and, correspondingly, no good theoretical values for the transition parameter.

4.2. The long-time tails of the velocity autocorrelation function for hard disks and spheres

Although we will discuss in a later section some current machine results for the velocity autocorrelation function of hard disks and spheres, it seems appropriate to include here, because of its importance in motivating much recent and current theoretical work, a very brief discussion of the Alder and Wainwright[34)] results on the long time decay of these functions shown in Fig. 4.2.

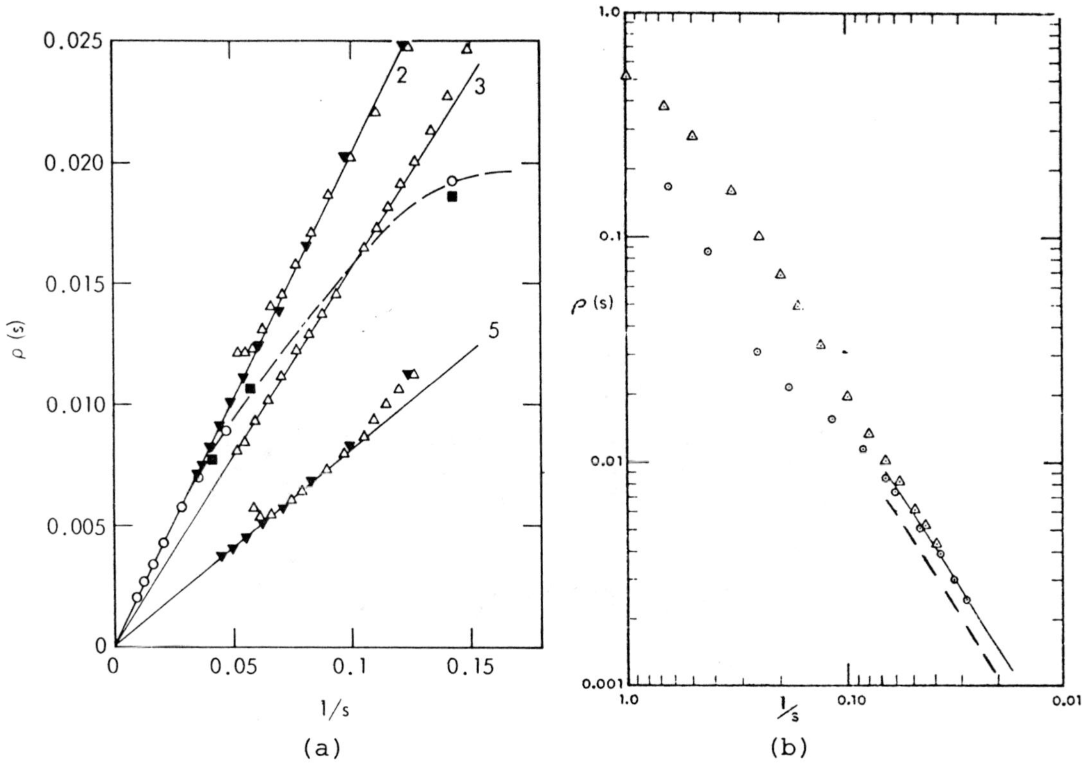

Fig. 4.2. The velocity autocorrelation function $\hat{\rho}_D(t)$ [here denoted by $\rho(s)$] versus $s^{-1} = (t/t_o)^{-1}$ for hard disks (a) and spheres (b), from Alder and Wainwright[34)]. See the text for the meaning of the various symbols. The molecular dynamics points include the Alder and Wainwright additive $1/(N-1)$ correction.

The interested reader should consult the original work for many of the details. For hard disks, Fig. 4.2.a., the figure shows molecular dynamics results at three different densities (V/V_o = 2, 3, and 5) for systems of 504 (Δ) and 986 (▼) particles. The straight lines are drawn with the slopes given by the hydrodynamic and kinetic theories discussed by Prof. Dorfman, using Enskog values for the transport coefficients. The circles and squares, and the associated dashed curve, are from a numerical (finite-mesh) hydrodynamic calculation with which we need not be concerned here. The evident linearity in t^{-1} implied of course a divergent self-diffusion coefficient, whose consequences Prof. Dorfman has discussed. The upward deviation of the molecular dynamics points for the smaller system (N = 504, Δ) at the longest times plotted were attributed to finite system effects. We note that these deviations appear somewhat earlier than the corresponding acoustic traversal times in Table 3.1, which indicates that the latter are no better than crude estimates of the times beyond which finite system effects may appear in $\rho_D(s)$.

The Alder and Wainwright[34] results for hard spheres were less extensive and less conclusive for the $t^{-3/2}$ behavior. Only the single calculation shown in Fig. 4.2.b was presented, the triangles giving molecular dynamics results for a system of 500 hard spheres at V/V_o = 3 extending out to t/t_o = 25. (From Table 3.1 we note that finite system effects might be expected to appear by t/t_o equal to about 20). The circles in the figure again refer to a numerical hydrodynamic calculation, with which we will not concern ourselves. The solid straight line was intended to represent the theoretical prediction $\rho_D(s) = \alpha_D^{(3)} s^{-3/2}$, but unfortunately a factor $\eta/(D + \eta)$, equal to about 0.76 at this density, was inadvertently omitted. Including this factor gives the dashed line shown in the figure, which lies significantly below the molecular dynamics points. Thus, in spite of frequent statements in the literature to the contrary, for hard spheres the so-far published molecular dynamics calculations are only very marginally in agreement with the theoretical predictions. We will mention some more recent, as yet unpublished, results later.

4.3. Lorentz Models

We mention very briefly the two machine calculations known to us on Lorentz models.

4.3.1. The Ehrenfest Wind-Tree.

In the Ehrenfest wind-tree model, a point particle ("wind particle") moves parallel to the diagonals of infinitely massive oriented parallel squares ("trees") of edge σ, the particle reflecting specularly when it collides with a square. Two cases are defined according to whether the squares are allowed to overlap each other (denoted by OV) or forbidden to do so (NOV). Hauge and Cohen[36,37] predicted from kinetic theory analysis that the wind particle would exhibit normal diffusive behavior in the NOV case, i.e., a finite, non-zero diffusion constant and a mean-square displacement growing asymptotically linearly with time, but an abnormal behavior in the OV case corresponding to a vanishing diffusion constant (mean-square displacement growing asymptotically less rapidly than linearly in time). Wood and Lado[38] verified these predictions by a combined Monte Carlo-molecular dynamics calculation of the type described in Section 3.4. The computed behavior of the variable $S = \langle\Delta r(t)^2\rangle/\ell_B^2 t^*$ where $t^* = t/t_B$, with t_B being the low-density mean-free-time, and ℓ_B the corresponding mean free path, is shown in Fig. 4.3.

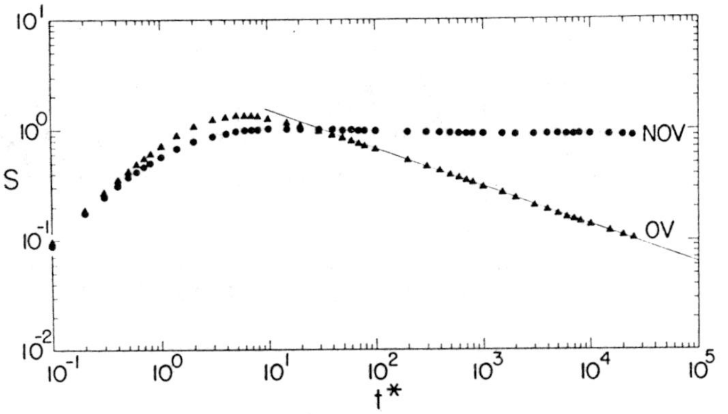

Fig. 4.3. $S = \langle\Delta r(t)^2\rangle/\ell_B^2 t^*$ plotted against $t^* = t/t_B$, for the Ehrenfest wind-tree model, using periodic boundary conditions with N = 8192 scattering squares ("trees") at $V/V_o = 2$, $V_o = N\sigma^2$. [Wood and Lado[38]].

We see that the mean square displacement is indeed, within the accuracy of the machine calculation, growing aysmptotically linearly with time in the NOV case, and certainly less rapidly in the OV case. Van Beyeren and Hauge[39] were subsequently able to account for the power law decay of S displayed in the figure by a heuristic extension of the Hauge-Cohen analysis. The importance of this computer experiment on an admittedly very pathological dynamical system is in the verification of the ability of the theoretical techniques to cope with gross dynamical abnormalities, yet ones which to a certain extent mimic events that occur in more physically realistic systems.

4.3.2. The Lorentz gas with overlapping disks as scatterers.

Here we consider a system similar to that in the previous section, except that the scatterers are now disks of radius σ which are permitted to overlap. The system is of particular interest because the diffusion coefficient $D^{(o)}$ has, according to kinetic theory calculations by Weijland and Van Leeuwen[40] and Bruin[41], the density dependence

$$v\sigma/D^{(o)} = c_1 n^* + c_2' n^{*2} \ln n^* + c_2 n^{*2} + c_3'' n^{*3} (\ln n^*)^2 + \dots \tag{4.10}$$

$$c_1 = 16/3, \quad c_2' = -64/9, \quad c_2 = -4.68, \quad c_3'' = 24.10$$

Here v is the velocity of the moving particle and $n^* = n\sigma^2$, with $n = N/V$ being the number density of scatterers. The importance of the system lies in the appearance of logarithmic terms similar to those which are believed to be present in real three-dimensional systems, but for which conclusive experimental evidence is lacking. In the present case the logarithm appears one order lower in the density than is believed to be the case in real systems, and its coefficient is not small compared to the leading (Boltzmann) term, both of which circumstances should be favorable to its detection. Bruin[41] has carried out an extensive computer study of this system by methods similar to those already described. In a short summary, one cannot really do justice to the wealth of data he reports. With respect to the presence of the logarithmic term, the situation is perhaps best summarized by Fig. 4.4., taken from Bruin's paper.

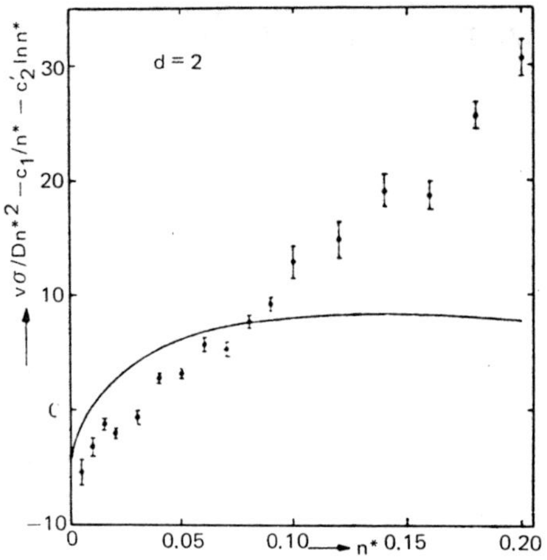

Fig. 4.4. The deviation $(v\sigma/D - c_1 n^*)n^{*-2} - c_2' \ln n^*$ versus n^* for the Lorentz gas with overlapping disks as scatterers [Bruin[41]]; here D is the same as our $D^{(o)}$. The points are the molecular dynamics results; the curve is the locus of the known terms in the density expansion, i.e., $c_2 + c_3'' n^*(\ln n^*)^2$.

Note that in the form so displayed, the deviation of the computed quantity $v\sigma/D^{(o)}$ from the first two terms on the right hand side of eq. (4.10) is multiplied by n^{*-2}, the latter factor being very large at the lowest densities. The "experimental" error is of course multiplied by the same factor; the relatively small error bars which nevertheless result are an indication of the precision of the computed low density diffusion coefficients. [At the lowest density, for example, $n^* = .005$, Bruin reports $D^{(o)}/v\sigma = 36.398 \pm 0.037$.] One wishes the agreement between the points and the theoretical curve in the figure were better at the lowest densities, but the disagreement may be due to slow convergence of the theoretical expansion. Even at the lowest density $n^* = .005$ the magnitude of the last known term $c_3'' n^*(\ln n^*)^2$ is 72% of that of the preceding term c_2. The interested reader should refer to the original work for a more thorough discussion.

5. SOME CURRENT WORK ON HARD DISKS AND SPHERES

5.1. Velocity autocorrelation function; hydrodynamic theory for periodic systems

As mentioned previously one of the first objectives of the current work at Los Alamos was to confirm and, if possible, extend the results of Alder and Wainwright for the long-time behavior of the velocity autocorrelation function for hard spheres and disks. By calculating for systems of more particles we hoped to be able to extend the comparison with the theoretical predictions to significantly larger values of t/t_o than their largest value (about 29 for hard disks; see Fig. 4.2). In the course of this work it occurred to us that the success of the hydrodynamic theories, in accounting for the long-time behavior of the velocity autocorrelation function in infinite systems, strongly suggests that they might be capable of giving a quantitative account of finite periodic system effects on $\rho_D(t)$. Leaving aside for the present the already-mentioned questions concerning the accuracy of the trajectory calculation, it is such finite system effects which have heretofore limited the time scale over which the theories and the molecular dynamics results can be compared. If the agreement could be extended to longer times by applying the theory to periodic systems, this would considerably strengthen our confidence in it. There are various hints and suggestions along these lines in the work of Alder and Wainwright, but apparently no systematic investigation has been carried out. In this section we will first outline very briefly how the hydrodynamic theory can be applied to periodic systems, and then use it as a framework for discussing some of our recent molecular dynamics results.

We use the hydrodynamic theory of Ernst, Hauge, and van Leeuwen[42], which Prof. Dorfman has summarized in his lectures. In applying this theory, hereinafter referred to as "EHvL", to a finite periodic system, we observe the following points.

1. We use the canonical ensemble instead of the grand canonical ensemble of EHvL; see the lectures of Prof. Dorfman on this point.

2. From the hydrodynamic theory we obtain $\rho_D(t)$ in the canonical ensemble, whereas the machine calculation gives $\hat{\rho}_D(t)$ in the microcanonical ensemble. A small correction can be applied to account for the different ensembles, while within either ensemble the two functions are related by

$$\hat{\rho}_D(t) = [N\,\rho_D(t) - 1]/(N - 1) \; . \qquad (5.1)$$

3. In transforming the hydrodynamic fields back into coordinate space from Fourier space, a discrete summation over the wave vectors $\vec{k}$ appropriate to the given periodic system replaces the Fourier integrals used by EHvL. No short wavelength cutoff is used.

4. In the comparisons with the molecular dynamics calculations reported here, the $\vec{k}$-sum mentioned in 3. above has been carried out numerically. We have not

yet succeeded in finding analytical asymptotic approximations for large N at fixed t.

5. We include the contributions of both the longitudinal (sonic) and transverse (shear) components of the hydrodynamic velocity field.

6. For numerical evaluation, we use Enskog values of the collision time and the transport coefficients, and the Ree-Hoover[17] Padé approximants for the equations of state.

7. We set the initial tagged particle distribution function $W(\vec{r})$ of EHvL equal to a δ-function.

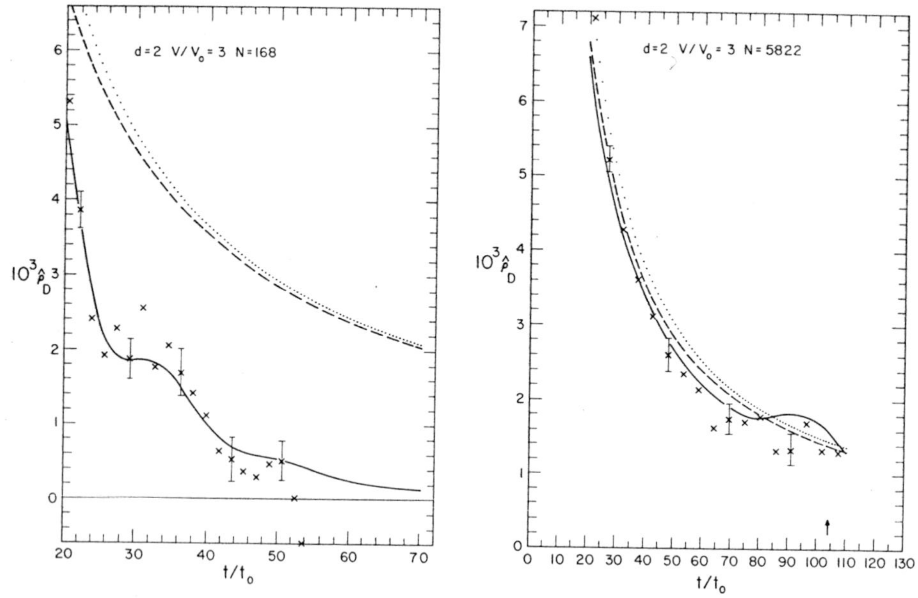

Fig. 5.1. Comparison of $\hat{\rho}_D(t)$ as a function of t/t_o obtained from the finite system hydrodynamic theory with molecular dynamics results for hard disks. See the text for the coding of the theoretical curves.

Fig. 5.1.a compares $\hat{\rho}_D(t)$ calculated in this way for a system of 168 hard disks at $V/V_o = 3$ with our molecular dynamics results for the same system. In this figure and the subsequent similar figures, three theoretical curves are shown:

(a) The dotted curve is the familiar result of the several theories for an infinite system at long times

$$\rho_D(t) = \alpha_D^{(d)} (t/t_o)^{-d/2}$$
$$\alpha_D^{(d)} = [(d-1)/dn]\,[4\pi(D_E^{(o)} + \nu_E)t_o]^{-d/2} . \qquad (5.2)$$

Here $n = N/V$, the subscript E indicates the use of Enskog values of the transport coefficient, and ν is the kinematic viscosity.

(b) The dashed curve contains, in addition to the infinite-system contribution of the transverse modes as given in eq. (5.2), the infinite-system limit of the contribution of the longitudinal modes. This contribution decays exponentially for d = 3 and (asymptotically) as $(t/t_o)^{-2}$ for d = 2. Note that the dotted curve and the dashed curve both apply to an infinite system.

(c) The solid curve is the complete, numerically calculated, result for the finite system, calculated as just described.

(d) The points, with representative error bars shown, are the molecular dynamics results. The small vertical arrows locate the acoustic traversal time t_a/t_o given in Table 3.1 when they fall within the abscissa limits of the figure.

Returning to Fig. 5.1.a., we note that the finite system hydrodynamic calculation gives a quite satisfactory account of the rather large departures from infinite system behavior out to times appreciably longer ($t/t_o \approx 50$) than the maximum times reported by Alder and Wainwright[34]. Only the point at the longest time calculated ($t/t_o \approx 54$), for reasons not understood, appears to exhibit an abnormally large deviation from the solid curve.

Fig. 5.1.b. shows a similar comparison for the largest system studied, 5822 hard disks, at the same density ($V/V_o = 3$), and out to the longest time so far explored. For this large system the three theoretical curves are quite close together, and the agreement seems on the whole satisfactory. Beyond about $t/t_o = 40$

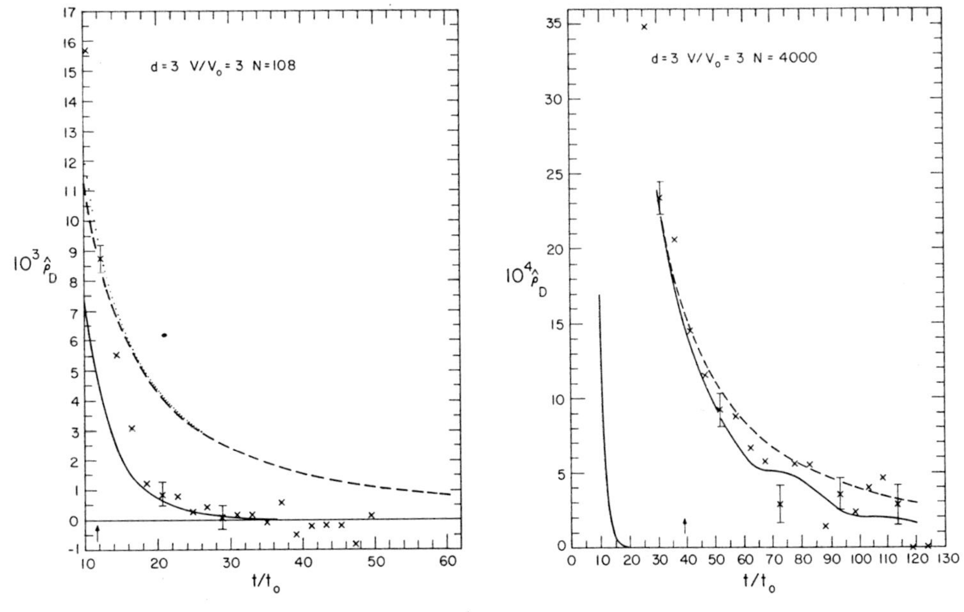

Fig. 5.2. Comparison of $\hat{\rho}_D(t)$ as a function of t/t_o obtained from the finite system hydrodynamic theory with molecular dynamics results for hard spheres at $V/V_o = 3$. See the text for the coding of the theoretical curves (a) N = 108; (b) N = 4000. In (b) the dotted curve and the dashed curve coincide on the scale of the figure, and only the latter is shown. The steeply falling curve at the left edge of the figure is $\hat{\rho}_D(t)$ as given by the Boltzmann equation.

almost all the points lie slightly below the theoretical finite system curve. One possible explanation of such a tendency would lie in the supposition that eq. (5.2) should be modified by allowing $\alpha_D^{(d)}$ to be time-dependent, corresponding to replacing the Enskog values of the transport coefficients by slowly divergent, time dependent values.

Similar agreement is obtained at other densities. In summary, it seems correct to say that these current investigations of the hard disk velocity autocorrelation function have indeed confirmed Alder and Wainwright's previous work, and have extended the time interval of sybstantial agreement with the theoretical t^{-1} decay law out to $t/t_o \approx 100$ in one case.

Figs. 5.2.a. and b. exhibit similar comparisons for hard spheres at $V/V_o = 3$. Note, by comparing Fig. 5.1.b. and 5.2.b., that at $t/t_o \approx 120$ the theoretical infinite system velocity autocorrelation function for hard spheres is only about one-quarter that of hard disks. A given absolute statistical error corresponds, accordingly, to a much larger relative error in the three-dimensional case. Nevertheless, the observed agreement between the theory and the molecular dynamics results seems reasonably satisfying. Note that the calculation in the larger system (4000 particles) has been extended out to more than three times the acoustic traversal time. Without the estimate of finite system effects provided by the hydrodynamic theory we would be quite doubtful of their significance.

Before leaving the subject of the hard-core velocity autocorrelation function, we wish to fulfill our promise to give some further discussion of the effect of varying the accuracy with which the dynamical trajectories are calculated.

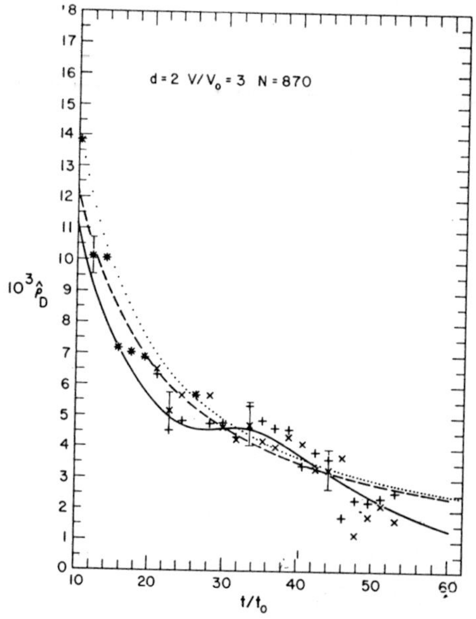

Fig. 5.3. $\hat{\rho}_D(t)$ versus t/t_o for 870 hard disks at $V/V_o=3$, from molecular dynamics calculations in "single-precision (14 decimal places)" arithmetic (+ symbols) and "double-precision (29 decimal places)" (x symbols). The theoretical curves are coded as in the immediately preceding figures.

Fig. 5.3. is in the same format as the two preceding figures, except that it contains points for two different molecular dynamics calculations for a system of 870 hard disks at $V/V_o = 3$. In one calculation (+ symbols) "single-precision" arithmetic on the CDC7600 was used, corresponding to about 14 decimal places being carried in the (floating point) positions and velocities. In the second calculation (x symbols) "double-precision" arithmetic was used, corresponding to twice as many decimal places. In order to avoid confounding different effects, no time averaging was used in either calculation [i.e., in eq.(3.42) the parameter ν was set equal to one]. In each calculation trajectories were developed from the same set of 1500 different initial phases, sampled from the micro-canonical ensemble as described in Section 3.4. This set of 1500 initial phases was identical in the two calculations, the "low-order" half of the "double-precision" positions and velocities being taken to be zero. Thus, the "true" set of 1500 trajectories is the same for both calculations, and comparing the results for $\hat{\rho}_D(t)$ from the two runs should give an indication of the accuracy of the velocities at time t. From Fig. 5.3. we see that the values of $\hat{\rho}_D(t)$ agree, within the plotting accuracy, up to about $t/t_o = 20$, but differ beyond that point, typically in the first or second significant decimal place. From the magnitude of $\hat{\rho}_D(t)$ we see that roughly two significant decimal places must be lost in forming the correlation function. Thus, it seems likely that shortly after $t/t_o = 20$ the single precision velocities are inaccurate in their third decimal place. From other evidence it seems likely that, on the average, phase significance is lost along the trajectory at a constant rate (depending significantly on the density and perhaps the system size), so that it follows that in the present case the single precision velocities are probably totally imprecise, particle by particle, somewhere between $t/t_o = 20$ and 30. Then, ipso facto, the same will be true of the double-precision velocities at twice the value of t/t_o.

Yet from the figure we see that at all times up to the maximum time studied ($t/t_o \approx 54$), the single-precision and double-precision averages are in statistical agreement. That is, they agree within the statistical accuracy of the double-precision average, the latter being estimated in the usual way from the set of 1500 "observed" values. This seems, at least at first sight, quite surprising. It means, that at, say, $t/t_o = 40$ the single-precision velocity of any particular particle has no apparent relation to its true value (it may well have the opposite sign). Yet we nevertheless obtain, by averaging its correlation with its initial velocity over some number of trajectories, an estimate of the true correlation which is as statistically reliable as the one we would obtain by computing the same average value using the true velocities on the same number of trajectories.

It seems clear that the above conjectured behavior can occur only subject to appropriate limitation. For instance, we would not expect it to be the case if the number of decimal places carried in the calculation is reduced ad absurdum.

But is does appear that in practice useful results can be obtained from time-correlation functions at values of t longer than the times over which the trajectory integration is precise with respect to the phases of individual particles. It would be interesting to understand the limitations under which this is true. The Los Alamos work reported here was done in double precision.

5.2. The (super) Burnett self-diffusion coefficient

Several theoretical calculations[43-46] have predicted a divergence of the (super) Burnett coefficient $D^{(2)}(t)$, appearing in eqs. (3.29) and (3.35) through (3.37) and mentioned in the lectures of Prof. Dorfman, in both two and three dimensions. Molecular dynamics calculations of $D^{(2)}(t)$ for hard disks and spheres are in progress at Los Alamos and for hard disks at Livermore, and we will mention here a few of the preliminary results of the Los Alamos work. The two sets of results for hard disks are in good agreement, and a joint publication is planned in the immediate future.

5.2.1. Hard disks.

For hard disks de Schepper, van Beyeren, and Ernst[45] have obtained the expressions

$$\begin{aligned} D^{(2)}(t) &= D^{(2)}_{LB} + e_1 t + e_2 t \ln t/t^*_o + e_3 t(\ln t/t^*_o)^2 + \ldots \\ e_1 &= -\frac{1}{2} d_o D^2/(D+\nu) \\ e_2 &= -d_o^2 \frac{D}{D+\nu}\left(\frac{\nu}{D+\nu} - \frac{D}{8\Gamma_s} - \frac{D}{4\nu}\right) \\ d_o &= [8\pi\beta m n(D+\nu)]^{-1} \\ \Gamma_s &= \zeta/nm + \nu + (\gamma-1)\lambda/nC_p \end{aligned} \tag{5.3}$$

in which $D = D^{(o)}$ is the ordinary Fick's law self-diffusion coefficient, ν the kinematic viscosity, n the number density, ζ the bulk viscosity, C_p and C_v the heat capacities per particle, and $\gamma = C_p/C_v$. $D^{(2)}_{LB}$ is the (super) Burnett coefficient given by the Lorentz-Boltzmann equation[†)].

[†)] One might consistently use either the time-dependent coefficient $D^{(2)}_{LB}(t)$ from the Lorentz-Boltzmann equation, as an approximation for intermediate times, or its limit $D^{(2)}_{LB}(\infty)$. We have obtained preliminary values for both $D^{(2)}_{LB}(t)$ and $D^{(2)}_{LB}(\infty)$ by solving the Lorentz-Boltzmann equation through the fifth and ninth Enskog approximations, respectively. We find $(\beta m)^2 D^{(2)}_{LB}(\infty)/t_o^3 = 0.306$ for $d = 2$, and 0.817 for $d = 3$. The latter value differs by several percent from the value implicit in a numerical calculation by Desai and Nelkin[47]; we do not yet understand the cause of the discrepancy.

The quantity t_o^* is a time-constant related to the mean free time, but the theory has not yet yielded an explicit expression for it. This theoretical result gives in each term the leading contribution for large t. At low density the transport coefficients appearing in the coefficients take on their corresponding Boltzmann values, so that $D_{LB}^{(2)}$ is proportional to n^{-3}, $e_1 t_o$ to n^{-2}, $e_2 t_o$ to n^{-1}, etc. With the reduced time t/t_o held fixed at some reasonably large value compared to unity the expansion is then presumed to be physically significant only at densities low enough that the successive terms decrease. The coefficient e_1 arises from the same class of dynamical events ("rings") which gives the leading contribution to the asymptotic decay of the velocity autocorrelation function, and at higher densities there is some theoretical justification for replacing the transport coefficients appearing in its definition with their Enskog values. The e_2 and higher order terms represent the dominant contribution for low density and long time of more complex dynamical events than the simple rings contained in e_1. It can be argued that such events will only contribute on a significantly longer time scale than the ring events, but there is at present no quantitative estimate for this time scale. For this reason, and also because of the uncertain value of t_o^*, we limit this preliminary comparison of eq. (5.3) and the molecular dynamics results to the terms containing $D_{LB}^{(2)}$ and e_1, using Enskog values for the transport coefficients and the Ree-Hoover[17)] Padé approximant for the equation of state. The omission of the e_2 and higher order terms is not expected to be important at low densities, but would presumably become more so as the density increases.

Eq. (5.3) differs from the earlier result of Keyes and Oppenheim[43)] in the presence of the e_1 term, and the e_3 and higher order terms (the existence of which are inferred from the theory although no expressions for the coefficients are known), and also in the expression for the coefficient e_2. The molecular dynamics results and eq. (5.3) through the e_1 term are compared in Fig. 5.4. in terms of the dimensionless variable

$$\tilde{D}^{(2)}(t) = (\beta m)^2 D^{(2)}(t)/t_o^3 \qquad (5.4)$$

Considering first the molecular dynamics results by themselves, we note that after agreeing well with the Lorentz-Boltzmann equation for t/t_o up to about 2, the computed values pass through a maximum in the interval between $t/t_o = 5$ and 10, and then decrease, becoming definitely negative at the higher density. The increase at long times in the lower density case ($V/V_o = 10$) may possibly be due to finite system effects. Thus, the negative divergence predicted by the theory does indeed seem to be present, especially at the higher density. The quantitative agreement with de Schepper, <u>et al</u>, also seems quite good, perhaps surprisingly so at the higher density.

5.2.2. Hard spheres

For hard spheres de Schepper, van Beyeren, and Ernst[46)] find

$$D^{(2)}(t) = D^{(2)}_{LB} + e_1 t^{1/2} + e_2 t^{1/4} + O(t^{1/8})$$

$$e_1 = -D^2[10\pi^{3/2}\ \beta mn(D+\nu)^{5/2}]^{-1}$$

$$e_2 = -\frac{4D^2\ \Delta_\eta(1)\Gamma(15/4)}{15\pi^2\beta mn(D+\nu)^{15/4}} \qquad (5.5)$$

$$\Delta_\eta(1) = c^{1/2}[77\pi\sqrt{2}\beta mn\Gamma_s^{3/2}]^{-1}$$

where c is the adiabatic sound speed, $\Gamma(x)$ is the usual gamma-function, and the remaining symbols have the same meaning as in the two-dimensional case. We note that in eq. (5.5) the e_2 term is less divergent than the e_1 term, in contrast to eq. (5.3). Comparisons with the molecular dynamics results, carried out in the same manner as before but including all three of the known terms, are shown in Fig. 5.5., using again the reduced coefficient defined in eq. (5.4). Here it should be noted that in both cases the calculations of $\tilde{D}^{(2)}(t)$ extend to times much longer than the acoustic traversal time, and so are suspect with regard to perturbations from finite system effects. We presently lack any means, such as we described for the case of the velocity autocorrelation function, of estimating these systematic effects on the Burnett coefficient, and consequently we can not make any quantitative comparison with the theoretical prediction. Only at the higher density are negative values of $\tilde{D}^{(2)}(t)$ actually attained, and then much less strikingly than was the case for hard disks.

5.3. Asymptotic behavior of the van Hove self-correlation function.

Aside from the hydrodynamic significance of the (super) Burnett coefficient, the time dependence of the fourth cumulant $\kappa_4(t) = \langle\Delta x_1(t)^4\rangle - 3\langle\Delta x_1(t)^2\rangle^2$ appearing in its definition [eq. (3.35)] is relevant to the validity of the frequently made assumption that the distribution function[†)] $G(x,t) = \langle\delta[\Delta x_1(t)-x]\rangle$ of the x-component of displacement of the tagged particle becomes gaussian at long times,

$$G(x,t) \sim [2\pi\langle\Delta x_1(t)^2\rangle]^{-1/2}\ \exp(-x^2/2\langle\Delta x_1(t)^2\rangle). \qquad (5.6)$$

If eq. (5.6) is correct, then the reduced cumulant $\tilde{\kappa}_4(t) = \kappa_4(t)/3\langle\Delta x_1(t)^2\rangle^2$ should approach zero for large t.

Considering first the behavior of $\tilde{\kappa}_4(t)$ which follows from the theoretically predicted $t^{1/2}$ divergence of $D^{(2)}(t)$ for hard spheres, and omitting positive

†) The function G(x,t) is closely related to the van Hove self-correlation function $G_s(\vec{r},t) = \langle\delta[\Delta\vec{r}_1(t)-\vec{r}]\rangle$.

(a)

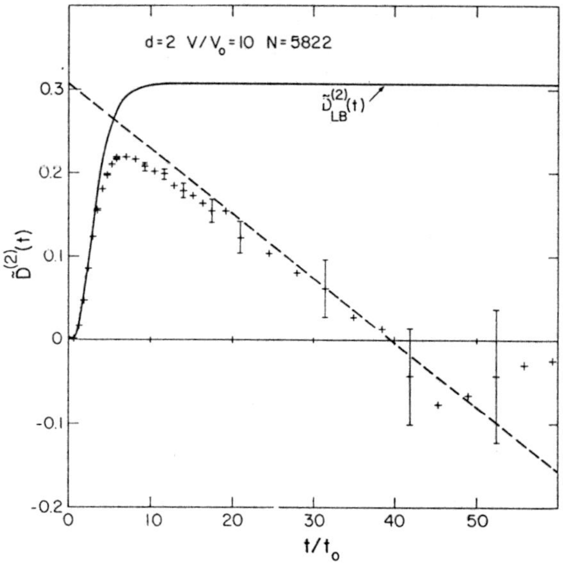

(b)

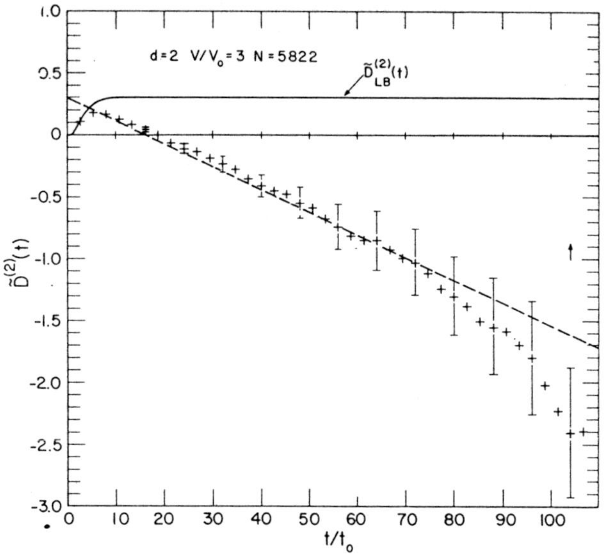

Fig. 5.4. Molecular dynamics results (+ signs, with representative error bars) for the reduced (super) Burnett coefficient $\tilde{D}^{(2)}(t)$ for 5822 hard disks versus t/t_o, compared with the $D^{(2)}_{LB}(\infty)$ and e_1 terms of the de Schepper, et al, theoretical expression given in eq. (5.3). In (a) $V/V_o = 10$, in (b) $V/V_o = 3$.

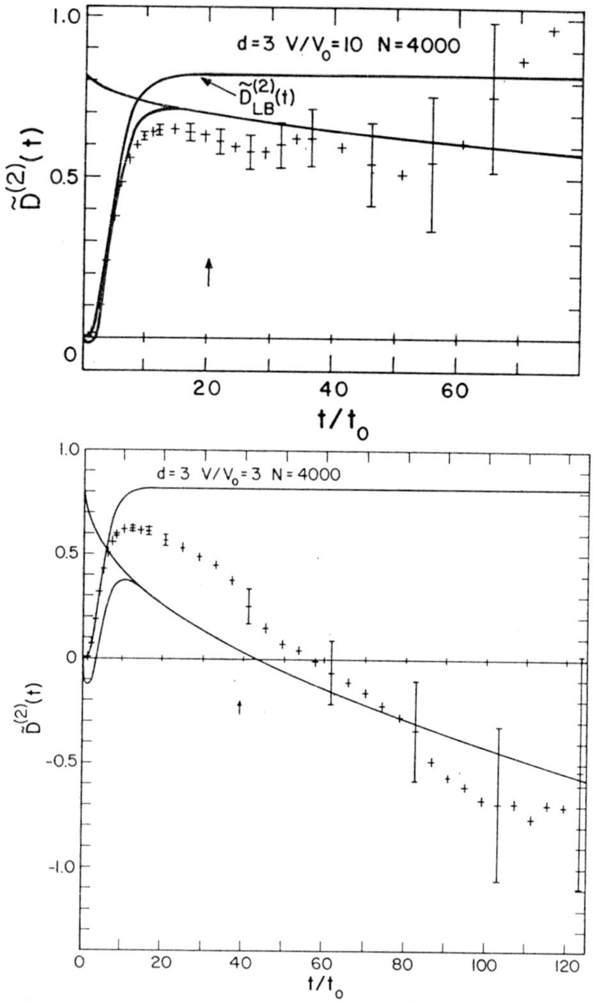

(a)

(b)

Fig. 5.5. Molecular dynamics results (+ signs, with representative error bars) for the reduced (super) Burnett coefficient $\tilde{D}^{(2)}(t)$ versus t/t_o for 4000 hard spheres, compared with the de Schepper, et al, theoretical expression given in eq. (5.5). Both choices $D_{LB}^{(2)}(t)$ and $D_{LB}^{(2)}(\infty)$ for $D_{LB}^{(2)}$ are shown, along with $\tilde{D}_{LB}^{(2)}(t)$ for comparison. The e_2 term is essentially negligible in both cases. In (a) $V/V_o = 10$, in (b) $V/V_o = 3$.

multiplicative factors, we have $\kappa_4(t) \sim -t^{3/2}$ and $\langle \Delta x_1(t)^2 \rangle \sim t$, so that $\tilde{\kappa}_4(t) \sim -t^{-1/2}$. That is, the predicted divergence in the three-dimensional Burnett coefficient $D^{(2)}(t)$ is consistent with $G(x,t)$ becoming gaussian at long times. The situation is much more problemmatical in two dimensions, due to lack of valid asymptotic estimates for $D^{(2)}(t)$ or $\kappa_4(t)$, and we refrain from speculation. It should be noted that $\kappa_4(t)$ is by its nature slow in adjusting its behavior to that of $D^{(2)}(t)$, since it is the integral of the latter.

Fig. 5.6. shows the reduced cumulant $\tilde{\kappa}_4(t)$ obtained from the molecular dynamics calculations at $V/V_o = 3$. In the two-dimensional case it is negative and

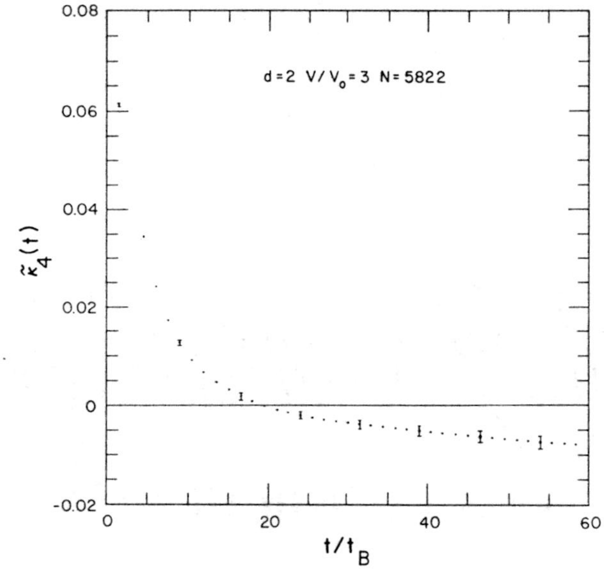

(a)

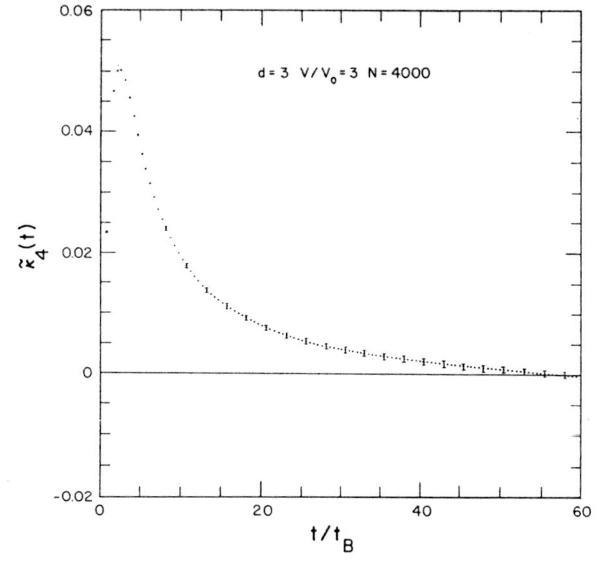

(b)

Fig. 5.6. The fourth cumulant $\tilde{\kappa}_4(t)$ versus t/t_B at $V/V_o = 3$ for (a) 5822 hard disks, $t_B/t_o \approx 1.781$ and (b) 4000 hard spheres, $t_B/t_o \approx 2.058$; t_B denotes the low-density (Boltzmann) mean free time.

slowly decreasing at the longest times calculated. In the three dimensional case, it is very slightly negative, with the error bars overlapping zero. Thus, at this density the machine results are consistent with G(x,t) becoming gaussian for hard spheres (but subject to uncertainty with respect to finite system effects), while in the case of hard disks it is definitely non-gaussian, and becoming more so, at the longest times calculated.

5.4. Non-equilibrium molecular dynamics; steady-state self-diffusion

Recently a new approach to computer studies of transport processes has been initiated by Ashurst and Hoover[48], with other somewhat similar methods being also introduced by Gosling, McDonald, and Singer[49] and Lees and Edwards[50]. In the Ashurst-Hoover method the basic notion is to alter the boundary conditions on the system in such a way as to drive the system into a non-equilibrium steady state. From the computer one obtains directly "observed" values of the appropriate gradients and currents, and then studies the relation between these quantities as the driving forces at the boundary are varied. In this way, for example, Ashurst and Hoover have simulated Couette flow in liquid argon, finding reasonable agreement with experimentally measured values of the shear viscosity.

Limitations of time and the intended scope of these lectures prevent our giving here a detailed discussion of this very interesting work. For pedagogical purposes it is probably more to the point to illustrate the ideas within the context of the self-diffusion process in systems of hard disks and spheres, by describing very briefly a similar calculation for non-equilibrium, steady state self-diffusion which is being carried out at Los Alamos with Dr. B. Holian and Dr. J.J. Erpenbeck, and which was directly inspired by the work of Ashurst and Hoover. We use the standard molecular dynamics procedure to study a binary mixture of hard disks or spheres in which the two components are completely mechanically identical but differ in their "colors", being respectively "red" and "white", say. The usual periodic boundary conditions are employed, with only the following modification. Whenever a red particle crosses in the positive x-direction any of the boundary planes $x = \nu L$ of the infinite "checker-board" array of cells of volume $V = L^d$ (ν being any positive, negative, or zero integer), its color changes to white with some specified probability p. Similarly, a white particle crossing in the negative direction becomes red with the same probability. Particles of either color traveling in the opposite direction from those specified remain unchanged in color. These boundary conditions force the number density $n_1(x,t)$ of red particles to increase with x within a given cell, on the average, and accordingly a diffusion current $J_1(x,t)$ of red particles develops in the negative x-direction. Intuitively one expects the system to approach a steady state in which the time-averaged quantities $\bar{n}_1(x)$ and $\bar{J}_1(x)$ become independent of the length t of the time-averaging interval, and this is indeed observed. Note that if one ignores the colors of the particles the system is completely "at equilibrium"; we can and do calculate the various equilibrium time correlation functions of interest by simply disregarding the particle colors.

From number conservation we expect $\bar{J}_1(x)$ to be independent of x (aside from fluctuations) in the steady-state, and this also is observed in the preliminary calculations discussed here. In addition, the number density $\bar{n}_1(x)$ of red particles is found to be quite linear in x (our spatial resolution being too small to observe any boundary layer effects near $x = \nu L$). This suggests that the steady-state self-diffusion coefficient is independent of the local red particle number density $\bar{n}_1(x)$, and we accordingly calculate the self-diffusion coefficient from the mean gradient and current, i.e., $D^{(o)} = -\bar{J}/[\partial\bar{n}_1(x)/\partial x]$. Finally, within the precision of our preliminary results, the resulting values of $D^{(o)}$ appear to be independent of the magnitude of the red particle number density gradient[†)], which can be varied by varying the probability p with which the color changes are forced at the boundary. Note also that finite system effects are strongly felt in experiments of this type, since the time-averaging must necessarily be carried out over a time long compared to the hydrodynamic relaxation time of the system.

Table 5.1. gives some very preliminary values of $D^{(o)}/D_E$ calculated in this way for several values of N at $V/V_o = 3$, for both hard disks and hard spheres, with D_E being the Enskog dense gas value of the self-diffusion coefficient.

TABLE 5.1.

Preliminary non-equilibrium molecular dynamics values of $D^{(o)}/D_E$ for hard disks and spheres at $V/V_o = 3$.

d	N	$D^{(o)}/D_E$
2	168	1.40 ± .03
	1512	1.79 ± .04
3	108	1.17 ± .02
	500	1.23 ± .02
	4000	1.29 ± .02

The very large N-dependence in the two-dimensional case is qualitatively consistent with the expectation that, while finite system effects are expected to result in a finite value of $D^{(o)}$ for any given value of N, this value should increase without limit with increasing N. In the three-dimensional case, on the other hand, one expects a noticeable N-dependence arising from the $t^{-3/2}$ decay, but with a finite limiting value being approached as N increases. The values given in the table for hard spheres seem consistent with the estimate $D^{(o)}/D_E = 1.34$ given for

†) This observation suggests the absence of any non-linear Burnett self-diffusion coefficient, i.e., the absence in the self-diffusion current of any contributions proportional to higher powers of the gradient than the first. The role of the linear (super) Burnett coefficient $D^{(2)}$ in the present computer experiment is problemmatical. If the red particle number density is strictly linear, then the super Burnett self-diffusion current $-D^{(2)}\partial^3\bar{n}_1(x)/\partial x^3$ of course vanishes, at least for a finite value of $D^{(2)}$.

this limiting value by Alder, Gass, and Wainwright[51]. At present we lack a quantitative theoretical estimate of the expected value of the self-diffusion coefficient for such a steady state process in a finite system. A plausible guess might be the long-time integral of the finite-system velocity correlation function as extrapolated using the EHvL theory described in Section 5.A., but we have not yet carried out this calculation.

6. CONCLUSION

We close this survey of computer studies on hard-core systems by mentioning a few directions in which further work may be useful.

1. It would be useful in theoretical studies of transport processes to take as much account as possible of finite system effects, in order to extend the time scale over which meaningful comparisons with computer experiments can be made. For example, it is not at all clear why the finite system EHvL theory works as well as it apparently does. At the same time, a similar, or better, treatment of the (super) Burnett coefficient would be very helpful in comparing the theoretical predictions with the computer calculations, especially in three dimensions.
2. What is the asymptotic character of the Burnett and super-Burnett coefficients for other transport processes such as viscosity and heat conduction?
3. In particular, with respect to the preceding question, what can be learned about non-linear transport processes? From the computational point of view, are non-equilibrium molecular dynamics techniques such as that of Ashurst and Hoover the best ones for the study of such effects?
4. It would be desirable to understand better the effect on the accuracy of molecular dynamics time correlation functions of inaccuracy in the trajectory integration.
5. It might be of interest to investigate the (super) Burnett coefficient for the Lorentz models.

7. ACKNOWLEDGEMENTS

The work at Los Alamos mentioned here is in large measure that of my colleagues, Drs. J.J. Erpenbeck and B. Holian. Our molecular dynamics studies of the (super) Burnett self-diffusion coefficient have been carried on in close collaboration with similar studies by Dr. B.J. Alder at Livermore. I am greatly indepted to Professors E.G.D. Cohen, J.R. Dorfman, and M.H. Ernst for many helpful discussions and comments.

REFERENCES

*) This work has been conducted under the auspices of the U.S. Atomic Energy Commission.

1) B.J. Alder, Ann. Rev. Phys. Chem., 24 (1973), 325.
2) B.J. Berne, "Time Dependent Properties of Condensed Media", Chapter 9 of Volume VIIIB, Liquid State, in Physical Chemistry, An Advanced Treatise, H. Eyring, D. Henderson, and W. Jost, editors, (Academic Press), 1971.
3) B.J. Berne and D. Forster, Ann. Rev. Phys. Chem., 22 (1971), 563.
4) F.H. Ree, "Computer Calculation for Model Systems", Chapter 3 of Volume VIIIA, Liquid State, in Physical Chemistry, An Advanced Treatise, H. Eyring, D. Henderson, and W. Jost, editors, (Academic Press), 1971.
5) I.R. McDonald and K. Singer, Quaterly Reviews XXIV (1970), 238.
6) L. Verlet, Studies in Appl. Math., 3 (1969), 112.
7) J.M. Hammersley and D.C. Handscomb, Monte Carlo Methods, (John Wiley and Sons, Inc., New York), 1964.
8) Birger Jansson, Random Number Generators, (Pettersons, Stockholm), 1966.
9) U. Dieter and J.H. Ahrens, "Uniform Random Number Generators", to be published, 1974.
10) F. Stockmal, J. Assoc. for Computing Machinery, 11 (1964), 41-52.
11) W.W. Wood, J. Chem. Phys., 48 (1968a), 415-434.
12) W.A. Beyer, R.B. Roof, and D. Williamson, Mathematics of Computation, 25 (1971), 345-363.
13) M.H. Kalos, D. Levesque, and L. Verlet, Phys. Rev. A 9 (1974), 2178-2195.
14) W.W. Wood, J. Chem. Phys., 52 (1970), 729.
15) I.R. McDonald, Molecular Physics, 23 (1972), 41.
16) W.W. Wood, "Monte Carlo Studies of Simple Liquid Models", Chapter 5 in Physics of Simple Liquids, H.N.V. Temperley, J.S. Rowlinson, and G.S. Rushbrooke, editors, (North Holland Publishing Company, Amsterdam), 1968b.
17) F.H. Ree and W.G. Hoover, J. Chem. Phys., 40 (1964), 939.
18) W.G. Hoover and F.H. Ree, J. Chem. Phys., 49 (1968), 3609.
19) B. Widom, J. Chem. Phys., 44 (1966), 3888.
20) B.J. Alder, S.P. Frankel, and V.A. Lewinson, J. Chem. Phys., 23 (1955), 417.
21) N.C. Metropolis, A.W. Rosenbluth, M.N. Rosenbluth, A.H. Teller, and E. Teller, J. Chem. Phys., 21 (1953), 1087.
22) M.N. Rosenbluth and A.W. Rosenbluth, J. Chem. Phys., 22 (1954), 881.
23) W. Feller, An Introduction to Probability Theory and Its Applications, Vol. I, (John Wiley and Sons, Inc., New York), 1950.
24) J.L. Doob, Stochastic Processes, (John Wiley and Sons, Inc., New York), 1953.
25) J.G. Kemeny and J.L. Snell, Finite Markov Chains, (Van Nostrand, New York), 1960.

26) B.J. Alder and T.E. Wainwright, "International Symposium on Statistical Mechanical Theory of Transport Processes", Brussels, 1956, I. Prigogine, editor, (Interscience), 1958, p. 97.

27) A. Rahman, Phys. Rev. A 136 (1964), 405.

28) E. Fermi, I.R. Pasta, and S.M. Ulam, "Studies of Non-Linear Problems", Los Alamos Scientific Laboratory report, LA-1940, (Los Alamos, New Mexico), 1955.

29) J. Orban and A. Bellemans, Phys. Letters, 24A (1967), 620.

30) B.J. Alder and T.E. Wainwright, Phys. Rev., 127 (1962), 359.

31) J.O. Hirschfelder, C.F. Curtiss, and R.B. Bird, Molecular Theory of Gases and Liquids, (John Wiley and Sons, Inc., New York), 1954, p. 134.

32) W.G. Hoover and B.J. Alder, J. Chem. Phys., 46 (1967), 686.

33) B.J. Alder and T.E. Wainwright, "Proceedings of the International Conference on Statistical Mechanics", Japan, J. Phys. Soc. of Japan 26 Supplement, (1968), 267.

34) B.J. Alder and T.E. Wainwright, Phys. Rev., A 1 (1970), 18.

35) G. Torrie, J.P. Valleau, and A. Bain, J. Chem. Phys., 58 (1973), 5479.

36) E.H. Hauge and E.G.D. Cohen, Phys. Letters, 25A (1967), 78.

37) E.H. Hauge and E.G.D. Cohen, J. Math. Phys., 10 (1969), 397.

38) W.W. Wood and F. Lado, J. Computational Phys., 7 (1971), 528.

39) H. van Beyeren and E.H. Hauge, Phys. Letters, 39A (1972), 397.

40) A. Weijland and J.M.J. van Leeuwen, Physica, 38 (1969), 35.

41) C. Bruin, Physica, 72 (1974), 261.

42) M.H. Ernst, E.H. Hauge, J.M.J. van Leeuwen, Phys. Rev., A 4 (1971), 2055.

43) T. Keyes and I. Oppenheim, Physica, 70 (1973), 100.

44) J.W. Dufty and J.A. McLennan, Phys. Rev., A 9 (1974), 1266.

45) I.M. de Schepper, H. van Beyeren, and M.H. Ernst, private communication (1974).

46) I.M. de Schepper, H. van Beyeren, and M.H. Ernst, preprint "The Non-Existence of the Linear Diffusion Equation Beyond Fick's Law", (1974).

47) R.C. Desai and M. Nelkin, Nucl. Science and Engineering, 24 (1966), 142.

48) W.T. Ashurst and W.G. Hoover, Phys. Rev. Letters, 31 (1973), 206.

49) E.M. Gosling, I.R. McDonald, and K. Singer, preprint (1973).

50) A.W. Lees and S.F. Edwards, J. Phys. C, Solid State, 5 (1972), 1921.

51) B.J. Alder, D.M. Gass, and T.E. Wainwright, J. Chem. Phys., 53 (1970), 3813.

FLUCTUATING HYDRODYNAMICS AND RENORMALIZATION OF SUSCEPTIBILITIES AND TRANSPORT COEFFICIENTS

P. MAZUR[†]

Instituut-Lorentz, University of Leiden, the Netherlands

1. GENERAL INTRODUCTION [*]

1.1. Fluctuating hydrodynamics and renormalization of transport coefficients

In recent years relaxation phenomena in non-linear systems have been studied extensively. Two aspects of this problem have in particular been investigated. On the one hand the renormalization of transport coefficients in the critical region has been discussed within the framework of the mode-mode theory by Kawasaki and others[4,5]. On the other hand slow decaying contributions to time correlation functions and memory kernels, as first found in a computer experiment by Alder and Wainwright[6], were studied using either hydrodynamic, kinetic or related arguments (ref. 6-13). As has been pointed out, for example, by Kawasaki[14] and Zwanzig[15] both aspects are intimately related.

In these lectures we shall discuss the renormalization of certain transport-coefficients or susceptibilities consistently within the framework of fluctuating hydrodynamics[*]. To this end we extend, so to say, the Landau-Lifshitz theory of linear fluctuating hydrodynamics[16], to include the non-linear (fluctuating) terms which occur in the hydrodynamic equations. A theory of this type is particularly well suited to study phenomena which occur at small wave vectors and long times when hydrodynamic considerations are applicable. We shall restrict ourselves to situations in which the non-linearity of the fluctuating equations considered has a very simple structure.

We shall on the one hand consider the behaviour of the dielectric constant in a fluctuating non-polar fluid and show that the deviations from the validity of the Clausius-Mossotti formula may be interpreted, within this framework, as being due to a renormalization of the dielectric constant as a result of density fluctuations. Explicit formulae can then be obtained to describe the behaviour of the frequency and wave vector dependent dielectric tensor in the critical region.

We shall furthermore study the diffusion of tagged particles through an incompressible fluctuating fluid, starting from a non-linear generalized Langevin

---

† These lectures are also published in the Springer series "Lecture notes in physics", Proceedings of the Sitges International School on Statistical Mechanics, 1974.

* The subject matter of these lectures is essentially contained in a series of papers by D. Bedeaux and the author[1-3]

** A similar point of view was taken by Gitterman and Gorodetskii[31].

equation for the density of the tagged particles (the non-linear Landau-Lifshitz equation for the diffusion problem). We show that averaging this equation over the fluctuations, a linear macroscopic diffusion equation is obtained with a renormalized wave vector and frequency dependent diffusion coefficient, for which we obtain a closed expression. An analysis of this expression leads amongst other things to the well known $t^{-3/2}$ asymptotic behaviour for the diffusion memory kernel. We are able to discuss in detail the question whether the expression for the asymptotic behaviour of the memory kernel should contain the renormalized diffusion coefficient, as argued by several authors[4-8], rather than the bare one.

We will first discuss briefly a class of stochastic differential equations in their relation to the theory presented.

1.2. Stochastic differential equations

The theory which we will present is essentially based on the consideration of stochastic differential equations of a certain class. Basically these stochastic differential equations may be of the form

$$L^* x(t) = K(t) \tag{1.1}$$

Here $x(t)$ is a random process, $K(t)$ some "external generalized force" (a given function of time t) and L^* a stochastic differential operator of the form

$$L^* = \frac{\partial}{\partial t} + \gamma_o + \gamma_1 \, y(t) \tag{1.2}$$

where γ_o and γ_1 are constants, and $y(t)$ is a second stationary random process, with zero mean

$$\langle y(t) \rangle = 0 \tag{1.3}$$

and given stochastic properties.

The formal solution of eq. (1.1) is

$$x(t) = L^{*-1} K(t) = G^* K(t) \tag{1.4}$$

with L^{*-1} the inverse of L^* and $G^* = L^{*-1}$ the random Green function operator of the problem. If one averages eq. (1.4) one obtains

$$\langle x(t) \rangle = \langle L^{*-1} \rangle K(t) = \langle G^* \rangle K(t) = G^* K(t) \tag{1.5}$$

where G is the propagator for the averaged equation. Defining

$$L = G^{-1} \tag{1.6}$$

we obtain for $<x(t)>$ the equation

$$L<x(t)> = K(t) \tag{1.7}$$

with

$$L = <L^{*-1}>^{-1} \tag{1.8}$$

Let us now define an operator γ' through

$$L \equiv \frac{\partial}{\partial t} + \gamma_o + \gamma' = L_o + \gamma' \tag{1.9}$$

so that

$$L = L_o(1 + L_o^{-1}\gamma') = L_o(1 + G_o\gamma') \tag{1.10}$$

with

$$G_o = L_o^{-1} \tag{1.11}$$

On the other hand

$$L^* = L_o(1 + \gamma_1 G_o\, y(t)) \tag{1.12}$$

so that

$$<L^{*-1}>^{-1} = L_o<(1 + \gamma_1 G_o\, y)^{-1}>^{-1} \tag{1.13}$$

If we then substitute eqs. (1.9) and (1.13) into eq. (1.8) we obtain

$$\begin{aligned}\gamma' &= -L_o + L_o<(1 + \gamma_1 G_o y)^{-1}>^{-1} \\ &= <-L_o(1 + \gamma_1 G_o y)^{-1} + L_o><(1 + \gamma_1 G_o y)^{-1}>^{-1} \\ &= \gamma_1<y(1 + \gamma_1 G_o y)^{-1}><(1 + \gamma_1 G_o y)^{-1}>^{-1}\end{aligned} \tag{1.14}$$

Equation (1.14) defines the macroscopic operator γ' in terms of correlation functions of $y(t)$. If we were to call γ_o the bare kinetic coefficient and

$\gamma_o + \gamma_1 y(t)$ the random kinetic coefficient, then $\gamma_o + \gamma'$ represents, so to say, the macroscopic "renormalized" kinetic coefficient since, according to eqs. (1.7) and (1.9), $\langle x \rangle$ obeys the equation

$$\frac{\partial \langle x(t) \rangle}{\partial t} = - (\gamma_o + \gamma') \langle x(t) \rangle + K(t) \tag{1.15}$$

Note that γ' is still an operator, which turns out to be a convulution operator in time such that eq. (1.15) has the form

$$\frac{\partial \langle x(t) \rangle}{\partial t} = - \gamma_o \langle x(t) \rangle - \int_{-\infty}^{t} \gamma'(t - t') \langle x(t) \rangle dt' + K(t')$$

In the next chapters we shall consider specific problems described by stochastic differential equations, more or less of the type of eq. (1.1). We will consider as stated in Section 1.1. the dielectric properties of a fluctuating fluid, and the diffusion of tagged particles through a fluctuating fluid. We shall evaluate the corresponding "renormalized kinetic coefficient", i.e. the dielectric tensor, and the diffusion memory kernel, to some order of approximation. Stochastic differential equations of the type of eq. (1.1) have recently been studied by van Kampen[17]. We refer to his papers for further references

2. ON THE CRITICAL BEHAVIOUR OF THE DIELECTRIC CONSTANT FOR A NON-POLAR FLUID

2.1. Introduction

In the theory of the propagation of light through a fluid two aspects have received special attention. On the one hand one has studied the scattering of light from an incident beam. The phenomenological theory of this phenomenon goes back to the work of Smoluchowski[18] and Einstein[19]. Molecular theories of light scattering have subsequently been given by, among others, Yvon[20] and Zimm[21] and also by Fixmann[22], who was able to justify Einstein's result. On the other hand the propagation of the transmitted beam has been studied by calculation of the refractive index of the system. Theories for the refractive index have been given by, among others, Yvon[20], Hoek[23], Rosenfeld[24], Mazur and Mandel[25]. All these theories start essentially from a molecular basis. The theory of the refractive index is related to the theory of light scattering to the extent that the imaginary part of the refractive index, in the absence of true absorption, is directly related to the toral intensity of the scattered light.

All molecular theories both of light scattering and of the refractive index suffer from the drawback that they are based on series expansions in the polarizability per unit volume and the calculation of the first few terms of the series. Strictly speaking they are therefore limited to systems where the refractive index is not appreciably different from unity. This makes their application questionable, for instance, in the critical region. The phenomenological theory does not suffer from this drawback.

We shall develop here a theory of the dielectric constant in a fluctuating fluid, which yields an expression for the macroscopic wave vector and frequency dependent dielectric tensor in terms of density fluctuation correlation functions. This tensor describes the response of the system to an arbitrary electromagnetic field. Its transverse part, with k and ω satisfying the usual dispersion relation, yields the index of refraction of the medium in terms of these correlation functions. The theory is not restricted to small values of the polarizability per unit volume and is therefore well suited to the study of the behaviour of the dielectric tensor in the critical region. In particular we shall study the dispersion of the velocity of light in the medium when it is close to the critical point. For small values of the polarizability per unit of volume the results can be shown to be in agreement with those of previous molecular theories.

2.2. Formal theory

The Maxwell equations in a fluctuating fluid are

$$\text{curl}\,\vec{E} = -\frac{\partial\vec{B}}{\partial t} \quad , \quad \text{div}\,\vec{D} = 0 \quad , \quad \text{curl}\,\vec{H} = \frac{\partial\vec{D}}{\partial t} \quad , \quad \text{div}\,\vec{B} = 0 \quad , \tag{2.1}$$

where $\vec{E}(\vec{r},t)$ and $\vec{B}(\vec{r},t)$ are the fluctuating electric and magnetic fields respectively, and $\vec{D}(\vec{r},t)$ and $\vec{H}(\vec{r},t)$ the fluctuating inductions; units are chosen in such a way that the velocity of light is unity in vacuum. Neglecting the magnetic properties we have

$$\vec{H} = \vec{B} \quad , \quad \vec{D} = \vec{E} + \vec{P} \tag{2.2}$$

with $\vec{P}$ the fluctuating polarization.

We define Fourier transforms with respect to $\vec{r}$ and t of a field f by

$$f(\vec{k},\omega) = \int d\vec{r}\,dt\,e^{-i(\vec{k}\cdot\vec{r}-\omega t)}f(\vec{r},t) \quad . \tag{2.3}$$

From equations (2.1) and (2.2) we then obtain the vector wave equation

$$(\vec{k}\vec{k} - k^2 + \omega^2)\vec{E}(\vec{k},\omega) = -\,\omega^2\vec{P}(\vec{k},\omega) \quad . \tag{2.4}$$

The general retarded solution of this equation is

$$\vec{E}(\vec{k},\omega) = \vec{E}^{o}(\vec{k},\omega) - \vec{\vec{F}}(\vec{k},\omega) \cdot \vec{P}(\vec{k},\omega) \qquad (2.5)$$

where $\vec{E}^{o}$ is a solution of the homogeneous equation and is therefore the incident field in vacuum. In the presence of externally controlled sources $\vec{E}^{o}$ contains also the vacuum fields generated by these sources. The retarded propagator of the electromagnetic field in vacuum $\vec{\vec{F}}$ is given by the diagonal elements $\vec{k},\omega$ representation

$$\vec{\vec{F}}(\vec{k},\omega) = \left[\vec{k}\vec{k} - k^2 + (\omega+i0)^2\right]^{-1}\omega^2 = \left[k^2 - (\omega+i0)^2\right]^{-1}(\vec{k}\vec{k} - \omega^2)$$

$$= \left[\frac{1}{2}\, i\pi k^{-1}\{\delta(k-\omega) - \delta(k+\omega)\} + \mathcal{P}\frac{1}{k^2-\omega^2}\right](\vec{k}\vec{k} - \omega^2) \quad , \qquad (2.6)$$

where 0 represents an infinitesimally small positive number.

From eq. (2.4) or (2.5) it can be seen that the electric field will fluctuate because of the fluctuations in the polarization of the dielectric. These in turn will be caused for a non-polar fluid by fluctuations in the density $\rho(\vec{r},t)$ and in other thermodynamic variables. Averaging over these fluctuations, denoted by $\langle\ldots\rangle$, yields the macroscopic quantities. In order to come to a closed description we must relate the polarization to the electric field. In linear optics $P(r,t)$ is given by

$$\vec{P}(\vec{r},t) = \chi^*(\rho(\vec{r},t))\vec{E}(\vec{r},t) \qquad (2.7)$$

where $\chi^*(\rho(\vec{r},t))$, the fluctuating susceptibility, is related to the density by the Clausius-Mossotti formula

$$\chi^*(\rho) = \alpha_o\rho(1 - \tfrac{1}{3}\alpha_o\rho)^{-1} \qquad (2.8)$$

where α_o is a constant frequency independent molecular polarizability. This restricts the applicability of the theory to the transmission of fields at non-resonant frequencies. The validity of eq. (2.8) is assumed here for density fields which vary sufficiently slowly in time and space. Eq. (2.8) can be justified on a molecular basis. Deviations from eq. (2.8) occur if ρ varies appreciably over molecular distances. Now upon substitution of eq. (2.8) into eq. (2.5) one obtains

$$\vec{E} = \vec{E}^{o} - \vec{\vec{F}} \cdot \chi^*\vec{E} \qquad (2.9)$$

with the formal solution

$$\vec{E} = (1 + \overleftrightarrow{F} \cdot \chi^*)^{-1} \cdot \vec{E}^o \quad . \tag{2.10}$$

In both eqs. (2.9) and (2.10), χ^* has to be interpreted as an operator. According to eq. (2.8), χ^* is diagonal in the $\vec{r},t$ representation. It is therefore a convolution operator in the $\vec{k},\omega$ representation. The propagator $\overleftrightarrow{F}$ is diagonal in the $\vec{k},\omega$ representation (cf. eq. (2.6)) and a convolution operator in the $\vec{r},t$ representation.

The macroscopic electric field is obtained if one averages eq. (2.10),

$$\langle\vec{E}\rangle = \langle(1 + \overleftrightarrow{F}\chi^*)^{-1}\rangle \cdot \vec{E}^o \quad . \tag{2.11}$$

On the other hand, substituting eq. (2.10) into eq. (2.7), and using also eq. (2.11), yields for the average polarization

$$\langle\vec{P}\rangle = \langle\chi^*\vec{E}\rangle = \langle\chi^*(1 + \overleftrightarrow{F}\chi^*)^{-1}\rangle \cdot \vec{E}^o$$

$$= \langle\chi^*(1 + \overleftrightarrow{F}\chi^*)^{-1}\rangle \cdot \langle(1 + \overleftrightarrow{F}\chi^*)^{-1}\rangle^{-1} \cdot \langle\vec{E}\rangle \quad . \tag{2.12}$$

This equation defines the macroscopic dielectric susceptibility tensor $\overleftrightarrow{\chi}$ and dielectric tensor $\overleftrightarrow{\varepsilon}$

$$\overleftrightarrow{\varepsilon} - 1 = \overleftrightarrow{\chi} = \langle\chi^*(1 + \overleftrightarrow{F}\chi^*)^{-1}\rangle \cdot \langle(1 + \overleftrightarrow{F}\chi^*)^{-1}\rangle^{-1} \quad . \tag{2.13}$$

It will be the starting point of our further discussion.

In the absence of fluctuations it follows from the above equation that the macroscopic dielectric constant is given by the Clausius-Mossotti formula

$$\varepsilon_o - 1 = \chi_o = \alpha_o\rho_o(1 - \tfrac{1}{3}\alpha_o\rho_o)^{-1} \quad , \quad \rho_o = \langle\rho\rangle \quad . \tag{2.14}$$

We will now investigate in more detail the deviations from the Clausius-Mossotti formula, caused by the density fluctuations. We define the propagator in the absence of fluctuations

$$\overleftrightarrow{F}_{\varepsilon_o}(\vec{k},\omega) = (1 + \overleftrightarrow{F}\chi_o)^{-1}\overleftrightarrow{F}(\vec{k},\omega) = \left[\vec{k}\vec{k} - k^2 + (\omega + i0)^2\varepsilon_o\right]^{-1}\omega^2$$

$$= \varepsilon_o^{-1}\left[k^2 - (\omega + i0)^2\varepsilon_o\right]^{-1}(\vec{k}\vec{k} - \omega^2\varepsilon_o) \tag{2.15}$$

and write

$$\chi^* = \chi_o + \Delta\chi^* \quad . \tag{2.16}$$

If we then substitute eq. (2.16) into eq. (2.13), we find that

$$\varepsilon = \varepsilon_o + \langle\Delta\chi^*(1 + \overleftrightarrow{F}_{\varepsilon_o}\,\Delta\chi^*)^{-1}\rangle \cdot \langle(1 + \overleftrightarrow{F}_{\varepsilon_o}\,\Delta\chi^*)^{-1}\rangle \quad . \tag{2.17}$$

Equation (2.17), which is equivalent to equation (2.13), may be used to obtain expansions for $\overleftrightarrow{\varepsilon}$ in terms of density-density fluctuation correlation functions. We note that the "renormalized" propagator $\overleftrightarrow{F}_{\varepsilon_o}$ accounts for the fact that the fluctuations in χ^* interact via the medium rather than through vacuum. Each term in the expansion of eq. (2.17) corresponds to a partial resummation of the terms in the expansion of eq. (2.13) in powers of χ^*. The formal transformation from eq. (2.13) to eq. (2.17) performs these resummations to all orders. It should also be mentioned that one can easily convince oneself, using the fact that the fluid is translationally invariant in space and time, that $\overleftrightarrow{\varepsilon}$ is diagonal in the $\vec{k},\omega$ representation, as of course it should be.

Before proceeding with the analysis of the influence of density fluctuations on the behaviour of the dielectric constant, we shall derive two further identities.

Define the "cut-out" propagator:

$$\overleftrightarrow{H} = \overleftrightarrow{F} - \frac{1}{3} \tag{2.18}$$

and the Clausius-Mossotti function:

$$\overleftrightarrow{\gamma} = 3(\overleftrightarrow{\varepsilon} - 1)(\overleftrightarrow{\varepsilon} + 2)^{-1} \tag{2.19}$$

or

$$\overleftrightarrow{\varepsilon} - 1 = \overleftrightarrow{\gamma} \cdot (1 - \frac{1}{3}\overleftrightarrow{\gamma})^{-1} \quad . \tag{2.20}$$

With these definitions and eq. (2.8), one finds after some straightforward transformations from eq. (2.13) that

$$\overleftrightarrow{\gamma} = \langle\rho\alpha_o(1 + \overleftrightarrow{H}\rho\alpha_o)^{-1}\rangle \cdot \langle(1 + \overleftrightarrow{H}\rho\alpha_o)^{-1}\rangle \quad , \tag{2.21}$$

an expression for the Clausius-Mossotti function in terms of the density correlation functions.

In the absence of fluctuations, eq. (2.21) leads to the Clausius-Mossotti formula in its usual form. An even more useful identity is found if we write

$$\rho = \rho_o + \Delta\rho \quad , \quad \rho_o = \langle\rho\rangle \quad . \tag{2.22}$$

Substitution of eq. (2.22) into eq. (2.21) leads to

$$\overleftrightarrow{\gamma} = \rho_o\alpha_o + \langle\alpha_o\Delta\rho(1 + \overleftrightarrow{K}\alpha_o\Delta\rho)^{-1}\rangle \cdot \langle(1 + \overleftrightarrow{K}\alpha_o\Delta\rho)^{-1}\rangle \tag{2.23}$$

with the renormalized "cut-out" propagator

$$\overleftrightarrow{K} \equiv (1 + \overleftrightarrow{H}\alpha_o\rho_o)^{-1} \cdot \overleftrightarrow{H}$$

$$= [1 + (\overleftrightarrow{F} - \tfrac{1}{3})\ \alpha_o\rho_o]^{-1} \cdot (\overleftrightarrow{F} - \tfrac{1}{3}) \tag{2.24}$$

If one uses the relations (cf. eq. (2.14) and (2.15))

$$\frac{\varepsilon_o - 1}{\varepsilon_o + 2} = \frac{1}{3}\rho_o\alpha_o \tag{2.25}$$

$$\overleftrightarrow{F}_{\varepsilon_o} = [1 + \overleftrightarrow{F}(\varepsilon_o - 1)]^{-1} \cdot \overleftrightarrow{F}$$

$$\overleftrightarrow{F} = [1 - \overleftrightarrow{F}_{\varepsilon_o}(\varepsilon_o - 1)]^{-1} \cdot \overleftrightarrow{F}_{\varepsilon_o} \tag{2.26}$$

one finds from eq. (2.24) a relation between the propagator $\overleftrightarrow{K}$ and the propagator $\overleftrightarrow{F}_{\varepsilon_o}$ occurring in eq. (2.17)

$$\overleftrightarrow{K} = \left(\frac{\varepsilon_o + 2}{3}\right)^2 \left(\overleftrightarrow{F}_{\varepsilon_o} - \frac{1}{\varepsilon_o + 2}\right) \tag{2.27}$$

The general expression eq. (2.23) relates the corrections to the Clausius-Mossotti formula directly to density fluctuation correlation functions. The propagator $\overleftrightarrow{K}$ accounts for the fact that these density fluctuations interact via the medium. As we see from eq. (2.27), $\overleftrightarrow{K}$ is essentially the propagator in the medium with dielectric constant ε_o, modified by Lorentz corrections.

2.3. Expansion of the dielectric tensor in terms of density-density correlation functions

We shall now study eq. (2.23) in more detail. Expanding the right hand side in powers of $\alpha_o \Delta\rho$, we obtain

$$\overleftrightarrow{\gamma}(\vec{k},\omega) = \alpha_o\rho_o \left\{ 1 - (2\pi)^{-4}\alpha_o\rho_o \int_{k'<k_o} S_2(\vec{k}-\vec{k}',\omega-\omega')\overleftrightarrow{K}(\vec{k}',\omega')d\vec{k}'d\omega' \right.$$
$$\left. + \text{ higher order terms} \right\} \tag{2.28}$$

where the density-density correlation function S_2 is defined as

$$S_2(\vec{r}_2-\vec{r}_1,t_2-t_1) = \rho_o^{-2}\langle\Delta\rho(\vec{r}_1,t_1)\Delta\rho(\vec{r}_2,t_2)\rangle \tag{2.29}$$

and where the integral in (2.28) is cut off at some inverse molecular distance. The introduction of the cut off in eq. (2.28) is related to the fact that eq. (2.8) does not hold any more if ρ varies appreciably over molecular distances. In a molecular version of the present theory, in which corrections to eq. (2.8) are taken into account, it is not necessary to introduce an explicit cut off[1]. The Fourier transform of S_2 is defined in the usual manner. If one also expands $\overleftrightarrow{K}$ in $\alpha_o\rho_o$, one obtains a series expansion in powers of $\alpha_o\rho_o$, which is in fact closely related to the series obtained by previous authors from molecular theories. Such a series will rapidly converge if $\alpha_o\rho_o \ll 1$ or if $||\overleftrightarrow{\varepsilon} - 1|| \ll 1$, i.e. for sufficiently low densities. However, the expansion in eq. (2.28) will also rapidly converge if $\alpha_o\rho_o$ is of order unity, but the integrals involving the correlation functions become progressively smaller, i.e. if the density fluctuations are sufficiently small, so that $||\overleftrightarrow{\varepsilon} - \varepsilon_o|| \ll 1$. Such an expansion is therefore well suited to study the behaviour of the dielectric tensor in the critical region.

In the next sections we will calculate the correction to the Clausius-Mossotti function originating from the density-density function S_2, assuming therefore that under most circumstances this is the dominant contribution. Using (2.25), eq. (2.28) yields for $\overleftrightarrow{\varepsilon}$:

$$\overleftrightarrow{\varepsilon}(\vec{k},\omega) \cong \varepsilon_o - (\varepsilon_o-1)^2(2\pi)^{-4}\int S_2(\vec{k}-\vec{k}',\omega-\omega')\overleftrightarrow{K}(\vec{k}',\omega')d\vec{k}'d\omega'$$

$$= \varepsilon_o - (\varepsilon_o-1)^2\left(\frac{\varepsilon_o+2}{3}\right)^2(2\pi)^{-4}\int S_2(\vec{k}-\vec{k}',\omega-\omega')\left[\overleftrightarrow{F}_{\varepsilon_o}(\vec{k}',\omega') - \frac{1}{\varepsilon_o+2}\right]d\vec{k}'d\omega' \tag{2.30}$$

where we have also used eq. (2.27).

At this point it should be mentioned that eq. (2.30) can also be obtained from the general formula (2.17), if one expands the r.h.s. consistently up to powers quadratic in $\Delta\rho$.

The correction to the dielectric tensor in eq. (2.30) has the form of a mode-mode coupling expression, encountered in the now familiar theories for the renormalization of transport coefficients. Here the coupling is between the electromagnetic mode and the modes governing the behaviour of S_2 (hydrodynamic modes). In the language of the mode-mode coupling theories we may call ε_o the "bare" dielectric constant and $\overleftrightarrow{\varepsilon}$ the renormalized dielectric tensor.

Up to corrections of order $(v/c)^2$ (v is the thermal velocity in the fluid) we may neglect the motion of the fluid, so that we can use the static approximation for the correlation function S_2

$$S_2(\vec{k} - \vec{k}', \omega - \omega') = 2\pi S_2(\vec{k} - \vec{k}')\,\delta(\omega - \omega') \quad . \tag{2.31}$$

Equation (2.30) then becomes

$$\overleftrightarrow{\varepsilon} = \varepsilon_o - (\varepsilon_o - 1)^2 \left(\frac{\varepsilon_o+2}{3}\right)^2 (2\pi)^{-3} \int S_2(\vec{k} - \vec{k}') \left[\overleftrightarrow{F}_{\varepsilon_o}(\vec{k}', \omega) - \frac{1}{\varepsilon_o+2}\right] d\vec{k}' \quad . \tag{2.32}$$

For isotropic systems we may write

$$\overleftrightarrow{\varepsilon}(\vec{k}, \omega) = \varepsilon_{tr}(k, \omega)(1 - \vec{k}\vec{k}/k^2) + \varepsilon_\ell(k, \omega)\vec{k}\vec{k}/k^2 \quad , \tag{2.33}$$

where the transverse and longitudinal dielectric constants are given by

$$\varepsilon_{tr}(k, \omega) = \varepsilon_o - (2\pi)^{-3}(\varepsilon_o - 1)^2 \left(\frac{\varepsilon_o+2}{3}\right)^2 \int S_2(|\vec{k}-\vec{k}'|)$$

$$\vec{u} \cdot \left[\overleftrightarrow{F}_{\varepsilon_o}(\vec{k}', \omega) - \frac{1}{\varepsilon_o+2}\right] \cdot \vec{u}\,d\vec{k}' \tag{2.34}$$

with $\vec{u}$ a unit vector orthogonal to $\vec{k}$, $\vec{u}\cdot\vec{k} = 0$,

$$\varepsilon_\ell(k, \omega) = \varepsilon_o - (\varepsilon_o - 1)^2 \left(\frac{\varepsilon_o+2}{3}\right)^2 (2\pi)^{-3} \int S_2(|\vec{k}-\vec{k}'|)$$

$$\frac{\vec{k}}{k} \cdot \left[\overleftrightarrow{F}_{\varepsilon_o}(\vec{k}', \omega) - \frac{1}{\varepsilon_o+2}\right] \cdot \frac{\vec{k}}{k}\,d\vec{k}' \quad . \tag{2.35}$$

For k in the hydrodynamic region the density-density correlation function has, in good approximation the Ornstein-Zernike*) [26,27] form

$$S_2^H(k) = k_B T\kappa(1 + k^2\xi^2)^{-1} \tag{2.36}$$

where k_B is Boltzmann's constant, T the temperature, κ the isothermal compressibility and ξ the hydrodynamic correlation length.

For larger values of k one has to add terms describing the molecular structure at small intermolecular distances. We therefore write in general

$$S_2(k) = S_2^H(k) + S_2^M(k) \tag{2.37}$$

We shall assume that S_2^M is a sufficiently slowly varying function of k/k_o and becomes small for hydrodynamic values of k.

In the following sections we shall evaluate the various contributions to $\vec{\varepsilon}(\vec{k},\omega)$ by substituting eq. (2.37) into eq. (2.32).

2.4. The extinction coefficient

We shall first compute the imaginary part of dielectric tensor in the approximation given in eq. (2.31). This quantity is directly related to the extinction of light in the fluid. Substituting eq. (2.15) into eqs. (2.34) and (2.35), gives after integration over k' and with $\vec{\Omega} = \vec{k}'/k'$,

$$\mathrm{Im}\,\varepsilon_{tr}(k,\omega) = \frac{\omega^3}{32\pi^2} n_o(\varepsilon_o - 1)^2 \left(\frac{\varepsilon_o+2}{3}\right)^2 \int d\vec{\Omega} S_2(|\vec{k} - \omega n_o\vec{\Omega}|)(1+\cos^2\Theta) \tag{2.38}$$

where Θ is the angle between $\vec{k}$ and $\vec{\Omega}$, and also

$$\mathrm{Im}\,\varepsilon_\ell(k,\omega) = \frac{\omega^3}{16\pi^2} n_o(\varepsilon_o - 1)^2 \left(\frac{\varepsilon_o+2}{3}\right)^2 \int d\vec{\Omega} S_2(|\vec{k} - \omega n_o\vec{\Omega}|)\sin^2\Theta \tag{2.39}$$

$n_o \equiv \varepsilon_o^{1/2}$ is the "bare" index of refraction.

The extinction coefficient is defined as

$$\alpha(\omega) \equiv 2\,\omega\,\mathrm{Im}\,n(\omega) \tag{2.40}$$

with the refractive index given by

---

* The calculations of sections 4-6 can, in principle, also be made by assuming that the Ornstein-Zernike form is slightly modified:

$$S_2^H = k_B T\kappa(1 + k^2\xi^2)^{-1+\eta/2}$$

$$n(\omega) = (\varepsilon_{tr}(k(\omega),\omega))^{1/2} \tag{2.41}$$

where $k(\omega)$ is the solution of the dispersion relation

$$k^2 = \omega^2 \varepsilon_{tr}(k,\omega) \tag{2.42}$$

To lowest order,

$$k(\omega) = n_o \omega \tag{2.43}$$

so that we have to first order from eqs. (2.40)-(2.42) together with eq. (2.38) that

$$\alpha(\omega) = \frac{\omega^4}{32\pi^2} (\varepsilon_o - 1)^2 \left(\frac{\varepsilon_o+2}{3}\right)^2 \int d\vec{\Omega}\, S_2\,(n_o\omega|\vec{\Omega}_o-\vec{\Omega}|)\,(1+\cos^2\Theta) \tag{2.44}$$

where $\vec{\Omega}_o = \vec{k}/n_o\omega$.

In formulae (2.38), (2.39) and (2.44) we can substitute the Ornstein-Zernike form for S_2, since only hydrodynamic values of the argument occur. The integrations can then be performed.[1] This yields in particular for $\alpha(\omega)$

$$\alpha(\omega) = -\frac{\omega^4}{32\pi\varepsilon_o} (\varepsilon_o - 1)^2 \left(\frac{\varepsilon_o+2}{3}\right)^2 \frac{k_B T\kappa}{\omega^2\xi^2} \alpha'(\xi\omega n_o) \tag{2.45}$$

with

$$\alpha'(\xi\omega n_o) = \frac{1+u^2}{u^2} + \left[\left(\frac{1+u^2}{2u^2}\right)^2 + 1\right] \ln\left(\frac{1-u^2}{1+3u^2}\right) \tag{2.46}$$

$$u \equiv \xi\omega n_o (1+\xi^2\omega^2 n_o^2)^{-1/2} \tag{2.47}$$

Furthermore,

$$\alpha'(\xi\omega n_o) \cong -\frac{16}{3} n_o^2\omega^2\xi^2 \qquad \text{if} \qquad \omega^2\xi^2 << 1 \tag{2.48}$$

$$\alpha'(\xi\omega n_o) \cong -4[\ln(2\omega\xi n_o) - 1/2] \tag{2.49}$$

For the explicit results for Im $\varepsilon_{tr}(k,\omega)$ and Im $\varepsilon_\ell(k,\omega)$, the reader is referred to ref. 1.

The expression for the extinction coefficient contains the factor $((\varepsilon_o+2)/3)^2$, which also appears in the expressions obtained from the phenomenological theory of light scattering. The first molecular derivation of this factor was given by Fixman[22]. For $\alpha_o\rho_o \ll 1$, eq. (2.45) reduces to the expression derived by Rosenfeld in that limit. For $\alpha_o\rho_o$ of order unity Rosenfeld's theory does not strictly apply.

We also note that if the system is in the critical region, but not extremely close to the critical point, eq. (2.48) applies and $\alpha(\omega)$ appears to diverge as κ, which diverges as ξ^2. However, extremely close to the critical point, the behaviour is described by eq. (2.49), and $\alpha(\omega)$ is logarithmically divergent. Furthermore the extinction coefficient close to the critical point behaves roughly as ω^2 rather than ω^4. This is the phenomenon of critical opalescence.

2.5. The static, non-dispersive dielectric tensor

Let us now study $\overleftrightarrow{\varepsilon}(\vec{k},\omega)$, for $\omega = 0$ and $\vec{k} = 0$. We have in this case from eq. (2.32), using also eqs. (2.15) and (2.37)

$$\overleftrightarrow{\varepsilon}(0,0) = \varepsilon_o + \varepsilon^M + \varepsilon^H \quad , \tag{2.50}$$

where

$$\varepsilon^M = (27\pi^2\varepsilon_o)^{-1}(\varepsilon_o - 1)^3(\varepsilon_o + 2)\int_0^{k_o} S_2^M(k)k^2dk \tag{2.51}$$

$$\varepsilon^H = (27\pi^2\varepsilon_o)^{-1}(\varepsilon_o - 1)^3(\varepsilon_o + 2)k_BT\kappa\xi^{-3}\int_0^{k_o\xi}(1+x^2)^{-1}x^2dx \quad . \tag{2.52}$$

We cannot evaluate the contribution $\Delta\varepsilon^M$ explicitly. It does not depend critically, however, on the thermodynamic variables. On the other hand the integral in (2.52) is elementary, and one obtains if $k_o\xi \gg 1$

$$\varepsilon^H = (27\pi^2\varepsilon_o)^{-1}(\varepsilon_o - 1)^3(\varepsilon_o + 2)k_BT\kappa\xi^{-3}(k_o\xi - \tfrac{\pi}{2}) \quad , \quad k_o\xi \gg 1 \quad . \tag{2.53}$$

If $k_o\xi \ll 1$, which is typically the case if the system is sufficiently dilute, eq. (2.52) gives

$$\varepsilon^H = (81\pi^2\varepsilon_o)^{-1}(\varepsilon_o - 1)^3(\varepsilon_o + 2)k_BT\kappa\, k_o^3 \quad . \tag{2.54}$$

As is seen from eq. (2.53), the contribution $\Delta\varepsilon^H$ to the static dielectric constant exhibits a marked critical behaviour. In the next section it will become apparent that this term must be taken into account when discussing the critical behaviour of the velocity of light.

2.6. The real dispersive part of the dielectric tensor and the velocity of light

If we define the dispersive part of $\overleftrightarrow{\varepsilon}(\vec{k},\omega)$ as

$$\Delta\overleftrightarrow{\varepsilon}(\vec{k},\omega) = \overleftrightarrow{\varepsilon}(\vec{k},\omega) - \overleftrightarrow{\varepsilon}(0,0) \tag{2.55}$$

we obtain from eq. (2.32), using eqs. (2.15) and (2.37),

$$\mathrm{Re}\,\Delta\overleftrightarrow{\varepsilon}(\vec{k},\omega) = \varepsilon_o^{-1}(6\pi)^{-3}(\varepsilon_o - 1)^2(\varepsilon_o + 2)^2 k_B T\kappa\xi^{-3}\,\overleftrightarrow{I}(\vec{k}\xi,\omega n_o) \tag{2.56}$$

where

$$\overleftrightarrow{I}(\vec{x},y) = \int_{x'<\xi k_o} d\vec{x}'\,(1+|\vec{x}-\vec{x}'|^2)^{-1}\left[(1-3\frac{\vec{x}'\vec{x}'}{x'^2}) + 3y^2(x'^2-y^2)^{-1}(1-\frac{\vec{x}'\vec{x}'}{x'^2})\right] . \tag{2.57}$$

In eq. (2.57) we have neglected the contribution to the integral arising from the molecular part S_2^M of S_2. This implies that we have neglected terms of order $(\omega/k_o)^2$ and $(k/k_o)^2$, which is certainly permissible for optical frequencies and wave numbers. If furthermore $k_o\xi >> 1$, the integrations in eq. (2.57) may be performed and analytic expressions for the real part of $\Delta\overleftrightarrow{\varepsilon}$ can be obtained. We again refer to ref. 1 for these expressions. Here we shall only discuss explicitly the velocity of light, which is defined as

$$c(\omega) \equiv [\mathrm{Re}\; n(\omega)]^{-1} \tag{2.58}$$

where $n(\omega)$ is given by (2.41) with (2.42). To first order in the corrections, we can again use eq. (2.43) so that

$$c(\omega) = \{\mathrm{Re}[\varepsilon_{tr}(n_o\omega,\omega)]^{1/2}\}^{-1}$$

$$= n_o^{-1}\{1 - \tfrac{1}{2}n_o^{-2}\varepsilon^M - \tfrac{1}{2}n_o^{-2}\varepsilon^H - \tfrac{1}{2}n_o^{-2}\mathrm{Re}\;\Delta\varepsilon_{tr}(n_o\omega,\omega) \quad . \tag{2.59}$$

With the result of the integrations in eq. (2.57), and using also eq. (2.53), one then finds that

$$c(\omega) = n_o^{-1} - \frac{1}{2} n_o^{-3} \varepsilon^M - \frac{n_o^{-5}}{54\pi^2} (\varepsilon_o - 1)^3 (\varepsilon_o + 2)(k_o \xi - \pi/2) k_B T \kappa \xi^{-3}$$

$$- \frac{1}{32\pi} \varepsilon_o^{-2} (\varepsilon_o - 1)^2 \left(\frac{\varepsilon_o + 2}{3}\right)^2 k_B T \kappa \xi^{-2} \omega\, \Xi(\xi\omega n_o) \tag{2.60}$$

where

$$\Xi(\xi\omega n_o) = \frac{1}{4u^4} (5u^4 + 2u^2 + 1) \text{arc sin}\, u - \frac{1}{6u^3} (5u^2 + 3)(1 - u^2)^{1/2} +$$

$$+ \left[1 + \left(\frac{1+u^2}{2u^2}\right)^2\right] \text{arc tan} \left(\frac{u(1-u^2)^{1/2}}{1+u^2}\right) \tag{2.61}$$

with u given by eq. (2.47).

Furthermore

$$\Xi(\xi\omega n_o) = \frac{44}{15} \xi\omega n_o \quad , \quad \xi\omega n_o \ll 1 \tag{2.62}$$

$$\Xi(\xi\omega n_o) = \pi \quad , \quad \xi\omega n_o \gg 1 \quad . \tag{2.63}$$

Equation (2.60) describes the behaviour of $c(\omega)$ in the critical region: not too close to the critical point $c(\omega)$ appears to diverge like ξ. Close to the critical point eq. (2.63) applies and shows that $c(\omega)$ remains finite. If one expands eq. (2.60) in powers of $\alpha_o \rho_o$ and only retains quadratic terms, one obtains an expression identical with the expression obtained in that order for $c(\omega)$ by Larsen, Mountain and Zwanzig[28] from a molecular theory. Inspection of expression (2.60) shows, however, that the critical non-dispersive term in c, which is of order $\alpha_o^3 \rho_o^3$ can have the same magnitude, not too close to the critical point, as the dispersive contribution which is of order $\alpha_o^2 \rho_o^2$.

To conclude we may remark that the theory developed in this chapter for the dielectric tensor, on the basis of a theoretical phenomenological-fluctuation approach, enables one to give a detailed description of the behaviour of the dielectric tensor in the critical region, and applies even when the refractive index is appreciably different from unity. The theory has been generalized to the description of binary fluids (liquids)[29].

3. RENORMALIZATION OF THE DIFFUSION COEFFICIENT IN A FLUCTUATING FLUID

3.1. Derivation of a general formula for the renormalized diffusion coefficient

We consider a density distribution $n(\vec{r},t)$ of tagged particles in an incompressible fluid. It is assumed that the solution of the tagged particles is sufficiently dilute so that the fluctuations of the fluid are those of the pure fluid in equilibrium. The density $n(\vec{r},t)$ satisfies the conservation law

$$\frac{\partial}{\partial t} n(\vec{r},t) = - \operatorname{div} \vec{j}(\vec{r},t) \tag{3.1}$$

where $j(\vec{r},t)$ is the current density of the tagged particles. In the hydrodynamic regime this current is assumed to be given by

$$\vec{j}(\vec{r},t) = \vec{v}(\vec{r},t)n(\vec{r},t) - D_o \operatorname{grad} n(\vec{r},t) + \vec{j}_R(\vec{r},t) \tag{3.2}$$

where $\vec{v}(\vec{r},t)$ is the fluctuating velocity field of the fluid. The first term on the right hand side of eq. (3.2) represents the convective part of the current. The second term represents the diffusive part of the current with respect to the moving fluid, with a "bare" diffusion coefficient D_o which is assumed to be constant. The last term represents the random current which is assumed to have the property that

$$\langle \vec{j}_R(\vec{r},t) \rangle_{fl} = 0 \tag{3.3}$$

where the average is taken for given values of the hydrodynamic fluid field $\vec{v}(\vec{r},t)$.

Substituting eq. (3.2) into eq. (3.1), we find that $n(\vec{r},t)$ obeys the non-linear Langevin-equation

$$\left(\frac{\partial}{\partial t} - D_o \nabla^2\right) n(\vec{r},t) = - \operatorname{div} \vec{v}n(\vec{r},t) - \operatorname{div} \vec{j}_R(\vec{r},t) \tag{3.4}$$

where $\vec{v}$ is a vector operator. Even though this equation is linear in the density of the tagged particles the coupling to the fluid is non-linear.

The Fourier transform of a field $f(\vec{r},t)$ is defined as

$$f(\vec{k},\omega) \equiv \int e^{-i(\vec{k}.\vec{r}-\omega t)} f(\vec{r},t) d\vec{r}dt \tag{3.5}$$

In the $\vec{k},\omega$ representation eq. (3.4) becomes

$$(i\omega - D_o k^2) n(\vec{k},\omega) = i\vec{k}.\vec{v}n(\vec{k},\omega) + i\vec{k}.\vec{j}_R(\vec{k},\omega) \tag{3.6}$$

where we note that the operator $\vec{v}$ in this representation has matrix elements

$$\vec{v}(\vec{k},\omega|\vec{k}',\omega') = (2\pi)^{-4}\vec{v}(\vec{k}-\vec{k}',\omega-\omega') \quad . \tag{3.7}$$

Eq. (3.6) has the formal solution

$$n(\vec{k},\omega) = n_o(\vec{k},\omega) - iG_o\vec{k}.\vec{v}n(\vec{k},\omega) - iG_o\vec{k}.\vec{j}_R(\vec{k},\omega) \tag{3.8}$$

where $n_o(\vec{k},\omega)$ is a solution of the homogeneous equation and therefore a non-fluctuating quantity. G_o is the bare diffusion propagator (in the absence of fluctuations)

$$G_o(\vec{k},\omega) \equiv -(i\omega-D_ok^2)^{-1} \quad . \tag{3.9}$$

The formal solution can be rewritten as

$$n(\vec{k},\omega) = [1 + iG_o\vec{k}.\vec{v}]^{-1}\{n_o(\vec{k},\omega) - iG_o\vec{k}.\vec{j}_R(\vec{k},\omega)\} \quad . \tag{3.10}$$

This yields for the current of the tagged particles

$$\vec{j}(\vec{k},\omega) = (\vec{v}-iD_o\vec{k})[1+iG_o\vec{k}.\vec{v}]^{-1}\{n_o(\vec{k},\omega) - iG_o\vec{k}.\vec{j}_R(\vec{k},\omega)\} + \vec{j}_R(\vec{k},\omega) \quad . \tag{3.11}$$

Averaging eqs. (3.10) and (3.11) first over the random current and then over the fluctuations of the fluid we find for the mean particle and current density of the tagged particles using also eq. (3.3)

$$\langle n(\vec{k},\omega)\rangle = \langle[1 + iG_o\vec{k}.\vec{v}]^{-1}\rangle n_o(\vec{k},\omega) \tag{3.12}$$

$$\langle\vec{j}(\vec{k},\omega)\rangle = \langle(\vec{v}-iD_o\vec{k})[1+iG_o\vec{k}.\vec{v}]^{-1}\rangle n_o(\vec{k},\omega) \tag{3.13}$$

where we have introduced the shorthand notation

$$\langle\ldots\rangle = \langle\langle\ldots\rangle_{fl}\rangle \quad . \tag{3.14}$$

Eliminating n_o, the mean current can be written as

$$\langle\vec{j}(\vec{k},\omega)\rangle = \{-iD_o\vec{k} + \langle\vec{v}[1+iG_o\vec{k}.\vec{v}]^{-1}\rangle\langle[1+iG_o\vec{k}.\vec{v}]^{-1}\rangle^{-1}\} \langle n(\vec{k},\omega)\rangle \quad . \tag{3.15}$$

This relation defines the "renormalized" diffusion coefficient

$$D' = D_o + k^{-2}\langle i\vec{k}.\vec{v}[1+iG_o\vec{k}.\vec{v}]^{-1}\rangle\langle[1+iG_o\vec{k}.\vec{v}]^{-1}\rangle^{-1} \quad . \tag{3.16}$$

D is an operator which is, using translational invariance and stationarity of the fluid, diagonal in the $\vec{k},\omega$ representation. From eqs. (3.1), (3.15) and (3.16) it then follows that the mean tagged particle density satisfies the diffusion equation with the renormalized diffusion coefficient

$$(i\omega - D(\vec{k},\omega)k^2)\langle n(\vec{k},\omega)\rangle = 0 \tag{3.17}$$

The macroscopic diffusion propagator is therefore diagonal in the $\vec{k},\omega$ representation and is given by

$$G(\vec{k},\omega) \equiv -(i\omega - k^2 D(\vec{k},\omega))^{-1} \tag{3.18}$$

In subsequent sections we will evaluate D by expanding the right hand side of eq. (3.16) in fluctuation correlation functions of the fluid. Note also that

$$G = \langle G^* \rangle \tag{3.19}$$

where G^* is the fluctuating diffusion propagator

$$G^* \equiv -(i\omega - D_o k^2 - i\vec{k}.\vec{v})^{-1} = [1 + iG_o\vec{k}.\vec{v}]^{-1} G_o \tag{3.20}$$

Eq. (3.19) can be obtained from eq. (3.16) with some straightforward algebra. See in this connection section 1.2.

3.2. An expansion of the renormalized transport coefficient in correlation functions

In this section we will expand the renormalized transport coefficient in terms of the correlation functions of the fluid. Expanding eq. (3.16) in powers of $\vec{v}$ yields

$$D = D_o + k^{-2}\langle\vec{k}.\vec{v}G_o\vec{k}.\vec{v}\rangle - ik^2\langle\vec{k}.\vec{v}G_o\vec{k}.\vec{v}G_o\vec{k}.\vec{v}\rangle - k^{-2}\langle\vec{k}.\vec{v}G_o\vec{k}.\vec{v}G_o\vec{k}.\vec{v}G_o\vec{k}.\vec{v}\rangle$$

$$+ k^{-2}\langle\vec{k}.\vec{v}G_o\vec{k}.\vec{v}\rangle G_o \langle\vec{k}.\vec{v}G_o\vec{k}.\vec{v}\rangle + \text{higher order terms} . \tag{3.21}$$

To second order in $\vec{v}$ one has

$$D = D_o + k^{-2}\langle\vec{k}.\vec{v}G_o\vec{k}.\vec{v}\rangle = D_o + D_1 \tag{3.22}$$

where all contributions are diagonal in $\vec{k},\omega$ representation due to translational invariance and stationarity of the fluid. We note that $\vec{v}$ in eq. (3.22) should be interpreted as an operator which is diagonal in the $\vec{r},t$ representation and a convolution operator in the $\vec{k},\omega$ representation (c.f. (3.7)). The diagonal elements of D_1 can now be written as

$$D_1(\vec{k},\omega) = k^{-2}(2\pi)^{-4}\int d\vec{k}'d\omega'\vec{k}.\overleftrightarrow{S}^{vv}(\vec{k}',\omega').(\vec{k}-\vec{k}')G_0(\vec{k}-\vec{k}',\omega-\omega') \tag{3.23}$$

where the correlation function of $\vec{v}$ is given by

$$\langle\vec{v}(\vec{k},\omega)\vec{v}(\vec{k}',\omega') = (2\pi)^4\overleftrightarrow{S}^{vv}(\vec{k},\omega)\delta(\vec{k}-\vec{k}')\delta(\omega-\omega') \tag{3.24}$$

For an isotropic incompressible fluid we furthermore have

$$\overleftrightarrow{S}(\vec{k},\omega) = \left(1 - \frac{\vec{k}\vec{k}}{k^2}\right)\overleftrightarrow{S}^{vv}_{tr}(\vec{k},\omega) \tag{3.25}$$

Substituting eq. (3.25) into eq. (3.6) we therefore have

$$D_1(\vec{k},\omega) = k^{-2}(2\pi)^{-4}\int d\vec{k}'d\omega'(k^2-k'^{-2}(\vec{k}'.\vec{k})^2)S^{vv}_{tr}(\vec{k}',\omega')G_o(\vec{k}-\vec{k}',\omega-\omega') \tag{3.26}$$

or in $\vec{k},t$ representation

$$D_1(\vec{k},t) = k^{-2}(2\pi)^{-3}\int d\vec{k}'(k^2-k'^{-2}(\vec{k}',\vec{k})^2)S^{vv}_{tr}(\vec{k}',t)G_o(\vec{k}-\vec{k}',t) \tag{3.27}$$

This is the memory kernel for the diffusion process.

The coefficient $D_1(\vec{k},\omega)$ as given in eq. (3.26) will in general diverge because we use a continuum description of the system. One therefore has to impose a cut off k_o in k space where k_o is of the order of an inverse molecular length. The coefficient $D_1(\vec{k},t)$ does not suffer from this drawback, however the answer will only be reliable for sufficiently small k and sufficiently large t. As a final remark we note that $G_o(\vec{k},t)$ is according to eq. (3.9) given by

$$G_o(\vec{k},t) = -\frac{1}{2\pi}\int d\omega e^{-i\omega t}(i\omega-D_o k^2)^{-1} = \begin{cases} 0 & \text{if} \quad t < 0 \\ e^{-k^2 D_o t} & \text{if} \quad t \geq 0 \end{cases} \tag{3.28}$$

and therefore satisfies a causality condition. Consequently $D_1(\vec{k},t)$ satisfies a similar causality condition.

3.3. The long time behaviour of the diffusion memory kernel, and the $\vec{k},\omega$ dependent renormalized diffusion constant

In this section we will first evaluate the memory kernel $D_1(k,t)$ as given in eq. (3.27). For this purpose we shall first use the fluid correlation function, as found from linearized hydrodynamics with constant coefficients. We will come back to the more general case. The correlation function S_{tr}^{vv} for hydrodynamic values of k and t is then given by[15)]

$$S_{tr}^{vv}(k,t) = \rho_o^{-1} k_B T_o \exp(-\nu k^2 |t|) \tag{3.29}$$

where k_B is Boltzmann's constant and ν the kinematic viscosity.

Substitution of eqs. (3.28) and (3.29) into eq. (3.27) yields

$$D_1(k,t) = \begin{cases} 0 \quad \text{if} \quad t < 0 \\ \frac{1}{2}\rho_o^{-1} k_B T_o (2\pi)^{-2} \int_{-\infty}^{\infty} dk' \int_{-1}^{1} d\xi k'^2 (1-\xi^2) \exp[-t\nu k'^2 - tD_o(k'^2+k^2-2kk'\xi)] \\ \qquad \text{if} \quad t > 0 \end{cases} \tag{3.30}$$

Performing the integrals one obtains for hydrodynamic times and wave vectors

$$D_1(k,t) = \frac{2}{3}\rho_o^{-1} k_B T_o [4\pi t(\nu+D_o)]^{-3/2} f\left(\frac{k^2 t D_o^2}{\nu + D_o}\right) \exp -\left(\frac{k^2 D_o \nu t}{\nu+D_o}\right) \quad \text{if} \quad t > 0 \tag{3.31}$$

where

$$f(\alpha) = \frac{3}{2}\alpha^{-1}\left[1 + \frac{i}{2}\sqrt{\pi}\,\alpha^{-1/2} e^{-\alpha} \operatorname{erf}(i\sqrt{\alpha})\right] \quad . \tag{3.32}$$

The notation erf indicates the error function. Furthermore $f(\alpha)$ is positive and real for positive values of α. For small values of α

$$f(\alpha) = 1 - \frac{2}{5}\alpha + \mathcal{O}(\alpha^2) \quad . \tag{3.33}$$

For large values of

$$f(\alpha) = \frac{3}{4}\alpha^{-2}[1 + 2\alpha] + \mathcal{O}(\alpha^{-3}) \quad . \tag{3.34}$$

For $k = 0$ one finds the usual form

$$D_1(0,t) = \frac{2}{3}\rho_o^{-1} k_B T_o [4\pi t(\nu+D_o)]^{-3/2} \quad , \quad t > 0 \quad . \tag{3.35}$$

For k larger than zero one can distinguish two regions in which the time dependence is essentially different

$$D_1(k,t) = \begin{cases} \frac{2}{3}\rho_o^{-1}k_BT_o[4\pi t(\nu+D_o)]^{-3/2} & \text{if } 0 \le \frac{k^2tD_o}{D_o+\nu}\max\{\nu,D_o\} \ll 1 \\ \frac{3}{4\pi}\frac{k^2D_o^2}{(D_o+\nu)^2}\rho_o^{-1}k_BT_o[4\pi t(\nu+D_o)]^{-1/2}\exp-\left(\frac{k^2\nu D_o t}{\nu+D_o}\right) & \text{if } \frac{k^2tD_o^2}{D_o+\nu} \gg 1 . \end{cases} \tag{3.36}$$

In the general case when the transport coefficients of the fluid are wave vector and frequency dependent, eq. (3.29) is still valid asymptotically for large times using the value of the transport coefficient ν in the hydrodynamic limit

$$\left(\lim_{\omega\to 0}\ \lim_{k\to 0}\right)$$

These transport coefficients may then also be interpreted as the renormalized coefficients of the fluid. All the results derived in this section for the long time tails are therefore still valid asymptotically in this order of the expansion (3.21). In a subsequent section we will discuss the behaviour of higher order terms in eq. (3.21). These contain, it turns out, next to faster decaying terms, contributions to the asymptotic $t^{-3/2}$ behaviour. It should also be mentioned that the $t^{-7/4}$ contribution to the long time behaviour of $D(0,t)$ found by Pomeau[8] and Ernst and Dorfmann[10] would follow if one takes into account a term proportional to $k^{1/2}$ in the viscosity of the fluid, as found by these authors.

We shall now calculate the diffusion coefficient $D(k,\omega)$ as given in eq. (3.26) by choosing a suitable molecular cut off wave vector k_o. The correlation in the (k,ω) representation is

$$S^{vv}_{tr}(k,\omega) = 2\,\frac{k_BT_o}{\rho_o}\,\frac{k^2}{\omega^2+\nu^2k^4} \tag{3.37}$$

the Fourier transform of eq. (3.30). Substitution of eqs. (3.9) and (3.37) into eq. (3.26) yields

$$D_1(k,\omega) = \frac{k_BT_o}{4\pi^3\rho_o}\int_0^{k_o}dk'\int_{-1}^{1}d\xi\int_{-\infty}^{\infty}d\omega' k'^2(\xi^2-1)\,\frac{\nu k'^2}{\omega'^2+\nu^2k'^4}$$
$$\times\,[\,i(\omega-\omega') - D_o(k^2+k'^2-2kk'\xi)]^{-1} \tag{3.38}$$

If one evaluates the integral in eq. (3.38) one obtains[2)]

$$D_1(k,\omega) = \frac{k_BT_o}{3\pi^2(D_o+\nu)\rho_o}\{k_o - \frac{3}{8}\pi(D_o+\nu)^{-1/2}(D_ok^2-i\omega)^{1/2}f(r)\} \tag{3.39}$$

with

$$r \equiv \left(\frac{D_o}{D_o+\nu}\right)^{1/2}\left(1-\frac{i\omega}{D_ok^2}\right)^{-1/2} \quad \text{and} \quad f(r) \equiv (1-\frac{1}{2}r^2)\sqrt{1-r^2}+\frac{1}{2}r^{-3}\arcsin r \tag{3.40}$$

For small values of $|r|$, which is the case if $D_ok^2 << |\omega|$

$$f(r) = \frac{4}{3} - \frac{2}{5}r^2 + \mathcal{O}(r^4) \tag{3.41}$$

so that

$$D_1(0,\omega) = \frac{k_BT_o}{3\pi^2(D_o+\nu)\rho_o}\{k_o - \frac{1}{2}\pi(D_o+\nu)^{-1/2}(-i\omega)^{1/2}\} \quad . \tag{3.42}$$

Furthermore one finds that

$$D_1(k,0) = \frac{k_BT_o}{3\pi^2(D_o+\nu)\rho_o}\left[k_o - \frac{3}{8}\pi k\left(\frac{D_o}{D_o+\nu}\right)^{1/2} f\left(\left\{\frac{D_o}{D_o+\nu}\right\}^{1/2}\right)\right] \quad . \tag{3.43}$$

In the zero frequency and wave vector limit we find

$$D_1(0,0) = \lim_{\omega\to 0}\lim_{k\to 0} D_1(k,\omega) = \lim_{k\to 0}\lim_{\omega\to 0} D_1(k,\omega) = \frac{k_BT_ok_o}{3\pi^2(D_o+\nu)\rho_o} \quad . \tag{3.44}$$

If the tagged particle is sufficiently large so that $D_o = 0$, eq. (3.44) gives, with $\eta = \nu\rho_o$ the viscosity,

$$D(0,0) = \frac{k_BT_ok_o}{3\pi^2\eta} \quad . \tag{3.45}$$

This is the Stokes-Einstein law if one chooses the cut off equal to

$$k_o = \pi(\text{diameter})^{-1} = \frac{1}{2}\pi R^{-1} \tag{3.46}$$

where R is the radius of the tagged particles. See for a proper derivation of this result ref. 30.

3.4. Expansion of the renormalized diffusion coefficient in terms of the renormalized diffusion propagator

If one investigates the behaviour of the higher order terms in the expansion (3.21) one finds that they also contain contributions to the $t^{-3/2}$ long time behaviour, next to faster decaying terms. Some of these contributions can easily be resummed and then lead for $k = 0$ to an asymptotic behaviour

$$D^{r}(k=0,t) - \frac{2}{3}\rho_o^{-1} k_B T_o [4\pi t(\nu+D_o+D_1(k=0,\omega=0))]^{-3/2} \quad (3.47)$$

where D^{r} is the resummed part of D and where $D_1(k=0,\omega=0)$ is given by the second order approximation to $D(k,\omega)$, eq. (3.44).

Formula (3.41) suggests that summation over all the contributions to the $t^{-3/2}$ behaviour leads to the asymptotic formula

$$D(k=0,t) = \frac{2}{3}\rho_o^{-1} k_B T_o [4\pi t(\nu+D(k=0,\omega=0)]^{-3/2} \quad (3.48)$$

containing the full rather than the bare diffusion coefficient. Eq. (3.48) could be obtained by extensive partial resummation as is in fact done by Kawasaki[4)] in the context of the mode-mode coupling theory. We shall obtain this result here by an alternative method, without the use of resummation techniques.

In order to proceed with our analysis we rewrite the full diffusion propagator eq. (3.18) in the form

$$G = -(i\omega-k^2D)^{-1} = G_0 - G_o k^2 (D-D_o)G = [1+G_o k^2 (D-D_o)]^{-1} G_o \quad . \quad (3.49)$$

With the help of this equality one can rewrite after some straightforward algebra the general formula (3.16) for the diffusion coefficient in the form

$$D - D_o = k^{-2} \langle i\vec{k}.\vec{v}[1-G\{k^2(D-D_o)-i\vec{k}.\vec{v}\}]^{-1}\rangle \langle[1-G\{k^2(D-D_o)-i\vec{k}.\vec{v}\}]^{-1}\rangle^{-1} . \quad (3.50) .$$

The right hand side can be expanded in powers of correlation functions of $\vec{v}$ and of $(D-D_o)k^2$. The quantity $(D-D_o)k^2$ can then be eliminated from the r.h.s. by iteration. The result is an expansion for $(D-D_o)k^2$ in terms of correlation functions of $\vec{v}$, but always contains the full diffusion propagator rather than the bare one. Up to second order one finds

$$D - D_o = k^{-2} \langle \vec{k}.\vec{v}\, G\, \vec{k}.\vec{v}\rangle \quad (3.51)$$

This expression which has again the well known mode-mode coupling form gives, for the asymptotic long time behaviour, after an analysis similar to the one in section 3.3. the result (3.48).

If one analyses the contributions of fourth order in $\vec{v}$ (assuming $\vec{v}$ to be a Gaussian process for hydrodynamic k, ω, so that odd orders in $\vec{v}$ vanish) one finds that these decay for $k = 0$ as t^{-2}. The sixth order contributions, which have also been analysed, decay as $t^{-5/2} \ln t$. For details of this analysis we refer to reference 3.

To summarize, it would therefore seem that an expansion starting from formula (3.50), in terms of the fluid correlation functions and the renormalized diffusion propagator, is indeed a systematic one for the long time behaviour and that eq. (3.48) is asymptotically correct to all orders.

REFERENCES

1) D. Bedeaux and P. Mazur, Physica 67(1973)23.
2) D. Bedeaux and P. Mazur, Physica 73(1974)431.
3) P. Mazur and D. Bedeaux, Physica (1974), to be published.
4) K. Kawasaki, Ann.Phys. 61(1970)1 and references therein.
5) L.P. Kadanoff and J. Swift, Phys.Rev. 166(1968)89.
6) B.J. Alder and T.E. Wainwright, Phys.Rev.Lett. 18(1967)988; Phys.Rev. A1(1970)18.
7) M.H. Ernst, E.H. Hauge and J.M.J. van Leeuwen, Phys.Rev.Lett. 25(1970)1254; Phys.Rev. A4(1971)2055.
8) Y. Pomeau, Phys.Rev. A5(1972)2569; A7(1973)1134.
9) J.R. Dorfman and E.G.D. Cohen, Phys.Rev.Lett. 25(1970)1257; Phys.Rev. A6(1972)776.
10) M.H. Ernst and J.R. Dorfman, Phys.Lett. 38A(1972)269; Physica 61(1972)157.
11) P. Résibois, preprint.
12) R. Zwanzig and M. Bixon, Phys.Rev. A2(1970)2005.
13) T. Keyes and I. Oppenheim, Phys.Rev. A7(1973)1384.
14) K. Kawasaki, Phys.Lett. 32A(1970)379; 34A(1971)12.
15) R. Zwanzig, Statistical Mechanics, Proc. Sixth I.U.P.A.P. Conf. on Statistical Mechanics (The University of Chicago Press 1972).
16) L. Landau and E. Lifshitz, Fluid Mechanics, Pergamon Press (New York, 1959).
17) N.G. van Kampen, these proceedings.
18) M. Smoluchowski, Ann.Physik 25(1908)205.
19) A. Einstein, Ann.Physik 33(1910)1275.
20) J. Yvon, Recherches sur la Théorie Cinétique des Liquides, Hermann et Cie. (Paris, 1937).
21) B.H. Zimm, J.chem.Phys. 13(1945)141.

22) M. Fixmann, J.chem.Phys. 23(1955)2074.

23) H. Hoek, Thesis (Leiden, 1939).

24) L. Rosenfeld, Theory of Electrons, North-Holland Publ.Comp. (Amsterdam, 1951).

25) P. Mazur and M. Mandel, Physica 22(1956)299.

26) F. Zernike, Proc.Acad.Sci. Amsterdam 18(1916)1520.

27) L.D. Landau and E.M. Lifshitz, Statistical Physics, Pergamon Press (London-Paris, 1958).

28) S.V. Larsen, R.D. Mountain and R. Zwanzig, J.chem.Phys. 42(1965)2187.

29) Shoon K. Kim and P. Mazur, Physica 71(1974)579.

30) D. Bedeaux and P. Mazur, to be published.

31) M.Sh. Giterman and E.E. Gorodetskii, JETP 29(1969)347, JETP 30(1970)348.